A TEXT-BOOK

ON

SOUND

Wm. H. George

BY

EDWIN H. BARTON, D.Sc. (Lond.), F.R.S.E.

A.M.I.E.E., F.Ph.S.L.

PROFESSOR OF EXPERIMENTAL PHYSICS
UNIVERSITY COLLEGE
NOTTINGHAM

MACMILLAN AND CO., LIMITED
ST. MARTIN'S STREET, LONDON

1908

PREFACE

In writing the following pages the aim has been to provide students with a text-book on Sound, embracing both its experimental and theoretical aspects.

To make it more widely useful, the mathematical portions are restricted to the elements of the calculus. Thus, when Fourier's Theorem or Differential Equations are introduced, the treatment is simple and the physical bearings of the problem are carefully discussed, so as to meet the needs of those readers having no previous acquaintance with such methods. All higher analysis is entirely excluded. Indeed, much of the work is intelligible to those not familiar with the calculus at all. For, in the parts where it is used, simpler alternative methods are often provided, chiefly for the sake of emphasising certain important physical aspects of the subject.

Experiments suitable either for laboratory exercise or lecture illustration are described in some detail, and distinguished by smaller type and numbered headings.

The various typical musical instruments are discussed more fully than usual, though always from the view-point of the physicist rather than that of the musician.

At the close of the book a number of original examples on the various chapters and sections are given to afford a

gauge of the student's progress and grasp of the text.
These include enunciations, proofs, numerical and descrip-
tive examples, essay-writing, and actual manipulation in
the laboratory. They are for the most part fairly straightforward, it being assumed that Pass or Honours candidates
for Degrees or other Diplomas will further test themselves
by working special problems from papers previously set at
the particular examination they are taking.

Like every other modern work on Sound, the present
text-book obviously owes much to the classical treatises of
Helmholtz, Lord Rayleigh, and Tyndall. The excellent
Continental courses on physics by Müller-Pouillet, Wüllner,
and Jamin and Bouty also deserve mention. On special
subjects a number of other works have been consulted
with advantage, and references given in the text where
necessary.

The endeavour has been made to bring the treatment
up to date by insertion of the more important recent
researches at home and abroad, the respective authorities
being in each case quoted.

Thanks are hereby tendered to Messrs. Newton and Co.
for permission to reproduce one of Prof. C. V. Boys'
photographs of a bullet in flight; to Messrs. Taylor and
Francis for a like favour with respect to any illustrations
in the *Philosophical Magazine*; and to Prof. J. G. M'Kendrick,
F.R.S., who kindly allowed some of the highly-interesting
curves obtained from his Phonograph Recorder to appear
in these pages.

To Mr. Ambrose Wilkinson, B.Sc., Lecturer in Physics
at University College, Nottingham, special thanks are given
for his valuable help in reading the proofs; but, as it can
scarcely be expected that any single reader, however

careful, would succeed in noting every inaccuracy, it is feared that some errors or obscurities still remain. Should such be found by any users of the book, their kindness in forwarding either corrections or suggestions would be heartily appreciated.

UNIVERSITY COLLEGE, NOTTINGHAM.
    February 1908.

CONTENTS

PART I. PRELIMINARY SURVEY

CHAPTER I

INTRODUCTORY

PART II. MATHEMATICAL

CHAPTER II

KINEMATICS

CHAPTER III

ELASTICITY

CHAPTER IV

DYNAMICAL BASIS

PART III. PHYSICAL

CHAPTER V

VIBRATING SYSTEMS

CHAPTER VI

RESONANCE AND RESPONSE

CHAPTER VII

INTERFERENCE AND COMBINATIONAL TONES

PART IV. MUSICAL

CHAPTER VIII

MUSICAL INSTRUMENTS

CHAPTER IX

CONSONANCE AND TEMPERAMENT

PART V. EXPERIMENTAL

CHAPTER X

ACOUSTIC DETERMINATIONS

CHAPTER XI

RECORDERS AND REPRODUCERS

EXAMPLES

CHAPTER I

1. THE word sound is commonly used in two different senses : (1) to denote the *sensation* perceived by means of the ear when the auditory nerves are excited ; and (2) to denote the *external physical disturbance* which, under ordinary conditions, suitably excites the auditory nerves.

This usage will generally be followed here. It rarely leads to any ambiguity, the context generally showing in which of the two senses the word is employed. When necessary, for clearness' sake, the first or subjective sense will be represented by " the sensation of sound," and the second, or objective sense, by " sound waves," or other similar expressions.

It is a matter of common knowledge that the source of sound is always a body in a state of vibration, or rapid to-and-fro motion. This body may be a solid, as the string of a harp ; or fluid, as the column of air in a wind instrument.

We may, therefore, define *Acoustics*, or the study of sound, as that branch of physics which deals with vibratory motion as perceived by the sense of hearing. It is usual, however, to include with this a few other closely allied phenomena.

2. Production of Sound.—But in order to produce sound it is not sufficient to have some body in a state of vibration as its source. We need also (1) some medium to

1

B

receive and transmit this vibratory motion, otherwise neither the sensation of sound nor the external disturbance would be present. (2) It is imperative that the parts of the body in vibratory motion should have such shape, size, and motion as to cause a disturbance to advance through the air, and not such as to produce a local flow and reflow of the air simply. (3) Our ears enable us to perceive the sensation of sound only when affected by to-and-fro movements whose number per second lies between certain limits.

Therefore, to produce sound sensations, it is necessary that our vibrating body should conform to this requirement also. These points are respectively illustrated by the following experiments :—

EXPT. 1. *A Medium Essential.*—To illustrate the necessity of a medium to convey sound from its source to the ear, hang a bell by india-rubber cords within a glass bulb fitted with a tap. Sound the bell in the bulb full of air with the tap open, and then with the tap closed, so as to indicate its loudness in each case. Next, exhaust the bulb as completely as possible by an air-pump. Detach the bulb when exhausted and shake so as to attempt to make the bell sound. No sound, or only an extremely feeble one is heard. While the bell is inaudibly shaking, open the tap so as to admit the air ; the sound is very quickly restored. Contrast with this the case of an ordinary electric glow-lamp, whose incandescent filament sends light to us across the space within its bulb although it is practically devoid of air. Light, like sound, needs a medium for its propagation. But the medium essential to the propagation of light is the ether which we are at present unable to remove from any space.

EXPT. 2. *Importance of Sound Board.*—Fit up two steel wires each about 1 mm. diameter—one on a monochord, the other on the bars of two 56 lb. weights. The latter should have the same length between the bars that the former has between the bridges, and they should be tuned to the same pitch. It is desirable that the 56 lb. weights should not rest upon wood. They may both be on a level tiled floor, or slab of stone or slate. Or, the wire might be vertical, the upper weight being on an iron or stone bracket from a wall, and the lower one hanging freely. On plucking or bowing the wire on the 56 lb. weights, only a very feeble sound will be heard. But on plucking or bowing the wire on the monochord the sound is easily heard by an audience of a thousand persons.

It is thus seen that the wire whose ends are on the massive iron weights, although moving to and fro like the other, is yet unable to produce vigorous waves of sound in the air. But the precisely similar wire on the monochord passes over bridges which are moved by its vibrations. And the bridges in turn set the belly or upper board of the sound box in motion. It is true the motions of the bridges and belly are very small, but the shape of the latter forces the air near it to take up a vigorous vibratory motion which can advance to distant parts of a large room. Any mere local flow or reflow of the air, which is almost all that the wire on the weights could produce, is impossible in the case of the monochord sound box. Hence the distinction between the effects produced in the two cases.

EXPT. 3. *Right Frequency needed.*—Take a piece of steel about 1 m. long, 2 cm. wide, and 1 mm. thick. Clamp it firmly in a vice, allowing at first, say, 80 cm. to project. Pull this projecting end aside and let it go. It is seen to execute vibrations, but no sound is heard. Decrease the length of the projecting part, and again test the vibrations for audibility. Repeat the shortening and the test until the vibrations are audible as well as visible. This simple experiment shows that very slow vibrations are inadequate to produce an audible effect, although absolutely similar ones executed a greater number of times per second produce a distinct sound. We shall see later that vibrations executed too quickly fall beyond the limits of audition.

3. Noises and Musical Sounds.—All sounds may be divided roughly into two classes, noises and musical sounds. Noises are characterised by irregularity or suddenness, musical sounds by their comparatively smooth and even flow. But the line of demarcation between them cannot be sharply drawn. Throughout the irregularity of some noises may be perceived, now more and now less plainly, a persistent

musical sound. On the other hand, very few musical sounds are entirely free from accompanying noises which disturb to some slight extent their regularity and smoothness. These differences can be illustrated better than defined. The following experiments afford typical examples :—

EXPT. 4. *Extreme Cases.*—(1) Drop from a height of 6 ft. a 2 lb. ball of iron upon a tin plate a foot square resting upon sawdust in a box on the floor. (2) Take a tuning-fork mounted upon its resonance box, and excite it gently with a carefully rosined bow. The first sound is unquestionably a noise, and the second just as surely a musical sound.

EXPT. 5. *Intermediate Cases.*—Pour water from a jug into a water bottle or tall jar until the bottle or jar is full. The sound produced by the falling water seems at first to be merely a confused noise. But, after a few seconds, it will be noticed that throughout the noise a sustained musical sound is also present. Moreover, the musical sound rises as the jar becomes nearer full, and this continuous rise makes it easier to detect. Bars of steel, bells, and gongs, when struck with another hard body, furnish examples of sounds in which noises and musical elements are both clearly present. The harder the hammer with which they are struck, the harsher and less musical will the sound usually be.

Since sounding bodies are in a state of vibration, and musical sounds are characterised by their regularity and smoothness, it seems natural to infer that they are produced by *regular* or periodic vibrations. We shall afterwards see distinct proof that this is the case. Noises, on the other hand, are produced by *irregular* or non-periodic vibrations. We shall, henceforth, be concerned almost solely with musical sounds, noises being practically dismissed with this brief notice.

4. Propagation of Sound.—Let us now examine the general nature of the process by which sound advances from its source to the ear or other recipient. The medium of this advance is usually the air, and this will serve our present purpose, as the essentials with which we are now concerned are the same whatever the medium. The features in question may be illustrated as follows :—

EXPT. 6. *Air Waves.*—Arrange a pipe AB, about 6 feet long and 4 inches diameter, with a glass funnel F and a lighted candle C in a line with it at one end. At the end remote from the funnel introduce into the pipe two watch-glasses, one containing strong hydrochloric acid and the other ammonium hydrate, so as to produce dense white fumes. Or, instead of producing fumes in this way, the smoke from smouldering brown paper will serve. Near the end containing the fumes or smoke make a sharp report by clapping together smartly two blocks of wood or two books. When everything is rightly adjusted the candle

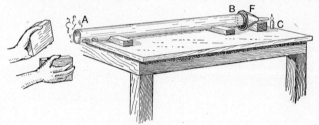

FIG. 1.—AIR WAVES.

flame is seen to duck at each clap. But, although abundant fumes may be evolved within the tube at the end next the source of sound, no trace of fume is seen to issue at the end next the candle.

Hence we conclude that when sound passes from one point to another it is not the medium of its propagation which advances. On the contrary, the parts of this medium make only quite small excursions to and fro. And it is this state of minute to-and-fro motion that advances. Thus the medium as a whole, after the disturbance has passed, is practically where it was to begin with. Illustrations of this advance of a state of motion through a medium which does not itself appreciably advance may easily be multiplied. The following will repay consideration :—

EXPT. 7. *Water Waves.*—Obtain a trough about 6 feet

long, 8 inches wide, and 6 inches deep. Let this be placed level and about half-filled with water. Next float upon the water about six pieces of cork, each about 7 inches square and a quarter of an inch thick, and each carrying a straw mast and a paper flag. Agitate the water at one end by alternately depressing and raising a block of wood. The disturbed state of the water thus produced at one end is shown by the floats to advance to the other, the flags, one by one, nodding as the waves pass them. On carefully watching this phenomenon it will be observed that the corks move not only up and down, but also exhibit a little movement lengthwise of the trough. But if the agitation is slight they do not leave their place

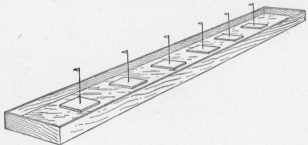

FIG. 2.—WATER WAVES.

entirely to advance with the wave. The motion of the water at any point is really round and round in a closed loop in a vertical plane.

EXPT. 8. *Rope Waves.*—Obtain a solid india-rubber cord, about half an inch in diameter, and about 20 or 30 feet long. Fix one end on a hook or staple in a wall, and take the other end in the hand. On shaking sidewise the end held in the hand a series of corresponding displacements will be seen to pass along the cord to the farther end. Here the motion of the separate parts of the cord is clearly not one of advance, but only a to-and-fro motion sideways or *transversely.* But this state of motion advances, each part of the rope executing in turn the motion that a neighbouring part executed a little before.

EXPT. 9. *Spring Waves.*—The apparatus shown in Fig. 3 affords a valuable illustration of the phenomena now under discussion, and although more elaborate than those

previously referred to, is well worth the expense and
trouble required for its preparation. A helical coil should
be wound in a lathe, the wire being of soft copper about
1·5 mm. diameter, its turns being 10 cm. diameter, their
pitch, or distance apart longitudinally, may be about 1 cm.,
the whole coil being about 2 m. long, thus containing
about 200 turns. Each turn of the coil should be supported
by a fine silk thread in the form of a V as shown, each limb
of the V being about 1 m. long, its two upper ends being
half a metre apart where the threads are fixed to the wood
framework. The coil may require to be wound of a rather
smaller diameter, and with its turns somewhat closer together,

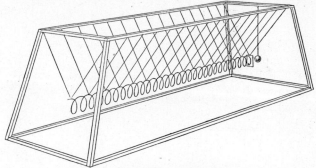

FIG. 3.—SPRING-WAVE APPARATUS.

in order that, when liberated, it should assume the dimensions
given above, which are those it should have when finished
and in use. These sizes are chosen to insure a slow advance
of the disturbance from one end to the other, and cannot
without disadvantage be departed from at random. A
very slight increase in the diameter of the wire, for example,
would greatly increase the speed at which any disturbance
would advance along the coil. It would thus render it
difficult for the eye to follow its movements and so detract
from the illustrative value of the apparatus.

To use the coil, it is sufficient for our present purpose
to take one end in the hand and move it to and fro endwise.
A corresponding endwise or *longitudinal* state of motion is
then seen to pass slowly along to the other end. If this end
is provided with a disc of cardboard with a pendulum bob
resting against it, as shown in the figure, the bob will be

agitated on the reception of the disturbance. We should thus have an imitation, in a very crude fashion, of the reception of sound by the human ear.

5. In these four experiments we have illustrations of progressive wave motion, or the advance at a finite speed of a disturbance among parts which do not themselves advance. In the case of the india-rubber cord the waves are called *transverse*, because the small excursions of the separate parts were performed transversely to the line of advance of the disturbance. In the case of the coil of wire the waves are called *longitudinal*, because the small excursions of the separate coils were executed longitudinally, or along the line of advance of the disturbance. In the case of the water waves the motion of the separate parts is more complicated, being a combination of the two forms just referred to. The question arises, which of these three, if any, represents the waves of sound in air which were produced in the first of the present set of four experiments? We shall see later considerations which show us that waves in the air must be of the longitudinal type like those were which passed along the coil of wire. This apparatus, therefore, gives us the best illustration of the passage of sound waves through the air.

6. Vibrations.—We shall conclude this introductory chapter by defining or explaining various terms and phrases of frequent occurrence and fundamental importance :—

DEFINITIONS (1). The *period* of a vibration is the time from the instant when the vibrating point passes through any position to the instant when it next passes through the same position moving in the same direction (symbol for period τ—unit for its measurement, the second).

(2) The *frequency* of a vibration is the number of vibrations performed per unit time. Thus frequency is the reciprocal of period. (Symbol for frequency $N = 1/\tau$—unit for its measurement, "*per* second.")

(3) The *amplitude* of a vibration is the maximum displacement assumed by the vibrating point in the course of its motion. (Symbol, *a*—unit the centimetre, foot, etc.)

(4) The *phase* of a vibrating point at any instant is the state of its displacement and motion at the instant in question. The various methods of measuring phase will be dealt with later. (See arts. 22 and 24.)

All musical sounds are characterised during their steady continuance by three features : *pitch, intensity,* and *quality.* Each of these needs a little notice here.

7. Pitch.—The pitch of a musical sound is a feature recognised by every one. It depends upon the period or frequency of the vibrations constituting the sound, and upon that alone. The greater the frequency, the higher the pitch. This may be illustrated by rubbing the fingernail, first slowly and then quickly, across a finely-grooved surface, such as a book-cover of ribbed cloth. Pitch is specified in two distinct ways, namely : (1) scientifically, by the statement of the period or frequency of the vibration, or by the logarithm of its frequency ; (2) musically, by assigning to the sound in question its position in a certain accepted series of sounds constituting a musical scale.

Perhaps the simplest proof that pitch depends only upon the frequency, is that afforded by the following experiment with the siren :—

EXPT. 10. *Pitch fixed by Frequency.*—For the present purpose it will suffice to use the disc siren due to Seebeck. This is shown in Fig. 4. It consists essentially of a disc capable of rotation about its centre, and pierced with one or more sets of holes arranged equidistantly in circles concentric with the axis. Opposite to each circle is a jet through which air may be blown perpendicularly to the disc. Thus as the disc revolves the air will alternately pass through the holes and strike the blank spaces between them, thus giving rise to a series of puffs which produce a musical sound. The disc may be driven by hand, or preferably by an electric motor. Experiments with this apparatus show that the pitch of the sound obtained depends in no way upon the size or shape of the holes or the pressure of the blast, but only upon the number of holes which pass the jet per second. The air blast may even be replaced by a quill or cord touching the edges of the holes, but still the pitch will be found to depend simply on the frequency.

Fig. 4.—Seebeck's Siren.

8. Musical Notation.—The ordinary or staff notation of notes for the representation of musical sounds is given in Fig. 5. Underneath the several notes are placed the letters used as names for them. The various notes of the same name are distinguished by capitals, small letters, subscripts, and accents, on the plan introduced by Helmholtz.

The relative frequencies are shown next, and, lastly, the actual frequencies for the pitch generally used in physical

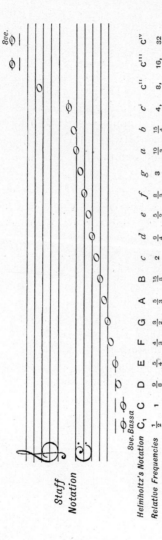

FIG. 5.—STAFF NOTATION, ETC.

apparatus. This has been purposely chosen for simplicity's sake, so that all the c's have for their frequencies powers of the number 2. The absolute frequencies used in musical practice varies in different countries, and has changed considerably in the course of time (see end of Chap. IX.).

9. Musical Intervals.—It may be noticed from Fig. 5 that the *differences* of frequencies between consecutive notes bearing the same name are very various. Thus between the c's we have, beginning with the higher notes, the following differences between relative frequencies : 16, 8, 4, 2, 1, $\frac{1}{2}$. Again, the difference between the relative frequencies of g and G is $\frac{3}{2}$, and so on, each pair of notes of like name yielding a new value. If, on the other hand, we take the *ratios* of frequencies of consecutive notes bearing the same name, and beginning at the higher of the two, we find the value of this ratio to be always the same, namely, 2. This is not due to chance. Take now some other step or musical interval, that from one note to another of different name. Then, again, keeping to a pair of notes of the same names, we find the ratio of their frequencies the same whether they are taken from one or another part of the scale. Thus the ratio $\frac{4}{3}$ is yielded by f and c, and also by F and C ; whereas the differences are, in the one case $\frac{2}{3}$, in the other $\frac{1}{3}$. The notation is thus arranged because it has been found that the relationship between two sounds, or their *musical interval*, is the *same* whatever their absolute frequencies may be, provided that the *ratio* of their frequencies remains constant. This is conclusively shown by the following experiment :—

Expt. 11. *Musical Interval determined by Ratio of Frequencies.*—Use again the disc siren shown in Fig. 4. But this time use alternately two jets directed upon circles of holes whose numbers are in the desired ratio ; let this at first be 2 : 1. Let the disc be rotated at first at a constant speed, and only quick enough to give low notes. Then, on opening first one only of the air jets, and next the other only, the two sounds will be recognised by any one having a musical ear to be at the interval known as an *octave*. Let the speed be increased, and again maintained constant. Again, in the same way as before, it may be found that, although each sound is now higher in pitch than at first, the interval between them is still an octave. And so it may be shown, for any speeds whatever which produce audible results, that the interval is an octave when the frequencies have the ratio 2 : 1. Choose now two circles of holes whose numbers are in the ratio 3 : 2. Then proceeding as before, the two sounds produced, whatever their absolute pitch, will be found to have the interval known musically as a *fifth*. It is the interval between C and G, E and B, F and *c* in the scales previously given. To those sufficiently musical to recognise the exactness of the interval between two notes sounded simultaneously, this experiment may be more quickly performed by sounding the two notes together and increasing the speed of the siren continuously.

10. Logarithmic Cents.—Since pitch depends upon frequency and interval upon ratio of frequencies, we have the following important result. Let it be required to measure intervals so that the sum of the measures of component intervals shall be the measure of the resultant interval. Then the only method possible is that of taking for each interval a number proportional to the logarithm of the ratio of the frequencies of the notes composing that interval. Thus, let the frequencies of three notes, beginning at the highest and proceeding in order of pitch, be L, M, and N. Also let the intervals be I_1 between L and M, I_2 between M and N, and I between L and N. Then, if each interval be measured by k times the logarithm of the ratio of frequencies, we have

$$I_1 = k \log \frac{L}{M} = k (\log L - \log M) \qquad (1).$$

$$I_2 = k \log \frac{M}{N} = k (\log M - \log N) \qquad (2).$$

$$I = k \log \frac{L}{N} = k (\log L - \log N) \qquad (3).$$

But by addition of (1) and (2)

$$I_1 + I_2 = k \, (\log L - \log N) \qquad (4),$$

so by (3) and (4)

$$I = I_1 + I_2 \qquad (5).$$

For k any convenient number could be chosen, as (5) shows that the relation desired is independent of it. But the late Mr. A. J. Ellis (the translator of Helmholtz's *Sensations of Tone*) has adopted as the unit for this logarithmic measure the *cent*, 1200 of which make the octave. The name cent is used because 100 cents make the semitone of those instruments in which twelve equal semitones are the intervals occurring in an octave. Hence the clue to reduction of any intervals to these logarithmic cents would be found in the following equations, where I is the interval in cents between notes of frequencies M and N :—

$$I = k \log M/N \qquad (6).$$
$$1200 = k \log 2 \qquad (7).$$

Whence by $(6) \div (7)$.

$$I = 1200 \, \frac{\log M - \log N}{\log 2} \qquad (8).$$

11. Intensity and Loudness.—The intensity of sound waves is a purely physical quantity independent of the ear. It is proportional to the wave energy passing per unit time through unit area. It will be shown later that for a given medium of propagation and given frequency of vibration the energy of a wave motion is proportional to the square of the amplitude. Thus the intensity of sound waves of a given frequency in air is proportional to the square of their amplitude. But a distinction must be drawn between this physical quantity intensity and the meaning to be understood for the term loudness.

The loudness of a sound depends upon the intensity of

the waves producing it, and increases and decreases with
the intensity for a sound of given frequency, but in a way
difficult precisely to define, and scarcely susceptible of
strictly quantitative statement. It is thus seen that the
intensity of a sound is a physical quantity having objective
existence and capable of precise definition and quantitative
comparison. Loudness, on the other hand, corresponding to
degree of sensation, is not wholly physical, but is, in part
at least, subjective, and depends therefore upon the ear and
the hearer. To the electrical student the relation between
intensity and loudness may be illustrated by that between
electric current and deflections of galvanometer needles
produced when it passes. The current is the physical
quantity which can be defined, and has only one value at
any one time and place. The deflection of the galvanometer,
on the other hand, though it depends upon the current and
increases with increase of current, yet depends also upon
the galvanometer itself. Thus different galvanometers may
give different deflections for the same current, and a double
current will not necessarily give a double deflection with
any of the galvanometers in question.

12. Quality.—We now pass to consider the third
feature, quality, which serves to distinguish between
musical sounds of the same pitch and intensity produced
on different instruments, say, the voice, the violin, the
organ or harmonium. Since pitch depends upon the
frequency, and intensity upon the amplitude of the vibration,
at first sight it may seem that there is nothing left whose
variation can account for the different qualities observable
in the various musical sounds with which we are familiar.
A moment's reflection, however, suffices to dispel this
illusion. Let, for example, a vibrating point move to and
fro a given number of times per second. Then its
frequency, and therefore the pitch of the corresponding
sound, is fixed. Let also its excursions extend over a
prescribed distance. Then the amplitude of the vibration,

and consequently the intensity of the corresponding sound, will be fixed. But we still have at our disposal the character of the motion, *i.e.* the displacement and velocity at each instant of the motion, and it is upon these that the quality of the sound depends. The discovery of this fact is due to Helmholtz. Perhaps the two simplest cases to imagine are the following marked (1) and (2):—

(1) Suppose a point to move to and fro with given frequency and amplitude, its speed being uniform in one direction for half the period, next suddenly reversed, and, lastly, maintained with an equal uniform speed in the opposite direction for the second half of the period.

(2) Suppose the motions in one direction to be quite suddenly changed into a reverse motion as before, but let the speeds in the two directions be unequal, though each speed is constant till the next reversal.

The above two cases, though easy to imagine and describe, are not so often realised in practice as might be supposed. The following case is easier to realise and of great importance, though apparently a little more complicated:—

(3) Let the speed of the point in its to-and-fro motion suffer no violent change, but gradually wax, wane, reverse, then wax and wane in the opposite direction, and so forth again and again.

It will be seen later, that a vibration of this kind, with specific definition as to the precise velocity at each point, is one of fundamental importance, and is taken as the type in terms of which all others can be expressed.

The characteristics of the above vibrations can be conveniently exhibited graphically by plotting curves having times for abscissæ, and displacements for ordinates. We thus obtain Fig. 6, where the curves are numbered to correspond to the paragraphs in which are described the vibrations in question.

Order of Treatment.—The preliminary survey of the

subject contained in this introductory chapter shows that
we are concerned primarily with—

    (1) Vibrating bodies and their possible rates and modes
        of vibration.

    (2) The propagation through the air, or other media, of
        the disturbances which these vibrations generate, and

    (3) The reception of the vibratory disturbances and the
        effects produced by them.

We have thus to deal very largely with motions, which
are, for the most part, of a somewhat complicated order,
that is to say, beyond those usually given in text-books of

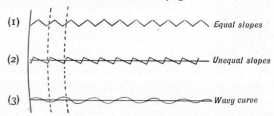

FIG. 6.—VIBRATION CURVES.

mechanics for beginners. We shall, accordingly, commence
the systematic treatment of the subject with a study of
motion itself without reference to the causes which produce
it. This is contained in the next chapter on Kinematics.
Again, vibrating bodies and the media in which they
generate waves have this in common, that a displacement
calls forth a restoring force. This property is popularly
referred to as elasticity. The quantitative study of
elasticity, therefore, fitly occupies the third chapter. We
shall then proceed to apply dynamical principles in conjunction with what has been deduced respecting kinematics
and elasticity. And then the foundations of the subject
being laid, we pass to a number of physical, musical, and
electrical applications.

CHAPTER II

13. DEFINITIONS.—*Kinematics* is that branch of science which treats of motion purely, *i.e.* apart from any consideration of the causes which produce it.

As already mentioned in art. 12, there is one type of vibration regarded as fundamental. It is named and defined as follows :—*Simple harmonic motion* is the resolved part, parallel to a fixed straight line, of uniform circular motion. Any other periodic motion may be called a *compound* harmonic motion, and may be obtained by compounding two or more appropriate simple harmonic motions. Any periodic motion in a straight line may be regarded as the projection of a point describing some closed curve according to some particular law as to speed at each point of the path. Taking this view, we see from the definition above the appropriateness of the term *simple* harmonic motion. For the motion so called is the projection of a point describing the simplest closed curve (a circle), with the simplest law of speed (uniform all round).

14. Discussion of Simple Harmonic Motion.—Let the point P (Fig. 7), describe the circle XPYX'Y' with uniform speed, then the point M, the foot of the perpendicular from P on the fixed line YOY', executes along that line the particular to-and-fro movement called simple harmonic motion.

Let the radius of the circle be *a* cm., and the speed of

P be v cm. per second. Then a is obviously the amplitude of the vibration. Also the period τ is given by

$$\tau = 2\pi a/v = 2\pi/\omega \tag{1},$$

where ω denotes the angular velocity of P round O in radians per second, and therefore $\omega = v/a$. The frequency N is, of course, given by

$$N = 1/\tau = \omega/2\pi, \text{ or } \omega = 2\pi N \tag{2}.$$

The phase of the vibration at the instant depicted in the figure depends upon the angle POX, which may accordingly be termed the phase angle.

If the point describing the circle started from X at the commencement of the time t, the angle POX would equal ωt, P being the position of the point at the time t. Hence XOX' and YOY' being perpendicular diameters, the displacement of the point executing the simple harmonic motion is given by OM = OP sin POX, or

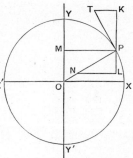

Fig. 7.—Simple Harmonic Motion.

$$y = a \sin \omega t \tag{3},$$

where y denotes OM.

15. Velocity in Simple Harmonic Motion.—In figure 7, let PT represent the velocity v of the point P. Draw PK parallel to OY, and let TK be drawn parallel to OX. Then PK represents in magnitude and direction the velocity of M. But the angle TPK is equal to the angle POX, which equals the angle OPM.

Hence, we have

velocity of M = PK = PT cos TPK = PT cos OPM = $v \cdot$ MP$/a$,

or $$\dot{y} = \omega \cdot \text{MP} \tag{4},$$

where $\dot{y}$ represents the velocity of M whose ordinate is y, the dot converting a displacement into a velocity in the same direction. In the interpretation of (4) we must take distances to the right or upwards as positive, and those to the left or downwards as negative. Note also that the line MP must be taken in the order of the letters, and not in the reverse order. Then, on tracing the path of P throughout the four quadrants of the circle, we see that the general features of equation (4) are justified. The angular velocity ω of the point P is constant. Hence, we see by (4) that the velocity of M varies directly as MP. Thus when M is at O, and P at X, MP is positive and has its greatest value, hence the velocity of M has also its greatest value. As P moves through the first quadrant, namely, from X to Y, MP is positive, but continually decreases, hence the velocity of M is always positive, that is, directed upwards, but is diminishing, which is obviously the case. When M arrives at Y, P is at Y also, that is, MP has vanished, consequently the velocity of M has vanished. And we easily see this to be the case, for M is in the act of reversing its motion. As P moves through the second quadrant, MP is negative, and the velocity of M is negative also. But MP is increasing numerically from zero to its full value, and M's velocity is increasing also as to numerical value. While P describes the third quadrant, MP is negative, but decreasing numerically, or M's motion is still downwards, but slower and slower. Finally, as P describes the fourth quadrant, MP is positive and increasing, hence M's velocity is upward and increasing also.

16. Acceleration in Simple Harmonic Motion.— Referring again to Fig. 7, let PN represent the acceleration of P. This is shown in elementary text-books (1) to be along the normal PO, (2) to be directed towards the centre of the circle, and (3) to have the magnitude $v^2/a = \omega^2 a$.

Thus, drawing PL parallel to OY, and letting NL fall perpendicularly upon it, we have the acceleration of M represented in magnitude and direction by PL. By construction, the angle PNL equals the angles POX and OPM $= \omega t$. Hence, we may write—

The acceleration of M $=$ PL $=$ PN sin PNL $= (-\omega^2 a) \cdot$ OM$/a$,

or $$\ddot{y} = -\omega^2 y \qquad (5),$$

where $\ddot{y}$ denotes the acceleration of M. The minus sign is needed because the acceleration PN and its component parallel to OY, PL, are negative when the displacement of M is positive. The result expressed in equation (5) is of great importance, and may be put in words as follows. The acceleration of a point executing a simple harmonic motion is proportional to its displacement, but is oppositely directed.

Further, equation (5) shows us that equations (1) and (2) for period and frequency are susceptible of the following useful forms—

$$\tau = 2\pi \sqrt{-y/\ddot{y}}, \qquad (6),$$

and $$2\pi N = \sqrt{-\ddot{y}/y} \qquad (7).$$

The values of the acceleration of M may be traced throughout the whole vibration, just as was done for the velocity. It may thus be seen that when the displacement is zero and the velocity has its maximum numerical value, positive or negative, the acceleration is zero. Again, when the displacement has its greatest numerical value, positive or negative, and the velocity is zero, the acceleration has its greatest numerical value, but of sign opposite to that of the displacement.

17. Analytical Treatment.—By aid of the differential calculus the velocity and acceleration of a point executing simple harmonic motion are immediately obtained. Thus, we have for the displacement of the point,

$$y = a \sin \omega t.$$

Differentiating with respect to the time, we get

$$\dot{y} = \omega a \cos \omega t = \omega \cdot \text{MP}.$$

A second differentiation gives

$$\ddot{y} = -\omega^2 a \sin \omega t = -\omega^2 y.$$

These equations correspond to (3), (4), and (5) previously given.

18. Graphic Representation of Simple Harmonic Motion.—The characteristics of any rectilinear motion may be very conveniently exhibited by its displacement curve. This is a line whose abscissæ represent the times, and whose ordinates represent the corresponding displacements. Such a curve for simple harmonic motion is shown in Fig. 8, the auxiliary circle to the left being used to obtain the displacements corresponding to equal intervals of time. This curve may be easily plotted on squared paper. The circle to the left may be dispensed with if a table of sines is used.

This curve is identical with that often plotted in studying trigonometry, and called a *sine-graph*. Evidently it is also a curve described by a point which simultaneously executes a simple harmonic motion and a rectangular uniform translation, that is to say, a simple harmonic motion along YOY′, and a translation with uniform speed along OX. In order to grasp the full meaning and utility of a displacement curve it is necessary to note (1) that the *slope* of the curve represents the *velocity* of the moving point, and (2) that the *rate of change of slope* represents the *acceleration* of that point. These facts follow immediately from the method of plotting

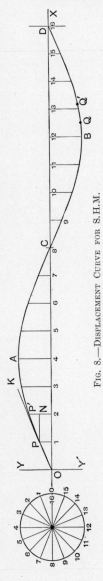

FIG. 8.—DISPLACEMENT CURVE FOR S.H.M.

the curve and the definitions of the terms involved. Thus, if the displacement curve is anywhere horizontal, as at A and B, we have, at the instants in question, the velocity equal to zero. This we know to be the case, for here the vibrating point is at its greatest elongation and is just about to return. Again, at O, C and D we have parts of the curve where the slope is greatest, and at the corresponding instants the vibrating point must accordingly have its greatest velocity. This also agrees with what we have seen as the result of equation (4), namely, that when the displacement is zero the velocity is a maximum. Regarding now the rate of change of slope, we see that this is greatest at A and B, for there the curvature is seen in the figure to be greatest. Accordingly at the instants corresponding to A and B, the acceleration of the vibrating point should have its greatest value. At O, C and D the curvatures are seen to be small and are indeed zero. These zero curvatures denote that the acceleration of the vibrating point at the corresponding instants is zero also. Both these results agree with equation (5). We may thus draw up the following scheme (see Table I.) as the meanings of the various features of a displacement curve :—

TABLE I.—DISPLACEMENT CURVE

Features of Curve.	Significance.
Abscissa	Time.
Ordinate . . .	Displacement of vibrating point.
Slope	Velocity of vibrating point.
Rate of change of slope .	Acceleration of vibrating point.
Horizontal part . .	Zero velocity, or rest of vibrating point.
Steepest part . . .	Greatest velocity of vibrating point.
Straight part . . .	Zero acceleration, or uniform velocity of vibrating point.
Sharpest curvature . .	Greatest acceleration of vibrating point.

19. Quantitative Use of Displacement Curve.—
Consider now points P and P′ on the curve (see Fig. 8),
and draw PN parallel to OX meeting in N, P′N parallel
to OY.   Let the ordinates at P and P′ be y and $y′$, and
the corresponding times from O be t and $t′$ respectively.
Then the mean speed of the vibrating point during the
short time $t′ - t$ is given by

$$\dot{y} = \frac{y′ - y}{t′ - t} \tag{1}.$$

But this ratio is represented on the diagram by NP′/PN,
hence we have

$$\dot{y} = \tan P′PN \tag{2}$$

Draw PK the geometrical tangent to the curve at P,
and making the angle ϕ with PN and OX.   Then, in the
limit where P′ approaches very near to P, the chord PP′
becomes PK, and we obtain

$$\dot{y} = \tan \phi, \tag{3},$$

or from (1) by the calculus

$$\dot{y} = \frac{dy}{dx} \tag{4}.$$

In drawing the geometrical inferences contained in
equations (2), (3), and (4), it should be noted that these are
true just as printed *only if* unit time and unit distance are
represented by the *same* lengths of the axes of abscissæ
and ordinates in the displacement curve.

Let us now inquire exactly how the acceleration of the
vibrating point can be inferred from the curvature of the
displacement curve.   At Q, between B and D on Fig. 8,
let the geometrical tangent to the curve make the angle ψ
with OX, and at the adjacent point Q′ let the corresponding
angle be $\psi′$.   Then, by definition, between A and Q′ we
have

$$curvature = \frac{\psi′ - \psi}{QQ′}, \tag{5},$$

where QQ′ refers to the length of the arc. But, from (3), tan ψ represents the velocity at Q, and tan ψ' represents the velocity at Q′. Also the horizontal distance between Q and Q′ represents the time in which the velocity changes from one value to the other. Hence the mean acceleration between Q and Q′ is practically given by

$$\ddot{y} = \frac{\tan \psi' - \tan \psi}{QQ'}, \qquad (6),$$

where QQ′ is strictly the horizontal distance between these points, but may be assimilated to the value in (5). But, since the angles are everywhere supposed small, tan $\psi = \psi$ nearly, and the same holds for ψ'. Thus, (6) may be written

$$\ddot{y} = \frac{\psi' - \psi}{QQ'} \text{ nearly} \qquad (7).$$

And from (5) and (7) we obtain the approximate equation,

$$acceleration = \ddot{y} = curvature \qquad (8).$$

By the calculus these steps may be put more briefly as follows,

$$\text{Acceleration} = \frac{d\dot{y}}{dt} = \frac{d(\tan \phi)}{dx} = \frac{d^2 y}{dx^2} =$$
$$\text{rate of change of slope} \qquad (9).$$

But, $curvature = \dfrac{d\phi}{ds}$, where s is arc, and for small curvatures reduces to (9),

$$\text{and so} = acceleration \qquad (10).$$

Note that tan $\phi > \phi$ and $x < s$, hence by (9) and (10) we have *strictly*

$$acceleration > curvature \qquad (11).$$

20. Transverse Progressive Waves.—The simpler wave motions may now be illustrated and discussed.

EXPT. 12.—The lantern-slide model represented in Fig. 9 will be found useful for demonstrating the various features of progressive waves. It consists essentially of a sliding bar cut to a sine-graph, upon which ride a number of uprights carrying balls at their tops. These uprights slide through vertical holes in the two horizontal bars. The uprights may be suitably made from darning-needles whose eyes, when broken, will form the fork for resting on the sliding bar. The balls may be made by beads cemented on the needle-points, or by small pellets of sealing-wax. The illustration is from a photograph of the original model used by the writer. This shows the glass cover buttoned on, which holds all in place, but can easily be removed for any adjustments.

FIG. 9.—WAVE MODEL FOR LANTERN.

The experiment with this model consists simply in moving the bar uniformly along, and watching the consequent motion of the beads as seen projected on the lantern-screen.

From the construction of the apparatus, the points noted in this paragraph immediately follow for the state of things when the guide-plate is sliding uniformly along at speed v, viz.—

(1) Each bead executes a simple harmonic vibration vertically, the amplitude being the *same* for all the beads, but the phase *varying* continuously from bead to bead according to distance along the row.

(2) The arrangement of the beads at any instant is in a series of crests and troughs, something like gentle water waves. We call this a wave form. In the case under consideration it should be noted that a crest is like an inverted trough.

(3) This wave form, without changing its type, advances horizontally at speed v. This form of wave motion is called transverse, because the vibration of the beads is at right angles to the advance of the waves.

(4) The instantaneous form or arrangement of the beads exactly repeats itself at intervals called wave lengths (λ).

(5) The velocity and acceleration of any one bead, at any instant, are precisely like those, at the same instant, of certain other beads distant longitudinally an integral number of wave lengths (λ, 2λ, 3λ, etc.).

(6) If λ is the wave length of the pattern cut in the guide-plate, v the speed at which it is moved, and τ the period of the vibration of the beads thus produced, we have $v = \lambda/\tau = N\lambda$ (1),

N being, as usual, the frequency.

Hence, a sine-graph of wave length λ and amplitude a moving along its axis at speed v, represents a transverse progressive wave of simple harmonic type of wave length λ and amplitude a, and propagated at speed v, the frequency of vibration of the particles being given by $N = v/\lambda$. The amplitude a of the waves is, of course, represented on the same scale by the extreme ordinates of the graph, and the velocity and acceleration follow in the usual manner for simple harmonic motion.

Suppose now a guide plate were cut to any other exactly repeating pattern of a type that the rods could work on. Then, on moving it at constant speed, we should still have a transverse progressive wave motion executed by the beads, but now of a more complicated type. For, just

as a simple harmonic motion is the simplest type of vibration, so the corresponding or simple harmonic wave is the
simplest type of wave motion. We previously mentioned
that any periodic motion of a particle along a straight line
could be made by compounding two or more suitable simple
harmonic motions. It accordingly follows that any wave
motion, whose type does not change as it advances, can be
formed by compounding two or more simple harmonic wave
motions.

21. Longitudinal Progressive Waves.—Let us now
consider the kind of wave motion executed by the spring
model shown in Fig. 3. This kind is called longitudinal
because the line of vibration of the particles is along the
line of advance of the waves instead of transverse as in the
case just considered. Suppose then we start with a straight
row of particles, which when undisplaced are equidistant.
It is evident that, as the longitudinal waves pass along
them, they will remain in a straight row, but will no
longer be equidistant. Thus the arrangement is never along
a wavy line as in transverse waves. Nevertheless, it is a
matter of great convenience to represent the instantaneous
state of all the particles by a single curved line, instead of
having to show by a number of dots the position of each
particle. And this convenience can readily be attained for
longitudinal waves if we agree to plot a curve whose
ordinates mean displacements *parallel to the axis of abscissæ,*
the abscissæ denoting, of course, the undisplaced positions of
the various particles; that is to say, the displacements,
though actually occurring to right and left, are represented
on the curve by ordinates up and down respectively. A
longitudinal wave passing along a row of particles is
exhibited in various ways by the different lines of the
diagram in Fig. 10.

The first line gives an actual picture of the particles,
their equilibrium or undisplaced positions being indicated
by small crosses, and their actual or displaced positions by

small circles. The second line exhibits the same wave by
the displacement curve drawn on the convention described
above, namely, ordinates up and down denote displacements
to the right and left respectively. The third and fourth
lines representing the velocities and accelerations may be
deduced from the displacement curve by supposing it to
move to the right, while the fifth line showing the linear
densities may be inferred from either the same curve or the

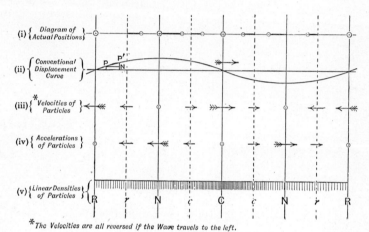

*The Velocities are all reversed if the Wave travels to the left.

FIG. 10.—LONGITUDINAL PROGRESSIVE WAVES.

first line which gives actual positions. The R's denote
rarefactions, the C's condensations, the N's places of normal
linear density.

We may therefore state the elements of a longitudinal
progressive wave of simple harmonic type as follows :—

(1) Each particle executes a simple harmonic motion
along the line of advance of the wave, the amplitude
being the same, but the phase varying continuously
for every particle according to distance along the
line.

(2) The arrangement of all the particles at any instant

is along a straight line, but such as may be represented by a sine-graph on the conventions that displacements to the right are denoted by positive
ordinates, and displacements to the left by negative
ordinates.

(3) This arrangement, without changing its type,
advances with uniform velocity, v say, and so may
be represented on a working diagram or model by a
uniform advance of the displacement curve already
referred to. (See (2) of this article and line (ii) in
Fig. 10.)

(4) This instantaneous arrangement repeats itself at
regular distances called wave lengths (and denoted
by λ say).

(5) The velocity and acceleration of any one particle at
any instant are precisely like those, at the same
instant, of certain other particles whose distances
longitudinally are λ, 2λ, 3λ, etc.

(6) With the same notation as before, we have $v = \lambda/\tau$
$= N\lambda$.

The above statement corresponds to the like-numbered
sections in art. 20 for transverse waves. We may now
add here another section special to the case of longitudinal
waves and not before needed.

(7) It follows from sections (3) and (4) that the linear
density of the particles, or their state of condensation
or rarefaction, is, at any instant, arranged in a pattern
which repeats itself at intervals of a wave length.
Further, this state of alternate condensation and rarefaction, without changing its type, advances with the
uniform velocity v.

The significance of the various features of the conventional displacement curve for longitudinal waves may be
seen from Fig. 10 and Table II. The relation between any
feature of the curve and the algebraic sign of the quantity
denoted by it is best seen from the figure. It should be

noted that if the wave travels to the left the *velocities* of the particles are thereby reversed, all else remaining the same.

TABLE II.—DISPLACEMENT CURVE FOR LONGITUDINAL WAVES

Features of the Curve.	Their Significance.
Abscissæ . . .	Lengths along line of advance of waves.
Ordinates . . .	Displacements along axis of abscissæ.
Slope *proportional* to .	Velocity of particles longitudinally.
Rate of change of slope *proportional* to . .	Acceleration of particles longitudinally.
Slope also indicates .	Linear density differs from its normal value.

As to the various quantitative relations here involved, it is easily seen that what was stated for vibrations and transverse progressive waves (arts. 19 and 20) will guide us here also. To deal with the new feature of linear density, let its value at x be σ and its normal value σ_0. Then, since these densities are inversely as lengths occupied by given material, we have on reference to line (ii) of Fig. 10, $\sigma_0(\mathrm{PN}) = \sigma(\mathrm{PN} + \mathrm{NP}')$, or $\sigma_0/\sigma = 1 + \mathrm{NP}'/\mathrm{PN} = 1 + \tan \phi$, where ϕ is the angle between the axis of abscissæ and the tangent at P. Or, if $\sigma = \sigma_0(1 + s)$, we have $\dfrac{1}{1 + s} = 1 + \tan \phi$,

whence $\qquad\qquad s = - \tan \phi$ nearly $\qquad\qquad$ (1).

We may also derive from Fig. 10 the following relations:—

Velocity of particle at $\mathrm{P} = \dfrac{-\mathrm{NP}'}{\mathrm{PN}/v} = - v \tan \phi$

$$= - v \times \text{slope} \qquad (2).$$

Also *acceleration* at P

$$= \frac{- v \tan \phi - (- v \tan \phi')}{\mathrm{PN}/v} = v^2 \times \text{curvature} \quad (3).$$

22. Phase and its Measurement.—During its motion the displacement, velocity, and acceleration of a vibrating particle wax, wane, and change sign, passing in the course of a complete vibration through the whole sequence of values possible to them. The place in this sequence which is occupied by the displacement and velocity, at any instant, of a vibrating point, is called its phase at the instant in question. Or, we may define as follows :—

The phase of a vibrating point, at any instant, is its state of displacement and motion at that instant, judged with respect to those which it successively assumes in the course of its vibration.

Thus, if two vibrating points pass simultaneously through their undisplaced positions in the same direction, they are at the instant of such passage in the same phase. And this is true whether their velocities were numerically equal or not. If, however, the direction of one were reversed, all else remaining the same, they would at the instant of such passage be in opposite phases. Again, if two vibrating points simultaneously reach their maximum displacements in the same direction they are then in the same phase ; if in opposite directions, in opposite phases. And this is the case whether the amplitudes are equal or unequal. The consideration which decides the phase is always the relation borne by the displacement and velocity to those possible in the given vibration. The absolute value of the displacement and velocity of two vibrating points in the same phase may be quite different.

When wishing to specify phase to a greater nicety than simply equal or opposite, we must choose some standard state to reckon from, and some method or methods of measuring from that state to the state in question whose phase is to be specified. The state usually chosen as standard is that possessed by the vibrating point when passing through its undisplaced position in the positive direction. As to measuring from this state, evidently every state of motion possible to a given vibrating particle is defined by the corresponding position of the point describing the auxiliary circle. But the position of this point in the auxiliary circle may be specified in three ways as follows :—

(1) By the *fraction of a period* which has elapsed since last the point passed through its standard position (which of course corresponds to the standard state of the vibrating point).

(2) By the *angle* which it has described since last it passed through its standard position.

(3) By the *fraction of a wave length* traversed by the waves since the point last passed through its standard position. This third method is, of course, applicable only when waves are proceeding from a vibrating source. It is then often very convenient.

The relation of these three methods of measuring phase difference is easily seen and remembered by taking as an example that of opposite phases. Then, clearly, this may be expressed (1) by half the period, (2) by the angle π radians, or $180°$, and (3) by half a wave length of path. It is often necessary to pass from the fraction of a period to the actual time in order to insert the corresponding value in our equation, or from the fraction of a wave length to the actual length, but in each case it is the *fraction* that measures the phase or the phase difference in question. If the fractions are alike in two cases, then the phase differences so measured are alike, no matter what the actual times or lengths may amount to.

This distinction may be illustrated by the following equations representing vibrations, in which $\tau = 2\pi/\omega$:—

$$y_1 = a \sin \omega t \tag{1},$$

$$y_2 = a \sin \omega\left(t + \frac{\tau}{2}\right) = a \sin\left(\omega t + \pi\right) \tag{2},$$

$$y_3 = a \sin \frac{\omega}{2} t \tag{3},$$

$$y_4 = a \sin \frac{\omega}{2}\left(t + \frac{\tau}{2}\right) \tag{4},$$

$$= a \sin \frac{\omega}{2}\left(t + \frac{2\tau}{4}\right) = a \sin\left(\frac{\omega}{2} t + \frac{\pi}{2}\right) \tag{5}.$$

Thus (1) and (3), at the instant $t = 0$, are in like phases. Vibrations (1) and (2) are at every instant in opposite phases. Equations (3) and (4) represent vibrations, which at first sight might seem to be in opposite phases also, but in reality, as shown by (5), y_4 differs in phase from y_3 by a quarter of a period only; or the angle $\pi/2$ and not π. Here, since the ω of equations (1) and (2) is replaced by $\frac{\omega}{2}$, the period is changed from τ to 2τ, thus the extra time in equation (4) $\frac{\tau}{2}$ is only a quarter of a period, and the phase angle in consequence $\frac{\pi}{2}$ only. The measurement of phase by fraction of wave length will be exemplified in a subsequent article (24).

Epoch is the term used to denote the phase at the commencement of the time. It may be expressed in any of the ways by which phase is measurable. Thus in equation (2) the epoch is half a period, or π radians; in equations (4) and (5) a quarter of a period, or $\frac{\pi}{2}$ radians; while in (1) and (3) the epoch is zero.

23. Analytical Representation of Progressive Waves.—Let a progressive wave proceed in the positive direction along the axis of x. Denote by y the displacement at time t of a point whose equilibrium position is x. Then, if the waves are of the simple harmonic type, they may be represented by the following equations :—

$$y = a \sin 2\pi\left(\frac{t}{\tau} - \frac{x}{\lambda}\right) \tag{1},$$

or, $$y = a \sin 2\pi(Nt - x/\lambda) \tag{2},$$

where τ and N are respectively the period and frequency of the vibrations, a their amplitude, and λ is the wave length. The speed of advance of the waves does not appear in the above, but is evidently given by

$$v = \frac{\lambda}{\tau} = N\lambda \tag{3}.$$

Instead of equation (1) or (2) we may write the equivalent form $$y = a \sin \omega(t - x/v) \tag{4}.$$

This has the advantage of brevity and also introduces v explicitly, but it omits both N and λ, which are sometimes disadvantages. The three forms are easily seen to be identical. To verify their representation of progressive waves it is sufficient to compare either of them with the sections (1)-(6) of articles 20 and 21. We will take them in order, pointing out in each case how the verification is to be made.

(1) Give to x any constant value, and let t grow continuously from zero to τ or beyond. The displacement is then seen to pass through the changes characteristic of simple harmonic motion, the phase depending upon x.

(2) Give to t any constant value, and give to x all values possible from zero to λ or beyond. The displacements simultaneously occurring at all the different points along the line are then seen to be those of a sine-graph.

(3) Fix upon any point the co-ordinate of whose equilibrium position is x' say, and let its displacement at time t' be y'. Then, taking equation (2), we have

$$y' = a \sin 2\pi\, (Nt' - x'/\lambda) \tag{5}.$$

Now, in order to find whether the wave travels without
change of type, we must examine whether for any
change in x a corresponding change in t can be
found and such as will leave y unaltered. If so,
the wave evidently advances, without change of
type, and at speed equal to change in x divided by
corresponding change in t to leave y unaltered.

Suppose, therefore, that after the lapse of time t from
the instant represented by equation (5), the point
whose equilibrium position is $x' + x$ has the displacement y'. Then we shall have

$$y' = a \sin 2\pi \left(N \overline{t' + t} - \frac{x' + x}{\lambda} \right) \qquad (6),$$

and we must find the relation between x and t to
satisfy both (5) and (6). Obviously the condition
needed is that the value in the brackets is the same
in each equation. A value differing by any integer
would indeed make y' the same, but it would
correspond to the passage from one wave to another
and must accordingly be rejected. We therefore
derive

$$Nt - x/\lambda = 0, \text{ or } \frac{x}{t} = N\lambda = v \text{ say} \qquad (7).$$

Hence, no matter what the displacement y' was
originally, it remains unchanged if we pass in time
t to another part of the wave at a distance vt farther
on. And this is true for all values of t and vt,
provided v is given by equation (7). But this
constitutes the verification sought that the wave,
without change of type, advances at speed v.

(4) Keeping t constant add to the x co-ordinate any
multiple of λ, and it is then seen that the displacement is unaltered.

(5) Again, keep t constant and increase x by any multiple
of λ, and it is evident that we have the vibration

in the same phase as before, or in other words, the velocity and acceleration of the vibrating point are unchanged.

(6) The statement of this section has already been verified with section (3).

(7) The statement of the additional section of art. 21, occurring only in connection with longitudinal waves, follows from what has already been given in sections (3) and (4) above.

24. Phase measured by Path of Waves.—We may now recur to the third method of measuring phase difference, namely, by the fraction of a wave length passed over by the waves while the vibration changes from one phase to the other. Thus, consider the following two waves :—

$$y_1 = a_1 \sin 2\pi\left(\frac{t}{\tau} - \frac{x}{\lambda}\right) \tag{8},$$

and

$$y_2 = a_2 \sin 2\pi\left(\frac{t + \tau/4}{\tau} - \frac{x}{\lambda}\right) = a_2 \sin 2\pi\left(\frac{t}{\tau} - \frac{x - \lambda/4}{\lambda}\right) \tag{9}.$$

On comparing these two equations we see that the phase difference of the vibrations at a given point for the two waves is a quarter of a period, or, by the second form of (9) we may say the second wave is a quarter wave length ahead of the other at any given time.

Negatively-travelling Waves.—It should be noted that the equations just dealt with represent positively-travelling waves. In order to represent those travelling in the negative direction along the axis of x ,we must change the sign of λ or v, whichever occurs in the form of equation used. Thus, the following equations represent negative waves :—

$$y = a \sin 2\pi\left(\frac{t}{\tau} + \frac{x}{\lambda}\right) = a \sin \omega(t + x/v) \tag{10}.$$

25. Condensation in Longitudinal Waves.—Consider now the linear density σ of a slice of material whose zero positions lie between x and $x + dx$, the corresponding displacements being ξ and $\xi + d\xi$. Then if the normal linear density is σ_0, we have

$$\sigma_0 dx = \sigma(dx + d\xi) \tag{11}.$$

Now let us write $\quad \sigma = \sigma_0(1 + s) \tag{12},$

s being called the " condensation." Then from (11) and (12) we have

$$1 = (1 + s)\left(1 + \frac{d\xi}{dx}\right) \text{ so } s = -\frac{d\xi}{dx} \text{ nearly} \tag{13}.$$

Thus in the displacement curve where ξ is represented by y we have

$$s = -\frac{dy}{dx} \tag{14}.$$

Velocity of Particles in Progressive Waves.—Write the equation in the form (3)

$$y = a \sin \omega(t - x/v).$$

Then we have for the velocity of the particles

$$\frac{dy}{dt} = \omega a \cos \omega(t - x/v) \tag{15}.$$

But this may be expressed in terms of the slope of the displacement curve. For

$$\frac{dy}{dx} = -\frac{\omega}{v} a \cos \omega(t - x/v) \tag{16}.$$

Hence $\qquad \dfrac{dy}{dt} = -v\dfrac{dy}{dx} \tag{17}.$

Or:—velocity of particle $= -v$ times slope of curve nearly, as obtained in equation (2) near the end of article 21. This result applies to either transverse or longitudinal waves.

Acceleration of Particles in Progressive Waves.— Differentiating again, we obtain for the acceleration

$$\frac{d^2y}{dt^2} = -\omega^2 a \sin \omega(t - x/v) \tag{18}.$$

Also $$\frac{d^2y}{dx^2} = -\frac{\omega^2}{v^2}a \sin \omega(t - x/v) \qquad (19).$$

Hence $$\frac{d^2y}{dt^2} = +v^2\frac{d^2y}{dx^2} \qquad (20).$$

Or :—acceleration of particle $= +v$ times curvature nearly, as obtained in equation (3) at end of article 21.

26. Composition of Simple Harmonic Motions along the same Line.—For the solution of this problem several courses are open to us. It may be treated graphically by the triangle or polygon method and by the method of displacement curves. We shall take these in the above order, concluding with the analytical method, and point out the special cases for which each method is most convenient.

Polygon Method for Vibrations of same Period.— This graphical method is suitable only for equal periods, but can deal quite well with any number of vibrations of different amplitudes and phases. When two vibrations only have to be dealt with the polygon reduces to a triangle. It is this simple case which is illustrated in Fig. 11.

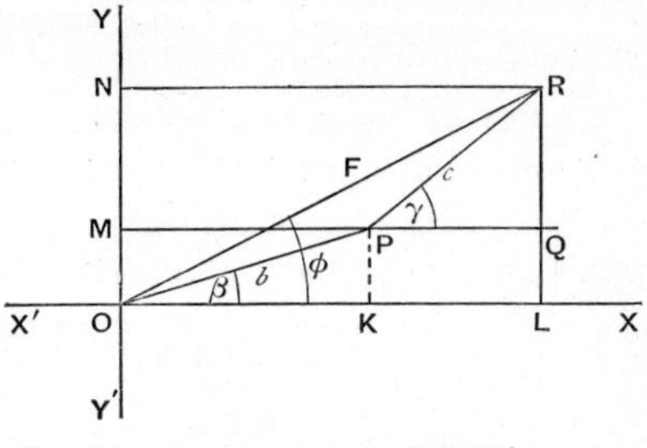

Let the vibrations be each of period τ and

FIG. 11.—COMPOSITION OF S.H.M.'S BY THE POLYGON METHOD.

occur along YOY'. Let the amplitudes and epoch angles of one be b and β, and of the other c and γ respectively. It is required to find the resultant motion of a point simultaneously obeying both these vibrations. In other words, we need an expression for a displacement which is at every instant the algebraic sum of the displacements at that instant of the component vibrations.

Construction.—Take XOX' at right angles to YOY'. Lay off from O, OP of length b and at the angle β with OX.

Lay off from P, PR of length c and at the angle γ with OX. Draw PM, RN parallel to OX, and meeting OY in M and N, also join OR. Then as OR rotates about O with angular velocity $\omega = 2\pi/\tau$, N shall execute along YOY' the motion which is the resultant of the two given component vibrations. In other words, the resultant sought is itself a simple harmonic motion of period τ of amplitude F = OR and of epoch angle ϕ = ROX.

Proof.—By construction OM is the displacement at $t = 0$ due to the first component vibration, while MN is that due to the other at the same instant. Hence at $t = 0$ the resultant displacement is OM + MN = ON. But in order that ON shall always represent the resultant displacement, its components OM and MN must always represent their respective component displacements, *i.e.* the lines OP and PR must rotate each at angular speed ω. Thus they remain at the *same angle* to each other, hence OR is of constant length and rotates at angular speed ω also. ON accordingly continues to represent the resultant of the two vibrations to be compounded, and so solves the problem. .

Analytical Expression for Resultant.—In Fig. 11 draw PK and RL parallel to YO, and produce MP to meet RL in Q. Then we have for the resultant amplitude

$$OR^2 = OP^2 + PR^2 - 2OP.PR \cos OPR,$$

or, $$F^2 = b^2 + c^2 + 2bc \cos (\beta \sim \gamma) \qquad (1),$$

since the angle $(\beta \sim \gamma)$ is the supplement of OPR.

Again, for the epoch of the resultant, we have

$$\tan ROX = \frac{LR}{OL} = \frac{KP + QR}{OK + PQ},$$

or, $$\tan \phi = \frac{b \sin \beta + c \sin \gamma}{b \cos \beta + c \cos \gamma} \qquad (2).$$

Finally, since the resultant of the two vibrations is given by the motion of N as OR rotates at angular velocity ω, we see that it may be expressed by

$$y = F \sin (\omega t + \phi) \qquad (3),$$

F and ϕ having the values in (1) and (2).

27. Method of Displacement Curves.—This method may be used for any case whatever, but is specially good for two or more components whose periods are different. When the periods are equal the polygon method is quicker. We shall illustrate its use by compounding two vibrations whose periods are as $2:1$. Each component must be represented on the same scale by its appropriate sine-graph. A third curve is then plotted whose ordinate at each point is the algebraic sum of those of the components at the same point. Then this resultant curve is obviously the displace-

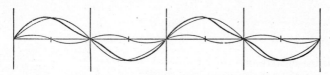

Fig. 12.—Composition of S.H.M.'s by Displacement Curves.

ment curve of the vibration which results from the composition of the two given simple harmonic motions.

The method is illustrated in Fig. 12, in which the thin lines represent the components and the thick line the resultant.

28. Analytical Method.—This method becomes complicated if the periods have no simple relation. We shall therefore illustrate its use for the following cases : (1) Equal periods, (2) Periods nearly equal, and shall just notice its application to (3) Periods commensurate or nearly so.

Equal Periods.—For the sake of comparison with the polygon method, we will write the two component vibrations the same and in the same notation as there used. We have thus

$$y_1 = b \sin (\omega t + \beta) \qquad (1),$$

and $$y_2 = c \sin (\omega t + \gamma) \qquad (2).$$

Hence for the resultant vibration, we obtain

$$y = y_1 + y_2 = b \sin(\omega t + \beta) + c \sin(\omega t + \gamma)$$
$$= (b \cos \beta + c \cos \gamma) \sin \omega t$$
$$+ (b \sin \beta + c \sin \gamma) \cos \omega t \qquad (3),$$

or say,
$$y = (F \cos \phi) \sin \omega t$$
$$+ (F \sin \phi) \cos \omega t \qquad (4).$$

On comparing (3) and (4) it is evident they are identical, provided that

$$F \cos \phi = b \cos \beta + c \cos \gamma \qquad (5),$$

and
$$F \sin \phi = b \sin \beta + c \sin \gamma \qquad (6).$$

Now from (5) and (6) we obtain

$$F^2 = b^2 + c^2 + 2bc \cos(\beta \sim \gamma) \qquad (7),$$

and
$$\tan \phi = \frac{b \sin \beta + c \sin \gamma}{b \cos \beta + c \cos \gamma} \qquad (8),$$

which clearly give real values of F and ϕ for any values of b, c, β and γ. Thus equation (4) is justified, and the solution may be written

$$y = F \sin(\omega t + \phi) \qquad (9),$$

the F and ϕ being expressed by (7) and (8).

This result is seen to be that obtained by the polygon method.

Special Cases.——We may now with advantage examine a few special cases——

(1) Let $\beta \sim \gamma = 0$, then $F = b + c$ (10).

(2) ,, $\beta \sim \gamma = \pi$, ,, $F = b \sim c$ and $= 0$ if $b = c$ (11).

(3) ,, $\beta \sim \gamma = \dfrac{\pi}{2}$, ,, $F^2 = b^2 + c^2$ (12).

(4) ,, $b = c$,   ,, $\phi = \dfrac{\beta + \gamma}{2}$ (13).

Equation (11) illustrates the case in which two equal vibrations in opposite phases nullify one another, and is usually referred to under the term "interference." The

term is objected to by some writers on the ground that each
vibration has its full natural effect. The subject is of
great interest and importance both in acoustics and optics,
and will be dealt with experimentally in the seventh
chapter.

29. Frequencies nearly Equal: Beats.—Let the two
vibrations we have to sum be represented by the right
side of the following equation:—

$$y = a \sin (m + n)t + b \sin (m - n)t \qquad (1),$$

in which n is supposed small compared to m.

Hence we have to determine y to solve the problem.
Assume

$$y = f \sin (mt + \phi) \qquad (2);$$

then expanding the right sides of (1) and (2), and comparing,
we have

$$f \cos \phi = (a + b) \cos nt \qquad (3),$$

and

$$f \sin \phi = (a - b) \sin nt \qquad (4).$$

Whence

$$f^2 = a^2 + b^2 + 2ab \cos 2nt \qquad (5),$$

and

$$\tan \phi = \frac{a - b}{a + b} \tan nt \qquad (6).$$

Thus f varies in value between $(a + b)$ and $(a - b)$ with
the frequency $\frac{2n}{2\pi}$, which equals the difference of the frequencies of the components $\frac{m + n}{2\pi}$ and $\frac{m - n}{2\pi}$. Also ϕ, the
phase angle of the resultant, varies as shown by (6), being
a function of the time of frequency $n/2\pi$, and not a
constant. Lastly, the quasi-frequency of the resultant is
$\frac{m}{2\pi}$, being the arithmetic mean of the frequencies of the
components which are respectively $\frac{m + n}{2\pi}$ and $\frac{m - n}{2\pi}$.

Thus, we may say that the resultant of two simple
harmonic vibrations of nearly equal frequencies may be

regarded as approximately a simple harmonic motion whose quasi-frequency is the arithmetic mean of the component frequencies, whose amplitude is alternately the sum and difference of the component amplitudes, the variation having a frequency equal to the difference of the component frequencies, and whose phase varies with a frequency half the difference of the component frequencies. This change of phase expressed by ϕ assimilates the frequency of the resultant to that of the component having the greater amplitude. The resultant could also be expressed as a vibration with the frequency of either of its components, the phase angle would then be different so as to make the various expressions equivalent.

If the difference of frequencies were large the solutions contained in equations (2), (5), and (6) would still be valid, but would no longer be a convenient form in which to present it. And the verbal statement of the solution by which those equations were followed would be misleading except when the difference of frequencies is small. For obviously, if, during the course of a single vibration, the amplitude changes to double or treble its value, it becomes misleading to speak of the vibration as simple harmonic. If, on the other hand, fifty or more vibrations occur while the amplitude experiences such a change, any single vibration differs but little from the simple harmonic type. It then becomes permissible to regard the vibrations as simple harmonic of given frequency, but with a slowly fluctuating amplitude.

Since f, the amplitude of the resultant, varies between the limits $a + b$ and $a - b$, $i.e.$ the sum and difference of the component amplitudes, the case in which these are equal is of special interest. For it makes the minimum value of f equal to zero, and thus renders the change in the resultant the more striking.

Putting $b = a$ in (5) and (6) we may write
$$\phi = 0, \tag{7}$$

and $\qquad f^2 = 2a^2 (1 + \cos 2nt) = 4a^2 \cos^2 nt,$

or, $\qquad f = 2a \cos nt \qquad\qquad\qquad\qquad (8).$

If we wrote $f = + a \sqrt{2 + 2 \cos 2 nt}$ we should have to retain ϕ with values derived from (6). Thus ϕ would be zero for

$nt = 0$ to $\dfrac{\pi}{2}$, $\phi = \dfrac{\pi}{2}$ for $nt = \dfrac{\pi}{2}$, $\phi = \pi$ for $nt = \dfrac{\pi}{2}$ to $\dfrac{3\pi}{2}$, etc.

From (7) and (8) equation (2) becomes

$$y = 2a \cos nt \sin mt \qquad\qquad (9).$$

The term *beats* is applied to the phenomenon of the waxing and waning of loudness noticed when two musical sounds of nearly but not quite the same frequency are simultaneously heard. The reason for it is seen from the above examination, which also shows clearly the practical importance of making and preserving the component amplitudes nearly equal when using the phenomenon. We shall frequently have recourse to the observation of beats for a number of purposes later. An illustrative diagram showing the displacement curve for the resultant of two beating tones is included in Fig 13.

30. Frequencies Commensurate or nearly so.—Let us now consider the case in which the vibrations along the same line to be compounded have commensurate frequencies. We can represent the resultant of such vibrations by the following equation :—

$y = a_1 \sin (pt + q_1) + a_2 \sin (2pt + q_2)$
$$+ a_3 \sin (3pt + q_3) + \ .\ .\ .\quad (1).$$

A second method consists of introducing cosines instead of phase-angles in the sines. This is illustrated in the next equation :—

$$y = a_1 \sin pt + a_2 \sin 2pt + a_3 \sin 3pt + \ .\ .\ .$$
$$+ b_1 \cos pt + b_2 \cos 2pt + b_3 \cos 3pt + \ .\ .\ .\quad (2).$$

It might naturally be supposed that the problem now before us was the reduction of the right sides of these equations just as was accomplished previously in cases apparently similar. But this is not so. We shall see later that with special values of the constants these equations can be made to represent any periodic motion of frequency $p/2\pi$. It is not, however, easy, or indeed possible, in general to simplify the above expressions for the resultant displacement. They stand, therefore, as the analytical representation of what may be termed a *compound harmonic motion* of frequency $p/2\pi$.

If the periods of the components are not commensurate we then have a vibration which is *not* periodic. It never repeats itself. If, however, the periods of the components are very nearly commensurate we shall have a type of vibration which, for a time, closely approximates to that represented by equations (1) and (2). The deviation of the periods from strict commensurability would be susceptible of approximate representation in equation (1) by a continuous change in the values of the q's, and in equation (2) by corresponding changes in the a's and b's.

31. Typical Examples of Composition.—The following examples shown by displacement curves are fairly representative of the most important types of composition of simple harmonic motions. The data are given at the left and the curves at the right of Fig. 13, the components being in thin lines and the resultants in thick ones.

In cases I. to III. the resultant is simple harmonic, the first being simply doubled in amplitude, the third changed in amplitude and intermediate in phase, while in the second the amplitude is obliterated, the two components being equal and opposite. Case VII., illustrating the phenomenon of beats, approximates to a combination of cases I. and II. alternately, the components being at the outset in like phases, and after 12 periods of one and $12\frac{1}{2}$ of the other in opposite phases. In case IV. we have a tone and its octave, to use the musical expression. This introduces the appearance of a *compound* harmonic motion

| Curve | Components | | | Resultant | Displacement Curves |
	Frequencies	Amplitudes	Phases		
i	1:1	equal	same	Simple harmonic. Amplitude doubled	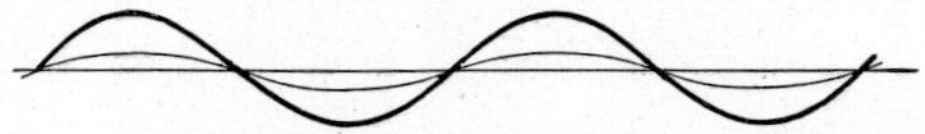
ii	1:1	equal	opposite	Amplitude zero	
iii	1:1	equal	2θ	Simple harmonic. Phase difference of $+\theta$ from each component	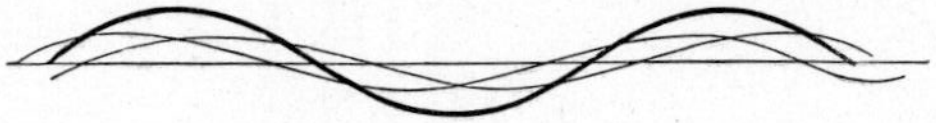
iv	1:2	$1:\frac{1}{3}$	crest on crest & on trough	Tone and octave	
v	1:3	$1:\frac{1}{8}$	crest on crest	Tone and twelfth. Sharp peaks in curve	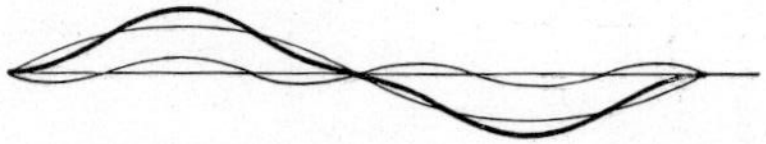
vi	1:3	$1:\frac{1}{5}$	crest on trough	Tone and twelfth. Trough shaped curve	
vii	24:25	equal	various	Beats	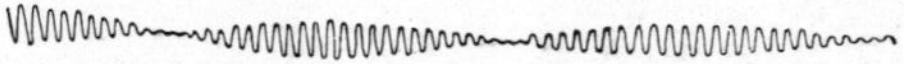
viii	1:2:3:4	$1:\frac{1}{4}:\frac{1}{9}:\frac{1}{16}$	zero at $t=0$	Good musical tone; curve approaching two-step zig-zag	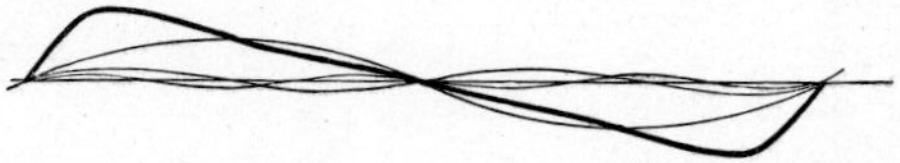

FIG. 13.—TYPICAL EXAMPLES OF COMPOSITION.

already referred to when first discussing the method of composition by displacement curves. Cases V. and VI. correspond to the tone and its twelfth to use the musical term again. The diagrams illustrate the great difference in form of curve depending on the phase relation of components of given frequencies and amplitudes. Case VIII. illustrates the composition of a number of vibrations of commensurate frequencies with amplitudes diminishing regularly according to a certain law as their frequencies increase. The resultant is an example of the kind of vibration sought from the essential parts of a musical instrument. The term *note* has been used by Lord Rayleigh for this kind of compound musical sound whose vibrations are composed of commensurate simple harmonic motions, and of which case VIII. is the type. Both Tyndall and Rayleigh used the word *tone* for those sounds whose vibrations are *simple harmonic*. The same practice will be followed here.

It should be noticed that displacement curves are most readily drawn on squared paper, the ordinates being taken from tables of sines.

32. Composition of Rectangular Vibrations.— We shall now consider the composition of two simple harmonic motions along lines at right angles to each other. It will be convenient to start with equal frequencies, and to pass afterwards to examples of commensurate frequencies expressed by simple ratios. Each case will be dealt with graphically and analytically ; the effect of a slight departure of one frequency from the strict value assigned to it will also be discussed.

Equal Frequencies : *Graphical Method.*—The graphical method of attacking this problem is illustrated in Fig. 14. In this figure the projection upon OX of the point P describing the lower circle uniformly gives the point M, executing simple harmonic motion along XOX'. Similarly the projection upon OY of the point Q describing the right-hand circle, gives the point N executing simple harmonic motion along YOY.' By compounding these two displacements OM and ON, we obtain the resultant displacement OR. In the case drawn, the point R is found to execute along the inclined line AOA' a simple harmonic motion which is the resultant of the two given rectangular vibrations. This statement is verified by the graphical method, which will be readily understood from the corresponding

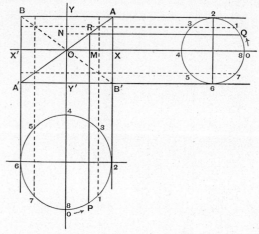

Fig. 14.—Composition of Rectangular Vibrations of Equal Periods.

numerals round the circles and the dotted lines indicating the projections.

The above is for the case of no phase difference, for when M is at O, moving in the positive direction OX, N is at O moving in its positive direction OY. To obtain the resultant for any specified phase difference, we have simply to shift the numerals round one of the circles by the requisite amount, allowing those on the other circle to remain where they were, then compound as before.

Thus, if the case of opposite phases be desired, we have only to shift the numerals on either circle through 180°, the others remaining undisturbed, and we obtain the path BOB'.

Again, let the phase difference be a quarter of a period, that is, its angular measure is $\pi/2$. It is then easily seen that the resultant is an ellipse whose axes are XOX' and YOY', and which is inscribed within the rectangle AB'A'B. If the vibrations have equal amplitudes, the auxiliary circles in the figure are equal, and the ellipse just referred to becomes

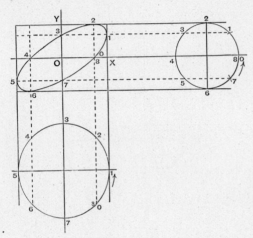

FIG. 15.—MORE GENERAL CASE OF COMPOSITION.

a circle also, and is described by R with constant speed. The fact that two rectangular simple harmonic motions of equal period and amplitude and phase difference $\pi/2$ compound into a uniform circular motion is also obvious from the definition of simple harmonic motion.

If the phase difference is neither zero, π nor $\pi/2$, we have as the resultant an ellipse with oblique axes, but still inscribed in the same rectangle as before. Such a case is illustrated in Fig. 15, in which the phase difference is $\pi/4$, or one-eighth of a period.

In this case the numerals in the lower circle are shifted

forwards by the angle $\pi/4$, those in the other circle
remaining in the standard position. The resultant inclined
ellipse shown then follows from the ordinary method of
projection.

Analytical Method.—To treat the problem analytically
it is convenient to take a general symbol for the phase
difference, and afterwards assign to it any required values.
We accordingly write for the two rectangular components:

$$x = a \sin (\omega t + \delta) \qquad (1),$$

$$y = b \sin \omega t \qquad (2).$$

Now to obtain the equation of the path we need to
eliminate t between these two equations, we shall then have
a single relation between x and y instead of having each
expressed in terms of t and other constants. The result
may be written

$$b^2x^2 - 2abxy \cos \delta + a^2y^2 = a^2b^2 \sin^2 \delta \qquad (3).$$

This is, in general, the equation of an ellipse with axes
inclined to the co-ordinate axes. To test the effect of
various phase differences, consider the following cases:—

(i) For $\delta = 0$, (3) becomes

$$(bx - ay)^2 = 0 \qquad (4),$$

which represents a pair of coincident straight lines through
the origin, and lying in the first and third quadrant as
AOA', Fig. 14. The analytical representation of a *pair*
of coincident lines corresponds to the fact that the line
AOA' is described *twice* (in opposite directions) in each
period.

(ii) For $\delta = \pi$, (3) becomes

$$(bx + ay)^2 = 0 \qquad (5),$$

representing the other diagonal BOB'.

(iii) For $\delta = \pi/2$, (3) becomes

$$b^2x^2 + a^2y^2 = a^2b^2 \qquad (6),$$

which is the equation of an ellipse with semi-axes a and b

along OX and OY respectively. Further, if $b = a$, this becomes a circle.

(iv) For $\delta = \pi/4$, (3) becomes

$$b^2x^2 - 2abxy/\sqrt{2} + a^2y^2 = a^2b^2/2 \qquad (7),$$

which is the oblique ellipse in Fig. 15.

33. Frequencies nearly Equal.—We have just seen the results of compounding two simple harmonic motions of equal period and various phase-differences. Now, let the periods be very nearly but not quite equal, and let the initial phase-difference be zero. Then it is evident that initially the resultant will be practically that corresponding to vibrations of equal period and like phases. When, however, one vibration has gained an eighth of a period on the other, we shall have as resultant a figure closely resembling the oblique ellipse just dealt with above. When the phase-difference has become a quarter of a period we shall have for resultant something closely like the ellipse with axes parallel to the component vibrations, and so forth, passing through all possible phase-differences while one vibration gains a period on the other. Thus, when the difference between the frequencies is very small, the phase-difference, though gradually changing, can be regarded as almost constant through any one period. Hence, for any such period, the resultant may be taken as practically represented by that closed loop obtained for two vibrations of equal frequencies and of the phase-difference which ruled at the time in question. If, on the other hand, the difference of frequencies is considerable, the resultant at any time differs materially from a closed loop, because an appreciable change in the phase-difference has occurred in the course of a single period.

34. EXPT. 13. *Composition illustrated by Spherical Pendulum.* —Take a thread about a metre long, fasten it rigidly at its upper end, and attach a metal bob to the free end below. There should be space enough for the bob to move, say 50 cm., in any direction from its resting position. With

this simple form of spherical pendulum we may illustrate
the composition of two simple harmonic motions at right
angles to each other with periods sensibly equal, or distinctly
unequal at pleasure. These facts are seen from the following
sketch of the theory of the pendulum :—

It is shown in elementary text-books on mechanics that
the period of a simple pendulum is given by $\tau = 2\pi \sqrt{l/g}$,
where l denotes the length of the pendulum and g the
acceleration due to gravity. This expression is obtained for
vibration through angles small enough to make their sines
and circular measures practically equal. For somewhat
larger amplitudes of a radians, it is shown in more advanced
treatises that the period is approximately expressed by

$$\tau = 2\pi \sqrt{l/g}\left(1 + \frac{a^2}{16}\right).$$

Thus, if our pendulum of 100 cm. long vibrates through
an arc of 40 cm. we have $a = 0\cdot4$, and $a^2/16 = 0\cdot01$. In
other words, such vibrations have a period longer by one per
cent than infinitely small vibrations of the same pendulum.
And this would make an appreciable difference in the
behaviour of our pendulum as we shall notice presently. If,
however, the arcs used are 20 cm., the period is lengthened
by only one-fourth per cent, for halving the amplitude
reduces the correction to one-quarter. Again, for arcs of
10 cm. (or about 4 inches) we have the correction term
reduced to $\frac{1}{16}$ per cent, which is negligible for our present
purpose. Hence for vibrations within 10 cm. amplitude,
we have practically the same period as for infinitely small
arcs ; whereas with the extreme of 40 cm. arcs, or $0\cdot4$ radian
amplitude, the addition to the period reaches one per cent.

To compound vibrations with equal periods, start the bob
by a slight tap to the east say, and when it next passes
through its equilibrium position give it another similar tap
to the north or south. Then we shall have illustrated the
composition of vibrations in like or opposite phases. Then,
whether the taps were equal or not, provided they were
both feeble enough to keep the amplitudes under 10 cm., we
see, from the results of theory just quoted, that the periods
will be practically equal in the two directions at right
angles.

Hence the resultant will be an oblique straight line since the phase-difference is zero or π.

To obtain any other desired phase difference it is only necessary to time the two taps accordingly. Thus if the second tap is given to the bob when it is at either end of the swing due to the first, we have the phase-difference one-quarter or three-quarters of a period, and the resultant figure an ellipse with axes along the directions of the component vibrations. If, however, the second tap is given when the bob is neither at the zero position nor the end of its swing, we have a phase-difference between zero and a quarter of a period, and, accordingly, an oblique ellipse is described as the resultant motion.

Now let the taps be such as to give amplitudes of 40 cm. and 5 cm. respectively in two directions at right angles, the phase-difference being one-quarter. Then the figure initially described is approximately a long, narrow ellipse of semi-axes 40 cm. and 5 cm. But the period lengthwise is about one per cent greater than the cross period. And this slight inequality produces a striking effect which is at once noticed when performing the experiment. Before seeing this result it might be expected that the various figures described would be those treated in the theory of composition with various phase-differences, namely, figures all of which are inscribed in the same rectangle unchanged in size and position. This, however, is not the case. On the contrary, the quasi-ellipse shifts round, or " precesses " as it is termed, the direction of precession being the same as that of description. The explanation is easy. Suppose the large amplitude to have been originally east and west, and the small one north and south. Then the slightly longer period corresponds initially to the east and west vibration. Let the original phase-difference be $\pi/2$, so that the initial figure described is an ellipse with major axis east and west. Consider the bob as it passes round from the end of the major axis, in, say, the counter-clockwise direction. It goes north for a quarter of the shorter period, south for half that period, north for another quarter, and again crosses the major axis of the original ellipse. But its vibrations east and west have been slower, corresponding to the longer period due to large amplitude. Hence at the instant of crossing the major axis to the northward it has not quite finished its motion eastwards. It thus crosses the axis northerly and *easterly,* and at a point short of the end of the axis. Thus the second description will give a quasi-ellipse whose major axis is not exactly east and west, but has turned slightly from that position in a counter clockwise direction. But the longest period still corresponds to the major axis of this displaced ellipse, hence the cause for its further rotation holds good as before, and results in its continued rotation in the sense of description.

Of course, any of these pendulum curves are subject to a slight shrinkage of amplitude as time goes on, which causes them to fail of being quite re-entrant, apart from the special phenomenon now under notice.

35. EXPT. 14. *Composition illustrated by Stöhrer's Projection Apparatus.*—In the apparatus due to Stöhrer and illustrated in Fig. 15A, it is seen that two opaque discs are mechanically made to execute simple harmonic motions along directions at right angles. Each disc has a slit at right angles to the direction of its own motion. Hence these slits are mutually perpendicular, and leave only a small square open for light to pass through. An optical lantern is used, and so we obtain focused on the screen an image of this square hole. When the handle of the apparatus is turned to put the discs in motion, the spot of light on the screen executes a motion which is obviously the resultant of the two rectangular simple harmonic components. By means of a number of wheels supplied with the apparatus, and which may be changed at will, the periods may be made precisely equal, nearly but not quite equal, or of various simple ratios. Moreover the phase-difference can be arranged to have any desired value by springing the wheel of one disc out of gear, and setting it by any specified angle ahead of the other. If the handle is turned slowly so that the resultant motion is performed say only once or twice per second, the spot is seen in motion, but the exact shape of its path can scarcely be ascertained. If, however, the handle be turned quick enough to cause the whole cycle to be passed through not less than ten times per second, then the complete path of the resultant motion will be exhibited as a bright line. This is owing to the phenomenon of persistence of vision, in virtue of which the impression on the retina persists for about a tenth of a second after the removal of the stimulus which produced it. Hence if the periods of the components are exactly equal, we have a steady or stationary figure whose form depends upon the phase-difference chosen. If, however, the periods are slightly different (say 59 : 60, by using wheels of 60 and 59 teeth driven by the same driver), then the phase-difference passes through all its possible values in 60

Fig. 15a.—Stöhrer's Apparatus.

of the smaller periods, and hence the figure appears to slowly melt or dissolve from one characteristic form to another, passing in turn through all the forms possible for practically equal periods.

Unlike the spherical pendulum just described, the component vibrations in this apparatus preserve their original direction, amplitude, and period. Hence the rectangle which circumscribes the initial figure contains also the whole series of figures subsequently described. This apparatus may, of course, be used for periods as 1 : 2, 2 : 3, etc. But in such cases where several turns of each wheel are needed before the cycle of the resultant is completed, it is difficult to attain such speed of working as to make the whole figure apparent. Thus if the cycle occupied two-tenths of a second in description, only about half of it would be visible at any one time. The result is then far from satisfactory. Hence such cases dealt with in the next article are illustrated by a special pendulum.

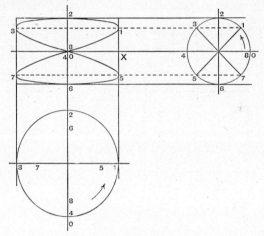

FIG. 16.—COMPOSITION OF RECTANGULAR VIBRATIONS OF PERIODS 2 : 1.

36. Periods Commensurate or nearly so.—*Periods* 2 : 1.—We shall treat this first by the graphical method previously adopted for equal periods. In Figures 16 and 17 this is illustrated for like phases and for an *initial* phase-difference corresponding to a quarter of the smaller period. It should be noted that here, since the periods are quite different, the phase is not constant, hence the term *initial* phase-difference.

The previous description of Figs. 14 and 15, and the numerals on these two figures, will make the method of description clear enough.

Analytical Treatment.—The general case for rectangular vibrations of periods as 2 : 1 is analytically represented by

$$x = a \sin (2\omega t + \delta)$$

and $$y = b \sin \omega t.$$

On eliminating t between these two, we obtain

$$\frac{4y^2}{b^2}\left(\frac{y^2}{b^2} + \frac{x}{a}\sin\delta - 1\right) + \left(\frac{x}{a} - \sin\delta\right)^2 = 0 \qquad (1),$$

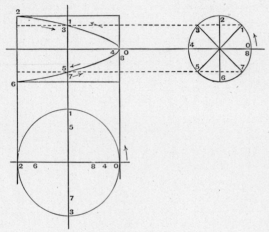

Fig. 17.—Composition with Periods 2 : 1, but in Different Phases.

which is the general equation for any phase-difference and amplitudes.

Hence, for $\delta = 0$, this becomes

$$\frac{4y^2}{b^2}\left(\frac{y^2}{b^2} - 1\right) + \frac{x^2}{a^2} = 0 \qquad (2),$$

which is the equation of the curve in Fig. 16.   For $\delta = \pi/2$ as in Figure 17, we obtain

$$\left(\frac{2y^2}{b^2} + \frac{x}{a} - 1\right)^2 = 0 \qquad (3),$$

which represents the two coincident parabolas. The equation to the single parabola may be written

$$y^2 = -\frac{b^2}{2a}(x-a) \qquad (4),$$

which gives the curve shown in the figure. Equation (3) gives two coincident curves as it should do since the single curve of (4) is described twice (viz. in opposite directions) in each cycle of the resultant motion. These two results may, of course, be obtained by giving to δ the appropriate value before eliminating t, but that method lacks generality.

Periods 3 : 1.—This need not be treated in detail by the graphical method. For it is clear that no new difficulty will arise beyond the more mechanical labour. On the other hand, in the analytical method, to avoid undue complication, it becomes advisable to sink full generality and put in at the outset the particular value of the phase-difference chosen.

Thus for $\delta = 0$ we have as the components

$$x = a \sin 3\omega t$$

and
$$y = b \sin \omega t.$$

Whence we obtain as the equation of the resultant

$$\frac{4y^3}{b^3} - \frac{3y}{b} + \frac{x}{a} = 0 \qquad (5).$$

This is a cubic or an equation of the third degree. In reality the path of the point is two coincident cubics described opposite ways. This would be seen from the graphical method. It could also be obtained analytically by elimination of t with δ unspecified, and then writing $\delta = 0$ in the equation so obtained.

Take now the following case :—

$$x = a \sin (3\omega t + \pi/2) = a \cos 3\omega t,$$

and
$$y = b \sin \omega t.$$

We then find on elimination of t,

$$\frac{x^2}{a^2} = \left(1 - \frac{y^2}{b^2}\right)\left(1 - \frac{4y^2}{b^2}\right)^2 \qquad (6).$$

This is a curve of the sixth degree.

Other Ratios.—For periods of any ratios whatever, commensurate or incommensurate, the graphical method is applicable, and gives, as readily as can be expected, the result sought. The analytical method, on the other hand, soon becomes exceedingly cumbrous, and is perhaps hardly worth using for ratios beyond those just given. Where the periods are nearly but not quite of a given simple ratio, the resultant may be approximately expressed as that for the simple ratio in question, but with a continuously changing phase-difference. A special case of this has already been dwelt upon at some length, namely, that in which the frequencies are nearly equal.

37. Typical Examples of Composition of Rectangular Vibrations.—Let the two vibrations be respectively

$$x = a \sin (r\omega t + \delta) \text{ and } y = b \sin \omega t.$$

The type of the resultant then depends upon the value of the ratio, r, of the periods and the phase-difference as expressed by δ. The ratio of length and width of the circumscribing rectangle is of course dependent on the value of a/b, the ratio of the amplitudes, but this affects the dimensions only, and not the type of the resultant curve. Fig. 18 shows a few typical cases, the value of the ratios being given in the first column and those of δ vary from 0 to π along the lines.

EXPT. 15. *Composition illustrated by Blackburn's Pendulum.* —All the cases just given in Fig. 18 and any others can be illustrated in a very clear and interesting manner by a simple apparatus known as Blackburn's pendulum. Fig. 19 shows an outline of the instrument, which is seen to consist essentially of a bob and funnel with a **Y**-shaped suspension. The stem of the **Y** has a length l, while the whole length to

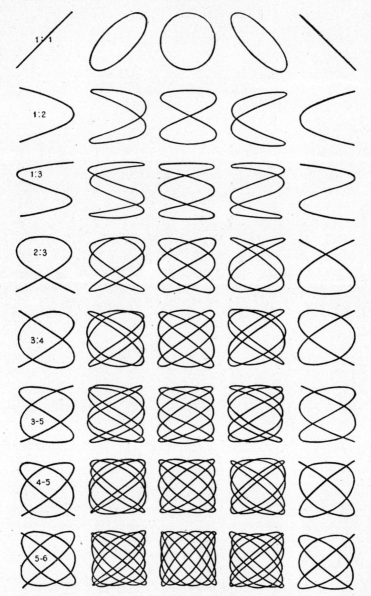

Fig. 18.—Typical Cases of Rectangular Vibrations.

the level of the top points is L. Thus for vibrations normal
to the plane of the **Y** the period is given by $T = 2\pi \sqrt{L/g}$,
while for vibrations in the plane of the **Y** executed by the
stem of the **Y** only, the period in $t = 2\pi \sqrt{l/g}$. So the ratio
of the periods is given by $r = \sqrt{L/l}$, and by altering the L
and l, r may be made what we please. To form a trace of
the path the funnel may contain fine silver sand which is
received on a blackened surface. Some ready means of
changing the lengths is required ; one simple method consists
in fixing the position A, of the top of the stem of the **Y**, by
a metal clip which can be slid up and down, and remains by

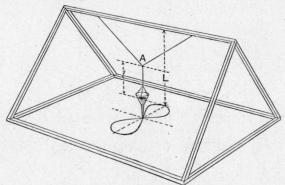

FIG. 19.—BLACKBURN'S PENDULUM.

friction where set. It is also desirable to have packing
blocks or wedges under the board to bring it near to the
funnel, as if too far away the sand spreads too much. The
bob may be a simple ring of lead round the funnel, or a piece
of cast metal turned and bored true. Of course the greater
the mass of the bob for a given size, the less quickly will the
vibrations die away. It is obvious that with this pendulum
the ratio of periods and amplitudes and the values of the
phase-difference can all be varied at pleasure within very
wide limits. When, as usually is the case, the adjustment
of periods aimed at is not quite attained, then the figure
passes successively through all the forms characteristic of the
various phases for the ratio in question. Thus the forms
appear successively like those in a given line of Fig. 18,
but those corresponding to different lines are not mixed.

38. Composition of Linear Progressive Waves.—The

problem of compounding wave motions progressing along the same line at the same speed naturally falls under two heads, according as their directions of motion are the same or opposite. When they are the same the matter is very simple and can readily be extended to embrace more than two components. It is sufficient to consider the form of each wave at a given instant, and then to compound them by addition of their respective ordinates. The resultant instantaneous wave-form so obtained must then be imagined to move with the speed of its components. It then represents the resultant wave motion sought. Thus, let the components be

$$y_1 = a_1 \sin \omega_1(t - x/v) \text{ and } y_2 = a_2 \sin \omega_2(t - x/v) \quad (1),$$

and for compounding them choose the instant $t = 0$. The above equations then reduce to

$$y_1 = -a_1 \sin (\omega_1 x/v) \text{ and } y_2 = -a_2 \sin (\omega_2 x/v) \quad (2).$$

Hence the resultant at $t = 0$ is given by

$$y_0 = -a_1 \sin (\omega_1 x/v) - a_2 \sin (\omega_2 x/v) \quad (3).$$

Thus the initial displacement is expressed in terms of x, and the curve so obtained must be shifted along in the positive direction of x at speed v to represent the resultant wave motion. This final result can be obtained and represented analytically by the simple addition of the original components as expressed by the equation (1). Thus, we have

$$y = a_1 \sin \omega_1(t - x/v) + a_2 \sin \omega_2(t - x/v) \quad (4),$$

which is equivalent to the statement made in words.

It is obvious that the resultant wave-forms at any instant, in the case now before us, are identical both in shape and process of derivation with the corresponding displacement curves shown in Fig. 13, art. 31. But in that case the abscissæ represented time, whereas now abscissæ represent actual lengths just as the ordinates do in both cases.

If the progressive waves to be compounded are longitudinal instead of transverse, they may still be represented by the above curves on the usual conventions for longitudinal waves.

39. Formation of Stationary Waves.—Let us now turn to the case of compounding waves progressing in opposite directions. In doing so we shall restrict our examination to the simple but important case of components of equal periods and amplitudes. And this is precisely the type which oftenest occurs. For either wave train may be

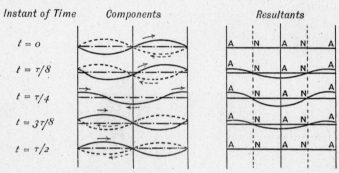

FIG. 20.—DERIVATION OF STATIONARY WAVES.

produced from the other by reflection, as will be seen in Expt. 16 and treated further in Chap. IV. The resultant of the components in question is a system of waves alternately waxing and waning, but without progression in either direction. To this the term *stationary waves* is applied. The process of graphical composition by displacement curves and the result obtained are sufficiently illustrated in Fig. 20. Five sets of curves are given showing the components and resultants after equal intervals of $\tau/8$.

Fig. 21 illustrates in more detail the state of things in stationary waves at two typical instants. In this figure the first three lines apply equally well to transverse or

longitudinal waves; the last line has reference to longitudinal
waves only. The points marked N and A in Figs. 20 and
21 denote respectively the places of no motion and
maximum motion. They are called *nodes* and *antinodes*.
The last line of Fig. 21 shows linear densities of longitudinal
waves, in which the U's mean undisturbed or normal
densities, and the C's and R's compressions and rarefactions
respectively.

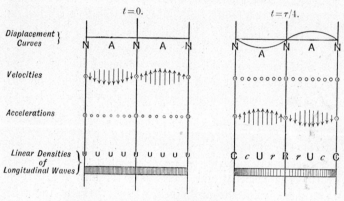

FIG. 21.—DETAILS OF STATIONARY WAVES.

40. Characteristics of Stationary Waves.—We are
now prepared for an explicit statement of the characteristics
of stationary waves of simple harmonic form, and in giving
it may fitly follow the order already adopted for progressive
waves in articles 20 and 21.

(1) With certain important exceptions each particle
    executes a simple harmonic motion. The amplitude
    of these vibrations varies continuously from point
    to point along the line of waves, passing through
    positive, zero, and negative values; whereas the
    phase, at any instant, is the same all along the line.
    The points where the amplitude is zero, and where,
    therefore, the particles never move at all, are called

F

nodes. Their distance apart is called half a wave length. The intervening portions are called ventral segments. The points midway between the nodes and where the amplitudes have their maximum values are called antinodes. The term loop is often used loosely, referring sometimes to a ventral segment and sometimes to an antinode.

(2) The arrangement of the particles at any instant is in general that of a sine-graph (or, if the waves are longitudinal, may be represented by one). But at certain instants, occurring twice in each period, this curve shrinks to a straight line.

(3) This wave-form neither changes its type nor advances, but only shrinks to a straight line by proportional diminution of all its ordinates. It then expands proportionally; all the ordinates being now reversed in sign, again shrinks, and so forth.

(4) The instantaneous form repeats itself at certain constant intervals called wave lengths.

(5) The velocity and acceleration of any one particle at any instant are precisely like those at the same instant of certain other particles whose distances longitudinally are any multiple of the wave length.

(6) If λ and τ denote respectively the wave length and period of vibration of a system of stationary waves, we have $\lambda/\tau = v$, where v represents the velocity of propagation of progressive waves of the same type which, by travelling in opposite directions, can produce the stationary waves in question.

The above sections apply to both transverse and longitudinal waves, the following section to longitudinal waves only.

(7) In longitudinal stationary waves the linear density of the particles, or their state of compression or dilatation is, at any instant, arranged in a pattern which repeats itself every wave length. Further,

this state of linear density neither changes its type
nor advances. It only changes, proportionally at
each point, to a state of uniform and normal density.
This occurs twice in each period. The deviations
from normal density then reverse sign at each point,
and experience proportional exaggeration until a
maximum is reached, when they again suffer a
shrinkage, and so forth. The nodes, or places of
no change of position, are places of maximum change
of linear density. Whereas the antinodes, or places
of maximum change of position, are places of no
change of linear density.

41. EXPT. 16. *Formation of Stationary Waves.*—The actual
experimental derivation of stationary waves may be demonstrated very simply by a solid india-rubber cord or thick-
walled tube of rubber, about half an inch in diameter, and
(say) 20 feet long. One end should be fixed, and the other
end held in the hand and moved to and fro at a suitable
rate. A train of waves is thus sent along the cord from
the hand to the fixed end where they are reflected. Thus
the incident and reflected wave trains moving in opposite
directions give us stationary waves. It is easy to arrange
that the whole length of the cord shall be $\lambda/2$, λ, $3\lambda/2$, etc.,
thus containing 1, 2, 3, etc., ventral segments. To form and
sustain clearly marked and regular stationary waves it is
necessary that the motions of the hand should be regular
and sustained.

EXPT. 16a. *Progressive and Stationary Waves Contrasted.*—
If a wire is wound uniformly round a cylinder so as to form
a helix, and then taken off and viewed from a distance, it is
easily seen that it must present the appearance of a sine-
graph. Moreover, if it is rotated uniformly, this sine-graph
will appear to move endwise, and thus represent a progressive
wave. Again, if a piece of the same wire be taken and bent
in a plane to the form of a sine-graph, with a piece left at
each end to form the axis of the graph, it is obvious that
this wire will, on rotation, represent a set of stationary
waves. For the amplitudes will all change proportionally
and vanish simultaneously when the wire is viewed edge-

wise. To exhibit these effects to an audience it would be inconvenient to view the wires direct. It is therefore desirable to mount the pair of wires as a small working model, and throw their image on the screen by the projection lantern. Fig. 22 shows the model used by the writer for this purpose.

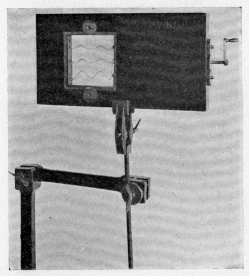

Fig. 22.—Lantern Model for Stationary and Progressive Waves.

42. Analytical Treatment of Stationary Waves.—

Let the two systems of oppositely travelling waves be represented by

$$y_1 = a \sin \omega(t - x/v) \text{ and } y_2 = a \sin \omega(t + x/v) \quad (1).$$

Then the equation of the resultant system of stationary waves is obtained by addition, and may be written—

$$y = 2 \cos (\omega x/v)a \sin \omega t \qquad (2).$$

The comparison of the part played by x in (1) and (2) shows at once the leading distinction between the two kinds of waves. The contrasting features have already been set forth in sections (1) of articles 20, 21, and 40, and may well be again referred to here as derivable from equations (1) and (2) above. In the equation for progressive waves, x enters into the argument of which the sine is taken and there only. It thus, by its change, can change the phase of the vibration, but is powerless to alter its amplitude. In the equation for stationary waves, on the other hand, x enters into the coefficient and there only. It is accordingly able, by its change, to change the amplitude, but is unable to affect the phase.

All the features shown in Figs. 20 and 21, and detailed in article 40 may be derived from equation (2) of this article. For the statement as to longitudinal density the y in equation (2) must be interpreted as a displacement along x.

To derive the characteristics from (2) it is as well to write it in the form—

$$y = 2 \cos (2\pi x/\lambda)a \sin \omega t \qquad (3).$$

Then for $t = 0$, $y = 0$ for all values of x. Also, for $x = \lambda/4$, $3\lambda/4$, $5\lambda/4$, etc., $y = 0$ for all values of t. These points correspond to the nodes and are seen to occur at intervals of $\lambda/2$. Again, for $x = 0$, $\lambda/2$, λ, etc., $y = \pm 2a \sin \omega t$ (4). These points $\lambda/2$ apart correspond, therefore, to the anti-nodes, since here the amplitude is a maximum, namely $\pm 2a$. By differentiating (3) with respect to t, we obtain for the velocity of any point x at time t—

$$\dot{y} = - 2\omega \cos (2\pi x/\lambda)a \cos \omega t \qquad (4).$$

Differentiating again, we have for the acceleration—

$$\ddot{y} = - \omega^2 y \qquad (5).$$

43. Diverging Waves. — Hitherto, for the sake of simplicity, we have considered waves advancing along a line merely. In actual fact, however, such waves are not usually met with. We must, accordingly, extend our ideas to waves starting from a given source and diverging thence in various directions, either (1) in a plane, or (2) in space of three dimensions. Waves diverging in all directions in a plane are familiarly illustrated by the ripples formed on the surface of calm water, in which a pebble is dropped. The waves diverging in solid space are illustrated by the case with which we are here most concerned, namely, sound waves in air. To give an example in which the divergence is of the most regular character, namely, spherical shells of alternately compressed and rarefied air, we may explode a gaseous mixture in a soap bubble. For this purpose the products of the electrolysis of dilute acid may be used.

Composition of Diverging Wave Systems.—Suppose we have two sources of exactly similar waves spreading in a plane. Then it is obvious that at some places the crests of one system will coincide with the crests of the other. We shall, accordingly, have unusually high crests at such places. Again, where the troughs of one system coincide with the troughs of the other, we shall have specially deep troughs. But where the crests of one system coincide with the troughs of the other, we may have a maintenance of the normal level. This phenomenon of the increased disturbance at some places, and the obliteration of disturbance at others, is often called the *interference* of the wave systems in question. The term is introduced under protest as one which has acquired such vogue that it should be known. Its reference is obviously to the annulment produced by opposite phases. But it has been pertinently asked, if that is interference in which the resultant is the algebraic sum of the components, what can non-interference be ?

The positions of the places of crest on crest, and crest on trough, can be easily seen from the circles in Fig. 23. In this the sources are the centres, the full lines show crests, and the dotted ones troughs. Hence where lines of the same kind intersect we have increased effects, where lines of opposite kinds cross we have no change from the normal level.

Figs. 84 and 85 are from photographs of such divergent wave systems obtained by Dr. J. H. Vincent on the surface of mercury by points from vibrating tuning-forks.

To extend either of these cases to that of the composition of wave systems radiating in three dimensions we must, in imagination, rotate the whole about an axis passing through the two point sources. Thus the ripples in the form of circles on a plane give place to spherical shells, and the

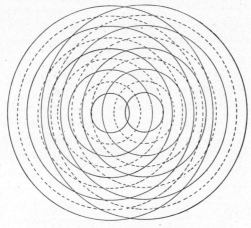

Fig. 23.—Composition of Divergent Waves.

points where crest falls on crest become circles whose centres lie upon the axis of rotation containing the two point sources. The same applies to the points where crest falls on trough, or trough on trough.

44. Huyghens' Principle of Wavelets and Envelopes. —Let us now consider, in more detail, the advance of waves in three dimensions in space from a point source. Let the velocity of propagation be the same in every direction. We can then regard the advance of the waves in two ways. First, we may think of them simply as emanating from the given source without any intermediate consideration. Second, we may think of the state of things at a certain instant as derivable from that at some previous instant when the disturbance was on its way from the source. This second view, which is often of great utility, was put forward by Huyghens in 1678 with reference to light, but may be applied equally to sound. In the original treatise by Huyghens the explanation and discussion of this principle occupies about seven pages, and is nowhere concisely enunciated. It accordingly appears in very different forms in the various text-books on optics and sound. This seems likely to lead to haziness of conception on the part of the student. Consequently, in the hope of making Huyghens' principle as clear as possible we shall here attempt to condense the pith of it for our purpose, in the following definition and enunciation :—

DEFINITION.—The locus of all points just reached by a wave disturbance at any instant is called the *wave front* at the instant in question.

HUYGHENS' PRINCIPLE.—The wave front at any instant may be derived as the *envelope* of *wavelets* whose origins are all the points constituting the wave front which existed *t* seconds previously. In an isotropic medium at rest these wavelets are spherical and of radius *vt*, where *v* is the velocity of propagation of the waves in all directions in the given medium.

The above statements, being highly condensed, will be understood better on reference to a concrete example, namely, that given in Fig. 24, which is a reproduction of one of Huyghens' original diagrams.

In this figure A represents the point source of a wave proceeding towards CE. At a certain instant the wave front is the arc CE whose centre is A. This, on the ordinary view, would be regarded simply as having emanated from A without any inquiry as to the intermediate stages in the process of propagation. But on Huyghens' view we may regard the wave front CE as derived from the concentric arc BG, which was the wave front at some previous instant. To construct CE on this principle, a number of points, B*bbbb*G, are taken on the wave front HBGI. From these points as centres circular arcs are described with the radius BC = GE. Then CE is easily seen to be the envelope of these secondary waves or wavelets. In this extremely simple case, that of the emanation of a wave from a point source, it is evident that no simplification of construction follows from the adoption of Huyghens' principle. In fact, it is much easier to describe CE as the circular arc whose centre is A, than to describe it as the envelope of half a dozen similar arcs. But the gain lies in the insight thus afforded into the process of propagation. The conception thus gained may be applied easily to other cases which cannot well be resolved by any other method.

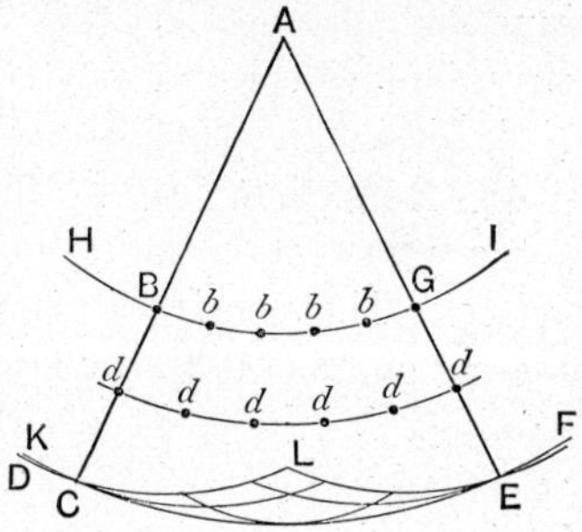

The grounds for accepting Huyghens' view of the matter

FIG. 24.—HUYGHENS' PRINCIPLE.

lie in its reasonableness, and in the agreement between its consequences and experiment. This agreement will be unfolded as we proceed, the reasonableness we may note now. Thus, since at some instant the wave starts from A, and at some later instant CE is the wave front, it may be assumed that all parts of space between A and CE have been traversed by the wave disturbance. Hence BG, concentric with CE, was at some instant the wave front. At this instant each point along BG was in a state of disturbance, and might therefore be regarded as the origin of an elementary disturbance; that is, each such point may be looked upon as the centre of a circular wave. Again, looking at the matter quantitatively, let the time for A to B be t_1, and from B to C be t_2, then the time from A to C would be $t_1 + t_2$. Thus, if the velocity of propagation be denoted by v, we have $AC = v(t_1 + t_2)$, taking the ordinary view of propagation without any reference to the intermediate wave front BG. Secondly, on taking Huyghens' view, we have $AB = vt_1$, and $BC = vt_2$, so that $AC = v(t_1 + t_2)$ as before. Hence the ordinary view, and that obtained on Huyghens' principle, are in agreement in the case considered.

Let us also notice here that the direction of advance of the wave is normal to the wave front. Further, if we take a very distant point source, our wave front is practically plane and advances at right angles to it. It will often be convenient to consider waves of this nature which we may briefly designate plane waves.

45. Reflection at a Plane Surface.—Suppose now that a plane wave falls obliquely upon a plane reflecting surface. The consideration of what happens is somewhat obscure on the ordinary view, but is very simple when examined in the light of Huyghens' principle, which we accordingly now apply. Fig. 25 is again from Huyghens' classical treatise of 1678.

In this figure AHHHC is the plane wave front at the instant of incidence of A upon the plane surface AKKKB of the obstacle. The angle of incidence may be measured by BAC, the angle between the wave front and the reflecting surface. It may be noted, in passing, that these planes have each an important physical meaning and objective reality ; whereas the angle of the same value, used in the ordinary method of geometrical optics, is taken between the normals to these surfaces, the normals being geometrical conceptions which are not in evidence in any experiment on reflection.

Consider now the passage of the wave front AC ; if no obstacle were present it would pass to GB, the opposite side of the rectangle ACBG. Owing, however, to the presence of the obstacle, the wavelet from any one of the points H can only reach in the original direction the corresponding point K, hence the equivalent of the remaining portion, KM, of the path must be executed, after reflection, on the original side of the surface AB. Thus, A, H, H, H, C, being the centres of the wavelets, we note first that the distance AG must be traversed wholly after reflection from A. We therefore describe from A the arc AN with radius AG. The path CB, on the other hand, is wholly described in the original direction before reflection. The paths from the intermediate points H, H, H, need treating in two parts as mentioned before. The first part HK is undisturbed in direction. The second part, equal in length to KM, is

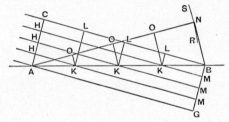

Fig. 25.—Plane Reflection on Huyghens' Principle.

then to be treated as the radius of a wavelet whose centre is K. We thus derive the plane wave front BN, reflected from AB, as the envelope of arcs whose centres are A, K, K, K, and radii AG, KM, KM, KM respectively. The three pairs of lines, each pair lettered LK and KO, trace the disappearance of the incident wave front and the growth of the reflected wave front. It is seen that only when the incident wave has wholly disappeared is the reflected wave front completely formed, and on the point of quitting the surface which has produced it. The angle of reflection, NBA, is easily seen to be equal to that of incidence, CAB; for AN is equal to CB, and AB is the common hypothenuse of the two right-angled triangles ACB and BNA. We accordingly have an agreement between the result of Huyghens' principle and the experimental facts to be dealt with later.

46. Refraction at a Plane Surface.—Huyghens' method of treating this problem is illustrated by Fig. 26, taken also from his original work.

Here AB represents the first face of a second medium in which the waves can advance, but with a speed bearing a constant ratio to that of their speed in the first medium. AC is the wave front at the instant when A is incident upon the face AB. If the first medium extended without

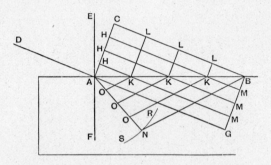

FIG. 26.—PLANE REFRACTION ON HUYGHENS' PRINCIPLE.

interruption, this wave front would advance to GB. Owing, however, to the presence of the second medium, in which the advance of the wave is retarded, some other line, NB, is reached instead of GB. To obtain NB on Huyghens' principle, we take a number of points, H, H, H, on the wave front AC, and draw from them lines HKM, parallel to the direction of advance of the wave, cutting the refracting face at K, K, K, and reaching at M, M, M, the line BG. Thus, at the instant when the wave front reaches any point K, K becomes the origin of a spherical wavelet spreading in the second medium. The radius of this wavelet after time t will be $v't$, where v' is the speed of the waves in the second medium. Let v be the cor-

responding speed for the first medium. Then, to obtain the
refracted wave front NB, we must (1) describe from A the
arc RNS of radius AN, where $AN : AG = v' : v$; (2) describe
from each point K an arc with radius (v'/v) times the corresponding KM. Thus, we obtain as the new wave after
refraction the line NB, which is the envelope of the
wavelets just described. The three pairs of lines, LK, KO,
trace the diminution of the incident wave front, and the
growth of the refracted wave front, as the process of refraction proceeds.

Let us now seek the relation between the angles of
incidence and refraction to which this principle leads.
Obviously the angles in question are respectively CAB and
NBA, in the two right-angled triangles whose common
hypothenuse is AB. Thus, taking sines of the angles, we
have by construction,

$$\frac{\sin \text{CAB}}{\sin \text{NBA}} = \frac{\text{CB}/\text{AB}}{\text{NA}/\text{AB}} = \frac{v}{v'},$$

or, $$\frac{\sin i}{\sin r} = \frac{v}{v'} = \mu \text{ say},\qquad\qquad (1),$$

where i and r denote the angle of incidence and refraction,
and μ, the ratio of the velocities, is called the index of
refraction for the pair of media in question. This consequence of Huyghens' principle, that the ratio of the sines
is constant, is seen to be in accord with the well-known
optical laws of refraction. The same laws are valid for
acoustics also. But the above treatment of Huyghens gives
further a physical significance to the index of refraction,
showing it to be the ratio of the velocities in the two
media. This, too, is in accord with the experimental facts
both of light and sound. In the domain of optics the
knowledge of this relation assisted in the rejection of
Newton's emission theory and the establishment of the
wave theory in its place, for Newton's emission theory
required the false relation $\mu = v'/v$.

47. Reflection and Refraction at Curved Surfaces.—
We have just seen that the ordinary laws of reflection and
refraction may be derived from Huyghens' principle. But
all the formulæ of geometrical optics are based upon these
laws, hence they may be derived from Huyghens' principle.
This could be done directly or by the use of the laws of
reflection and refraction just established. Thus all the
relations in use in optics between the distances of object
and image with spherical mirrors and lenses are valid for
the analogous cases of the reflection and refraction of sound.
The index of refraction from the first to the second of any
two media is always the ratio of the speed of sound in the
first to that in the second as already shown. As phenomena
of this kind occupy a subordinate place in acoustics we
must dismiss the subject now with this brief reference.

**48. From a Small Opening Waves Spread : Dif-
fraction.—**We must now pass to the consideration of
phenomena lying outside the domain of geometrical optics
of which some are not explainable even by Huyghens'
principle in its original form. First, consider the incidence
of a wave motion upon a small round opening, *i.e.* one
whose diameter is very small compared with the length
of the waves falling on it. We can then regard this
opening as practically a single point on the incident wave
front. Hence, by Huyghens' principle, it is the origin of
a spherical wavelet. Further, no other point on the wave
front is free to send wavelets, for the opening in question
is considered as a mere point. Hence, the new wave front,
which is the envelope of wavelets originating on the old
front, is, in this case, reduced to the spherical wavelet
whose centre is the opening under discussion. And this
is true whatever the form of the original wave front which
encountered the small opening. Thus if it were a plane
wave front, the waves would be advancing along *parallel*
lines, but after passing the opening the wave front is
spherical, and the directions of advance radial, and therefore

diverging. This is illustrated in Fig. 27, in which the incident waves are represented as plane. Partially opened doors and windows in a house or other building afford apertures which may be regarded as small in comparison with the wave length of many common sounds. Thus, the openings may be a few inches wide, and the wave length of the speaking voice of a man may be eight feet or more. Hence such sounds spread in all directions beyond those openings, as is well known, instead of proceeding in straight lines and giving sharp sound *shadows* as in the case of light through the same openings. Two such openings close together would be comparable to two small point sources of waves. They would, consequently, form an interfering

Fig. 27. — Waves Spread from Small Hole.

system like that discussed in article 43 and illustrated in Figure 23. In physical optics various phenomena due to the spreading of light waves when passing through narrow openings or round small obstacles are known and studied under the general term diffraction. In all such cases the openings in question bear about the same relation to the wave length of light as the openings for the analogous acoustical phenomena bear to the wave length of sound.

49. A Large Opening allows Rectilinear Propagation. —Now consider the passage of waves through an opening not small in comparison with the wave length, say of width equalling or exceeding it. We can here derive the main portion of the wave front beyond the opening, on Huyghens' principle, as the envelope of a number of wavelets.

Thus, as shown in Fig. 28, we obtain from a plane wave incident upon the opening AB, a transmitted wave whose main central part, equal to that width, is plane also. But, in addition, we have feebler curved portions which appear as continuations of the main central part. These curved parts project beyond the dotted lines AC and BD, which limit the central plane part, or transmitted wave proper, and are due to wavelets whose origins lie at A and B. In his discussion of the optical case, these curved portions were dismissed by Huyghens with the remark that the vibrations there were too feeble to produce light. This, however, falls short of a complete account of the phenomena. The fact is that, when we have rectilinear propagation, the wavelets interfere and mutually weaken each other outside the limits of the transmitted beam. This application of Young's principle of interference in

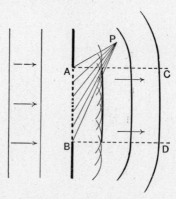

Fig. 28.—Rectilinear Propagation of Waves.

completion of Huyghens' principle was made by Fresnel. Hence, by what we may term the Huyghens-Fresnel principle, we are furnished with a satisfactory explanation of the rectilinear propagation of wave motion under certain circumstances. We thus see that the spreading, so usual in the case of sound, and the rectilinear propagation, so usual in the case of light, are simply matters of scale, and are both explicable on the wave theory. We are thus led to infer that under exceptional conditions we may have the rectilinear propagation of sound and the spreading of light after passing through a narrow slit. And both these phenomena have been observed, the phenomena due to the spreading of light, as already noticed, being termed diffraction effects.

Let us now examine a little more closely the conditions needed for the rectilinear propagation of a wave disturbance. Take a point P (Fig. 28) outside the track followed by the beam when rectilinear propagation occurs. Then, assuming that no resultant disturbance is felt at P, we see that, on the Fresnel extension of Huyghens' principle, this must be due to the destructive interference at P of all the wavelets whose origins lie along AB. In other words, although P is simultaneously affected by wavelets whose origins occupy the opening AB, yet the disturbances arriving at P have at every instant a zero resultant. Obviously, if AB is small compared to the wave length, the resultant could not be zero, for all the wavelets would reach P in practically the same phase. If, however, the opening AB is a number of wave lengths wide, theory and experiment alike show that a train of waves incident on the opening give a transmitted beam with rectilinear propagation, the intensity off the track of the beam being almost inappreciable.

49a. Failure of Rectilinear Propagation from Impulse.

—Suppose now, instead of a succession of waves of constant amplitude falling on AB where the width is several wave lengths, we had only a single wave or a still shorter disturbance of an impulsive character. In that case we cannot have the *simultaneous* arrival at P of wavelets proceeding from all points of AB, for that implies their starting from the various parts of AB at instants differing by several periods, which is now impossible, since, by the impulsive character of the source, AB is only disturbed for an instant or fraction of a period. Thus we should have, arriving *successively* at P, the wavelets that had started at the same instant from various parts of AB. But, in consequence of this successive arrival, no destructive interference is possible.

G

This interesting theoretical deduction receives a striking experimental confirmation in the instantaneous photographs by Professor C. V. Boys of bullets in flight. By kind permission of Newton and Co., the holders of the copyright, one of these photographs is reproduced in Fig. 29.

The bullet passes through a dark box in front of a sensitive plate, and is photographed at the right instant by an

FIG. 29.—HUYGHENS' WAVELETS FROM FLYING BULLET.

electric spark let off by the completion of a circuit by the bullet itself. In the photograph here reproduced reflectors were in use to test the reflection of the air waves from the point and rear of the projectile. The Huyghens' wavelets, shown so beautifully in this plate, came as a surprise, being neither sought nor expected by the experimenters.

50. EXPT. 17. *Huyghens' Principle illustrated by Ripple Tank.*—The wave effects just dealt with can be illustrated very well by ripples on the surface of water in a flat-bottomed vessel. It is desirable to have, for this purpose, a tank with a bottom of plate-glass painted white and carefully levelled, and then covered with inky water to a depth of about half a centimetre. About 3 feet by 2 feet will be found a convenient size for the tank if it is desired to exhibit the phenomena to a class. To start a train of plane waves, a lath, about a foot long, may be put in and suddenly moved to and fro broadside. If, in the path of the advancing ripples, two obstacles are placed so as to leave only a small opening, then the waves passing through are seen to spread. If, on the other hand, the opening is wide enough, a nearly plane wave may be obtained, thus showing propagation which is approximately rectilinear. Again, if only an impulsive wave be sent, the Huyghens' wavelets may be seen, as shown by the bullet in flight. The use of a tank for these purposes was pointed out by Professor S. P. Thompson.

51. Fourier's Theorem illustrated.—We have already seen in articles 27 and 31 that the composition of simple harmonic vibrations of commensurate periods may result in periodic motions of various characters. We now pass to the examination of a very important theorem which may be applied to this subject. It was discovered by Fourier, and is given in his renowned Analytical Theory of Heat (Paris, 1822). This theorem shows that the composition of commensurate simple harmonic motions of suitable amplitudes and phases is competent to produce a finite periodic motion of any form whatever. The theorem also shows how to determine the amplitudes and phases of the components requisite to produce any given resultant. In other words, it shows how to *analyse* any given periodic motion, however complicated, into the simple harmonic components of which it may be conceived to be built up.

Thus, in Fig. 30, line (i) is the displacement diagram of a given vibration of period τ and amplitude k. The diagram consists of two straight lines at equal but opposite slopes. It accordingly denotes a uniform motion in one direction followed, without any break, by a precisely similar motion in the opposite direction. Let it be required to analyse this motion into its simple harmonic components.

Fourier's theorem, applied to this case, gives as the components an infinite series of simple harmonic motions whose

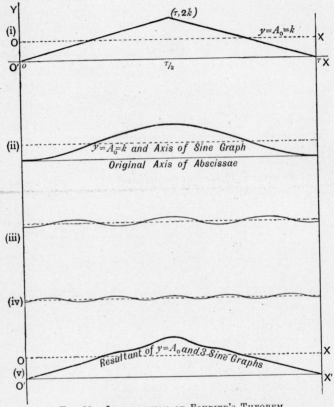

Fig. 30.—Illustration of Fourier's Theorem.

periods are τ, $\tau/3$, $\tau/5$, $\tau/7$, . . . and whose amplitudes are respectively

$$\frac{8k}{\pi^2}\left\{1,\ \frac{1}{3^2},\ \frac{1}{5^2},\ \frac{1}{7^2},\ \cdots\right\}$$

The phases are best seen by reference to the figure, the first three components being shown in lines (ii.), (iii.), and (iv.). Line (v.) shows the result of compounding these three components. It will be seen that the resultant of the first three of the infinite series comes very close to the required vibration. It is, therefore, easy to believe, what at first seemed almost impossible, that an infinite number of simple harmonic motions may yield as their resultant a broken line, or, indeed, any vibration whatever. Many other illustrations might be given, but considerations of space force us to conclude with a brief outline of the mathematical treatment and its application to a few typical cases.

52. Analytical Treatment of Fourier's Theorem.— Fourier's theorem is susceptible of many forms of expression. For our purpose the following is convenient :—

$$\left.\begin{aligned} y = A_0 + a_1 \cos \omega t + a_2 \cos 2\omega t + \ \ldots \\ + a_n \cos n\omega t + \ \ldots \\ + b_1 \sin \omega t + b_2 \sin 2\omega t + \ \ldots \\ + b_n \sin n\omega t + \ldots \end{aligned}\right\} \quad (1),$$

$$A_0 = \frac{1}{\tau} \int_0^\tau y \, dt \quad (2),$$

$$a_n = \frac{2}{\tau} \int_0^\tau y \cos (n\omega t) dt \quad (3),$$

$$b_n = \frac{2}{\tau} \int_0^\tau y \sin (n\omega t) dt \quad (4);$$

where, as usual, $\omega\tau = 2\pi$.

Here y denotes the displacements at time t, of a point executing a vibration of any type whatever of period τ. The fundamental fact of Fourier's theorem, *i.e.* the possibility of expressing such a vibration in terms of simple harmonic components, is stated in equation (1). The values of the constants in the right-hand side of (1) are given in the three following equations. The rigid proof of this theorem is beyond the scope of this text-book. It is well, however, to notice that, granting the possibility of the expansion given in equation (1), we may verify equations (2), (3), and (4) as follows :—

Multiply (1) by dt and integrate from 0 to τ, and we obtain (2).

Next, multiply (1) by $\cos(n\omega t)dt$ and integrate from 0 to τ, and we obtain (3).

Finally, multiply (1) by $\sin(n\omega t)dt$ and integrate from 0 to τ, and we obtain (4).

Equation (1) may be thrown into the form—

$$y = A_0 + A_1 \cos(\omega t - \epsilon_1) + A_2 \cos(2\omega t - \epsilon_2) + \cdots \\ + A_n \cos(n\omega t - \epsilon_n) + \cdots$$

or, still more compactly thus,

$$y = A_0 + \sum_{n=1}^{n=\infty} A_n \cos(n\omega t - \epsilon_n)$$

(5).

These forms correspond with (1) when the new constants fulfil the conditions—

$$A_n^2 = a_n^2 + b_n^2 \qquad (6),$$

and

$$\tan \epsilon_n = b_n / a_n \qquad (7).$$

Thus, the constants of (5) are expressible in terms of those given in (2), (3), and (4).

53. Analytical Illustration of Fourier's Theorem.—

Let us now illustrate the working of this theorem by its application to the case shown in Fig. 30. The values of y as a function of t are given by the ordinates in line (i.) of the figure, the middle point having co-ordinates $\left(\dfrac{\tau}{2}, 2k\right)$.

From this we have to determine the right side of equation (1) of art. 52, which expresses y analytically as the sum of sines or cosines, or both. It will now be convenient to take as our axes of abscissæ $O'X'$ in lines (i.) and (v.) instead of OX throughout as in the former references to this figure. Then, on turning to equations (2), (3), and (4), we see that it is necessary to express y in terms of t ready for insertion

under the sign of integration. It is obvious from line (i.)
in the figure that it is desirable to take two equations for
y, one for the first, or ascending half of the line, and
another for the second or descending half. These are
respectively

$$y = 4kt/\tau, \qquad \text{from } t = 0 \text{ to } t = \tau/2 ;$$

and $\qquad y = 4k(\tau - t)/\tau, \quad \text{from } t = \dfrac{\tau}{2} \text{ to } t = \tau \qquad (8).$

Hence each of the integrals in (2), (3), and (4) splits into
two. We accordingly obtain

$$\mathrm{A}_0 = \frac{1}{\tau}\left\{ \int_0^{\tau/2} \frac{4kt}{\tau}\,dt + \int_{\tau/2}^{\tau} \frac{4k(\tau - t)}{\tau}\,dt \right\} = k \qquad (9),$$

$$a_n = \frac{2}{\tau}\left\{ \int_0^{\tau/2} \frac{4kt}{\tau} \cos n\omega t\,dt + \int_{\tau/2}^{\tau} \frac{4k(\tau - t)}{\tau} \cos n\omega t\,dt \right\}$$

$$= \frac{4k}{n^2\pi^2}[(-1)^n - 1] \qquad (10),$$

$$b_n = \frac{2}{\tau}\left\{ \int_0^{\tau/2} \frac{4kt}{\tau} \sin n\omega t\,dt + \int_{\tau/2}^{\tau} \frac{4k(\tau - t)}{\tau} \sin n\omega t\,dt \right\} = 0 \qquad (11).$$

Putting now for n in equation (10) the values 1, 2, 3, 4,
etc., we see that for all even values of n the corresponding
a's become zero. The odd values of n give to the corresponding a's the following values:—

$$-\frac{8k}{\pi^2}\left\{ \frac{1}{1^2}, \frac{1}{3^2}, \frac{1}{5^2}, \text{ etc.} \right\} \qquad (12).$$

Hence inserting these values in (1) we have finally

$$y = k - \frac{8k}{\pi^2}\left\{ \frac{\cos \omega t}{1^2} + \frac{\cos 3\omega t}{3^2} + \frac{\cos 5\omega t}{5^2} + \cdots \right\} \qquad (13).$$

And from the first few terms of this expansion shown in
(13) the curves of figure 30 were plotted. To test this

equation, give to t in succession the values 0, $\tau/4$, $\tau/2$, and τ, and we find the corresponding values of y to be 0, k, $2k$, and 0, as should be the case.

When working out these values of y it should be remembered that the infinite series involved sums up as follows :—

$$\frac{1}{1^2} + \frac{1}{3^2} + \frac{1}{5^2} + \frac{1}{7^2} + \text{ad. inf.} = \frac{\pi^2}{8} \qquad (14).$$

This summation is given in Riemann's *Partielle Differential-gleichungen* and elsewhere.

54. Partial Fourier Series.—When it is known that the function to be expanded consists of sine terms only, or of cosine terms only, and extends over only half a wave length, other forms of the Fourier expansion will be found convenient. Thus, if w_1 and w_2 are functions of x extending over a half wave length, and involving respectively cosines only and sines only, we may write the expansions as follows :—

$$w_1 = \frac{a_0}{2} + a_1 \cos kx + \ldots + a_m \cos mkx + \ldots (15),$$

where

$$a_m = \frac{2}{\lambda/2} \int_0^{\lambda/2} w_1 \cos mkx\, dx \qquad (16);$$

and

$$w_2 = b_1 \sin kx + \ldots + b_m \sin mkx + \ldots (17),$$

where

$$b_m = \frac{2}{\lambda/2} \int_0^{\lambda/2} w_2 \sin mkx\, dx \qquad (18).$$

In these equations λ and k are connected by the relation

$$k\lambda = 2\pi \qquad (19).$$

It must also be noted that $\lambda/2 > x > 0$ \qquad (20).

These equations are susceptible of verification in the same manner as equations (1)-(4). Thus, multiply each side of (15) by $\cos mkx\, dx$, and integrate between the limits 0 and $\lambda/2$. Then all the terms on the right side disappear except that involving a_m, and the sole remaining term becomes $a_m \lambda/4$, thus reproducing equation (16). Similarly if we multiply each side of (17) by $\sin mkx\,dx$ and integrate between the limits 0 and $\lambda/2$, we verify (18), all the terms on the right side vanishing except the mth. It should be noted that the vanishing of all the terms but one on the right side is due to the fact that, except in the case reserved, we have after multiplying either a cosine, or products of cosines or of sines of *different* angles. These products will transform respectively into the sum and difference of cosines. But on integrating these cosines we obtain sines, which are zero for each of the limits of integration.

It is also to be carefully noticed that the values of a_m and b_m given in equations (16) and (18) apply only to those partial series, and must not be interchanged with those in equations (3) and (4) for a_n and b_n which apply to the full series. For, in the case of the full series, we have, on multiplying, products of sines and cosines. These transform to sums and differences of sines which accordingly integrate to cosines. But these cosines assume the values ± 1 for the limits 0 and π respectively, and so would not vanish for the integration over the half period which is employed for the partial series.

It will be seen that both for the full and the partial series the value of the coefficients of the integrals which express the a's and b's are : $(2 \div$ the extent over which the integration is to be effected).

The application of one of these partial series will be found in the treatment of vibrating membranes (see next art. and Chap. V.) and struck strings (Chapters IV. and VIII.).

55. Extension of Fourier's Theorem to Two Variables.—Fourier's theorem may be extended to represent an arbitrary function of two variables. For example, it may be used to represent the displacement of a surface at a given instant. For the sake of simplicity and its immediate application to the vibrations of membranes (see Chap. V.) let us take the following concrete case :—

Let the surface be a rectangle in the plane of xy and extending from the co-ordinate axes to $x = a$ and $y = b$. Let its displacements be represented by a sine series simply. Then, beginning first with the displacement as a function of x only, we may write

$$f(x) = \sum_{m=1}^{m=\infty} A_m \sin \frac{m\pi x}{a}$$

$$= \sum_{m=1}^{m=\infty} \sin \frac{m\pi x}{a} \cdot \frac{2}{a} \int_0^a f(a) \sin \frac{m\pi a}{a} da \qquad (21).$$

In the integral a new variable, a, is written for the sake of distinction. It is evident that any variable whatever may be written in this expression for the constant A_m, since in the evaluation of the definite integral the variable finally disappears. Let us now introduce the co-ordinate y into the function, but suppose it, at first, to be constant, as denoted by the subscript y outside the bracket. We thus have

$$f(x,y)_y = \sum_{m=1}^{m=\infty} \sin \frac{m\pi x}{a} \cdot \frac{2}{a} \int_0^a f(a,y) \sin \frac{m\pi a}{a} da \qquad (22).$$

From this equation, it will be seen that we may write by analogy

$$f(a,y) = \sum_{n=1}^{n=\infty} \sin \frac{n\pi y}{b} \cdot \frac{2}{b} \int_0^b f(a,\beta) \sin \frac{n\pi \beta}{b} d\beta \qquad (23).$$

Thus (23) in (22) gives the result sought, namely :—

$$f(x,y) = \frac{4}{ab} \sum_{m=1}^{m=\infty} \sum_{n=1}^{n=\infty} \int_0^a \int_0^b f(a,\beta) \sin \frac{m\pi x}{a}$$

$$\sin \frac{n\pi y}{b} \sin \frac{m\pi a}{a} \sin \frac{n\pi \beta}{b} da d\beta \qquad (24);$$

or, $$f(x,y) = \sum_{m=1}^{m=\infty} \sum_{n=1}^{n=\infty} A_{mn} \sin\frac{m\pi x}{a} \sin\frac{n\pi y}{b} \qquad (25),$$

where $$A_{mn} = \frac{4}{ab}\int_0^a \int_0^b f(\alpha,\beta)\, \sin\frac{m\pi\alpha}{a}\, \sin\frac{n\pi\beta}{b} d\alpha d\beta \qquad (26).$$

It is clear that in equation (26) any other variables (*e.g.* x and y) could be used under the sign of integration.

56. Damped Harmonic Motion.—We have already seen that simple harmonic motion may be regarded as the resolved part, in a given fixed direction, of uniform circular motion. In this case the amplitude of the vibration is constant and equals the radius of the circle from which the motion is derived by projection. We have now to consider another very important case in which the amplitude of the vibration is continually diminishing or suffers "damping," as it is often termed. Here, instead of a circle, we must use a spiral from which to derive the vibration. Let the amplitude be diminished by a constant fraction of itself for each period. We must, accordingly, use a logarithmic spiral. Then, this damped vibration may be obtained as the resolved part of the motion in a given fixed direction of a point which describes a logarithmic spiral with uniform angular speed about its pole. This curve is also called an equiangular spiral. The reason for each term and the exact nature of the curve will be seen from the following two ways in which it may be specified :—

Using polar co-ordinates the curve is analytically represented by the equation

$$r = ab^{-\theta} \qquad (1),$$

where a and b are constants, and the origin of the co-ordinates is termed the pole of the spiral. Equation (1) may be written

$$\left.\begin{array}{c} \log(r/a) = -\theta \log b \\ \log(r/a) \propto \theta \end{array}\right\} \qquad (2),$$

or,

which explains why the curve is called the "logarithmic" spiral. It is also called "equiangular" because it possesses the following geometrical property. From any point P on the spiral let PT the tangent to the curve be drawn; also let P be joined to the pole S. Then the angle SPT is *constant*, and is called the *angle* of the spiral. We may easily find this angle from (1) as follows:—Let θ change by a small amount δ, then the displacements of P along and at right angles to PS are respectively

$$r(b^\delta - 1) \text{ and } r\delta.$$

Thus taking their quotient, we have

$$\cot \mathrm{SPT} = \left(\frac{b^\delta - 1}{\delta} \right) = \left(\frac{1 + \delta \log_e b + \ldots - 1}{\delta} \right)$$
$$= \log_e b = \cot a \text{ say.}$$

If the angle a were $90°$, the spiral would become a circle. This corresponds with writing $\theta = 0$ in equation (1), in which case we obtain a circle of radius a for any value of b.

Following the method of the late Prof. P. G. Tait, we will now find the acceleration of the point describing the spiral. We can then infer that of the point executing the damped vibration. This is necessary in order to determine afterwards the force required to cause an actual body to vibrate in this manner.

57. Acceleration of Point describing a Logarithmic Spiral.—In Fig. 31 let S be the pole of the spiral and P the point describing the curve. Then, since the angular velocity of SP and the inclination a of this line to the tangent PT are each constant, the linear velocity of P is proportional to SP. Let this velocity be represented to scale by

$$\mathrm{PT} = p\mathrm{SP} \qquad (3),$$

where p is a constant. Draw SQ equal and parallel to PT. And, as P describes the spiral, let SQ retain its equality and parallelism to PT. Then Q will accordingly describe with an equal constant angular velocity another precisely similar spiral, but with radius-vector p times that of the first. Moreover, this second spiral is the hodograph of the first, *i.e.* its radius-vector SQ is always equal to the velocity of P. Hence the velocity QG of Q makes with SQ an angle a equal to SPT, and represents the acceleration of P.

Further $QG = p\mathrm{SQ} = p.\mathrm{PT} = p^2.\mathrm{SP}$ (4).

Thus, if PU be drawn parallel and equal to QG, and UV

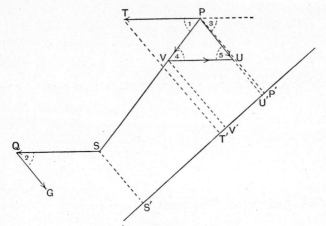

Fig. 31.—Acceleration in Spiral.

parallel to PT, cutting PS in V ; the whole acceleration PU may be resolved into PV and VU. Further, PVU is an isosceles triangle whose base angles at U and V are each equal to the angle a. (The angles a, taken in the order in which their equality may be readily seen, are figured in the diagram 1, 2, 3, 4 and 5.) Hence, as P describes the spiral, PVU remains isosceles with its sides proportional to SP, and therefore to PT also. The acceleration of P may, accordingly, be conceived as composed of a component PV directed towards S and proportional to SP, and a component parallel to VU and proportional to PT. Or, we may say that P has a *central* acceleration proportional to its *displacement* from S, and a *tangential* retardation proportional to its *velocity*. If we now take the components of P's motion parallel to any given line S'P' in the plane of the spiral, similar conditions will again hold. Namely, the acceleration consists of two parts : (i.) a central one proportional to the displacement, and (ii.) a retarding one proportional to the velocity. In the figure these two components of the acceleration are respectively P'V' proportional to P'S', and V'U' proportional to T'P'.

It should be noted that the two components of the acceleration of P in the spiral are each proportional to SP. But this does not necessarily hold true of the corresponding accelerations and displacements along the fixed direction S'P', since the accelerations PV and VU are not *both* parallel to SP. When, however, we state that the central and tangential acceleration of P in the spiral are proportional to SP and PT to which they are respectively *parallel*, this proportionality must needs hold in the corresponding accelerations, displacement, and velocity when projected on to any line S'P'.

58. Analytical Treatment.—Retaining the previous notation, the angle SPT of the spiral is denoted by a. Thus, if SP moves with the angular velocity q, we have PT $\sin a = q.$SP. Hence, on comparing with (3) we have

$$q = p \sin a \qquad\qquad (5).$$

Also by the figure the central acceleration is given by

$$\mathrm{PV} = \mathrm{PU} = \mathrm{QG} = p^2.\mathrm{SP} \qquad\qquad (6),$$

or, $= p^2$ times the displacement.

Again, the retardation of the motion is denoted by

$$\mathrm{VU} = 2\mathrm{PU} \cos a = 2\mathrm{QG} \cos a = 2p \cos a.\mathrm{PT} = 2\kappa.\mathrm{PT} \quad (7),$$

where κ is written for $p \cos a$. Thus, by (5) we have

$$p^2 = q^2 + \kappa^2 \qquad\qquad (8).$$

Hence the retardation of the motion is 2κ times the linear velocity. Writing now y for the "projected" displacement $S'P'$ and $\dot{y}$ for the projected velocity, we see that the relations expressed in (6) and (7) hold for the acceleration, displacement, and velocity along $S'P'$. We accordingly obtain, as the equation of motion of the point P' along $S'P'$,

$$\ddot{y} = -p^2 y - 2\kappa\dot{y} \qquad (9).$$

Referring again to the figure, we see that the diminution of SP in an infinitely short period dt is

$$\text{PT}.dt.\cos a = p.\text{SP}.dt.\cos a = \kappa.dt.\text{SP}.$$

Thus, in the time dt, SP is affected by the factor $(1 - \kappa dt)$ or $(1 + \kappa dt)^{-1}$. Accordingly, in the time t, SP is affected by the factor $(1 + \kappa dt)^{-t/dt}$. This may be written

$$\left\{ \left(1 + \frac{1}{n} \right)^n \right\}^{-\kappa t} = e^{-\kappa t},$$

where $n = 1/\kappa dt$ is infinite and e is the base of the Napierian logarithms. And, obviously, as SP diminishes, $S'P'$ its projected length is diminished in the same ratio. But, since it is this continuous diminution and this alone which distinguishes the motion of P' from simple harmonic motion, it is evident that we may write as representing its damped vibration

$$y = ae^{-\kappa t} \sin qt \qquad (10).$$

As a further check upon this result it is desirable to differentiate it to t, thus giving the velocity, and then again to obtain the acceleration, for comparison with (9).

Thus (10) yields

$$\dot{y} = ae^{-\kappa t}(q \cos qt - \kappa \sin qt) \qquad (11).$$

A second differentiation gives

$$\ddot{y} = ae^{-\kappa t}[-q^2 \sin qt - 2\kappa q \cos qt + \kappa^2 \sin qt]$$
$$= ae^{-\kappa t}[-2\kappa(q \cos qt - \kappa \sin qt) - (\kappa^2 + q^2) \sin qt];$$

or by (8) and (11) $\ddot{y} = -p^2 y - 2\kappa\dot{y} \qquad (12),$

which is identical with (9).

The significance of p, q, and κ will be seen more fully later when we deal with the physical aspect of the problem. It should be noticed that if $\kappa = 0$, (10), (11) and (12) reduce to the corresponding equations for undamped simple harmonic motions.

59. Damped Vibration as Infinite Series of Undamped Ones.—Fourier's theorem enables us to express *any periodic* motion in terms of *commensurate* simple harmonic motions. A somewhat similar and very striking relation has been pointed out [1] between a *damped simple harmonic* motion and an *infinite* series of *undamped* vibrations. This relation may be expressed in the following equation :—

$$y = e^{-kt}\sin(nt + \phi) = \frac{k}{\pi}\int_{-\infty}^{+\infty}\frac{\sin\{(n+z)t + \phi\}dz}{k^2 + z^2},$$

where k must not be zero.

That is, a damped vibration may be conceived as a superposition of an infinite series of undamped vibrations, whose frequencies vary continuously on both sides of that principal frequency defined by n, the amplitudes of these component vibrations, however, diminishing on each side as the central frequency is departed from.

60. Doppler's Principle.—In 1842 Doppler, considering the coloured light from the double stars, showed that a motion of approach between the source of waves and the recipient would cause an apparent increase of their frequency, and that a decrease of apparent frequency would occur with a motion of separation. In the corresponding acoustical phenomena, it is perhaps as well to consider at once the effect of a possible motion of the medium in which the waves occur as well as motions of both source and recipient. Thus, let v be the velocity of the waves through the medium, u_1 that of the source, u_2 that of the recipient, and w that of the medium itself; all being along the line

---

[1] *Annalen der Physik*, p. 356, June 1906, and 25, p. 650, 1885.

joining source and recipient, and reckoned positive when in the same direction, namely, from the source towards the recipient. These are shown in Fig. 32.

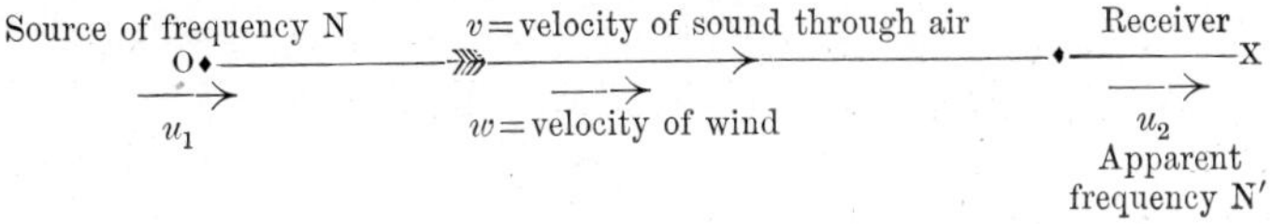

Source of frequency N　　　　v = velocity of sound through air　　　Receiver

　　　　　　　　　　　　　　　　　　　　　　　　　　　　　　　　X

u_1　　　　　　　w = velocity of wind　　　　　　u_2

Apparent
frequency N′

FIG. 32.—DOPPLER'S PRINCIPLE.

Now in the ordinary case with all at rest save the sound waves themselves, we have—

$$v = N\lambda$$

whence we may write　　$\lambda = v/N$　　　　　　　　(1),

and　　　　　　　　　　$N = v/\lambda$　　　　　　　　(2).

Hence, with source, medium, and recipient all in motion as above described, we have, by modification of (1)—

Disturbed wave length along OX = velocity of separation of wave fronts and source ÷ frequency of their emission from source,

or,　　　　　$\lambda' = (v + w - u_1)/N$　　　　　(3).

Again, by modification of (2), we obtain—

Frequency of receipt of waves = velocity of approach of waves and recipient ÷ disturbed wave length,

or,　　　　　$N' = (v + w - u_2)/\lambda'$　　　　　(4).

Thus (3) and (4) give finally—

$$N'/N = \frac{v + w - u_2}{v + w - u_1}$$　　　　　(5).

It should be noted that the above apply only to motions of source, recipient, and winds along the line joining source and recipient. An oblique wind would introduce a change, even if its component in the above direction remained

H

unaltered. For example, if $u_1 = u_2 = w = 0$, but a cross wind blew at right angles to OX, and of speed exceeding v, no waves from the source could ever reach the recipient however near. This may be easily seen by the method of the next article. When, however, the motions of medium, source, and recipient are all along OX, we have to note that the apparent rise of pitch due to a motion in one direction is different from the apparent fall due to a reversed motion of the same value. Of course, for $u_1 = u_2$, $N' = N$ for any value of w. A few typical illustrations are given in Table III.

TABLE III.—DOPPLER'S PRINCIPLE

Velocities of			Apparent Change in Pitch.	
Source u_1.	Recipient. u_2.	Wind w.	Ratio N'/N.	Musical Interval.
v/n 0	0 $-v/n$	0 $-v/n$ $\Big\}$	$\dfrac{n}{n-1}$	For $n=2$, note raised an octave
0	$-v/n$	0	$(n+1)/n$	For $n=2$, note raised a fifth
$-v/n$ 0	0 v/n	0 v/n $\Big\}$	$n/(n+1)$	For $n=2$, note lowered a fifth
0	v/n	0	$(n-1)/n$	For $n=2$, note lowered an octave
v/n $-v/n$	$-v/n'$ v/n'	0 0	$\dfrac{n(n'+1)}{n'(n-1)}$ $\dfrac{n(n'-1)}{n'(n+1)}$	If $n = 62 = n'$, the change from upper to lower line involves a fall of a diatonic semitone

The last case dealt with in the table corresponds to the change from a mutual approach of source and recipient to a mutual recession, the speed of each being about 12 miles per hour. Thus, if one cyclist riding at that speed meets another riding in the opposite direction at the same speed ringing his bell, at the instant of passing the pitch of the bell would appear to fall a diatonic semitone. Of course, at much lower speeds the effect of Doppler's principle is noticeable, especially in this case of double approach followed by double recession, a fourfold effect being involved.

"Doppler's principle has been experimentally verified by Buij's Ballot and Scott Russell, who examined the alterations of pitch of musical instruments carried on locomotives."

61. Oblique Propagation of Sound in a Wind.—Let a region be imagined, in all parts of which the wind is horizontal and of speed u. Let a plane wave front be inclined θ to the horizontal, and let the direction of propagation of these waves of sound be inclined ϕ to the vertical and in the same vertical plane as the wind. Then, on examination of this case, we shall find that ϕ is usually different from θ.

Let AB in Fig. 33 represent the wave front at a certain instant, and let CD represent it after the lapse of a short time denoted by t. Then the Huyghens' wavelet, whose origin is A, may be conceived as radiating from A in every direction with the speed of sound v, compounded with a horizontal velocity u. Hence, the wavelet from A after any time is a circle whose radius is vt, but whose centre is transferred a distance ut horizontally in the direction of the wind. Thus, lay off horizontally $AA' = ut$, then from A' describe with radius vt the arc ECF, and we have the wavelet required. Similarly, we obtain the wavelet originating at B and at any other intermediate points along AB. The new wave front is the envelope CD of these wavelets, and is obviously parallel to AB. Also the direction of propagation of the wave is AC, making with the vertical the angle $VAC = \phi$; whereas $A'C$ makes the angle θ with the vertical, since it is perpendicular to the wave front which is inclined θ to the horizontal. From C let fall CN perpendicular to the horizontal line AN. Then, for the relation between ϕ and θ, we have by construction—

$$\tan NCA = \frac{NA}{CN} = \frac{NA'}{CN} + \frac{A'A}{CA' \cos NCA},$$

or, $$\tan \phi = \tan \theta + \frac{u}{v} \sec \theta \qquad (1).$$

Hence the ray, instead of making the angle θ with the vertical, as it would do if normal to the wave front, makes

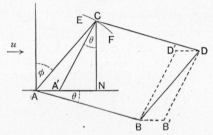

FIG. 33.—DRIFT OF SOUND RAYS IN A WIND.

the angle ϕ, which generally differs from θ whenever there is a wind in the region in question. The exception obviously occurs when the wave front ceases to be oblique. Thus for horizontal wind and vertical wave fronts, we have $\theta = 90°$ and $\phi = \theta$.

62. Refraction of Sound by Wind.[1]—Consider now two wind zones divided by a horizontal plane. Let the wind in the lower zone be everywhere in the same horizontal direction and of speed u_0, and in the upper zone in the same direction but of speed u_1. Let a plane wave front inclined θ_0 to the horizontal while in the lower zone assume the inclination θ_1 after passing into the upper zone, the directions of propagation being throughout in the same

[1] See *Phil. Mag.*, January 1901.

vertical plane as the wind.   Let us determine the relation
between θ_1 and θ_0.

In Fig. 34 let AC represent the wave front incident at
A upon AB, the plane of separation of the two zones.
Draw CB′ at right angles to AC and lay off B′B, making
B′B/CB′ = u_0/v, where v is the speed of sound.   Then by
art. 61, CB is the direction of propagation in the lower
zone (see lines BD′, D′D, and BD in Fig. 33).   If t be the
time occupied from C to B, we have CB′ = vt and B′B =
$u_0 t$.   To construct the new wave front in the upper zone,
we may consider A as the origin of a wavelet as in the

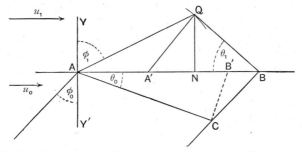

Fig. 34.—Refraction of Sound by Abrupt Change of Wind Speed.

first case.   This wavelet is obviously a spherical one of
radius A′Q = vt, described about a centre A′, distant horizontally $u_1 t$ from A.   Then from B draw BQ tangential to
the arc representing this sphere, then BQ denotes the
refracted wave front required.

To obtain the law of refraction, we have by the figure,

$$\operatorname{cosec} QBA' = \frac{BA'}{A'Q} = \frac{B'A - AA' + B'B}{vt} = \frac{B'A}{B'C} - \frac{u_1 t - u_0 t}{vt};$$

or, $\operatorname{cosec} \theta_1 = \operatorname{cosec} \theta_0 - \dfrac{u_1 - u_0}{v}$ (2).

This law of refraction should be contrasted with that
obtained for different conditions in art. 46.   We there
found: ratio of sines = constant, like the ordinary optical

law. Whereas here we find : difference of cosecants for wave fronts = constant. Now, by equation (1), or from the figure of the present article in which QN is drawn perpendicular to AB, thus making the angle $NQA' = \theta_1$,

$$\tan \phi_1 = \tan \theta_1 + \frac{u_1}{v} \sec \theta_1 \qquad (3).$$

This completes the solution, by giving the direction of propagation in terms of the inclination of the wave front.

63. Refraction through any Number of Wind Zones.— Let us now consider any number $(n + 1)$ of horizontal zones, let the wind be horizontal and in the same direction in all the zones, but differ in speed in the various zones, being u_0 in the lowest, u_1, u_2 . . . and u_n in the others. Further, let the angles which the wave fronts make with the horizontal, and the angles which the rays make with the vertical, be respectively denoted by θ and ϕ with corresponding subscripts for the different zones. Finally, let the rays be in the same vertical plane as the winds.

Then from equation (2) we have

$$\operatorname{cosec} \theta_1 = \operatorname{cosec} \theta_0 - (u_1 - u_0)/v,$$
$$\operatorname{cosec} \theta_2 = \operatorname{cosec} \theta_1 - (u_2 - u_1)/v,$$
$$\cdot \quad \cdot \quad \cdot \quad \cdot \quad \cdot \quad \cdot$$
$$\operatorname{cosec} \theta_n = \operatorname{cosec} \theta_{n-1} - (u_n - u_{n-1})/v.$$

Hence, on addition, we obtain

$$\operatorname{cosec} \theta_n = \operatorname{cosec} \theta_0 - \frac{u_n - u_0}{v} \qquad (4).$$

Also by (1) or (3) we have, for the final direction of propagation,

$$\tan \phi_n = \tan \theta_n + \frac{u_n}{v} \sec \theta_n \qquad (5).$$

We thus see that the final inclination of wave front and direction of propagation are each independent of the constants characterising the intermediate zones, though, of course, the path of the ray will depend on these constants, and also upon the thickness of each zone. It should be noted, further, that since a cosecant cannot have a value between $+1$ and -1, if any of the zones required such a value the series must cease there, equations (4) and (5) not holding for the higher zones. But this leads us to inquire what has become of the waves which could not penetrate the higher zone. If they cannot be refracted, are they reflected?

64. Total Reflection of Sound by Wind.—Although the cosecant law for the wave front obtaining here differs from the ordinary optical law of refraction, we still have, as in optics, the possibility of total reflection. And in this connection the distinction between wave front and direction of propagation is very striking. Thus, for the wave front, if the angle of refraction θ_n is put $\pi/2$, we have from equation (4) the critical case expressed by

$$\operatorname{cosec} \theta_0 - \frac{u_n - u_0}{v} = 1 \qquad (6).$$

Hence, any pair of values of θ_0 and $(u_n - u_0)$, which makes the left side of (6) numerically less than unity, affords an example of total reflection, the last zone not being entered by the beam, since no real angle θ_n can be found whose cosecant is less than unity.

Suppose now that we have a series of wind zones in which the wind speed increases as we ascend. Then, provided the initial inclination of the wave front were finite, it is clear that, at some point, we must have total reflection. But if, on the other hand, the wave front were initially horizontal, we should then have $\theta_0 = 0$. And, by equation (4), all the θ's would be zero also.

That is, we should have no refraction of the wave front, and consequently no total reflection anywhere. Whereas the ray, initially vertical, deviates as we ascend, without limit from the vertical. This is shown by the fact that equation (5) now reduces to

$$\tan \phi_n = u_n/v \qquad (7).$$

So that, in this case, we have zero refraction of the wave front associated with unlimited refraction of the rays, total reflection being impossible.

On consideration of the case by Huyghens' principle, it is seen that, when a zone cannot be penetrated and total reflection occurs, then such reflection follows the ordinary optical law—" angle of reflection equals angle of incidence."

65. Path of Sound Rays where Wind varies as Height.—Let the wind be everywhere horizontal and in the same vertical plane, but let its speed u vary continuously from one level to another according to the equation

$$u/v = c + ay \tag{8},$$

where v is the speed of sound, c and a constants, and y is measured vertically upwards. The sound rays are supposed to be in the same vertical plane as the wind, and the x co-ordinate of the ray will be taken horizontally to leeward. Let us now determine the inclinations of the wave front and the rays at any point, also the path of the rays. Then we need to express θ, ϕ, and x in terms of y. The equations for θ and ϕ are derived immediately from (4), (5), and (8). Thus, dropping subscripts, we have,

$$\operatorname{cosec} \theta = \operatorname{cosec} \theta_0 - ay \tag{9},$$

and

$$\tan \phi = \frac{dx}{dy} = \tan \theta + (c + ay) \sec \theta \tag{10}$$

whence

$$x = \int \frac{[1 + (c + ay)(\operatorname{cosec} \theta_0 - ay)]}{\sqrt{(\operatorname{cosec} \theta_0 - ay)^2 - 1}} \, dy \tag{11}.$$

On evaluation of (11), putting $x = 0$ for $y = 0$, we obtain

$$2ax = (b + 2c)\sqrt{b^2 - 1} - (b + 2c + ay)\sqrt{z^2 - 1}$$

$$+ \log_\epsilon \frac{b + \sqrt{b^2 - 1}}{z + \sqrt{z^2 - 1}} \tag{12},$$

where $\qquad b = \operatorname{cosec} \theta_0 \quad$ and $\quad z = b - ay.$

Thus, for any given ordinate, the abscissa is the sum of three terms; the first being a constant, the second forming with y a curve of the fourth degree, while the third is the abscissa of a catenary. This is the general expression exhibiting the relation between x and y, and therefore completes the required solution for the path of the rays in the general case.

If the wave front is initially horizontal, we have $\theta_0 = 0$, $b = \infty$, and (12) becomes indeterminate. But, either by evaluating this indeterminate form, or by use of (9) and (10), we obtain

$$2x = 2cy + ay^2,$$

or, $\qquad \left(y + \dfrac{c}{a}\right)^2 = \dfrac{2}{a}(x + c^2/2a) \qquad (13),$

showing that the path of the rays is now a parabola.

If the ray starts in still air, put $c = 0$ and (13) becomes

$$y^2 = 2x/a \qquad (14),$$

a parabola with vertex at the origin.

66. Numerical Illustration of Wind Refraction.—To illustrate the application of these equations take the following numerical case. Let $c = 0{\cdot}02$ and $a = 0{\cdot}0001$ per foot. Then, if the temperature is such as to make the speed of sound 1100 feet per second, the wind speed at the origin would be 22 ft./sec. or 15 miles per hour, and at a height of 1000 feet the wind speed would be six times its value at the origin. In this region consider the two following rays starting from the origin :—*First,* one with its wave front inclined at $60°$ to the horizontal; this suffers total reflection at a point about 1547 feet above, and 6195 to leeward of the origin. *Second,* let a ray start with its wave front horizontal, then it always remains so; but the ray describes a parabolic path, having, at a height of 3000 feet, drifted

about 500 feet to leeward. It would, however, never suffer total reflection, but would asymptote to the horizontal at an infinite height, the ray and the wave front tending to coincide.

67. Strains.—As an introduction to the subject of elasticity let us now consider a few of the simpler changes of volume and figure which may be experienced by a solid or fluid mass.

Any change in the dimensions of a body is called a *strain*. The change may be one of volume only, or of shape only, or of both together. Thus any mass of gas when compressed or dilated, or any solid when lengthened, shortened, bent, or twisted is said to be *strained*.

Homogeneous Strain.—The treatment of strains will here be restricted to what are called homogeneous strains. Following closely the treatment of the subject by Kelvin and Tait, strains of this class may be described thus. Parts of a body originally equal, similar and similarly situated remain, after a homogeneous strain, equal, similar and similarly situated, however much they may have been changed thereby in volume, form, and position. Hence, points originally in a straight line, or in a plane, remain in a straight line or in a plane respectively. Equal parallel lines remain equal parallel lines. Therefore a parallelogram remains a parallelogram, an ellipse remains an ellipse (a circle being included as a possible case of each ellipse), a parallelepiped remains a parallelepiped, and an ellipsoid remains an ellipsoid. Hence spheres may become ellipsoids and cubes may become parallelepipeds.

67a. Strain Ellipsoid.—Further, if the whole body before the strain be divided into equal cubes, it is possible so to choose their orientation that, after the strain, the original cubical portions of the substance will have become rectangular parallelepiped or brick-shaped figures with their edges at right angles. The possibility of so choosing the cubes as to obtain this simplification may be seen thus.

Let equal spheres be described in the unstrained body.
These become similar and similarly situated ellipsoids after
the homogeneous strain. Also, if tangent planes be drawn
to a sphere, at the extremities of three rectangular diameters,
then the plane through the end of any one diameter is
parallel to the plane containing the other two diameters.
But this *parallelism* will be maintained after the strain.
Thus, every set of three mutually perpendicular diameters
of the sphere becomes a set of conjugate diameters of the
ellipsoid into which the sphere is strained and conversely.
Hence the principal axes of the ellipsoid, which are conjugate diameters perpendicular to one another, were also
originally perpendicular to one another in the sphere from
which the ellipsoid has been derived.

The ellipsoid assumed in the strained condition by any
originally spherical portion of the body is called the *strain
ellipsoid*.

Along one of the principal axes of the general strain
ellipsoid the elongation is greater, and along another less, than
along any other direction in the body. Along the remaining
axis the elongation is less than that in any other line in
the plane of itself and the axis of greatest elongation, but
greater than that in any other line in the plane of itself
and the axis of least elongation. Thus if the x and z axes
are respectively those of greatest and least elongation, then
along the axis of y the elongation is a minimum for all
lines in the x-y plane, but a maximum for all lines in the
y-z plane. Contraction is to be reckoned as a negative
elongation, so the maximum elongation just referred to
may become a minimum contraction.

The above remarks apply to the most general case in
which all three axes of the strain ellipsoid differ from each
other and from the diameter of the original sphere. But in
special cases the strain ellipsoid may be an ellipsoid of
revolution, or it may be a sphere, in which case we have
change of volume only without change of shape of any part.

The principal axes of the strain are the principal axes of the strain ellipsoid. The principal elongations of a strain are the elongations along its principal axes. We shall estimate these per unit length, and may accordingly call them *fractional* elongations. It is sufficient for the purpose in view to treat only of strains in which the fractional elongations are indefinitely small. This restriction will therefore be made. But any or all of the elongations may be supposed replaced by contractions, in which case the corresponding symbols for the fractional " elongations " will have negative values.

68. Fractional Change of Volume.—Let the fractional elongations of a strain be a, b, and c. Then a sphere of radius r in the unstrained state becomes an ellipsoid of semi-axes $r(1 + a)$, $r(1 + b)$, and $r(1 + c)$ respectively.

Thus the fractional change of volume is given by

$$\left\{ \frac{4}{3}\pi r(1 + a)r(1 + b)r(1 + c) - \frac{4}{3}\pi r^3 \right\} \Big/ \frac{4}{3}\pi r^3.$$

But since a, b, and c are each small compared with unity, we may neglect their products. We thus obtain for the fractional change of volume due to the strain

$$\delta = a + b + c \tag{1}.$$

Typical Strains.—It is often convenient to specify a strain by its fractional elongations denoted by the early letters of the alphabet. Adopting this plan we may notice the typical cases shown in Table IV.

[TABLE

TABLE IV.—TYPICAL STRAINS

Case.	Fractional Elongations.			Name of Strain.
1	a	b	c	General strain.
2	a	b	0	Plane strain.
3	a	0	0	Simple elongation.
4	d	d	d	Uniform dilatation.
5	d	d	0	Uniform plane strain.
6	e	$-e$	0	Simple shear.
7	f	$-g$	$-g$	Elongation with lateral contractions or *axial* strain.

Of these strains, cases 1, 2, 3, and 5 call for no special remarks. Case 4, a *uniform dilatation*, is important as involving change of size only without change of shape. Similarly, case 6, a *simple shear*, is important, involving as it does change of shape only without change of size. This strain will receive further attention a little later. Case 7 is of importance because it is the strain produced by the simplest application of tractive or elongating forces to isotropic materials. For brevity, we may call this an *axial* strain. The ratio of g to f is a constant for a given substance, and is called *Poisson's ratio*. We shall denote it by σ.

69. Composition and Resolution of Strains.—We shall now notice how certain of the typical strains may be compounded to produce another, or how one may be resolved into components of specified types.

Case 1.—The simplest case of composition is that of a uniform plane strain and a simple shear. These may make any plane strain as specified in case 2. For if the component strains have respectively the fractional elongations, $(d, d, 0)$ and $(e, -e, 0)$, we obtain

$$d + e = a \qquad \text{and } d - e = b,$$

hence
$$\left. d = \frac{1}{2}(a + b) \text{ and } \qquad e = \frac{1}{2}(a - b) \right\} \qquad (2),$$

which give the formulæ of composition or solution; when

specifying the elongations it is understood that they are about the axes of x, y, and z taken in order.

Case 2.—Again, one uniform dilation $(d, d, d,)$ and two simple shears, say $(e_1, -e_1, 0)$ and $(e_2, 0, -e_2)$ will compound to a general strain (a, b, c), and therefore to anything whatever.

Obviously the equations are

$$\left.\begin{aligned} d + e_1 + e_2 &= a \\ d - e_1 &= b \\ d - e_2 &= c \end{aligned}\right\} \tag{3},$$

and

whence

$$\left.\begin{aligned} 3d &= a + b + c \\ 3e_1 &= a - 2b + c \\ 3e_2 &= a + b - 2c \end{aligned}\right\} \tag{4},$$

and

If $b = c = 0$, we have $d = e_1 = e_2 = a/3$.

Case 3.—Let us now use *three* strains of the last type in the table or *axial* strains, the ratio of g to f, being the same, σ, in each strain, but the axis of the unique elongation and its actual value different for each. With these components we can build up the general strain, and therefore any special case whatever. Take first the general case which includes the rest. Let the component strains be

$$(f_1, \ -\sigma f_1, \ -\sigma f_1)$$
$$(-\sigma f_2, \ f_2, \ -\sigma f_2)$$

and

$$(-\sigma f_3, \ -\sigma f_3, \ f_3)$$

the resultant being $(a, \quad b, \quad c)$.

Then we have by addition

$$\left.\begin{aligned} f_1 - \sigma f_2 - \sigma f_3 &= a \\ -\sigma f_1 + f_2 - \sigma f_3 &= b \\ -\sigma f_1 - \sigma f_2 + f_3 &= c \end{aligned}\right\} \tag{5},$$

and

whence we obtain, in solving for the f's,

$$\left.\begin{aligned} f_1(1 + \sigma)(1 - 2\sigma) &= a(1 - \sigma) + (b + c)\sigma \\ f_2(1 + \sigma)(1 - 2\sigma) &= b(1 - \sigma) + (c + a)\sigma \\ f_3(1 + \sigma)(1 - 2\sigma) &= c(1 - \sigma) + (a + b)\sigma \end{aligned}\right\} \tag{6}.$$

and

To produce the simple elongation $(a, 0, 0)$ by three such strains, we have merely to put $b = c = 0$ in (6) and we obtain

$$\left.\begin{array}{l} f_1(1 + \sigma)(1 - 2\sigma) = a(1 - \sigma) \\ f_2(1 + \sigma)(1 - 2\sigma) = a\sigma \\ f_3 = f_2 \end{array}\right\} \qquad (7),$$

and

This case will receive a special application in a later chapter.

The uniform dilation (d, d, d) may also be built up of three strains of the type now under notice. Thus, putting $a = b = c = d$ in (6) we have

$$f_1 = f_2 = f_3 = d/(1 - 2\sigma) \qquad (8).$$

Again, a simple shear may be regarded as composed of three strains of the type in question or axial strains. Thus putting $a = e$, $b = -e$, and $c = 0$ in (6), we have

$$\left.\begin{array}{l} f_1 = e/(1 + \sigma) \\ f_2 = -e/(1 + \sigma) \\ f_3 = 0 \end{array}\right\} \qquad (9).$$

and

Hence the system of axial strains required to make the given shear could be represented by

$$\left.\begin{array}{l} \left(\dfrac{e}{1 + \sigma}, \ \dfrac{-\sigma e}{1 + \sigma}, \ \dfrac{-\sigma e}{1 + \sigma}\right) \\[2mm] \left(\dfrac{+\sigma e}{1 + \sigma}, \ \dfrac{-e}{1 + \sigma}, \ \dfrac{+\sigma e}{1 + \sigma}\right) \end{array}\right\} \qquad (10);$$

and

which obviously result in $(e, -e, 0)$ as required.

70. Different View of Simple Shear.—It is important and instructive to take now another view of the particular strain called a simple shear. Let the fractional elongations of the shear be denoted as before by $(e, -e, 0)$. Let the full lines ABCD in Fig. 35 represent a portion of the substance before the strain, and the dotted lines A'B'C'D' the same portion after the strain. Let the unstrained figure have its horizontal semi-axes OB and OD each equal to 1, and its vertical semi-axes OA and OC each $1 + e$.

Thus, on the application of the respective fractional elongations e and $-e$ to these axes, they become OB′ and OD′
each equal to $1 + e$ and OA′ and OC′ each equal to 1.
Thus, the sides of the figure, originally equal, remain so and
of the same size after the strain.

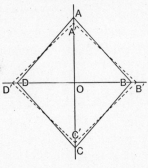

FIG. 35.—A RHOMBUS BEFORE
AND AFTER A SIMPLE SHEAR.

Further, the angles of the original
rhombus suffer a simple interchange when passing to the final
rhombus produced by the strain.
Thus the acute angles at A and
C change to the obtuse ones at
A′ and C′ equal to the original
obtuse angles at B and D, the
obtuse angles at B and D changing to the acute ones at B′ and
D′, equal to the original acute
angles at A and C.   Hence, apart
from a slight shift of the centre of the figure on rotation,
we could obtain the strain in question by keeping one
side, AB say, fixed, while CD moved parallel to itself till
the original acute and obtuse angles of the rhombus were
interchanged.   This is shown in Fig. 36.

Thus AB being kept at rest the simple shear is denoted
by the shift of CD to C′D′, whose position may also be
defined as obtained from the previous figure by applying
A′ to A and B′ to B.   Thinking now of the solid substance,
of which the diagram represents only a single plane, we see
that the strain may be described as the undistorted sliding
parallel to BA of all planes originally parallel to BA, the
amount of such sliding of each plane being proportional to
its distance from BA.

But instead of keeping AB fixed and taking the sliding
parallel to it, we might have kept BC fixed and taken the
sliding parallel to it.   This is illustrated in Fig. 37, in
which the unstrained rhombus is ABCD, and the strained
rhombus A′BCD′, obtained by sliding AD to A′D′ parallel

to BC. So in this case we could describe the strain as a proportional sliding parallel to BC without distortion of all planes originally parallel to BC. The plane of the diagram in each of the three figures 35, 36, and 37 is called the *plane* of the shear. It is obviously the plane containing the two equal and opposite elongations which specify it. It also contains the lines of relative motion of the planes regarded as sliding past one another in the second view we have just taken of the shear. Moreover, these lines of sliding, for an indefinitely small shear, are obviously at

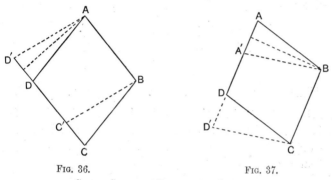

FIG. 36. FIG. 37.

SIMPLE SHEAR AS UNDISTORTED SLIDING.

angles of 45° with those of the elongation and equal contraction. The *angle* of the shear is that shown by CBC′ and DAD′ in Fig. 36, or by ABA′ and DCD′ in Fig. 37. It is therefore obviously given by the difference of the obtuse and acute angle of either the full line or dotted rhombus in these figures or in Fig. 35. The circular measure of this angle for an indefinitely small shear may be expressed as the displacement of any undistorted plane relative to another such plane divided by the perpendicular distance between them. This quotient is also termed the *amount* of the shear whether it is large or small.

The Amount of a Shear is twice its Fractional Elongation. —We may now easily obtain an important relation between

I

the amount of a shear and its fractional elongations. Thus, let the amount of the shear be χ, the elongations being $(e, -e, 0)$.

Then, on reference to Figs. 36 and 37 we see that

$$\chi/2 = \tan \frac{1}{2}\mathrm{DAD}' = \tan \frac{1}{2}\mathrm{ABA}'.$$

Also on referring to Fig. 35 we see that

$$\chi/2 = \tan(\mathrm{ABO} - \mathrm{OAB}).$$

But, $\tan \mathrm{ABO} = 1 + e$ and $\tan \mathrm{OAB} = 1/(1 + e)$.

Hence

$$\chi/2 = \frac{1 + e - \dfrac{1}{1 + e}}{1 + \dfrac{1 + e}{1 + e}} = e \text{ nearly.}$$

Thus
$$\chi = 2e. \tag{11}$$

Or, the *amount* of a simple shear is double its *elongation*. It is evident that for a small shear the same will be true of the *angle* of the shear *if* measured in *radians*. Hence, as for our purpose we have only to deal with small shears, we speak of the amount of the shear or its angle in circular measure. As a numerical illustration of the shears with which we are concerned, let $e = 0\cdot001$ then $\chi = 0\cdot002$.

Referring again to the strain ellipsoid, it will easily be seen, by those conversant with solid geometry, that the two sets of planes of no distortion in a shear correspond to the two circular sections of its strain ellipsoid.

CHAPTER III

71. General Conceptions: Stresses.—A set of forces in equilibrium applied to a body is called a *stress*. It is obvious from this definition that a stress does not tend to produce any motion of translation or rotation in the body as a whole. The stress only tends to change the size or shape of the body to which it is applied. In other words, a stress produces a strain and that only. Thus a uniform pressure exerted normally on the entire exterior surface of a body is an example of a stress. It has, of course, no tendency to move or rotate the body as a whole, but will simply compress it. And this compression will be uniform provided that the body is composed of a substance having the same properties in every direction. Such substances are said to be isotropic, and to them we restrict our attention throughout this work.

Nature of Elasticity.—Elasticity is that property of a substance in virtue of which (1) it requires a definite stress to produce in it a given strain, (2) it requires a continuance of the stress to maintain the strain, and (3) when set free from the stress, it springs back towards its unstrained condition. If, in order to maintain a given strain in a certain substance, the stress which produced it must be maintained absolutely undiminished, and if, when set free

115

from the stress, that substance springs back precisely to its original unstrained state, its elasticity is said to be perfect. Otherwise the elasticity is imperfect.

The elasticity of all substances in the solid state is distinctly imperfect if the limits of stress and strain are wide. Many solid substances, however, have an elasticity practically perfect within narrow limits of strain. These limits, within which the elasticity is sensibly perfect, are often called the " limits of elasticity " or the " elastic limits." Since the maintenance of a strain in an elastic body requires the continuance of a stress, we see that in the body itself, when strained, there is developed a stress equal and opposite to that applied to it from the outside.

Hooke's Law.—In 1678 Hooke enunciated the law still known by his name. Its original form was in Latin, as follows :—*Ut tensio sic vis.* His comments upon it show sufficiently in what sense Hooke intended the words *tensio* and *vis* to be understood. Extending the law to other cases besides those of mere elongation, we may state it thus : *Strain is proportional to stress.* The experimental evidence on which alone the law is based justifies also this extended statement of it. It should be noted here that this law implies further that an equal but reversed stress produces an equal but reversed strain. The law, of course, only applies within certain narrow limits, probably roughly comparable with those limits already defined as the limits of elasticity.

72. Measure of Elasticity. — Hooke's law may be thrown into the form :—Within narrow limits the quotient (stress ÷ strain) is a constant for a given substance. Then the value of this constant quotient for any substance is adopted as the measure for that substance of the kind of elasticity in question. For it is evident that as stresses and strains are of various kinds, we have correspondingly various kinds of elasticity. We may thus write the following as a general quantitative definition of elasticity. The elasticity of a substance is the quotient stress applied divided by strain thereby produced, the value of this quotient being taken in the limiting case where the stress and strain are each indefinitely small. This may be expressed in symbols as follows :—

$$\text{Elasticity} = \mathcal{L}_{s=0} \frac{\text{stress}}{\text{strain}},$$

in which the $\mathcal{L}$ prefixed denotes " limit of," and the subscript " $s = 0$ " means the strain is vanishingly small.

We shall now proceed to discuss the various simpler kinds of elasticity and the relations between them. We shall confine the treatment throughout to homogeneous isotropic substances, and, except in the case of gases, it will always be assumed that the substance is maintained at the same temperature throughout its mass and during the continuance of the strain. A homogeneous substance is one whose properties are the same at every point. An isotropic substance is one whose properties are the same in all directions at any point.

We saw in the last chapter (art. 69) that any small strain whatever could be resolved into a uniform dilatation and two shears. Hence the corresponding elasticities are specially important. For if known they give the key to the behaviour of the substance under any stresses that may be applied. They will be accordingly taken first.

73. Volume Elasticity.—For the elasticity of volume the stress is a uniform normal pressure over the whole exterior surface, and is measured by force per unit area. The strain is the fractional diminution of volume, that is the diminution of volume per unit original volume. Hence the stress may be measured in lbs. weight per square inch or dynes per square centimetre. Whereas the strain is of no dimensions, for being the ratio of like physical quantities, its value is a pure number. Hence the dimensions of volume elasticity (or bulk modulus as it is sometimes called) are those of force per unit area simply. It is thus expressible in the same units as the stress.

Let k denote the volume elasticity of a solid substance, then we may express its value by the following equation:—

$$k = \frac{p}{v/V} = \frac{p}{3d} \qquad (1),$$

where V is the original volume of the body, p is the pressure to which it is subjected, and v the consequent diminution of volume. The second expression on the right, in which $3d$ is written for v/V, is a reversion to the notation used in Chap. II. for fractional change of volume in the case of a uniform dilatation of amount d per unit length. It will serve equally well for a diminution when, as in the present case, the stress is a compressive one.

The reciprocal of an elasticity is sometimes referred to, a name and a symbol being adopted for it. Thus the reciprocal of the volume elasticity is called the compressibility, and is often denoted by β. We thus have—

$$\beta = \frac{1}{k} = \frac{v/V}{p} = \frac{3d}{p} \qquad (2).$$

In dealing with liquids the compressibility is often spoken of rather than the volume elasticity.

74. Elasticity of Gases.—Turning now to the case of gases we have to distinguish between the two chief methods of estimating the volume diminution. We may keep the temperature of the gas constant during compression, or, we may prevent the escape of heat from it and thus cause its temperature to rise during compression. These two methods of compression are called *isothermal* and *adiabatic* respectively. We have consequently two values for the volume elasticity of a gas. These are called the isothermal and adiabatic elasticities, and will be here denoted by E_t and E_h respectively. The subscripts signify that in the one case the temperature denoted by t is constant, and in the other that the quantity of heat denoted by h is constant. Now for a gas which obeys Boyle's law we may obtain a convenient expression for E_t as follows. Let P and V be its original pressure and volume, and $P+p$ and $V-v$ its pressure and volume at the same temperature after the infinitesimal compression.

Then, by definition of elasticity, we have

$$E_t = pV/v \qquad\qquad (3),$$

and by Boyle's law

$$(P+p)(V-v) = PV.$$

But, remembering that p and v are indefinitely small quantities whose product is accordingly negligible, this second equation becomes

$$pV - Pv = 0$$

or, $\qquad\qquad P = pV/v.$

Hence on comparison with (3) we have

$$E_t = P \qquad\qquad (4),$$

or, in words, the isothermal elasticity of a gas obeying Boyle's law is equal to its pressure.

The adiabatic elasticity is greater than this. In text-books on heat it is shown that the ratio of these two elasticities is equal to that of the two specific heats. Thus, we may write

$$E_h/E_t = S_p/S_v = \gamma, \text{ say} \qquad\qquad (5),$$

where S_p and S_v denote the specific heats at constant pressure and at constant volume respectively. Hence the adiabatic elasticity is given by

$$E_h = \gamma P \qquad\qquad (6),$$

γ being the ratio of the two specific heats for the gas in question. The determination of γ by acoustical methods will be dealt with later. We may note here that its values are approximately $1\frac{2}{3}$ for a monatomic gas, $1\cdot41$ for a diatomic gas, and 1·26 for a triatomic gas. The three cases are illustrated by argon, hydrogen, and carbon dioxide respectively.

It should be noted that gases, though limited to volume elasticity, exhibit this single kind without any imperfection. The narrowness of the limits assigned to the stresses and strains used for the value of an elasticity are here necessary simply to give definiteness to the result (see equations (4) and (6)), and not to prevent its becoming imperfect as in the case of solids.

75. Rigidity.—Rigidity or stiffness is a kind of elasticity which obviously applies only to solids. The strain which we are here concerned with is that known as a simple shear, and has been already discussed (arts. 68-70). The corresponding stress we may call a shearing stress, and it may be described as follows :—Take a cube in the substance in its unstrained state and subject it to uniform normal tension over one pair of opposite faces, to an equal normal pressure over another pair of opposite faces, leaving the third pair of faces unacted upon. The shearing stress is measured by force per unit area. We may now define rigidity thus. The rigidity of a substance is the quotient shearing stress divided by the amount of the shear thereby produced, the value of the quotient being taken in the limit when the shear is indefinitely small. Hence, writing n for rigidity, p for the force per unit area in the tensions and pressures, and χ for the amount of the shear, we have

$$n = p/\chi \qquad (7).$$

The above view of the shearing stress and rigidity corresponds to the view we first took of a simple shear, namely, an elongation one way accompanied by an equal contraction at right angles to it. But we saw in the last chapter (art. 70) that another view of a shear could be taken, namely, the relative sliding, without distortion, of parallel planes, their direction for a small shear being at angles of 45° to those of the elongation and contraction. And, corresponding to this second aspect of the strain, we have a second aspect of the shearing stress, namely, two equal but opposite couples in the same plane, which is the plane of the tensions and compressions on the other view of the stress. Further, the forces composing these couples will act along the directions of the sliding of the undistorted planes, and are accordingly at angles of 45° with the tensions and compressions which constituted the first aspect of the stress. They are, therefore, tangential forces applied parallel to the surfaces over which they act instead of normally as in the first view of the matter.

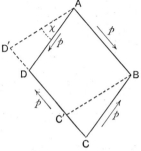

FIG. 38.—SECOND ASPECT OF SHEARING STRESS.

This aspect of the stress is illustrated in Fig. 38. The tangential forces are represented by the arrows, and are each of the magnitude p per unit area. Those along AB and CD obviously tend to produce the relative motion which carries CD to C′D′. But they would also tend to rotate the body clockwise since they constitute a couple. This tendency is counteracted by the forces along AD and CB which form an equal and opposite couple. And this second couple is seen to be able to produce the sliding parallel to AD and CB.

We have thus shown how the second view of shearing stress fits the corresponding view of shear. We have now to trace the quantitative relation between the two views of the stress. To change this set of four tangential forces to the pair of normal tensions and contractions, combine them as follows. Suppose all the edges to be of unit length and take together the forces along AD and CD, these yield a resultant along BD of value $p\sqrt{2}$, but spread over the diagonal plane AC of area $\sqrt{2}$. Similarly the forces along

AB and CB give an equal and opposite force along BD, but acting on the plane through AC of area $\sqrt{2}$. Thus the forces give a tension along BD of value p per unit area. Again, combining the forces along AB and AD to one resultant and the others to another resultant, we find a pressure exerted along AC, in which the force of magnitude $p\sqrt{2}$ is spread over the area $\sqrt{2}$ of the plane through BD. Thus the forces give a pressure of value p per unit area along AC. And, when the shear is infinitesimal, these directions are obviously at angles of 45° with those of the tangential forces. It should be particularly noted that whereas in the two views of the strain the amount of the shear is double the elongation, in the two views of the stress the normal tensions and pressures (per unit area) have precisely the same values as the tangential ones by which they may be replaced. Thus in equation (7) we may suppose the p to refer to either aspect of the stress at pleasure, and yet the validity of the equation remains.

76. Young's Modulus.—Here the stress is a uniform tension parallel to a given axis. This third kind of elasticity, though apparently simpler than either of the foregoing, is in reality more complicated. In the first place, it involves change of both shape and volume instead of a change of only one of these. Secondly, although like the other elasticities, it is represented by a fraction whose numerator is a stress, unlike them, the denominator of the fraction takes cognisance of only one aspect of the corresponding strain, namely, the fractional elongation produced. The lateral contraction, which is also caused by the stress in question, is ignored in estimating the value of Young's modulus, although this contraction bears no constant relation to the elongation. Writing q for Young's modulus, p for the tension in force per unit area of cross section, and f for the fractional elongation, we have

$$q = p/f \qquad (8).$$

77. Elasticity of Simple Elongation.—Suppose now lateral forces are applied so that no change in lateral dimensions occur in spite of the longitudinal tension. Let the tension be p as before, and let the fractional elongation be a. Then denoting the corresponding elasticity by j, we have

$$j = p/a \qquad (9).$$

It is seen that in the case of this elongational elasticity the denominator of the fraction fully specifies the strain, while the numerator of the fraction denotes only one part of the stress, its longitudinal tension, the lateral forces being unspecified and ignored. It is therefore the converse of Young's modulus.

78. Relation between the Elastic Constants.—It is now desirable to deduce certain useful relations between the stresses, strains, and the various elastic constants already dealt with and denoted by p, f, σ, k, n, q, and j. These are respectively tension or pressure, fractional elongation, Poisson's ratio, volume elasticity, rigidity, Young's modulus, and elongational elasticity. By the definitions and equations of this chapter, and the composition and resolution of strains in the preceding one, we have at once a number of important relations. Thus, by article 73 and article 69, equation (8), we have

$$k = \frac{p}{3d} = \frac{p}{3f(1-2\sigma)}. \qquad (10).$$

Again by article 75 and article 69, equation (9), we obtain

$$n = \frac{p}{\chi} = \frac{p}{2e} = \frac{p}{2f(1+\sigma)} \qquad (11).$$

Let us next rewrite here for convenience equation (8) of article 76.

$$q = p/f \qquad (12).$$

Finally, article 77 and equation (7) of article 69 yield

$$j = \frac{p}{a} = \frac{p(1 - \sigma)}{f(1 + \sigma)(1 - 2\sigma)} \qquad (13).$$

By cross multiplication of any pair of these equations p and f are eliminated and a relation obtained between the two elasticities concerned and Poisson's ratio. By combining the equations thus obtained it is obviously possible to express any one of the five quantities k, n, q, σ, and j in terms of any one of the six possible pairs of the remaining four quantities. Some of the more important of these relations are given in Table V., and will be found useful for reference. The first column is derived immediately from equations (10) to (13), and the other columns by further elimination as indicated above. The last two lines of the Table give expressions for the elongation and lateral contraction under a tension p without any forces acting laterally. The results in the column headed k and n are the most important.

[TABLE

TABLE V.—RELATION BETWEEN ELASTIC CONSTANTS

Elastic Constants.	Symbol.	Expressed in Terms of					
Name.		σ and q.	k and n.	n and q.	n and σ.	k and q.	σ and k.
Volume Elasticity	k	$\dfrac{q}{3(1-2\sigma)}$	k	$\dfrac{nq}{9n-3q}$	$\dfrac{2}{3}\cdot\dfrac{1+\sigma}{1-2\sigma}\cdot n$	k	k
Rigidity	n	$\dfrac{q}{2(1+\sigma)}$	n	n	n	$\dfrac{3kq}{9k-q}$	$\dfrac{3k(1-2\sigma)}{2(1+\sigma)}$
Young's Modulus	q	q	$\dfrac{9kn}{3k+n}$	q	$2(1+\sigma)n$	q	$3k(1-2\sigma)$
Poisson's Ratio	σ	σ	$\dfrac{3k-2n}{6k+2n}$	$\dfrac{q-2n}{2n}$	σ	$\dfrac{3k-q}{6k}$	σ
Elongational Elasticity	j	$\dfrac{q(1-\sigma)}{(1+\sigma)(1-2\sigma)}$	$k+\dfrac{4}{3}n$	$\dfrac{4n-q}{3n-q}n$	$\dfrac{2-2\sigma}{1-2\sigma}n$	$\dfrac{3(3k+q)k}{9k-q}$	$\dfrac{3k(1-\sigma)}{1+\sigma}$
Ratio of Elongation to simple tension p	f/p	$\dfrac{1}{q}$	$\left(\dfrac{1}{3n}+\dfrac{1}{9k}\right)$	$\dfrac{1}{q}$	$\dfrac{1}{2(1+\sigma)n}$	$\dfrac{1}{q}$	$\dfrac{1}{3k(1-2\sigma)}$
Ratio of Lateral Contraction to simple tension p	$\sigma f/p$	$\dfrac{\sigma}{q}$	$\left(\dfrac{1}{6n}-\dfrac{1}{9k}\right)$	$\dfrac{q-2n}{2nq}$	$\dfrac{\sigma}{2(1+\sigma)n}$	$\dfrac{3k-q}{6kq}$	$\dfrac{\sigma}{3k(1-2\sigma)}$

79. Experimental Determination of Elastic Constants.

—We shall now describe briefly a few simple experimental methods of determining the elastic constants. The easiest to determine directly in the laboratory is Young's modulus. Rigidity is also fairly easy to determine experimentally though more complicated theory is needed. The direct determination of volume elasticity for a solid presents such difficulties that most values for it have been deduced from the relation between it, the rigidity, and Young's modulus as given in Table V. We shall accordingly describe the experimental determination of the other two elasticities, and suppose the volume elasticity to be deduced from them. The value of the elongational elasticity may then be inferred from the values of k and n or q and n. The same applies also to Poisson's ratio. The above remarks refer, of course, to solids; for gases, the isothermal elasticity, being equal to the pressure, is found by reading the barometer and a pressure gauge. The adiabatic elasticity could then be calculated if the value of γ, the ratio of the specific heats, were known. It is more usual, however, to find the adiabatic elasticity directly by an acoustical method, and so obtain the value of γ indirectly. These determinations will be dealt with later (Chap. X.).

EXPT. 18. *Young's Modulus by Tension of a Wire.*—This experiment may be performed with any one of various methods for the measurement of the elongation. The essentials, however, are the same, namely, that a wire is loaded and the consequent lengthening observed. But the method used for noting the elongation governs the fineness with which it is possible to work and so dictates the total length of wire advisable. Suppose the simplest method of measurement to be adopted, the scale and vernier reading to say 1/20 of a millimetre. Then it is desirable to have a vertical wire about 10 metres long and about a millimetre diameter using loads of 1, 2, 3, and 4 kilograms successively. Further, to guard against a possible error due to the yielding of the support of the upper end of the wire when loaded,

the scale should be carried by another wire hanging from the
same support, the vernier being on the wire under examination.   Again, lest the temperature should change during the
experiment it is advisable to have the two wires of the same
material and diameter to obviate any unequal expansion or
contraction.   These arrangements being made, the experiment is performed by suitably loading the wire, reading
carefully the scale and vernier before and after each loading.
To guard against a violation of Hooke's law by exceeding
the elastic limits, the readings should also be taken after
removal of the weights one by one.   The loads and elongations may be plotted on squared paper and a curve drawn
showing the relation between them.   This should be a
straight line through the origin.   Suppose it makes an
angle θ with the axis on which the loads are plotted, then
cot θ denotes the quotient of load divided by elongation.
But Young's modulus is tension per unit area divided by
fractional elongation.   Thus writing r for the radius of the
wire and l for its length, we have

$$q = \frac{\text{load}}{\pi r^2} \div \frac{\text{elongation}}{l} = \frac{l}{\pi r^2} \cot \theta.$$

The diameter of the wire should be measured carefully in
several places by a micrometer gauge, the length may easily
be obtained with abundant accuracy.   To obtain the value
of q in $c.\ g.\ s.$ units (dynes per square cm.), the load must
be of course expressed in dynes by multiplying the weight
in grammes by 981, the value of the acceleration due to
gravity, also all linear measures must be expressed in
centimetres.

80. EXPT. 19. *Finer Methods for Young's Modulus.*—
Instead of using the scale and vernier we may use various
finer methods to measure the elongation in the determination
of Young's modulus.   Thus the spirit level and micrometer
gauge are used in an apparatus devised by Mr. G. F. C.
Searle.   The method of optical interference was adopted by
Mr. G. A. Shakespear (1899).   The electrical micrometer has
been used for this purpose by Dr. P. E. Shaw.   In this
arrangement the position in which the tip of the micrometer
screw touches a plate carried by the wire is known by its
completing an electric circuit containing a cell and a telephone.
Finally, the familiar apparatus called the optical lever may

be used for the purpose in question. With these finer methods the lengths of the wires operated upon may be proportionately reduced without loss of accuracy.

81. Theory of Torsion of a Cylinder.—As a preliminary to the determination of the rigidity of a substance by experiments on a cylinder of the material, we need the following theoretical investigations :—

Let a right cylinder of length l and radius a be held at one end while the other end is twisted through an angle θ radians, and there held by the application of a couple G dyne-centimetres. It is required to obtain the relation between these quantities and the rigidity n of the substance which is assumed to be homogeneous and isotropic.

Let a circular slice of thickness dl be bounded by planes at right angles to the axis of the cylinder. In this slice take a ring of radii r and $r + dr$ where $dr = dl$. Lastly in this ring consider a cube of sides $dr = dl$. Then, when the relative twist of the ends of the cylinder is θ, that of the planes bounding the slice will be $\theta dl/l$. Accordingly a face of the cube parallel to the base of the cylinder will be sheared relatively to the opposite face through the distance $r\theta dl/l$. To obtain the amount of the shear we must divide this quantity by the distance dl between the faces in question. Thus the amount of the shear is given by

$$\chi = r\theta/l \qquad (1).$$

But the rigidity is defined by $n = p/\chi$, where p is the tangential force per unit area. Hence we have

$$p = n\chi = nr\theta/l \qquad (2).$$

Thus the actual force distributed over a face of the cube parallel to the bases of the cylinder will be $(dr)^2$ times the above expression for p. Further, the moment of this force about the axis of the cylinder will be r times the force itself. Or, for the whole ring, the moment of the force will be $(2\pi r)dr$, r times p.

Thus
$$dG = \frac{2\pi n\theta}{l} r^3 dr \qquad (3).$$

Hence the moment for the slice of thickness dl and radius a is obtained from (3) by integrating from 0 to a. Further, this moment for the slice is the moment for the entire cylinder, for each slice into which we may divide the cylinder experiences the same twisting moment. Hence

$$G = \frac{2\pi n\theta}{l} \int_0^a r^3 dr = \frac{\pi}{2} \frac{\theta}{l} a^4 \qquad (4).$$

Thus $G \propto \theta$, so writing C for G/θ we have
$$C = G/\theta = \pi n a^4 / 2l \qquad (5)$$

as the expression for couple per radian of twist. Accordingly, to determine n we have simply to find C by some experimental method for a cylinder and measure its length and radius.

Some difficulty is occasionally felt by students as to the twisting of a cylinder making no change in the volume. Some imagine that a twist involves a shortening. But this is contrary to Hooke's law. For if stress and strain are proportional, and a twist one way shortened the cylinder, a twist in the opposite direction would lengthen it. This, however, is obviously contrary to our supposition that the substance is isotropic. Probably any expectation that a twist would involve a shortening is traceable to our experience of ropes and other fibrous twisted cords.

82. Expt. 20. *Static Determination of Rigidity.*—To determine the rigidity of a substance by holding a cylinder of it twisted, the apparatus shown in Fig. 39 designed by the author is suitable. The wire in a vertical position is held at the top and twisted at the bottom by the application of a couple due to the silk threads which are fastened to the wheel. These threads pass over smaller wheels at the side, and terminate at the ends of the horizontal cross bar which is loaded by weights placed in the scale pan at the centre. The angle of twist is read in degrees by observing each end

K

of the needle over the graduated circle which is provided with an anti-parallax mirror. Thus, suppose a mass of m grams in the pan produces a twist of d^0, and that the radius of the tread of the pulley on the wire is r cm., the length and radius of the wire being l cm. and a cm. respectively.

Fig. 39.—Rigidity Apparatus.

Then the tension on each thread is $\dfrac{mg}{2}$ dynes and the couple $2r$ times this, *i.e.* $mgr = G$ dyne-centimetres. Further, $d^0 = (\pi d / 180)$ radians, or $\theta = \pi d^0 / 180$. Hence from equation (4) or (5) we obtain for the rigidity of the material under test,

$$n = \frac{360gr}{\pi^2} \cdot \frac{l}{a^4} \cdot \frac{m}{d} \qquad (6).$$

The value of the last factor m/d^0 may be conveniently obtained from a curve plotted on squared paper from a number of loads and corresponding twists. In the apparatus shown in Fig. 39 the upper end of the wire is held by a crosshead which may be adjusted anywhere on the upright bars on which it slides. Thus the lengths of wire under test may be varied at will. When loads are applied at the scale pan, and so a twisting of the wire produced at the lower end, it is evident that an equal couple is experienced at the upper end of the wire also. But, if the arrangements to withstand this couple are insufficient the crosshead will yield appreciably, and the twist of the wire will be less than that of its lower end. Hence to test this point the two plummets shown are provided, and their readings on the circle should be observed before and after the loads are in the pan, corrections being made if necessary.

83. Other Methods for Elastic Constants.—We have only noticed so far very simple methods for the determination of Young's modules and rigidity. Many others are available and practicable. Thus Young's modules may be determined by the static or dynamic flexure of a bar, since the bending of a bar stretches its convex side and compresses the other, and thus involves the elasticity in question. Again, rigidity may be determined by the torsional oscillations of a mass suspended by a wire. The theories of bending and torsional oscillations will be developed in Chap. IV., but the application of them to the determinations under notice may be left to the student. An ingenious application of the method of oscillations has been made by Mr. G. F. C. Searle. He thus obtains with the same apparatus the rigidity of a wire about a foot long by torsional oscillations, and the Young's modulus by flexural oscillations. (See *Phil. Mag.*, Feb. 1900.)

A still simpler method introduced by the writer furnishes the Young's modulus for a wire or glass fibre by static bending and the rigidity by torsional oscillations. (See examples in Chap. II. No. 10.)

CHAPTER IV

DYNAMICAL BASIS

84. Examples of Simple Harmonic Motion. — In Chapter II. we saw that a simple harmonic motion of period τ involves the relation $\ddot{y} = -\omega^2 y$ where $\omega\tau = 2\pi$ and y and $\ddot{y}$ denote respectively the displacement and acceleration of the vibrating point. Now, by Newton's law of motion, $\ddot{y} = f/m$, where f is the force impressed upon a body of mass m to produce in it an acceleration $\ddot{y}$. Hence to cause a body of mass m to execute a S.H.M. of period τ we need that these two expressions for the acceleration should be equal. That is, we must have the body so conditioned that it is acted upon by a force expressed by

$$f = -\omega^2 m y \qquad (1).$$

This force may be due to elasticity, gravity, magnetic action, etc.

Simple Pendulum.—Take first an example in which the restoring force is due to gravity. Consider a simple pendulum of length l with bob of mass m. Then when the angular displacement is θ radians the restoring force is $-mg \sin \theta$, or, for very small values of θ, it is $-mg\theta$ nearly. But, the displacement y, being measured along the very slightly curved arc, we have $\theta = y/l$. Hence, on substitution of this value of θ, the restoring force, being the component along the arc of the weight of the bob, is given by

$$f = -mgy/l \qquad (2).$$

Thus, on reference to (1) we see that $\omega^2 = g/l$. Consequently, since $\tau = 2\pi/\omega$, we obtain

$$\tau = 2\pi \sqrt{l/g} \qquad (3),$$

the well-known expression for the period.

Elastically-suspended Bob.—Take now the case of a body of mass m hanging by an elastic cord, say of india-rubber, whose mass is negligible. Let the length of the cord be l, the area of its cross section c, and its Young's modulus q. Then, if the restoring force f corresponds to an extension y, we have

$$q = -\frac{fl}{cy}, \text{ or } f = -\frac{qc}{l}y \qquad (4).$$

Further, when the displacement is y, *i.e.* when the cord is stretched y more than when at rest with the mass m hanging on it, the total tension on the cord is $f + mg$, so that the force f is free to cause upward acceleration of the bob. Similarly, when the displacement is $-y$, or the bob is at a distance y above its position of hanging at rest, the total tension on the cord will be $mg - f$, so that the force $-f$ is free to produce a downward acceleration of the bob. Hence, by equations (1) and (4) we obtain

$$\omega^2 = qc/lm, \text{ whence}$$

$$\tau = 2\pi \sqrt{lm/qc} \qquad (5).$$

Now, we see from (4) that the restoring force per unit displacement is $f/y = -qc/l = -s$ say. Adopting this abbreviation, equation (5) then becomes

$$\tau = 2\pi \sqrt{m/s} \qquad (6).$$

85. *Generalised Expression for Period.*—This important result may be expressed in words as follows:—The period of oscillation of a particle is 2π times the square root of the quotient *inertia* factor divided by *spring* factor. On further examination this is found to be true for a rigid body executing rotary vibrations. In the linear case considered above the inertia factor is the simple mass of the bob, and the spring factor is the force per unit displacement. But if angular vibrations were under consideration, the inertia factor would be the moment of inertia of the rotating body taken about its axis of oscillation, and the spring factor would be the couple per unit of angular displacement.

Mass at Middle of String vibrating transversely.—Let a body of mass m be fixed at the middle of an elastic cord of negligible mass of length l and stretched by a force F. And let the transverse vibration executed be so small that the alterations of this stretching force are negligible in comparison with the force itself. Also, let f denote the restoring force called into play by the transverse displacement y of the bob or mass at the middle of the cord. Then, since f is the resultant of the two forces F,F due to the two parts of the string when drawn aside, we have by the parallelogram of forces $f : F = 2y : l/2$, or,

$$f = -\frac{4F}{l}y = -sy \text{ say} \qquad (7).$$

Thus, comparing with equation (1) we have $\omega^2 = 4F/lm = s/m$ say, and therefore

$$\tau = 2\pi \sqrt{lm/4F} = 2\pi \sqrt{m/s} \qquad (8).$$

86. *Energy of vibrating Particle.*—When a mass m is executing a S.H.M. represented by $y = a \sin \omega t$, it has been shown that its velocity is given by $\dot{y} = \omega a \cos \omega t$. Hence its kinetic energy is $\frac{1}{2}m\dot{y}^2 = \frac{1}{2}m\omega^2a^2 \cos^2 \omega t$. So the maximum value of its kinetic energy is $\frac{1}{2}m\omega^2a^2$. But the energy of the particle is usually part kinetic and part potential, the sum of the two remaining constant, but when the kinetic energy is a maximum the potential energy is zero. Thus, the expression obtained for the maximum kinetic energy gives the total energy at any point in the vibration, or,

$$E = \frac{1}{2}m\omega^2a^2 \qquad (9),$$

where E is the total energy in question.

We may accordingly say that the energy of a given vibrating mass is proportional to the square of the amplitude and to the square of the frequency.

87. More General Treatment of Small Oscillations.—

In any system whose kinetic and potential energies are expressible in terms of the displacements, velocities, and other quantities concerned, we have a general method of investigating its motion. For, by the doctrine of the conservation of energy, the sum of these two is constant, provided that no energy is being received or emitted by the system, or transformed internally into heat, etc., by friction or viscosity. Thus, let a particle of mass m execute a motion under the influence of a restoring force which is $-s$ times the displacement. Then its kinetic and potential energies are given respectively by

$$K = \frac{1}{2}m\dot{y}^2 \qquad (1),$$

and
$$P = \int_0^y sy\,dy = \frac{1}{2}sy^2 \qquad (2).$$

Hence $K + P = \text{constant}$, on substitution·from (1) and (2) and differentiation with respect to time, yields

$$m\ddot{y} + sy = 0 \qquad (3),$$

which is the equation of motion sought. Its solution may be written

$$y = a \sin(\omega t + \epsilon) \qquad (4),$$

where $\omega = \sqrt{s/m}$, a and ϵ being arbitrary constants depending on the initial conditions. That (4) is a solution of (3) may be verified by substitution, and the fact that it is the complete solution follows from its having a number of arbitrary constants equal to the order of the equation (3). Thus (3) contains $\ddot{y}$, a differential coefficient of the *second* order, and (4) contains *two* arbitrary constants.

From equation (4) we see that the motion in question is simple harmonic of period given by

$$\tau = 2\pi \sqrt{m/s} \qquad (5),$$

as previously obtained by the more elementary method. The advantage of the present more general method lies in its power to deal with cases beyond the scope of the elementary method. The following is an illustrative example :—

88. *Elastically-suspended Bob with Mass of Cord considered.*—Here let the assumption be made that the mass of the cord μ, though no longer negligible, is not great enough to materially change the distribution of strain throughout its length during the oscillation. That is, the cord is imagined as uniformly stretched at every instant of the motion. Consequently, on this assumption, the potential energy is not affected by the mass of the cord. We accordingly have

$$P = \frac{1}{2}sy^2 \text{ where } s = qc/l \qquad (6),$$

q being the Young's modulus, c the cross section, and l the length of the cord.

To calculate the kinetic energy of the cord, take the axis of x along the cord, the origin being at the upper or fixed end. Then $\dfrac{1}{2}\left(\dfrac{\mu}{l}dx\right)\left(\dfrac{x}{l}\dot{y}\right)^2$ is the kinetic energy of an element of the cord of length dx and abscissa x, while the lower end has the speed $\dot{y}$. Hence the kinetic energy of the whole cord and the bob at the same instant is given by

$$K = \frac{1}{2}m\dot{y}^2 + \frac{1}{2}\frac{\mu}{l}\int_0^l \left(\frac{x\dot{y}}{l}\right)^2 dx = \frac{1}{2}\left(m + \frac{\mu}{3}\right)\dot{y}^2 \qquad (7),$$

whence, proceeding as for equations (3), (4), and (5), we find for the period,

$$\tau = 2\pi \sqrt{(m + \mu/3)/s} \qquad (8).$$

Thus, the effect upon the period is represented by the addition to the mass of the bob of *one-third* the mass of the spring.

89. Resisted Oscillations.—We have already seen (arts. 57 and 58) that the acceleration of a point executing damped harmonic motion may be resolved into two components, one proportional to but opposite to its displacement, and the other proportional to and opposite to its velocity. Hence the motion in question will be realised by a particle subject to (1) a restoring force proportional to its displacement, together with (2) a retarding force proportional to its velocity. Such motions we may call resisted oscillations. Thus, if the motion is represented by

$$y = ae^{-\kappa t} \sin qt \qquad (1),$$

as in equation (10) of article 58, we have by equations (9) and (12), article 58,

$$\ddot{y} = -p^2 y - 2\kappa \dot{y}$$

or,

$$\frac{d^2 y}{dt^2} + 2\kappa \frac{dy}{dt} + p^2 y = 0 \qquad (2),$$

where

$$p^2 = q^2 + \kappa^2.$$

But if the mass of the particle be m, the restoring force $-s$ times the displacement, and the retarding force $-r$ times the velocity, we obtain by Newton's second law of motion,

$$\ddot{y} = -\frac{sy}{m} - \frac{r\dot{y}}{m} \qquad (3).$$

Hence, on comparison with equation (2) we find

$$p^2 = s/m, \ \kappa = r/2m, \ q^2 = \frac{s}{m} - \frac{r^2}{4m^2} \qquad (4),$$

which specify the constants of (1) in terms of those expressing the dynamical conditions under which the particle oscillates. We might thus rewrite (1) in the form

$$y = ae^{-rt/2m} \sin \left\{ \left(\frac{s}{m} - \frac{r^2}{4m^2} \right)^{\frac{1}{2}} t \right\} \qquad (5),$$

which is the solution required.

It should be carefully noted, that, in the acoustical cases with which we are here chiefly concerned, p and q are usually large and κ small. Further, in the exponential damping factor κ enters in the first power, whereas in the term characterising the frequency κ^2 subtracts from the value of p^2 to give q^2, see (4) and (5). Thus, while the damping due to κ may be quite appreciably large, it may well occur that the change of frequency due to it is inappreciably small. For example, if the *intensity* of the sound falls to $1/e$th of its value in the tenth of a second, we have $e^{-2\kappa t_0} = e^{-1}$ or $\kappa = 5$. But if the note have a pitch near the middle $C(c'256)$ we may write $p = 1600$, whence it appears that the change in frequency due to κ is $1/2000$th per cent only, and corresponds to a musical interval less than the hundredth of one of Mr. Ellis's logarithmic cents of which 1200 make an octave. Again, if the damping is such as to cause a lowering of the pitch of one logarithmic cent in a note of about 256 per second, we find $\kappa = 56$. Thus, the time t in which the intensity falls to $1/e$th of its value is $1/112$th of a second! If, however, the damping is such as to lower by one logarithmic cent a note of frequency about 40 per second, then $\kappa = 9$ nearly, and the intensity of the sound falls to $1/e$th of its value in about $1/18$th of a second.

It is thus seen that we may often ignore the distinction between p and q while retaining κ in the damping factor. We thus have for such cases the approximate solution—

$$y = ae^{-rt/2m} \sin\{(\sqrt{s/m})t\} \qquad (6).$$

We thus see, as might have been anticipated without the analysis, that if an isolated vibrating system have opposing resistances, the motion gradually dies away. The tones of a piano afford a good example of this. If the motion is to be maintained it is necessary that the system should be put into communication with a store of energy to make up the losses due to resistance. In some cases the connection between the two may be such as to depend for its action on the vibration itself. Thus, the assisting force might be conceived proportional to and in the same sense as the velocity of the vibrating particle. If, in addition, the assisting force were just equal in magnitude to the resisting force, they would then annul one another, we should accordingly have $\kappa = 0$, and the motion in consequence undamped simple harmonic. This is a very simple case of the general effect aimed at when endeavouring to produce sustained notes on musical instruments. The details are then usually much more complicated.

90. Alternative Treatment of Resisted Oscillations.— In the first treatment of resisted oscillations just given we assumed the kinematical results obtained in a previous chapter. But by the calculus we may easily and concisely obtain the same solution without any necessity for the preliminary kinematical investigation. This we now proceed to give. Using the same notation as before, the equation of motion is

$$m\ddot{y} + r\dot{y} + sy = 0 \qquad (1).$$

For a solution try $y = e^{xt}$. This satisfies (1) as found by substitution, provided that

$$mx^2 + rx + s = 0,$$

i.e. if
$$x = \frac{-r \pm \sqrt{r^2 - 4ms}}{2m} \qquad (2).$$

This evidently gives rise to two cases according to the algebraic sign of the quantity under the radical sign.

First, Suppose that this quantity is positive, then the values of x are real and both negative. Denoting them by $-a^2$ and $-\beta^2$, the solution may be written

$$y = Ae^{-a^2t} + Be^{-\beta^2t} \qquad (3).$$

Thus, instead of an oscillation, we have here a gradual

subsidence, and with such a case we are not at present concerned.

Second, Suppose $r^2 - 4ms$ is negative, and put

$$r/2m = \kappa \text{ and } \sqrt{4ms - r^2}/2m = q,$$

then we have
$$x = -\kappa \pm qi \qquad (4),$$

where i denotes $\sqrt{-1}$.

Thus the solution may be written

$$y = e^{-\kappa t}(Ae^{qit} + Be^{-qit}) \qquad (5),$$

or, in the equivalent form

$$y = ae^{-\kappa t} \sin(qt + \epsilon) \qquad (6).$$

In these two solutions the pairs of constants A and B in (5) and a and ϵ in (6) are arbitrary, and must be chosen to suit the initial conditions. The values of κ and q, on the other hand, are quite fixed, being defined by (4), and depend entirely upon the circumstances under which the motion occurs as expressed by the original constants m, s, and r. Thus (6) may be written in the form

$$y = ae^{-rt/2m} \sin\left(\frac{\sqrt{4ms - r^2}}{2m}t + \epsilon\right) \qquad (7).$$

It should be noted that the solution in (5) may be wholly real, and that the relation between the constants A and B in it, and those (a and ϵ) in (6) may be easily found. They may be written

$$a = 2\sqrt{AB} \text{ and } \tan \epsilon = \frac{A + B}{(A - B)i} \qquad (8).$$

91. Forced Vibrations.—We have just seen that an internally resisted oscillation, left to itself, dies away according to a certain law. And that if it be required to maintain its amplitude undiminished, some external impressed force must be applied to it for that purpose. This fact may be readily illustrated both mechanically and acoustically.

Thus a pendulum started and left to itself, without any clock movement in connection with it, finally comes to rest. The motive action of the clockwork is needed to maintain its oscillation. The sounds of a harp emitted by the strings plucked and let go immediately diminish and very quickly die away. In all musical instruments capable of producing sustained sounds some maintaining action is necessary, as the bow of the violin, the stream of air in the organ pipe or flute, and so forth in all other cases. But the maintenance of an oscillation often involves a slight change in its frequency. This leads us to the topic of forced vibrations, which will be first treated mathematically.

Let us consider the behaviour of a vibrating system when subjected both to internal friction and an external simple harmonic force. It has thus the friction to retard its motion, but also the impressed force to maintain that motion in spite of this retardation. The result will be found to be a settling down to a certain definite amplitude and phase which will remain constant while the impressed harmonic force continues, the frequency being that of the impressed force.

Let the impressed force vary as $\sin nt$ and have a maximum value f per unit mass of the vibrating particle. Then we may write the equation of motion as follows:—

$$m\ddot{y} + r\dot{y} + sy = mf \sin nt \qquad (1),$$

where the other symbols have the meanings previously assigned to them. This equation may be slightly abbreviated by the use of p and κ where $p^2 = s/m$ and $\kappa = r/2m$. It then becomes

$$\ddot{y} + 2\kappa\dot{y} + p^2 y = f \sin nt \qquad (2).$$

92. Suppose now some particular value of y, y_1 say, could be found which satisfies these equations. And let another value y_2 be that value of y_1 as found in the preceding article, which makes the left sides of (1) and (2) equal to zero.   Then since y does not enter into the right sides of the equations, obviously y_2 could be added to y_1 without impairing its validity as a solution.   Thus the solution sought may be written

$$y = y_1 + y_2 \qquad (3).$$

Let us assume as a trial

$$y_1 = A \sin (nt - \delta) \qquad (4).$$

Then, on substituting in (2), and regarding the right side of the equation as $f \sin (\delta + nt - \delta)$, we obtain

$$A(p^2 - n^2) \sin (nt - \delta) + A 2\kappa n \cos (nt - \delta)$$
$$= f \cos \delta \sin (nt - \delta) + f \sin \delta \cos (nt - \delta).$$

But, since this equation must hold for all values of t, we may equate the coefficients of the sine and cosine of $(nt - \delta)$. Whence

$$A(p^2 - n^2) = f \cos \delta \quad \text{and} \quad A 2\kappa n = f \sin \delta \qquad (5).$$

Thus, $$A = \frac{f \sin \delta}{2\kappa n} \quad \text{and} \quad \tan \delta = \frac{2\kappa n}{p^2 - n^2} \qquad (6).$$

That is, (4) is a solution of (1) and (2) provided A and δ are defined by (6).   If we construct a right-angled triangle of base $p^2 - n^2$ and perpendicular $2\kappa n$, then (6) may be construed as follows.   The amplitude A is the quotient of f and the hypothenuse of the triangle, while δ is the angle subtending the perpendicular.   It must be noted that p characterises the period of the vibrations *natural* to the system if the motion were *neither resisted nor assisted*.

If we now substitute (4) and (6) in (3), and also make use of the value previously obtained for y_2, we have the full solution of (1) and (2).   This may be written thus :—

$$y = \frac{f \sin \delta}{2\kappa n} \sin (nt - \delta) + ae^{-\kappa t} \sin (qt + \epsilon) \qquad (7),$$

where $$\tan \delta = \frac{2\kappa n}{p^2 - n^2}, \quad q^2 = p^2 - \kappa^2 \qquad (7a),$$

and a and ϵ are arbitrary constants depending on the initial conditions.

93. We now see that the two terms of the solution, which it is usually an analytical convenience to find separately, have also a distinct physical significance. The first term y_1 given in equations (4) and (6), denotes, as Rayleigh puts it, the "*forced* vibration; it is the response of the system to a force imposed upon it from without, and is maintained by the continued operation of that force, the amplitude is proportional to f, the magnitude of the force, and the period is the same as that of the force." It should be noted that it is only the presence of the damping which prevents y_1 from becoming infinite when $n = p$. Thus from (6) we may write

$$A = \frac{f}{\sqrt{(p^2 - n^2)^2 + 4\kappa^2 n^2}} \tag{8},$$

in which, if both $(p^2 - n^2)$ and κ vanish, $A = \infty$. The second term y_2, on the other hand, represents what is often called the *free* vibration. It is the vibration *natural* to the system when free from external impressed force. It should be understood, however, that it is not free in the sense of being unresisted from within. On the contrary, the amplitude of this vibration is continually diminishing on account of the internal friction, and the period is also slightly changed thereby as previously noticed.

94. Energy of Forced Vibration.—Suppose now that f in (1) and (2) remains constant while n varies. And let it be required to find how the energy of the forced vibration changes with the variation of n and κ. In order to make a comparison it is desirable to consider the forced vibration in the same phase in each case, say at the instant when $y_1 = 0$. At this instant the energy of the vibrating particle is wholly kinetic and expressed by $\frac{1}{2} m\dot{y}_1^2$. From (4), for $y_1 = 0$ we have $\sin(nt - \delta) = 0$, and therefore at the same instant $\cos(nt - \delta) = \pm 1$.

Again, by differentiation of (4) interpreted by (6), we have

$$\dot{y}_1 = \frac{f \sin \delta}{2\kappa} \cos(nt - \delta). \qquad (9).$$

Thus for $\quad y_1 = 0, \quad \dot{y}_1{}^2 = \frac{f^2 \sin^2 \delta}{4\kappa^2} = f^2 B$ say $\qquad (10).$

Thus, the variable factor in the kinetic energy, whose dependence on n and κ we are to determine, is expressed by

$$B = \frac{\sin^2 \delta}{4\kappa^2} \qquad (11).$$

Eliminating δ between this equation and (6) in which it was defined, we obtain

$$B = \frac{1}{\Delta^2 + 4\kappa^2} \qquad (12),$$

where $\qquad \Delta = \frac{n^2 - p^2}{n} = \left(\frac{n}{p} - \frac{p}{n} \right) p \qquad (13).$

If, therefore, values of B be taken as ordinates, and a curve plotted having for abscissæ the corresponding values of Δ, we see that for κ constant we have curves symmetrical about $\Delta = 0$, and with a maximum value of B at this place, *i.e.* for $n = p$. This maximum value is given by

$$B_m = 1/4\kappa^2 \qquad (14).$$

95. Thus, for any given value of κ, the kinetic energy of the forced vibration, when the particle is passing through the zero position, is a maximum when the period of the impressed force coincides with that of the vibration natural to the system if friction were absent. Moreover, the diminution of energy consequent upon the lack of this coincidence is the same for a given ratio of frequencies whether that of the impressed force is too great or too small. This will be seen from the second form for Δ in (13). For its value is there shown to depend upon that of n/p minus its reciprocal p/n. Hence a change of this ratio to its reciprocal simply changes the algebraic sign of Δ, leaving its numerical value and therefore its square unaltered. But this ratio n/p measures the *musical interval* between the impressed force and that of the system without damping. Thus an equal diminution of kinetic energy follows from the impressed force being a given interval above or below that which gives the maximum energy. But this symmetrical relation of *ratios* does not apply (except approximately, within narrow limits) to *differences* of frequencies. In other words, though the curves for B are symmetrical when plotted with Δ as abscissæ, they would not be symmetrical if plotted with n as abscissæ. Thus if $p = 100$, the maximum B follows when $n = 100$, and the same diminution in B follows when $n = 200$ or 50, but *not* when $n = 150$ or 50.

96. Referring to equation (10), we see that for the kinetic energy to be a maximum for a given value of κ we must have $\delta = \pi/2$. But by (2) and (4) that involves a *lag* of the displacement of the forced vibration of a quarter of a period behind the impressed force. The velocity of the vibrating point is, however, in phase with the impressed force. These facts are expressed by the following equations which are easily derived from (4), (6), and (9), putting $\delta = \pi/2$,

$$y_1 = -\frac{f \cos pt}{2\kappa p}, \quad \dot{y}_1 = \frac{f \sin pt}{2\kappa} \qquad (15).$$

In these equations p is written instead of n, as they only hold for this particular value of n. We see from (14) that if κ be allowed to vary, then B_m varies inversely as the square of κ. Thus, the less the damping, the greater is the absolute value of the maximum kinetic energy. Further, from (12) we see that for any given value of

L

Δ, the less κ is the greater is the absolute value of the
kinetic energy corresponding to this particular lack of
tuning. The variation of B and B_m with Δ and κ are
illustrated by the ordinates of the curves in Fig. 39a,
whose abscissæ are the values of Δ. Each curve is for
a specific value of κ as shown.

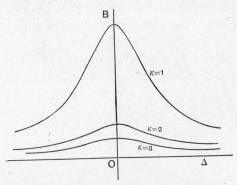

FIG. 39A.—KINETIC ENERGY OF FORCED VIBRATIONS.

97. Sharpness of Resonance.—We may now consider,
as a function of n and κ, not the absolute value of the
kinetic energy, but the ratio which it bears to its possible
maximum with the given κ, which value is only attained
for $\Delta = 0$. Denoting this ratio by b, we have from equations (12) and (14)

$$b = B/B_m = \frac{4\kappa^2}{\Delta^2 + 4\kappa^2} \qquad (16).$$

Thus, as we should anticipate from (12), b reaches its
maximum value, unity, for any value of κ, when $\Delta = 0$.
But we see also from (16) that, for a given value of Δ,
b increases with increase of κ, whereas with B it was just
the reverse. These points are illustrated by the curves
of Fig. 39B, in which the ordinates represent the values
of b and the abscissæ those of Δ, separate curves being
plotted for specific values of κ.

If the impressed harmonic force proceeds from one sound, and the forced vibration constitutes another, the latter is often called a resonance. This term has, however, been extended to cases where neither *driver* nor *driven* are sounds at all, but are very different primary forces and responsive motions. Further, the greater the dependence of the energy of the forced vibrations on exactitude of frequencies between driver and driven, the sharper is the resonance said to be. Let us now find a mathematical expression for the *sharpness of resonance*.

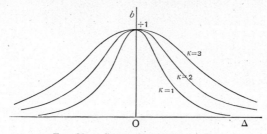

FIG. 39B.—SHARPNESS OF RESONANCE.

We find from equation (16) that

$$\frac{1-b}{b} \div \Delta^2 = \frac{1}{4\kappa^2} = S \text{ say} \qquad (17),$$

where S denotes what we may call the sharpness of resonance, since it expresses the ratio of the fractional diminution of b to the square of Δ which causes it. Hence the sharpness of resonance thus estimated varies inversely as the square of the damping coefficient. In other words, the smaller the frictional damping, the more important does exact tuning become in order to obtain the greatest energy in the forced vibration.

98. This dependence of sharpness of resonance on the damping has been exhibited in a different and very instructive way by Helmholtz.

Eliminating the damping coefficient, he obtains a relation between the resonance effect and the number of complete periods required for the energy of the vibration, when unforced, to diminish to a certain fraction of its initial amount. Thus from (17) and (13) we may write

$$\frac{p}{2\kappa} = \frac{\sqrt{(1-b)/b}}{\left(\dfrac{n}{p} - \dfrac{p}{n}\right)} \qquad (18).$$

But, if the amplitude of the vibration when left to itself is affected by the factor θ after x complete vibrations, we have $\theta = e^{-\kappa(x\tau)} = e^{-2\pi\kappa x/p}$, where p is written for q, to which it is practically equal for ordinary values of κ. Thus $\log_e \theta = -2\pi\kappa x/p$, or

$$x = -\frac{p}{2\pi\kappa} \log_e \theta \qquad (19).$$

Thus (18) in (19) gives

$$x = \frac{\log_e \theta}{\pi\left(\dfrac{n}{p} - \dfrac{p}{n}\right)} \sqrt{\frac{1-b}{b}} \qquad (20),$$

that algebraic sign being taken for the root which will make x positive. By this method Helmholtz obtained the numerical results given in Table VI. To deduce these we must write in (20) $b = \frac{1}{10}$, $\theta^2 = \frac{1}{10}$, and n/p equal to the ratio of the frequencies defining the musical interval required, thus $9/8$ for a tone, $5/4$ for a major third, and so forth. These being inserted the values of x may be calculated.

TABLE VI.—SHARPNESS OF RESONANCE AFTER HELMHOLTZ

Musical interval (of mistuning of impressed force) corresponding to the reduction of the forced vibration to $\frac{1}{10}$, i.e. interval to make $b = 1/10$.	Number of complete vibrations in which the intensity of the vibrations when unforced sinks to $\frac{1}{10}$, i.e. the value of x to make $\theta^2 = 1/10$.
1. An eighth of a tone . . .	38·00
2. A quarter of a tone . . .	19·00
3. A semitone	9·50
4. Three-quarters of a tone . .	6·33
5. A whole tone . . . : .	4·75
6. 5/4 of a tone	3·80
7. A minor third ($\frac{3}{2}$ tone) . . .	3·17
8. 7/4 of a tone	2·71
9. A major third (two whole tones) .	2·37

99. Amplitude of Forced Vibrations.—We have seen how the kinetic energy of a forced vibration varies with the frequency of the impressed forces, and that it is a maximum for $n = p$. Let us now inquire what value of n gives the forced vibration a maximum *amplitude*. We shall still suppose the impressed force to be given by $f \sin nt$, and keeping f constant shall examine the change in the amplitude y_1 consequent upon a change in n. Thus, referring to equations (4) and (8) of article 93, we have

$$y_1 = A \sin (nt - \delta) = \frac{f \sin (nt - \delta)}{\sqrt{(n^2 - p^2)^2 + 4\kappa^2 n^2}} \quad (21).$$

Thus,
$$f^2/A^2 = (n^2 - p^2)^2 + 4\kappa^2 n^2 \quad (22)$$

expresses the variable factor of the amplitude depending on n. Differentiating this to n and equating to zero, we find that

$$A/f \text{ is a maximum for } n^2 = p^2 - 2\kappa^2 \quad (23),$$

the maximum value itself being given by A_m in

$$f/A_m = 2\kappa q \quad (24),$$

where $\quad q^2 = p^2 - \kappa^2$, as in (7a) of article 92.

Another way of arriving at the same result is to throw equation (22) into the form

$$f^2/A^2 = (n^2 - p^2 + 2\kappa^2)^2 + 4\kappa^2 q^2 \qquad (25).$$

From this we may also derive the following conclusions. If a curve were plotted co-ordinating A/f and n^2, this curve would be symmetrical about the ordinate $n^2 = p^2 - 2\kappa^2$, and further, for a given value of n, A/f decreases with increase of κ.

If, on the other hand, we consider the ratio of A to its maximum value A_m for the same κ, then this ratio may increase with increases of κ. For, from (22) and (24) we have

$$\left(\frac{A}{A_m}\right)^2 = \frac{4\kappa^2(p^2 - \kappa^2)}{(n^2 - p^2)^2 + 4\kappa^2 n^2} = \frac{4\kappa^2 p^2}{(n^2 - p^2)^2 + 4\kappa^2 n^2} \text{ nearly } (26),$$

since κ is always small compared with p. Thus, when the relation of n^2 and p^2 is such that $4\kappa^2 n^2$ in the denominator is negligible, we see that

$$A/A_m = \frac{2\kappa p}{n^2 - p^2} \qquad (27),$$

or the ratio in question varies as κ.

It should be noted that the frequency of the impressed force to make the amplitude a maximum is lower than that natural to the system with friction; while the frequency of the impressed force to make the kinetic energy a maximum is above that natural to the system with friction, and equals that if friction were absent. Moreover, the squares of these three frequencies form an arithmetical progression whose common difference is proportional to the square of the damping coefficient. Thus, the vibrations of the system with friction being proportional to $e^{-\kappa t} \sin qt$, the force for maximum kinetic energy varies as $\sin pt$, and that for maximum amplitude varies as $\sin ht$, where

$$p^2 - q^2 = \kappa^2 = q^2 - h^2 \qquad (28).$$

100. Nature of Complete Solution when $n = q$.—Let us now return to the complete solution of vibrations executed under the action of an impressed force. We see from equation (7) in art. 92 that it consists of the sum of two sine functions with different amplitudes and different phases. In the general case the frequencies also are different and the composition is more complicated. So, for simplicity, we take first the case in which the frequencies are alike. This is obtained by putting $n = q$. In other words, this is the limiting case in which the " forcing " disappears. We may, therefore, compound these two vibrations by the methods of Chapter II., articles 26 and 28. We accordingly write the solution in the form

$$y = C \sin (qt - \gamma) \qquad (1),$$

where $$C^2 = A^2 + 2Aae^{-\kappa t} \cos (\delta + \epsilon) + a^2 e^{-2\kappa t} \qquad (2),$$

and $$\tan \gamma = \frac{A \sin \delta - ae^{-\kappa t} \sin \epsilon}{A \cos \delta + ae^{-\kappa t} \cos \epsilon} \qquad (3),$$

A being written for $(f \sin \delta)/2\kappa q$ $\qquad (4).$

Hence, if κ is very small, we may regard the motion, at any instant, as approximately simple harmonic motion, but the amplitude and phase angle are continually changing. Thus for $t = 0$, C and γ are each the same as if no damping were present. Next, when t is great enough to make the square of $e^{-\kappa t}$ negligible, we may write the approximation

$$C^2 = A^2 + 2Aae^{-\kappa t} \cos (\delta + \epsilon),$$

or, $$C = A\left[1 + \frac{a}{A} e^{-\kappa t} \cos (\delta + \epsilon) \right] \text{ nearly} \qquad (5),$$

and $$y = [A + ae^{-\kappa t} \cos (\delta + \epsilon)] \sin (qt - \gamma) \qquad (6).$$

Finally, when t is so great that $e^{-\kappa t}$ is negligible, C becomes A and γ becomes δ. The motion has then subsided to that of the forced vibration simply, and is, therefore, strictly simple

harmonic.   Or, in other words, y_2 has disappeared and y
has reduced to y_1.

This rather complicated motion may be simply illustrated
graphically as follows:—Let a radius of fixed length, A,
turn about a given point with constant angular velocity q.
Let another radius of continually diminishing length, $ae^{-\kappa t}$,
turn about the same point and with the same angular
velocity, the angle between the two radii being always
$(\delta + \epsilon)$.   Complete the parallelogram on these two lines.
Then it may easily be seen that the projections upon a

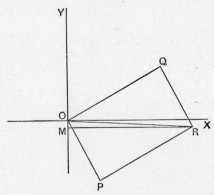

FIG. 40.—COMPLETE SOLUTION OF FORCED VIBRATIONS.

certain fixed line of the moving ends of the two radii give
the motions we wish to compound.   Similarly, the projection upon the same fixed line of the moving end of the
diagonal of the parallelogram gives the motion sought
which is the result of compounding the other two motions.
This construction is illustrated in Fig. 40, in which OP is
the radius of length A, OQ that of length $ae^{-\kappa t}$, the angle
POX $= -\delta$ and QOX $= +\epsilon$, the lines PR, QR complete
the parallelogram, M being the projection of R upon the
axis of y.   Thus OR $=$ C and the angle ROX $= -\gamma$.

It should be noted that although one pair of opposite
sides and all the angles of the parallelogram remain constant,

yet the shrinkage of the other pair of sides causes a shrinkage in the diagonal OR and a change in the angle it makes with the sides of the parallelogram.

101. Initial Conditions.—Let us now obtain expressions for the displacement and velocity at the commencement of the time. On equating these to the values which specify any initial condition of the vibrating system, we can then determine the arbitrary constants a and ϵ, and thus express our solution entirely in terms of known quantities. Thus, on writing $t = 0$ in equation (7) of art. 92 we have for the initial value of the displacement

$$y_0 = - A \sin \delta + a \sin \epsilon,$$

where A is written for $(f \sin \delta)/2\kappa q$, q being now equal to n.

Hence $$a \sin \epsilon = A \sin \delta + y_0 \qquad (7).$$

Again, differentiating to t, equation (7) of art. 92, we obtain

$$\dot{y} = qA \cos (qt - \delta) + ae^{-\kappa t}(q \cos \overline{qt + \epsilon} - \kappa \sin \overline{qt + \epsilon}),$$

so, for $t = 0$ we have

$$\dot{y}_0 = qA \cos \delta + a(q \cos \epsilon - \kappa \sin \epsilon),$$

whence, applying (7) of this article, we transform to

$$a \cos \epsilon = \frac{A}{q}(\kappa \sin \delta - q \cos \delta) + \frac{\kappa y_0 + \dot{y}_0}{q} \qquad (8).$$

Here y_0 and $\dot{y}_0$ denote respectively the initial value of displacement and velocity. Thus κ, q, A and δ being known from art. 91 and 92 in terms of the circumstances of the vibration system, if we now have given in addition the values of y_0 and $\dot{y}_0$, equations (7) and (8) above determine $a \cos \epsilon$ and $a \sin \epsilon$, and thus give a and ϵ. If these quantities are being determined graphically, equations (7) and (8) are in the form most convenient for use. If, however, the quantities are being determined algebraically, we may deduce from them the separate values of a and ϵ in any special case. For division of the two equations gives cot ϵ, squaring and adding them gives a^2.

Let us now consider several special cases with different initial conditions in which, however, $n = q$ throughout.

102. *Case I.*—Let the initial displacement and velocity be given by

$$y_0 = -A \sin \delta \text{ and } \dot{y}_0 - Aq \cos \delta \qquad (9).$$

Then, by substitution in (7) and (8), we obtain

$$a \sin \epsilon = a \cos \epsilon = 0. \quad \text{Thus } a = 0 \qquad (10).$$

That is, the motion is of the permanent type from the commencement, and accordingly suffers no change subsequently. In other words, $C = A$ and $\gamma = \delta$ from the beginning, and remain so while ever the impressed force acts. See equations (2) and (3) of art. 100. This is, of course, a very exceptional case.

Case II.—Let the initial conditions now be the very ordinary ones of no displacement and no velocity when the impressed force begins to act, *i.e.* let them be given by the equations

$$y_0 = 0 \text{ and } \dot{y}_0 = 0 \qquad (11).$$

Then (7) and (8) become

$$a \sin \epsilon = A \sin \delta$$

and $\qquad a \cos \epsilon = \dfrac{A}{q}(\kappa \sin \delta - q \cos \delta)\Big\} \qquad (12).$

Whence $\qquad \cot \epsilon = \dfrac{\kappa}{q} - \cot \delta.$

But by equation (7 *a*) of art. 92, $\kappa/q = 2 \cot \delta$.

Thus $\qquad \cot \epsilon = \cot \delta, \text{ or } \epsilon = \delta \qquad (13),$

and therefore $\qquad a = A \qquad (14).$

These values of ϵ and a put in equations (2) and (3) of art. 100, give, together with (1), the solution required.

103. *Case III.*—Now suppose the initial displacement to be zero, but the velocity finite, the equations being

$$y_0 = 0 \text{ and } \dot{y}_0 = Aq \qquad (15).$$

Then, on reference to (7) and (8), we have

$$a \sin \epsilon = A \sin \delta \text{ and } a \cos \epsilon = \frac{A}{q}(\kappa \sin \delta - q \cos \delta + q),$$

whence $$\cot \epsilon = \frac{\kappa \sin \delta - q \cos \delta + q}{q \sin \delta}$$

But, since $n = q$, $\cot \delta = (p^2 - q^2)/2\kappa q = \kappa/2q$,

and $$\operatorname{cosec} \delta = (\sqrt{4q^2 + \kappa^2})/2q.$$

Thus $$\cot \epsilon = \frac{2\kappa - \kappa + \sqrt{4q^2 + \kappa^2}}{2q} = 1 + \frac{\kappa}{2q} \text{ nearly} \quad (16),$$

the square of κ being regarded as negligible in comparison with $4q^2$. And, to the same approximation $\sin \delta = 1$ and $\cos \delta = \kappa/2q$,

thus $$a \sin \epsilon = A \text{ and } a \cos \epsilon = A\left(1 + \frac{\kappa}{2q}\right).$$

Whence $$a^2 = A^2(2 + \kappa/q) = A^2 2(1 + \kappa/2q),$$

or, $$a = A\sqrt{2}(1 + \kappa/4q) \qquad (17).$$

If, however, κ is negligible in comparison with q, we have

$$\cot \epsilon = 1, \text{ or } \epsilon = \pi/4, \text{ and } a = A\sqrt{2} \qquad (18).$$

The present case gives rise to a curious phenomenon which is readily made clear by Fig. 41.

104. Since the forced vibrations start from the undisplaced position it is obvious that $\gamma = 0$, and from (16) and (17) or (18) in (2) we find that C is practically equal to A. Thus in the figure OP and OQ represent the initial positions of the revolving lines whose projections on OY give the forced and free vibrations respectively. Therefore

the resultant motion is represented by the projection on
OY of R the moving corner of the parallelogram on OP and
OQ.   Hence OP has the length A, OR $= C = A$ nearly, and
OQ $= a =$ approximately $A \sqrt{2}$.   Further, the angle POX

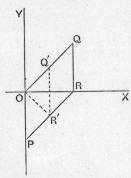

$= \delta = \pi/2$ nearly,   and   QOX $= \epsilon$
$= \pi/4$ nearly.   The line OR is seen
to lie on OX, thus making the angle
γ initially zero.   Then as time proceeds OP and OQ revolve at the
same angular speed q, thus keeping
the angle POQ constant, but while
OP is of constant value, OQ continually shrinks, since its value at time
t is $ae^{-\kappa t}$.   Consider the instant
when OP is again in its initial posi-

FIG. 41.—FORCED VIBRATIONS
STARTING FROM ZERO POSI-
TION.

tion, but OQ has shrunk to OQ′,
about half its initial value, then OR
occupies the position OR′.   Hence

at this instant C will be denoted by OR′ and γ by
the angle R′OX.   We thus see that as time increases γ
changes gradually from zero to about $90°$.   But C on the
other hand at first *diminishes* from A to about $A/\sqrt{2}$ while γ
grows to about $45°$, and then C *increases* from this minimum
to its final value A, while γ grows from about $45°$ to nearly
$90°$.   The minimum value of C occurs at the instant given

approximately by $e^{-\kappa t} = 1/2$ or $t = \dfrac{1}{\kappa}\log_e 2$.

105.—Let us now regard the matter analytically.   Take
the approximate values $\delta = \pi/2$, $\epsilon = \pi/4$, $a = A\sqrt{2}$ and
put them in equations (2) and (3), also rewriting (1).

We thus obtain $y = C \sin (qt - \gamma)$ $(18a)$,

where $C = A \sqrt{1 - 2e^{-\kappa t} + 2e^{-2\kappa t}}$ (19),

and $\tan \gamma = e^{\kappa t} - 1$ (20).

An examination of these equations shows an agreement with the results already illustrated graphically, and gives in addition more detailed information. Thus at various times $(18a)$ assumes successively the following forms :—

(i.) At $t = 0$,
$$e^{-\kappa t} = 1 \text{ and } y = A \sin qt ;$$

(ii.) when $e^{-\kappa t} = \frac{1}{2}$,
$$y = \frac{A}{\sqrt{2}} \sin \left(qt - \frac{\pi}{4} \right) ;$$

(iii.) when $e^{-2\kappa t}$ is negligibly small,
$$y = A(1 - e^{-\kappa t}) \sin (qt - \gamma) ;$$

(iv.) when $e^{-\kappa t}$ is negligibly small,
$$y = A \sin (qt - \delta) = - A \cos qt$$

$$(21).$$

By differentiation to t of (19) or writing it in the form

$$C = - \frac{A}{\sqrt{2}} \sqrt{1 + (1 - 2e^{-\kappa t})^2},$$

it is easily seen that C assumes a minimum value $A/\sqrt{2}$ for $e^{-\kappa t} = 1/2$.

106. General Case of Forced Vibrations : Beats.— Turning lastly to the case where n is not equal to q, *i.e.* to cases in which there is actual "forcing" of the vibrations out of their natural frequency, we see that equation (7) of article 92 no longer admits of the same simplification. It now represents the sum of two vibrations : one simple harmonic, the other damped harmonic, but of *different periods* as well as different amplitudes and phases. The cases of most interest are those in which the periods though different are but slightly so. We can treat such cases as follows. Let $q = n + g$ where g is very small compared with n. We may then write equation (7) in the form

$$y = A \sin (nt - \delta) + ae^{-\kappa t} \sin (nt + \epsilon + gt) \qquad (1),$$

and this by the composition of harmonic motions becomes

$$y = C \sin (nt - \gamma) \qquad (2),$$

where $\quad C'^2 = A^2 + a^2 e^{-2\kappa t} + 2Aae^{-\kappa t} \cos(\delta + \epsilon + gt) \quad$ (3),

and $\qquad \tan\gamma = \dfrac{A\sin\delta - ae^{-\kappa t}\sin(\epsilon + gt)}{A\cos\delta + ae^{-\kappa t}\cos(\epsilon + gt)} \qquad$ (4).

Thus the motion may be regarded as approximately simple harmonic of frequency equal to that of the impressed force. But, in the initial stages, the amplitude and phase are each complicated by slight fluctuations whose frequencies equal the difference between the frequencies of the impressed force and that of the damped vibrations natural to the system. In the course of time both these fluctuations subside, leaving the motion strictly simple harmonic. The amplitude and phase thus established are those which characterise the forced vibrations of the system under the given impressed force. They accordingly remain unchanged so long as the force in question acts.

The fluctuations of amplitude here referred to, afford another example of the phenomenon of " beats." In operating with any actual system they afford a valuable criterion of the closeness of the approximation between n and q. Moreover, if a change in a certain direction in one of these quantities makes the beats slower, it is known that the exact tuning is being still more closely approached.

Of course, here, as in the preceding articles, a and ϵ may be determined to suit any given initial conditions. And, if in any case $a = 0$, the beats will not appear, the permanent form of the vibration being immediately established. If, on the other hand, C is zero for $t = 0$, then the growth of amplitude from zero to A will occur gradually and be accompanied by the fluctuations as time goes on, the value of γ meanwhile changing from its initial amount to its final value δ. These circumstances are clearly deducible from equations (2), (3), and (4), when the appropriate values of a and ϵ for any given initial conditions are substituted.

107. Algebraical Method for Forced Vibrations.— The following algebraical method will serve as a check upon the results obtained by the calculus for forced vibrations and may be preferred by some readers. Assume that under the action of a periodic impressed force, $f \sin (nt + \delta)$, per unit mass of the particle, a vibration of the same frequency is maintained in it when subject to elastic restoring forces and frictional resistances. Let the resulting vibration be

$$y_1 = A \sin nt \tag{1}.$$

Then for the velocity and acceleration, we have by Chap. II. arts. 15 and 16,

$$\dot{y}_1 = nA \cos nt \tag{2},$$

and

$$\ddot{y}_1 = - n^2 A \sin nt \tag{3}.$$

Let the elastic force be $-p^2$-times the displacement, and the frictional force -2κ-times the velocity, each per unit mass. Now, applying Newton's second law of motion, equate the algebraic sum of the forces per unit mass to the acceleration of the vibrating particle. This gives

$$f \sin (nt + \delta) - p^2 A \sin nt - 2\kappa nA \cos nt = - n^2 A \sin nt \ (4).$$

Then, expanding $\sin (nt + \delta)$ and equating to zero the coefficients of $\sin nt$ and $\cos nt$, since the equation holds for every instant of time, we obtain

$$f \cos \delta = A(p^2 - n^2) \tag{5},$$

and

$$f \sin \delta = A 2\kappa n \tag{6}.$$

Thus from (6)

$$A = \frac{f \sin \delta}{2\kappa n} \tag{7},$$

and by (6)÷(5)

$$\tan \delta = \frac{2\kappa n}{p^2 - n^2} \tag{8}.$$

These results show the legitimacy of (1) and interpret it. They also agree with equations (6) of article 92. If the vibrating system be left to itself, we see from the hypotheses that the acceleration of the moving particle is given by

$$\ddot{y} = - p^2 y - 2\kappa \dot{y} \tag{9}.$$

Hence, by equations 9 and 10 of article 58 the vibration may be expressed by

$$y_2 = ae^{-\kappa t} \sin qt \qquad (10),$$

where $\qquad q^2 = p^2 - \kappa^2.$

Now, although the action of the impressed force causes the system to execute vibrations of the period of the force and of definite amplitude A and phase lag δ given by (7) and (8), yet this action by no means precludes the co-existence of the vibrations expressed by (10). Thus, any initial state of things may be regarded as the resultant of these two vibrations given by y_1 and y_2 with the appropriate values for amplitude and phase of y_2.

108. Graphical Treatment of Forced Vibrations.— The subject of forced vibrations may be instructively illustrated, and parts of the problem easily solved, graphically. Thus, taking the notation of the previous article let it be required to find graphically the values of A and δ in terms of the known constants.

In Fig. 42 let the forced vibration in question be represented by the projection upon OY of the point P moving with uniform angular velocity n round O. Now, when left to itself, the point executes damped vibrations represented by (10), the restoring force called into play by elasticity and the retarding force due to friction or other resistance being respectively $-p^2$-times the displacement, and -2κ-times the velocity, each per unit mass. But the displacement at time t is OP $\sin nt$ and the velocity n . OP $\cos nt$. To represent the corresponding forces, take on the axis of x, OS $= -p^2$.OP; and on the axis of y, OF $= -2\kappa n$. OP. Then, the projections upon the axis of y, of S and F revolving about O with angular velocity n will correctly denote the restoring and retarding forces during the forced vibration. The change from the axis of x to that of y in the case of the frictional force corresponds to the change from $\sin nt$ to $\cos nt$. But, for the particle to vibrate as represented by equation (1) the resultant force upon it must be $-n^2 OP \sin nt$. So take OR along the axis of x and equal to $-n^2 OP$. Then, if R rotate about O with angular velocity n, its projection upon the axis of y correctly represents the resultant force on the vibrating particle. It is thus evident that the impressed force to be applied to the vibrating particle can be represented by the projection upon OY of some point I rotating about O with angular velocity n, and such that OR must be the resultant of OS, OF, and OI. Hence the following construction for I. Take OK on the

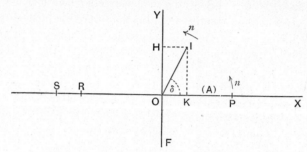

Fig. 42.—Graphical Treatment of Forced Vibrations.

axis of x and equal to SR and OH on the axis of y and equal to FO, complete the rectangle on OH, OK, and the new corner so obtained opposite to O is I, the point required. For, resolving OI, OS, and OF parallel to OX, the resultant is OR as it should be, and resolving the same three radii parallel to OY the resultant is, as required, zero. Which shows that OI is the radius required so as to give with OS and OF the resultant OR. Further, since OI represents f, the amplitude of the force in equation (4) and the angle IOP is the angle δ of the same equation, the figure forms the graphical solution sought, giving f if A is known, or A, $i.e.$ OP, if f is known. To see that this result agrees with the analytical solution previously obtained we may proceed thus:—

We have from the figure

$$f \sin \delta = \text{OH} = \text{FO} = 2\kappa n A,$$

and $\qquad f \cos \delta = \text{OK} = \text{SR} = \text{SO} - \text{RO} = (p^2 - n^2)\text{A}.$

Thus $\qquad A = \dfrac{f \sin \delta}{2\kappa n}$ and $\tan \delta = \dfrac{2\kappa n}{p^2 - n^2} \qquad (11).$

And these agree with the results obtained in articles 92 and 107.

109. Initial Conditions treated Graphically.—We can also exhibit graphically the completed solution under any given initial conditions. In the preceding article, for convenience of drawing, the phase angle δ was put in the expression for the force. Reverting now to the original notation of articles 91 and 92, let us write for the force $f \sin nt$, the forced vibration then becoming $A \sin (nt - \delta)$. This is shown in Fig. 43, in which as before OI and OP correspond respectively to the force and the displacement, and represent them on some convenient scale. The expressions for $a \sin \epsilon$ and $a \cos \epsilon$ in equations (7) and (8) of article 101 are now immediately applicable, and enable us to complete the solution for the given initial conditions.

Thus, we have only to insert the values of y_0, $\dot{y}_0$, and the other constants in the right sides of these equations to obtain $a \sin \epsilon$ and $a \cos \epsilon$. We must then set off ON along OY to represent to scale $a \sin \epsilon$, OL along OX to represent to the same scale $a \cos \epsilon$. The completion of the rectangle gives the point Q, and its diagonal OQ represents to scale the initial amplitude a of the damped vibration y_2 natural to the system, the angle QOX being its phase angle ϵ. This complete solution may then be expressed as follows. The impressed force and the forced vibration are represented by the projections upon OY of the points I and P respectively, each moving in circles about O as centre and with angular velocity n. The free but damped vibration natural to the system is represented by the projection upon OY of the point Q, the radius OQ rotating about O with angular velocity q and at the same time shrinking in length according to the factor $e^{-\kappa t}$. Thus, if K be the projection of P, the motion of the vibrating point will be given by a point M on OY whose ordinate OM is the algebraic sum of OK and ON. The figure represents the state of things for $t = 0$.

By drawing P, Q, and M for a number of positions, say, 8

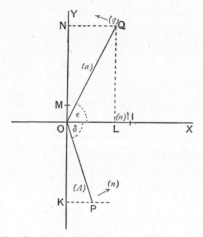

Fig. 43.—Completed Solution for Forced Vibrations.

or 12 times in each revolution, and continuing for several revolutions, and then combining with this actual vibratory motion of M a uniform translation parallel to OX, we could exhibit the graph showing the type of motion which the vibrating particle executes under these conditions. When $n = q$ no beats are possible, but we have usually a continuous growth of the vibration until the permanent amplitude and phase are attained. Though, under the conditions noted in Case III. of article 103, we have an exceptional case, in which a single diminution of amplitude may occur followed by a rise to the final steady state. When n is not equal to q, as

in article 106 (except when the initial conditions make
$a = 0$), beats must occur. Under these circumstances we
have at first repeated waxings and wanings of amplitude.
These, however, die away, leaving finally the permanent
form of vibration established, namely, that expressed by y_1, as
due to the impressed force.

110. Experimental Illustrations of Forced Vibrations.—Many illustrations of the phenomena of forced

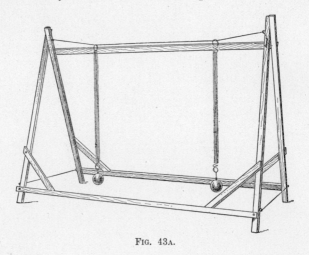

Fig. 43A.

vibrations may easily be called to mind or readily devised.
Of these two will be noticed here, others will occur later.

EXPT. 21. *Rough Illustrations of Forced Vibrations.*—From
a slightly stretched horizontal cord about a metre long,
preferably of india-rubber about half a centimetre diameter,
suspend, side by side, two pendulums. These may be
arranged with helical springs and heavy bobs, one of which is
adjustable in mass, and each bob oscillating vertically. Or,
they may be simple pendulums with metal bobs and silk
thread suspensions, one being adjustable in length. Both
arrangements are shown in Figs. 43A and 43B.

On starting one pendulum in oscillation the other is soon

seen to be moving also, and may, by its absorption of energy, almost reduce the first one to rest. In this case the "driven" becomes in turn the driver, and starts again the vibrations in the pendulum from which its own impulses were received. Indeed several such exchanges of energy between the two are possible and may be observed. The more correct the "tuning," the greater is the amplitude of the forced vibration, as theory shows. The frames shown in Figs. 43A and 43B are of wood about one inch square, and are stayed at the

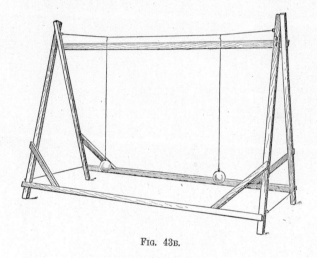

Fig. 43B.

bottom by strings only, in order that they may fold up for more compact storage in the apparatus cupboard.

This arrangement of forced vibrations may be modified so as to be more striking if space is available for a tight rope about 10 metres long. In that case a single simple pendulum 2 metres long may be hung about 2 metres from one end, and at 2 metres from the other end may be hung, say, three pendulums of lengths 1·8 m., 2 metres, and 2·2 m. respectively. Then, on setting the single pendulum in oscillation, the one of corresponding length, though so far away, is soon seen to be in vigorous oscillation, its fellows too long and too short only starting slightly and then stopping again, thus exhibiting "beats."

111. EXPT. 22. *Lord Rayleigh's Model for Forced Vibrations.*—This arrangement, shown in Fig. 44, is more elaborate than those just described, but well repays the trouble of making. In this case the simple pendulum PQ is forced to oscillate in time with the very massive pendulum from which it is suspended. This main pendulum is seen from the figure to be attached at the fixed points A and B by four wires supporting the points C and D which are connected by the strong bar CPD, carrying the large bobs exactly beneath

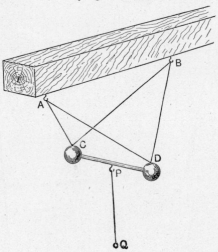

FIG. 44.—RAYLEIGH'S FORCED-VIBRATIONS MODEL.

the points C and D. It should be observed that the four wires are of equal lengths, thus causing the bar CD to set horizontally at right angles to the line joining the fixed points A and B. Hence, when this massive pendulum oscillates in small arcs, P moves almost horizontally. Further, this main pendulum moves with practical independence from the reaction of the forced pendulum PQ, since this latter has so small a mass in comparison with the former. By means of this apparatus the leading features of forced vibrations already enlarged upon may be readily illustrated. To facilitate accurate adjustment, the main suspensions AC, BC, AD, BD must be strong, say of steel wire. String quickly stretches and vitiates the tuning. The phenomenon of beats

is very well shown and needs no special endeavour to attain.
Setting the apparatus at random will almost certainly
produce them. On the other hand, to so adjust the model
that beats are absent is extremely difficult. To show the
effects of damping in reducing the actual amplitude and the
sharpness of resonance several methods are open to us.
Thus we may let the bob Q swing in water. Or we may
replace the small metal bob Q by a large woollen ball.

It is important in all these gravity pendulum arrangements that the amplitudes be kept fairly small, otherwise
the period is appreciably changed and the accuracy of the
tuning accordingly impaired. From the theory previously
developed it may be seen that the equation of motion of the
bob Q is $\ddot{y} + 2\kappa\dot{y} + p^2(y - y') = 0$ where y' is the displacement
of P and y that of Q. But since P's motion is nearly simple
harmonic we may write $p^2y' = f \sin nt$, thus obtaining the form
already used, viz.—

$$\ddot{y} + 2\kappa\dot{y} + p^2y = f \sin nt.$$

112. Large Vibrations.

112. Large Vibrations.—Let us now consider the
character of vibrations performed under the influence of
restoring forces not simply proportional to the displacement.
In strictness this is usually the case, but when the displacements are so small as to make the terms involving
their cubes and squares negligible, the lack of proportionality in the restoring force has no appreciable effect.
When, however, the vibrations are large, these squares and
cubes instead of being negligible may become paramount.
Both the square and cube of the displacement may be
involved in some actual case, but, for simplicity's sake, the
effect of each will be studied separately, and, further, the
frictional term will be omitted.

Asymmetrical Case.—Take first the case in which,
beyond the first power, only the square of the displacement
is involved. The equation of motion may then be written

$$\ddot{y} + p^2y + ay^2 = 0 \qquad (1).$$

It is thus seen that the restoring force changes its
numerical value as well as sign when the displacement
changes sign only.

Obviously, the asymmetry is represented by the term involving y^2, and its coefficient is supposed small. The straightforward, exact solution of this equation gives t as an elliptical integral of y, and is therefore not suitable for our purpose. We accordingly follow the method of successive approximations as used by Lord Rayleigh, and which gives y in a series of cosines involving t. Thus, at first, put $a = 0$ in (1). This yields the approximate solution

$$y = A \cos pt,$$

and this value, substituted in the term ay^2 of (1), gives the approximate differential equation

$$\ddot{y} + p^2 y = -a\frac{A^2}{2}(1 + \cos 2pt) \qquad (2).$$

The solution of this may be written

$$y = A \cos pt + B + C \cos 2pt \qquad (3),$$

where $$B = -\frac{aA^2}{2p^2} \text{ and } C = \frac{aA^2}{6p^2} \qquad (4),$$

A being arbitrary.

But, suppose this second approximate value of y were inserted in the term ay^2 in (1). Then, its first term $\cos pt$, would, in the solution, necessitate a term of the form $t \sin pt$. This term would imply that the displacement would grow indefinitely with the time, which is inadmissible. We thus see that the period involved, namely, $2\pi/p$, must be wrong, and so in time leads us quite astray. Let us therefore, in equation (3), replace p by another symbol q, whose value is to be determined. Then, on substituting in equation (1) we obtain the differential equation

$$\ddot{y} + p^2 y = -a(A \cos qt + B + C \cos 2qt)^2 \qquad (5).$$

The solution of this may be written

$$y = A(\cos qt + d + e \cos 2qt + f \cos 3qt + g \cos 4qt) \quad (6),$$

where A is the arbitrary amplitude,

$$\frac{q^2}{p^2} = 1 - \frac{5}{6}\frac{a^2 A^2}{p^4} = 1 - \frac{5}{6}\sigma^2 = \rho \text{ say,} \quad \Big\} \quad (7),$$

then
$$d = -\frac{\sigma}{2}\left(1 + \frac{19}{36}\sigma^2\right) \quad (8),$$

$$\left. \begin{aligned} e &= \frac{\sigma}{2} \cdot \frac{1 - \sigma^2/6}{4\rho - 1}, \\[1em] f &= \frac{\sigma^2}{6} \cdot \frac{1}{9\rho - 1}, \\[1em] g &= \frac{\sigma^3}{72} \cdot \frac{1}{16\rho - 1} \end{aligned} \right\} \quad (9).$$

113. Thus the asymmetry of the restoring force modifies the vibration in three ways :—

(1) It introduces the constant term expressed by d, see equations (6) and (8), that is, it displaces the vibration to one side.

(2) It slightly lowers the frequency, see equation (7).

(3) It causes the prime tone to be accompanied by the full harmonic series of overtones whose intensities diminish rapidly as they ascend in frequency, see equation (9).

It should be noted further, that the extent to which each of these effects occurs, depends upon the value of σ, and that when σ is fixed, these effects are all quantitatively fixed also. The relation of these effects will be shown more plainly by a few numerical illustrations. Let us take several values of σ and find, first, the ratio r of the intensity of the first overtone to that of the prime; and second, the lowering of the prime itself denoted by c cents. These are shown in Table VII. The numbers in the last column giving values of the quotient r/c being almost constant show that, over the range in question, r varies as c nearly.

TABLE VII.—ASYMMETRICAL VIBRATIONS

σ, Constant of Asymmetry.	c, Lowering of Prime in Logarithmic Cents.	r, Ratio of Intensities of Octave and Prime.	r/c
0·1	7	0·0012	0·000171
0·173	22	0·0036	0·000164
0·3	68	0·0120	0·000182
0·416	135	0·0280	0·000207

114. Symmetrical Case.—Take now the case in which the restoring force is symmetrical, its expression involving the displacement itself and its cube. We may then write the equation of motion in the form

$$\ddot{y} + n^2 y + \beta y^3 = 0 \qquad (10).$$

Let us, as before, obtain a first approximate solution by ignoring β. Thus, we have $y = A \cos nt$ nearly, and, substituting this in y^3 in (10), we get

$$\ddot{y} + n^2 y = -\frac{\beta B^3}{4}(\cos 3nt + 3 \cos nt) \qquad (11).$$

Then, as in the previous case, we must introduce a slightly different value, m say, instead of n in the right side of (11). We thus obtain the approximate equation

$$\ddot{y} + n^2 y = -\frac{3\beta B^3}{4} \cos mt - \frac{\beta B^3}{4} \cos 3mt \qquad (12).$$

And, trying as a solution of this,

$$y = B \cos mt + D \cos 3mt \qquad (13),$$

we find it satisfies (12), provided that

$$m^2 = n^2 + 3\beta B^2/4 \qquad (14),$$

and

$$D = \frac{\beta B^3}{4(9m^2 - n^2)} \qquad (15).$$

Thus, as before, we have a slight change in the pitch and the addition of a higher tone. But this time the higher tones begin at the twelfth, the octave being absent. Further, we no longer have in this case any shift of the equilibrium position.

115. Asymmetrical System under Double Forcing.— Let us now discuss the consequences of subjecting an asymmetrical system to two impressed harmonic forces. The equation of motion may be written

$$\ddot{y} + n^2 y + a y^2 = f \cos pt + g \cos (qt + \epsilon) \qquad (1).$$

Then, neglecting ay^2, we get the first approximate solution, namely—

$$y = a \cos pt + b \cos (qt + \epsilon) \qquad (2),$$

where $\qquad a = \dfrac{f}{n^2 - p^2}$ and $b = \dfrac{g}{n^2 - q^2} \qquad (3).$

It should be noted here that the displacement of each forced vibration is now exactly in phase with the corresponding impressed force, since the tangent of the angle of lag involves the frictional term as a factor of its numerator, see equation (6), article 92. Thus friction being supposed absent, the lag disappears also. Substituting in y^2 of (1) the value of y from (2), we then obtain the approximate differential equation

$$\ddot{y} + n^2 y = f \cos pt + g \cos (qt + \epsilon),$$

$$-\frac{a}{2} \Big\{ a^2 + b^2 + a^2 \cos 2pt + b^2 \cos 2(qt + \epsilon)$$

$$+ 2ab \cos (\delta . t - \epsilon) + 2ab \cos (\sigma t + \epsilon) \Big\} \qquad (4),$$

in which σ and δ denote respectively the sum and difference of p and q. The form of this equation suggests that the solution must contain corresponding terms involving frequencies equal to the double of the original ones and to their sum and difference also. And this suggestion is readily confirmed by analysis. Thus, assuming the form of solution in question, the terms having undetermined co-

efficients, substituting in the left side of (4) and equating
to the right side, we obtain

$$y = a \cos pt + b \cos (qt + \epsilon),$$

$$-\frac{a}{2} \left\{ \frac{a^2 + b^2}{n^2} + \frac{a^2 \cos 2pt}{n^2 - 4p^2} + \frac{b^2 \cos 2(qt + \epsilon)}{n^2 - 4q^2} \right.$$

$$+ \left. \frac{2ab \cos(\delta . t - \epsilon)}{n^2 - \delta^2} + \frac{2ab \cos (\sigma t + \epsilon)}{n^2 - \sigma^2} \right\} \qquad (5).$$

This, with equation (3), forms the second approximation
to a solution of (1). Hence, to the present approximation,
the vibration forced upon this system consists of the
primary tones and others whose frequencies are respectively
the double of those primary frequencies and their sum and
difference respectively. It should be noticed that these
four derived tones all have amplitudes proportional to the
second power of the amplitudes of the primaries. Hence
these derived tones increase in *relative* importance with the
intensity of the parent tones, being negligible in the case
of feeble primaries and paramount in the case of forcible
primaries. This subject has very important applications
to the theory of combinational tones and audition
generally, see Chaps. VI. and VII.

116. Principle of Superposition and its Limitations.—
Referring to equation (2) of the previous article, we may
derive the following important result. If a is absolutely
zero, then the vibrating system in question responds to any
frequency impressed upon it independently of the simultaneous action of other impressed forces. For what is
there shown for two forces would apply equally to a larger
number, or, to quote Lord Rayleigh, " the motion resulting
from the simultaneous action of any number of forces is
the simple sum of the motions due to the forces taken
separately." This is often referred to as the principle of
the superposition of small vibrations. But equation (3)
shows that the amplitude of each vibration depends both

upon that of the force producing it, and upon the closeness of its frequency to that of the free vibrations natural to the system. This last fact vitally affects the relation between the forces and the resulting vibrations. Indeed, it makes it possible for the whole composite vibration to be very unlike the aggregate of the forces producing it. Thus, let any *periodic* force be impressed upon the system. By Fourier's theorem this periodic force can be resolved into its harmonic elements. Each such element of the force excites a vibration of its own frequency and of determinate phase, *i.e.* of the same phase as the force if friction is negligible. But the amplitudes of these vibrations are not simply proportional to those of the corresponding forces. Thus, forces whose frequencies nearly synchronise with the free vibrations of the system call forth a disproportionately large vibration. Hence the aggregate of the vibrations may differ in character from the original periodic force. For, although the elements of the one may exactly correspond to those of the other in frequency, the amplitudes exhibit no such correspondence. Moreover, as shown in the previous article, if a is not absolutely negligible under all circumstances, vibrations are produced of frequencies not present at all in the forces used.

Now, the legitimacy of neglecting a obviously depends, not only on its own magnitude, but also on that of the factor y^2 with which it is associated. And, to discover what value y^2 may have, we must look at the amplitudes given in the full solution obtained by retaining a. Thus, if a were fairly small, and the amplitudes given in equations (2) and (3) small also, we might feel inclined to ignore a. In some cases this would be justifiable, in others it would not. For, suppose the frequency of the free vibrations of the system to be quite different from those of either of the forces, but nearly equal to the difference of their frequencies, *i.e.* n quite different from p and from q, but very nearly equal to the difference of p and q. Then, although the amplitudes in (2) and (3) would be quite small, that of the last term but one in (5) would be very large, because the denominator of the amplitude $n^2 - \delta^2$ would be almost zero. Now a is a factor of all the additional terms in the full solution, and thus though a may be negligibly small in association with any ordinary amplitude, it may need retention when in conjunction with the very large amplitude in question.

Take a numerical illustration. Let the frequency of the free vibrations of the system be that of the c (128) in the bass clef, or, say $n = 805$, and let p and q be 1,805·000001 and 1,000 respectively. Let the amplitudes a and b be each unity, and the value of a be unity also. Thus a is very small in comparison with n^2, and might seem negligible altogether. But if a is neglected entirely, all the added terms of the full solution disappear. Whereas if a is retained, the amplitude of the vibration given by $\cos(\delta.t - \epsilon)$ is found to be 625! And this is not the exaggeration of an element obscurely present in the forces impressed, but is entirely absent from them altogether, and so would never have been produced at all had the component forces involving $\cos pt$ and $\cos qt$ acted separately. Another instructive example will be found in article 402 in the eighth chapter, in which the amplitudes of the various vibrations forced upon a system are not simply proportional to the forces producing them, but depend vitally upon the closeness of tuning between the natural vibrations and the impressed forces.

117. Speed of Transverse Waves along a Cord.—Let it be required to determine the speed of transverse waves along a cord under tension. The cord will be supposed perfectly flexible, of mass σ per unit length and stretched by a force F absolute units. We shall follow the method of Professor Tait, and imagine the cord to be passed at speed v through a smooth tube. This tube has a curved portion, which causes a like disturbance of each part of the cord in turn as it passes through the tube. The tension of the cord produces a pressure which tends to straighten the cord and therefore also the tube. Whereas, the motion of the cord round the curve tends to exaggerate the curvature of the cord and the tube. When all the quantities are rightly adjusted, these two effects may become equal as well as opposite. And, when this balance is obtained, it is obvious that, if the tube were removed, the form of the curved portion of the cord would remain stationary in space, each

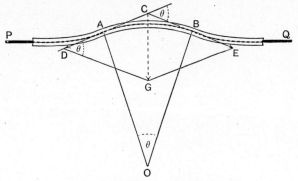

Fig. 45.—Speed of Rope Waves.

individual part of the cord passing in turn through that same stationary curved form. Hence, with respect to the cord itself, that curved portion would be moving backwards at speed v. This will now be dealt with in detail by reference to Fig. 45.

In Fig. 45 let AB of length s be the curved portion of the cord PQ passing at speed v through the stationary tube. Let O be the centre of curvature of the arc AB, and let CD, CE represent to scale the stretching forces F along the cord, CG showing to the same scale the force p thereby exerted by the part AB of the cord on the tube. Then the three angles marked θ on the figure are clearly equal, and

are supposed small enough to make θ (in circular measure)
equal to $\sin \theta$. Hence we have

$$\frac{p}{F} = \frac{CG}{CD} = 2 \sin \frac{\theta}{2} = \theta \text{ nearly.}$$

But $\theta = s/r$ where $r = AO$, the radius of curvature.
Thus $p = Fs/r$ (1).

Again, the centripetal constraint required to change the
direction of motion of a mass m moving with speed v, so
that it shall describe a curve of radius r, is well known to
be mv^2/r. Hence, denoting the force in the present case
by f, we have

$$f = \sigma s v^2/r \qquad (2),$$

where σ is the mass of the cord per unit length.

Thus, because the part AB of the cord is curved and
stretched it must experience, to preserve its form, an
outward force p given by (1), and to keep it curved though
moving it needs an inward force f given by (2). But if
these two forces were equal they would balance each other
and the tube would not be required. The condition for
dispensing with the tube without change of the curvature
of AB is evidently obtained by equating p and f. So from
(1) and (2) we have

$$F = \sigma v^2 \text{ or } v = \sqrt{F/\sigma} \qquad (3).$$

The dependence of v upon F and σ is illustrated by the
following experiment :—

118. EXPT. 23. *Speed of Rope Waves.*—Arrange horizontally, and side by side, two india-rubber cords each about 1 cm.
diameter and 5 to 10 metres long. Let one end of each be
fixed, and the other pass over a pulley and have a weight
attached. The weights should be so chosen that the speed
of advance of the waves along the cords is slow enough to
be easily followed by the eye. Keep one weight constant,
so that the speed of the waves along the cord to which it is
fixed remains constant also, and thus serves as a standard
for comparison. Let the other weight be at first equal to

the standard constant weight. Give to each cord simultaneously smart taps with the edge of the hand, then the pulses so produced are seen to travel along the cords side by side at the same speed. Now change the variable weight to four times its previous or standard value. Again tap the cords simultaneously at one end. This time the pulse on the tighter cord goes to the far end and back, while that on the standard cord reaches the far end only. In other words, the tension being increased fourfold the wave speed is doubled, as expressed by the theory in equation (3). The same increase of speed may also be attained by reverting to the original tension, but diminishing the diameter of the cord to half, for this reduces the linear density to a quarter, and so gives to the quotient F/σ the fourfold value as before. Similarly, the speed may be reduced to half by either doubling the diameter of the cord or using a tension one quarter the standard amount. There is, however, an advantage in the changes of tension over the changes in diameter. For weights of any multiple or submultiple are easily obtained, whereas cords whose diameter are in any simple ratio may not always be available. And it is desirable to make the ratio of the speeds on the two cords two to one, so that the eye may readily follow and appreciate the exact relation. If space allows, the cords may be placed vertically side by side, and the weights simply hung on, pulleys being dispensed with.

119. Speed of Sound in a Gas.—Let us now determine from elementary considerations the speed of sound in a gas. Lord Rayleigh treats this problem by supposing a wind whose speed equals that of the sound to oppose its advance. This is analogous to Professor Tait's treatment of the cord problem dealt with in art. 117. It seems the simplest and most elegant of the elementary methods, and forms the basis of the following treatment.

Let the speed of sound be v, and let the advance of the sound waves be opposed by a steady wind of the same mean speed v. The advance of the sound waves is accordingly prevented, just as, in the cord problem, the disturbance was kept stationary by the tube while the cord passed

N

along. But as the cord moved each part in turn took the
curvature imposed on it by the tube. So here with the gas,
as the wind carries it along, each portion assumes in turn the
various states of condensation or rarefaction appropriate to
the corresponding parts of the sound waves. These sound
waves, when once formed, are kept stationary in space by
the opposing wind, somewhat as the rope waves were by the
motion of the rope through the tube. Thus we have waves
not progressive and not stationary in the usual sense of the
term, but retained in their place by the contrary motion of
the medium. Hence the actual speed of the gas, its
pressure, and specific volume, vary from point to point in
the waves. Let these be characterised by v, P, and U, at
one point A, fixed in space, and by the same symbols with
dashes at another point A′ say.

120. Let us assume that the waves are practically unchanged in type as they advance. Then there can be no
accumulation or diminution of gas between the points
A and A′ under consideration. In other words, the motion
is what is called steady, a certain speed, pressure, and density
always characterising the gas particles which at *any time
occupy a given point fixed in space*. This gives the so-called
equation of continuity, viz.

$$v/U = v'/U' \qquad\qquad (1).$$

For each side of this equation represents the mass of gas
passing per unit area per unit time at the point to which it
refers.

But at the two places A and A′ these two equal masses
have different speeds, and therefore different momenta.
The cause of this change is to be sought in the difference
of pressures at the two points A and A′. For the prism of
gas between them is urged forward by the pressure felt
behind and retarded by that experienced in front. Thus
the *increase* of momentum between the ends of the prism is

due to the *decrease* of pressure throughout its length. We may accordingly write, as the equation of motion,

$$P - P' = (v'/U')v' - (v/U)v \qquad (2).$$

The substitution of (1) in (2) yields

$$P - P' = \frac{v^2}{U^2}(U' - U) \qquad (3),$$

whence

$$v^2 = \frac{P - P'}{(U' - U)/U}U,$$

or,

$$v = \sqrt{EU} = \sqrt{E/\rho} \qquad (4),$$

where E denotes the elasticity of the gas and ρ its density.

Now the expression for v in equation (4) gives the mean speed of the contrary wind required to prevent the advance of the waves. Hence it gives also the speed of sound relatively to the gas in any case. It thus furnishes a solution to the problem attacked, and gives, in the ordinary sense of the phrase, the speed of sound in the gas as required.

121. Newton's and Laplace's Formulæ.—The symbol E for the elasticity in equation (4) was left without a subscript, because we have yet to discuss the question whether the isothermal or the adiabatic elasticity is appropriate in this case. Newton, who first established this expression for the velocity of sound, took the isothermal elasticity. The value of this elasticity, as we have seen in the previous chapter, art. 74, is equal to the pressure of the gas. Hence, writing P for E in (4), we obtain what is known as Newton's formula, viz. :

$$v = \sqrt{P/\rho} \qquad (5).$$

But this value is in conflict with all good experimental results, and therefore fallacious. It was pointed out by Laplace that the elasticity appropriate to the case in question is the adiabatic elasticity. Hence, putting for E

in (4) γP, the value of the adiabatic elasticity, as shown in Chap. III. art. 74, we have Laplace's formula,

$$v = \sqrt{\gamma P / \rho} \qquad (6),$$

γ being the ratio of the specific heats of the gas. And this equation gives for v a value in agreement with experimental results.

Let us now examine the question more closely as to which elasticity must apply in the case of sound propagation. When sound waves pass along, any point fixed in space experiences alternately compressions and dilatations, the compressions involving generation of heat, the dilatations a cooling. But these opposite states follow each other too quickly for the temperature to be diffused from point to point, and so maintained practically constant everywhere. Hence clearly the isothermal elasticity cannot apply. It is not, however, quite so clear that we must go to the other extreme and use the adiabatic elasticity. We might naturally suppose that, if the heat conduction were insufficient to maintain the temperature constant, there would be at any rate sufficient conduction of heat to make the adiabatic elasticity inapplicable. But Stokes has shown that any appreciable departure from the adiabatic state of things would lead to a rapid stifling of the sound. And this we know is not the case. Hence Laplace's formula is upheld. We may, accordingly, trust the value of γ for air, deduced from the formula and the best experiments on the velocity of sound.

The effects of pressure and temperature on the velocity of sound will be seen easier if we transform (6) as follows :—

$$v = \sqrt{\gamma P U} \qquad (7),$$

where U is, as before, the volume per unit mass. Now, by Boyle's law, the product PU is a constant for temperature constant. Hence change of pressure without change of temperature has no effect on the speed of sound for a gas obeying Boyle's law. But if the temperature changes with or without change of pressure, then the product PU changes, and with it the speed of sound. Thus, writing U_0 and v_0 for the specific volume and speed of sound at $0°$C., we have

$$v = \sqrt{\gamma P U_0(1 + at)} = v_0 \sqrt{1 + at} \qquad (8),$$

where a is the coefficient of expansion of the gas at constant pressure. Now for any gas $a = 0{\cdot}003665$ or $\frac{1}{273}$ per $1°$ C. nearly, and for air we have approximately $v_0 = 33,150$ cm./sec., or 1090 ft./sec. These values put in (8) yield the useful approximate formulæ

$$v = (33,150 + 61t°\text{C.})\ \text{cm./sec. or } (1090 + 2t°\text{C.})\ \text{ft./sec.} \quad (9).$$

122. Distortion of Large Waves.—The foregoing determination of the expression for the speed of sound is based on the assumption that the waves remain precisely the same in character as they pass along, or, as it is often put, that the waves are of *permanent type*. This supposition is practically fulfilled provided the amplitudes concerned are very small. If they are large, then the assumption that they pass on unchanged is not in accordance with fact or possibility. This may be seen from equation (3), which yields

$$P + \frac{v^2}{U^2}U = P' + \frac{v^2}{U^2}U' = \text{a constant, } A \text{ say.}$$

But by (1), v^2/U^2 is also a constant, B say, in the case of steady motion corresponding to the propagation of waves of unchanging type. Hence we may write

$$P = A - BU \text{ or } y = A - Bx \qquad (10),$$

as the condition to be fulfilled by the pressure and volume, in order that waves may be propagated unchanged in character as they advance. But this is not the law for any known gas. For obviously (10) would give a straight line on the pressure-volume diagram, whereas both isothermals and adiabatics are always curves.

Suppose, however, that this straight line is taken tangentially to the actual adiabatic curve. Then, if the changes of pressure and volume are very small, the corresponding straight line will practically coincide with the curve for the length in question. Hence for such small changes the condition for steady motion is practically fulfilled, and the results obtained on the supposition of unchanged propagation remain valid.

If, however, the sound is very loud, then the pressures and volumes will change very considerably. The corresponding curve on the diagram of pressures and volumes, accordingly, departs sensibly from any straight line. Consider now the condensed portion of the wave. Here the slope of the adiabatic is appreciably steeper, and the volume less than at the normal or uncondensed parts of the wave. But the slope of the line given by (10) is expressed by the constant B which denotes v^2/U^2. Thus for the condensed part of a wave of large amplitude we have v^2/U^2 appreciably larger than normal, and U distinctly less. Hence for both reasons v is increased. We have thus obtained the important conclusion that the highly condensed portions of intense sound waves advance faster than those parts of the same waves at which the pressure is normal. Similarly, the highly rarefied portions of the wave travel rather slower. Accordingly, the condensed parts will outstrip the rarefied parts, and the type of the wave is modified or distorted as it advances. A similar change of type with advance is noticeable in water waves on a sloping sea beach. Here the crests gain on the troughs, and the faces of the waves become steeper and steeper until they curl over and break. This effect is clearly brought out in Maxwell's *Theory of Heat*, in the section dealing with the velocity of sound.

123. Speed of Longitudinal Waves along a Solid Prism.—We may here follow the method used for a gas, changing what needs to be changed to meet the present case. Thus let the prism be moved backwards at the mean speed v, that at which the sound waves move forward relatively to the prism. Also, let l denote the normal length of unit mass of the rod and l' that where the speed is v'.

Then the equation of continuity may be written

$$v'/l' = v/l \qquad (1).$$

Let F and F' be the stretching forces experienced by the prism over its entire cross section, where the speeds are respectively v and v'. Then the equation of motion becomes

$$F' - F = \left(\frac{v'}{l'}\right)v' - \left(\frac{v}{l}\right)v \qquad (2).$$

The substitution of (2) in (1) gives

$$F' - F = \frac{v^2}{l^2}(l' - l) \qquad (3),$$

whence

$$v^2 = \frac{(F' - F)l}{(l' - l)s} \cdot ls \qquad (4),$$

where s is the cross-sectional area of the prism. But the fraction on the right side of (4) is Young's modulus for the material of the prism, which we will denote by q. Again, ls is the specific volume or volume per unit mass, and is thus the reciprocal of the density ρ. Equation (4) may accordingly be transformed to

$$v = \sqrt{q/\rho} \qquad (5).$$

In this case the value of Young's modulus used should, in strictness, be the adiabatical value and not that obtained by any of the ordinary statical methods which give the isothermal Young's modulus. However, the difference between the two is small and is usually neglected.

If we examine the criterion for the permanence of the type of these longitudinal waves in an elastic solid, we see that it is fulfilled within the limits to which Hooke's law holds. For equation (3) shows that the increase of force is v^2/l^2 times that of the corresponding elongation. And by equation (1) v^2/l^2 is a constant. Hence (3) may be written $(F' - F) \propto (l' - l)$, which is the symbolic expression of Hooke's law.

Let us now inquire what stretching force is needed to make, if possible, the speed of transverse waves along a wire equal to that for longitudinal waves as just proved above. Referring to article 117 we have

$$\text{Speed of Transverse waves} = \sqrt{F/\sigma} = \sqrt{F/\rho s} \quad (6),$$

where σ is the linear density, ρ is the volume density, and s the cross-sectional area of the wire.

Again, from (5) we have

$$\text{Speed of Longitudinal waves} = \sqrt{q/\rho} = \sqrt{qs/\rho s} \quad (7).$$

Hence the stretching force required is qs, or a force of q units per unit area of cross section. But this is the force that, if Hooke's law held, would stretch the wire to double its length! Hence longitudinal waves in wires travel considerably faster than any transverse ones which we ever obtain.

124. Partial Differential Equations for Progressive Waves.—Let us now treat progressive wave-motion by the methods of the calculus. We have, first, to derive the differential equation; second, to obtain the solution of it; and third, to fit this solution to the various possible initial and terminal conditions. The derivation of the differential equation is, of course, different for strings, gases, solid prisms, and extended solids, dealing with the mechanics of each special case. They will accordingly be taken separately in the above order. But we shall find that, under the restriction of small amplitudes, each of these cases leads to the same approximate differential equation. The solution of it is accordingly deferred, until it has been established for each case. The common form arrived at will then be considered, the general results so obtained being applicable with slight modifications to any of the cases.

Transverse Waves along a Cord.—Let the mass of the

cord per unit length be σ and the stretching force F absolute units. Take the axis of x along the cord and let the transverse displacement at time t for a point whose abscissa is x be denoted by y. Then we have seen in article 117 that F/r expresses the pressure per unit length due to a curvature of radius r. Now, we shall suppose this curvature to be always very small, hence it may be approximately represented by d^2y/dx^2 instead of the fuller expression which is the above quantity divided by $\{1 + (dy/dx)^2\}^{3/2}$. Further, we may equate the restoring force to the product of mass per unit length and transverse acceleration. Thus, we obtain the differential equation of motion required, viz.

$$F\frac{d^2y}{dx^2} = \sigma\frac{d^2y}{dt^2},$$

or,
$$\frac{d^2y}{dt^2} = v^2\frac{d^2y}{dx^2} \qquad (1),$$

where
$$v^2 = F/\sigma \qquad (2).$$

125. *Plane Waves in a Gas.*—Let the plane of the wave front be at right angles to the axis of x. Also let x define the equilibrium position of particles and y their actual positions at time t. But y is to be measured from the same origin and along the *same line* as x. For the waves being in a gas must be longitudinal. Then, at a neighbouring layer at the same instant t let the equilibrium and actual positions of other particles be represented by $x + dx$ and $y + \dfrac{dy}{dx}dx$ respectively. Hence, if ρ_0 and ρ are respectively the normal and altered densities of the layer, we have

$$\rho_0 dx = \rho\frac{dy}{dx}dx,$$

or $\rho_0/\rho = dy/dx$. This and the adiabatic relation $P \propto \rho^\gamma$ or $P\rho^{-\gamma} = P_0\rho_0^{-\gamma}$, give

$$P = P_0\left(\frac{dy}{dx}\right)^{-\gamma} \qquad (3).$$

Also, the mass of unit area of the displaced and deformed slice is $\rho dy = \rho_0 dx$, and the corresponding moving force is

$$-\frac{dP}{dy}dy = -\frac{dP}{dx}dx.$$

Thus the equation of motion may be written

$$-\frac{dP}{dx} = \rho_0 \frac{d^2y}{dt^2} \tag{4}.$$

126. Eliminating P between equations (3) and (4) we obtain

$$\left(\frac{dy}{dx}\right)^{\gamma+1}\frac{d^2y}{dt^2} = \frac{\gamma P_0}{\rho_0}\frac{d^2y}{dx^2} \tag{5}.$$

This is the *exact* equation given by Lord Rayleigh defining the actual abscissa y in terms of the time t and the equilibrium abscissa x. We can easily transform this so as to exhibit the longitudinal *displacement* ξ in terms of x and t. Thus, by definition, $y = x + \xi$ and on substitution (5) becomes

$$\left(1 + \frac{d\xi}{dx}\right)^{\gamma+1}\frac{d^2\xi}{dt^2} = \frac{\gamma P_0}{\rho_0}\frac{d^2\xi}{dx^2} \tag{6}.$$

But on writing the approximate value unity for each of the quantities in brackets in equations (5) and (6), they reduce to the ordinary approximate forms, namely :—

$$\frac{d^2y}{dt^2} = v^2\frac{d^2y}{dx^2} \tag{7},$$

and

$$\frac{d^2\xi}{dt^2} = v^2\frac{d^2\xi}{dx^2} \tag{8},$$

in each of which

$$v^2 = \gamma P_0/\rho_0 \tag{9}.$$

127. Sometimes it is found convenient to use another dependent variable called the "condensation" instead of either the y or ξ just given. This is usually denoted by s and is defined by the relation $\rho = \rho_0(1 + s)$. Thus, since $\rho_0 = \rho(1 + d\xi/dx)$, we have $s = -d\xi/dx$. Differentiating (8) to x and then using this value of s we obtain successively

$$\frac{d^3\xi}{dt^2 dx} = v^2 \frac{d^3\xi}{dx^3},$$

and
$$\frac{d^2 s}{dt^2} = v^2 \frac{d^2 s}{dx^2} \qquad (10).$$

We thus see that the same form of equation is obtained whether y, ξ, or s is the dependent variable.

It forms a further useful exercise and check to derive directly the equation in s. At x let the density be ρ and the speed u. Then the equation of continuity for the slice between x and $x + dx$ is

$$\frac{-d(\rho u)}{dx}dx = \frac{d\rho}{dt}dx.$$

In this equation we may write

$$\frac{d}{dx}(\rho u) = \rho\frac{du}{dx} + u\frac{d\rho}{dx} = \rho_0\frac{du}{dx} \text{ nearly.}$$

For, in deriving the approximate equation for small motions, u is a small quantity and s negligible in comparison to unity. Thus $u\dfrac{d\rho}{dx}$ is omitted, and for $\rho = \rho_0(1 + s)$ is written ρ_0 simply. Again, $d\rho/dt$ on the right side of the same equation is $\rho_0 ds/dt$. Hence the equation of continuity in this approximate form becomes

$$\frac{-du}{dx} = \frac{ds}{dt} \qquad (11).$$

The mass of unit area of the slice is ρdx or $\rho_0 dx$ nearly. The corresponding moving force is $\dfrac{-dP}{dx}dx$. Thus the equation of motion may be written

$$\frac{-dP}{dx} = \rho_0\frac{du}{dt} \qquad (12).$$

Now the adiabatic relation may be written

$$P\rho^{-\gamma} = P_0\rho_0^{-\gamma} \text{ or } P = P_0(\rho/\rho_0)^\gamma = P_0(1 + s)^\gamma.$$

Hence $\qquad \dfrac{dP}{dx} = \gamma P_0 (1+s)^{\gamma-1} \dfrac{ds}{dx} = \gamma P_0 \dfrac{ds}{dx}$ nearly $\qquad$ (13).

Thus, by substitution from (13), equation (12) becomes

$$\frac{-\gamma P_0}{\rho_0} \frac{ds}{dx} = \frac{du}{dt} \qquad (14).$$

Then, on differentiating (11) to t and (14) to x, and equating the values thus found for the identical quantities $d^2u/dxdt$ and $d^2u/dtdx$, we obtain

$$\frac{d^2s}{dt^2} = \frac{\gamma P_0}{\rho_0} \frac{d^2s}{dx^2} = v^2 \frac{d^2s}{dx^2} \qquad (15),$$

which agrees with (10).

It should be noticed here that according to the kinetic theory of gases the speed of sound is determined by, and is directly proportional to, the velocity of mean square of its molecules. For on this theory we have

$$P = \frac{1}{3} \rho \bar{V}^2 \qquad (16),$$

where $\bar{V}^2$ is the mean square of the velocities of the various molecules and P the pressure. Hence, for the speed of sound in a gas of density ρ_0 at pressure P_0 we have

$$v = \sqrt{\gamma P_0/\rho_0} = \left(\sqrt{\gamma/3} \right) \bar{V} \qquad (17).$$

128. Longitudinal Waves along a Solid Rod.—Take the axis of x along the rod and let ξ denote the displacement at time t of a plane whose equilibrium position is x. Consider a neighbouring plane whose equilibrium position is $x + dx$. Then its displacement at time t is expressed by $\xi + \dfrac{d\xi}{dx}dx$. Thus the actual elongation of this layer is $\dfrac{d\xi}{dx}dx$ and its fractional elongation is $\dfrac{d\xi}{dx}$. Hence, if the value of Young's modulus for the material is denoted by q and the restoring force per unit area due to the stretching by f, we have $f = q\ d\xi/dx$. But the moving force per unit area on a slice of thickness dx will be the increase of this force in the thickness of the slice. It is accordingly represented by $\dfrac{df}{dx}dx$ $= q(d^2\xi/dx^2)dx$. And ρdx is the mass per unit area of the slice to be moved. Hence the equation of motion is

$$\rho dx\frac{d^2\xi}{dt^2} = qdx\frac{d^2\xi}{dx^2},$$

or,

$$\frac{d^2\xi}{dt^2} = v^2\frac{d^2\xi}{dx^2} \tag{18},$$

where

$$v^2 = q/\rho \tag{19}.$$

It might be supposed that the foregoing reasoning and result were rigorous; they are, however, in reality approximate, as may easily be seen thus. Since the elasticity used is Young's modulus, the supposition is that the sides of the rod are not prevented from bulging where longitudinal compression occurs, and shrinking laterally where elongation occurs. But this bulging and shrinking each involve a lateral motion which has not been taken into account in the equation of motion. Thus the above result is approximate and not rigidly true. It is, however, quite near enough for many purposes, provided that the wave length is great compared with the thickness or width of the rod or bar. This may be shown by examining the extent of the displacements longitudinally and laterally. Thus if the wave length is λ, we may regard a length $\lambda/4$ as being distinctly under compression or elongation at any one time. If the fractional elongation of this part of the rod is e, the actual elongation is $e\lambda/4$, which measures the extent of longitudinal motion. But if Poisson's ratio for the rod is σ, the lateral contraction would be σe per unit width; so for a width b, say, the actual contraction and possible motion would be σeb. Thus for this lateral motion to be negligible we need σb to be small compared with $\lambda/4$; or, since σ is about $1/4$, we may say b

must be small compared with λ. It should be noted that
only the outer portions of the rod would have the full value
of the lateral motion just written, but in like manner only
the end portions of a part elongated or compressed would
have the full value of the longitudinal motion just assigned
as due to this cause.

129. Longitudinal Waves in an Extended Solid.—
If, instead of a long thin rod, we have an unlimited solid,
and produce infinite plane longitudinal waves in it, then the
lateral bulging and shrinking which occurs in the rod is no
longer possible. Accordingly, Young's modulus no longer
applies as the elasticity appropriate to the case, its place
being taken by the simple longitudinal elasticity referred to
in articles 77 and 78 and Table V. Thus the differential
equation may be written

$$\frac{d^2\xi}{dt^2} = v^2 \frac{d^2\xi}{dx^2} \tag{20},$$

where $\qquad v^2 = \left(k + \frac{4}{3}n \right) \bigg/ \rho = \frac{(1-\sigma)q}{(1+\sigma)(1-2\sigma)\rho} \tag{21},.$

k denoting the volume elasticity, n the rigidity, and σ the
value of Poisson's ratio. Examples of waves approximately
of this type occur in the earthquake disturbances travelling
through the earth's crust, but we are not deeply concerned
with them here.

**130. Discussion of the Differential Equation for
Wave Motions.**—In the four cases just considered—viz.
transverse disturbances in a stretched cord, longitudinal
disturbances in a gas, a rod, or an extended solid—we have
found one common form of differential equation which
applies strictly or approximately to each case. The
constant denoted by v in these equations has, however,
different values for the different cases. But this fact does
not affect our discussion of the equation itself. Further, the
dependent variable used in the various cases is sometimes a
transverse displacement, sometimes a longitudinal one, and

at others the condensation. This again does not affect our treatment of the equation itself. We accordingly write, as the general type for solution and discussion,

$$\frac{d^2y}{dt^2} = v^2\frac{d^2y}{dx^2} \qquad (1).$$

This may be put into words, thus :—The second differential co-efficient of the dependent variable with respect to time is proportional to its second coefficient with respect to the co-ordinate along the axis of wave propagation. We shall afterwards see that this constant ratio v^2 is the square of the velocity of wave propagation.

The solution of this equation may be written

$$y = f_1(x - vt) + f_2(x + vt) \qquad (2),$$

where each of the f's denotes an *arbitrary function*. It may be seen from the respective arguments $(x - vt)$ and $(x + vt)$ that f_1 denotes a disturbance travelling in the positive direction, and f_2 one travelling in the negative direction. That this sum of functions satisfies the differential equation may be easily verified as follows :—Differentiate (2) twice with respect to t, thus giving the left side of (1), viz.

$$\frac{d^2y}{dt^2} = v^2f_1''(x - vt) + v^2f_2''(x + vt) \qquad (3),$$

where the dashes to the f's denote differentiations of the functions with respect to the arguments in brackets. Now differentiate (2) twice with respect to x, and multiply the result by v^2. We thus obtain the right side of (1), viz.

$$v^2\frac{d^2y}{dx^2} = v^2f_1''(x - vt) + v^2f_2''(x + vt) \qquad (4).$$

But the right sides of (3) and (4) are identical, hence we see that (2) satisfies (1) whatever the functions may be.

Equation (2) gives the displacement y, for completeness' sake we may add to this the value of the velocity $\dot{y}$.

Thus differentiating (2) once with respect to t, we obtain

$$\dot{y} = -vf_1'(x - vt) + vf_2'(x + vt) \qquad (5).$$

131. Now this solution for the dependent variable y applies equally to the same form of differential equation in which the dependent variable was ξ or the condensation s. Thus, applying this result to equation (15) of article 127 we see that

$$s = f_1(x - vt) + f_2(x + vt) \qquad (6).$$

But by equation (11) of article 127, we have

$$du = -\frac{ds}{dt}dx \qquad (7).$$

Thus differentiating (6) to t, substituting in (7) and integrating, we find

$$u = +v \int f_1'(x - vt)dx - v \int f_2'(x + vt)dx$$
$$= vf_1(x - vt) - vf_2(x + vt) \qquad (8),$$

or, for either the positive or negative part taken separately we have

$$u = \pm vs \qquad (9),$$

the upper sign referring to the wave disturbance denoted by f_1 which travels positively, and the negative sign to the wave travelling negatively. Thus u, the velocity of the particles, has the same sign as the condensation in a positively-travelling disturbance. Now in a condensed part of the wave s is positive; thus in a positively-travelling wave u is positive also, *i.e.* the velocity is there with the wave. Again, in the condensation of a negative wave, u would be negative, *i.e.* the velocity of the particle is still with the wave. On the other hand, where there is a rarefaction, s is negative, and the velocity u of the particles is against the direction of propagation of the wave.

132. Initial Conditions.—We have now to consider the various other conditions that may be imposed, and the forms that the arbitrary functions must assume to satisfy them. Let us at present suppose both the medium and the original disturbance to be unlimited. Suppose also that the initial displacements and velocities are given as functions of x. Then the problem is to satisfy the following three equations :—

The differential equation, $\dfrac{d^2y}{dt^2} = v^2\dfrac{d^2y}{dx^2}$ (1).

The initial displacement, $y = \phi(x)$, for $t = 0$ (2).

The initial velocity, $\dot{y} = \psi(x)$, for $t = 0$ (3).

We have already seen that (1) is satisfied by

$$y = f_1(x - vt) + f_2(x + vt) \tag{4}$$

It remains now to define f_1 and f_2 so as to fulfil (2) and (3) also.

By putting $t = 0$ in (4) and using (2), we have

$$\phi(x) = f_1(x) + f_2(x) \tag{5}$$

By differentiating (4) to t, then putting $t = 0$ and using (3), we obtain

$$\psi(x) = -vf_1{}'(x) + vf_2{}'(x) \tag{6}$$

On integrating (6) with respect to x, we find

$$\frac{1}{v}\int_0^x \psi(x)dx = -f_1(x) + f_2(x) \tag{7}$$

By addition and subtraction of (5) and (7) we then obtain the expressions sought for f_1 and f_2, viz.

$$f_1(x) = \frac{\phi(x)}{2} - \frac{1}{2v}\int_0^x \psi(x)dx \tag{8},$$

and $$f_2(x) = \frac{\phi(x)}{2} + \frac{1}{2v}\int_0^x \psi(x)dx \tag{9}$$

Then (8) and (9) substituted in (4) give the complete solution which fits the imposed initial conditions, viz.

$$y = \tfrac{1}{2}\phi(x - vt) - \frac{1}{2v}\int_0^x \psi(x - vt)dx + \tfrac{1}{2}\phi(x + vt)$$

$$+ \frac{1}{2v}\int_0^x \psi(x + vt)dx \qquad (10).$$

When the functions ϕ and ψ are of any ordinary well-known type, the integrations in (10) can, of course, be easily effected and the value of y fully expressed. Several cases of special simplicity or importance will now be considered.

133. Illustrative Examples of Initial Conditions.— *Case I.*—As the first illustration let the original disturbance be a displacement without velocity. Thus for $t = 0$ let

$$y = \phi(x) \text{ and } \dot{y} = 0 \qquad (11).$$

Then, in the previous notation, $\psi(x) = 0$. Thus we find by the foregoing that

$$f_1(x) = f_2(x) = \tfrac{1}{2}\phi(x), \text{ and therefore}$$

$$y = \tfrac{1}{2}\phi(x - vt) + \tfrac{1}{2}\phi(x + vt) \qquad (12),$$

or, in words, the wave motion consists of two equal waves travelling in opposite directions, their displacement being each half that of the initial displacement.

Thus, suppose $\qquad \phi(x) = -2a \sin \omega x/v \qquad (13)$, then we have

$$y = a \sin \{\omega(t - x/v)\} - a \sin\{\omega(t + x/v)\} \quad (14).$$

Case II.—Now let the original disturbance be an impressed velocity without displacement. Thus, for $t = 0$, let

$$y = 0 \text{ and } \dot{y} = \psi(x) \qquad (15).$$

Then, proceeding as before, we have

$$-f_1(x) = +f_2(x) = \frac{1}{2v}\int_0^x \psi(x)dx \qquad (16),$$

which by substitution in equation (4) or (10), gives

$$y = -\frac{1}{2v}\int_0^x \psi(x - vt)dx + \frac{1}{2v}\int_0^x \psi(x + vt)dx \quad (17).$$

It is seen that in this case we have two disturbances, each half the initial one, and travelling in opposite directions. The disturbances in this case are initially equal but opposite in their displacements, but have velocities which are alike in both magnitude and sign; this common velocity being $\frac{1}{2}\psi(x)$.

Thus, if $\psi(x) = -2a \sin (\omega x/v)$ (18),

we find $-f_1(x) = f_2(x) = -\dfrac{a}{\omega} \cos (\omega x/v),$

whence

$$y = -\frac{a}{\omega} \cos \left\{\omega(t - x/v)\right\} + \frac{a}{\omega} \cos\left\{\omega(t + x/v)\right\} \quad (19).$$

Case III.—Now let the initial disturbance involve both displacement and velocity. Thus at $t = 0$ let

$$y = \phi(x) \text{ and } \dot{y} = \psi(x) = -v\phi'(x) \quad (20).$$

Then $f_1(x) = \frac{1}{2}\phi(x) + \frac{1}{2}\displaystyle\int_0^x \phi'(x)dx = \phi(x)$

and $f_2(x) = \frac{1}{2}\phi(x) - \frac{1}{2}\displaystyle\int_0^x \phi'(x)dx = 0$ (21).

Thus $$y = \phi(x - vt) \quad (22).$$

That is, we have only a single wave, it is travelling in the positive direction, and has amplitude and velocity equal to those of the initial disturbance. Hence, if for $t = 0$,

$$y = -a \sin (\omega x/v) \text{ and } \dot{y} = \omega a \cos (\omega x/v) \quad (23),$$

we find as the solution $y = a \sin \left\{\omega(t - x/v)\right\}$ (24).

134. Original Disturbance Limited.—Now, while the medium remains unlimited as before, let the original disturbance be confined between the limits $x = 0$ and $x = l$.

Then the solution undergoes a slight corresponding modification, the disturbance produced having limitations in time and space. Thus, the original disturbance having length l, we have (in the general case) two disturbances, each of length l, travelling one in the positive and the other in the negative direction. If only one of these elements is present in the solution, say the positive wave, then we have only some one length l disturbed at any instant. Let us follow the single positive wave in its course. This disturbance of length l moves forward at speed v. Hence, at time t, the portion of medium disturbed has abscissæ vt and $l + vt$. Consider now the period during which any point experiences the disturbance. Let its abscissa be l'. Then obviously it is undisturbed until $t = (l' - l)/v$, when the head of the advancing wave train reaches it, it is then disturbed until $t = l'/v$ when the tail of the wave train passes it, after which it remains without further disturbance. Or, we may say that the point l' is disturbed only while t is not outside the limits l'/v and $(l' - l)/v$. Precisely similar considerations apply to points on the negative side of the origin when negatively-travelling waves are present in the solution.

135. Reflection at a Fixed End : Stopped Pipe.—In a medium of unlimited length we have seen that the solution of the differential equation may give a single positive or negative wave, or both superposed, the one case or the other being dependent upon the initial conditions. Suppose now the medium to be limited in length at one end, and let the initial conditions be such as to give only a single wave travelling towards that limit to the length of the medium. Then we shall show that the single initial disturbance gives rise to another travelling in the opposite direction. This result is produced by reflection at the end which limits the medium. But the nature of the reflection will depend upon the nature of this end of the medium. It may be what is termed a "fixed" end where no dis-

placement is possible. Or, it may be what is termed a
" free " end, where the displacement may be as large as we
please. Let us consider first the fixed end. This condition
is represented by the fixed end of a cord vibrating transversely, or of a rod vibrating longitudinally, or by the
" stopped " end of an organ pipe, or, for sounds in the free
air, by any large obstacle which produces the familiar
phenomenon of the echo. Let this end be situated at the
origin of co-ordinates, and let the medium extend only on
the negative side of the origin. Suppose, further, that the
initial conditions give rise to a disturbance represented by

$$y = f_1(vt - x) \qquad (1).$$

And, in order to represent this original or incident disturbance together with that produced by reflection at $x = 0$,
let us write

$$y = f_1(vt - x) + f_2(vt + x) \qquad (2).$$

We have then to determine f_2 subject to the conditions at
the fixed end, namely

$$y = 0 \text{ at } x = 0 \text{ for all values of } t \qquad (3).$$

Substituting (3) in (2), we have

$$0 = f_1(vt) + f_2(vt) \text{ or } f_2(z) = -f_1(z) \qquad (4),$$

where z is any variable. Thus (2) becomes

$$y = f_1(vt - x) - f_1(vt + x) \qquad (5).$$

We see by inspection that for $x = 0$, this gives $y = 0$ for
all values of t and for any form of the function f_1. Thus
the reflected wave is like the incident wave, but with
amplitude of reversed sign.

136. Equations (1) and (5), of course, apply under
certain restrictions of time and space which differ according
to circumstances. Precisely what the restrictions are for
any individual case can easily be ascertained by the method
of the previous article. It will suffice here to examine a
single case of special interest. Thus let the original

disturbance be confined to a portion of the medium of
length l.   Then equation (1) applies alone until the head
of the disturbance reaches the origin.   Let this occur at
time $t = 0$.   Then (5) begins to apply instead of (1).   But
its application is restricted in space, and the restriction is
different for the different terms.   Thus at time t, where
$t < l/v$, the first term applies only between the origin and
$x = -l + vt$, and the second term applies only between the
origin and $x = -vt$.   When $t = l/v$, the first term ceases
to apply, and the second term alone represents the value
of y.   That is to say, the act of reflection, which began at
$t = 0$, is now completed, and the value of y is henceforth
represented by the negatively-travelling wave—

$$y = -f_1(vt + x) \qquad (6).$$

These various stages are illustrated in Fig. 46, in which
the original function consists of two straight lines.   It is
thus seen that as the various portions of the incident
disturbance reach the reflecting point the corresponding
portions of the reflected disturbance emerge from it.   And
to show this fact the more clearly in the figure, *dotted* lines
are used for those parts of the reflected wave which are
represented by the general equation (5), but are excluded
from actual existence by the restrictions which apply to
that equation.   Thus, when the act of reflection is just
beginning, the dotted lines on the positive side of the
origin show a negatively-travelling wave as expressed by
the second term of equation (5).   But the dotted lines
indicate that as yet this wave has no physical existence.
At the next stage the incident wave has moved to the
right, the part which has passed the origin being now
dotted to show its fictitious character.   On the other hand,
the negatively-travelling wave has passed a like distance to
the left, that part which has passed the origin being in
full lines to show that it is now part of the actual reflected
wave, the remaining portion being dotted to show that it

has not as yet any actual physical reality. Hence the components of the wave disturbances to the left of the origin may be obtained by the following construction :—

137. Draw the displacements of the incident disturbance, and make on the other side of the origin a copy of them derived by rotating the incident wave through $180°$ about the axis of z (at right angles to the axes of both x and y). Let the original disturbance proceed in the positive direction at speed v, and the copy of it move in the negative direction at speed v; but at any instant account only those portions of these waves real which are then on the negative side of the origin along the axis of x.

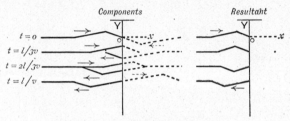

FIG. 46.—REFLECTION AT FIXED END.

138. Reflection at a Free End : Open Pipe.—Consider now the reflection of a positive wave at a " free " end situated at the origin of co-ordinates. A free end is represented by a free or loose end of a cord hanging vertically, a free end of a rod vibrating longitudinally, or the open end of an organ pipe.

The conditions imposed by such an end are represented by

$$\frac{dy}{dx} = 0 \text{ at } x = 0 \text{ for all values of } t \qquad (7).$$

It may be seen that this is equivalent to writing for the string the end must be always parallel to the axis of x, and for the open end of a pipe or the free end of a rod the density at the end must remain normal.

We have therefore now to combine equations (2) and (7), and determine the form of the function f_2.

Differentiating (2) with respect to x, we find

$$\frac{dy}{dx} = -f_1'(vt - x) + f_2'(vt + x),$$

where f' denotes the function obtained by differentiating the original function, or $f'(z)$ denotes $\dfrac{df(z)}{dz}$. Thus equation (7) gives

$$f_2'(vt) = f_1'(vt) \text{ for all values of } t \qquad (8).$$

Thus, integrating with respect to t from 0 to t, we have

$$\int_0^t f_2'(vt)dt = \int_0^t f_1'(vt)dt, \quad \text{or} \quad f_2(vt) = f_1(vt) \qquad (9).$$

Hence, for the free end, by substituting (9) in (2) we obtain the solution

$$y = f_1(vt - x) + f_1(vt + x) \qquad (10).$$

This shows that the reflected wave is like the incident one without reversal of sign of amplitude. In other words, by rotating the incident wave $180°$ about the axis of y, we obtain the form of a wave which, if made to move at speed v in the negative direction along the axis of x, will, on passing the origin, become the actual reflected wave.

It will afford good practice for the reader to draw for himself a diagram for this case similar to that illustrating the previous article.

It should be noted that various aspects of a wave motion may be singled out for consideration, and that if one is reversed by reflection another may be left unchanged. Thus, in the case of the stopped end, we saw that the displacement is reversed. The condensation, however, is left unchanged in sign by the reflection. For the condensation arriving at the end with the incident wave is associated with a motion of the particles towards the end (see Fig. 10, art. 21; and equation (9), art. 131). Now by the presence of the stopped end this motion is exactly annulled by the equal and opposite motion of the particles in the reflected wave. But this opposite motion in the oppositely-travelling wave is also associated with a condensation as in the incident wave. Thus a condensation is reflected as a condensation from a stopped end. Similarly at a stopped end a rarefaction is reflected as a rarefaction. Thus, though the displacement is reversed by reflection from a stopped end, the state of condensation is unchanged.

It is easy to see that the exact opposite of the above holds for reflection at an open end. That is, at an open end the displacement and motion of the particles are not reversed by reflection, but the condensation is thereby reversed in sign. Hence, at an open end an incident condensation is reflected as a rarefaction, and a rarefaction is reflected as a condensation.

139. Medium itself limited, Original Disturbance shorter still.—Suppose now that the medium is of finite length, and that the original or initiating disturbance occupies only a portion of this length. And let it be first assumed of such a nature as to give rise to only a single wave travelling in the positive direction. Then we see from the foregoing articles on reflection that this disturbance will course to and fro along the given length of medium suffering reflection at each end, the circumstances of those reflections depending on the natures of the ends. Suppose first both ends are fixed or stopped, then the amplitude or displacement is reversed in sign by such reflection. We are thus able to predict the whole future course of events. Second, suppose that both ends of the medium are free or open. Then such reflection occurs without change in magnitude or sign of the displacement. Here again we are able to follow out the whole phenomena as the wave disturbances pass to and fro along the given length of medium. Thirdly, suppose the medium in question to be terminated by one fixed and one free end. In this case the reflections occur alternately with and without change of algebraic sign of the amplitude.

It should be noticed that where the ends of the medium are *alike* in nature the original state of things is restored after the time required for the disturbance to traverse *twice* the length of the medium. Whereas, when the ends of the medium are *unlike*, the original state of things is not restored until after the time requisite for the waves to traverse a distance equal to *four times* the length of the medium.

We have hitherto supposed the original disturbance to give a positive wave only. Obviously, all the remarks just made would apply equally if the original wave were a negatively-travelling one. Finally, suppose the initial disturbance were quite general and, accordingly, gave rise to two waves travelling in opposite directions, and let it be required to find the state of things after time t. For this purpose it is necessary to take each wave separately, and find the state of things after time t due to each of them, and then superpose these states for the solution sought.

140. Displaced String.—Let us now consider the case of a string, extending from $x = 0$ to $x = l$, displaced and then let go. We have here then a finite length of elastic medium with both its ends fixed. Further, the initial disturbance is to consist of a displacement the whole length of the string, but without velocity. The solution of the differential equation (see equation (2), art. 130) may be written

$$y = f_1(x - vt) + f_2(x + vt) \qquad (1).$$

Let the initial conditions be expressed by

$$y = 2f(x) \quad \text{and} \quad \dot{y} = 0 \Big\} \qquad (2).$$

from $\qquad x = 0$ to $x = l$, when $t = 0$

The terminal conditions may be written—

For all values of t, $y = 0$ both at (and *outside*) the limits $x = 0$ and $x = l$ $\Big\}$ $\qquad (3).$

We must now determine f_1 and f_2 in (1) so as to satisfy (2) and (3). We have previously seen that to satisfy (2) we must have oppositely-travelling waves of like amplitude and sign, thus

$$y = f(x - vt) + f(x + vt) \qquad (4).$$

To make $y = 0$ at the limits, in accordance with equation (3), we have, on substitution in (4),

$$0 = f(-vt) + f(+vt),$$

and $$0 = f(l - vt) + f(l + vt).$$

Putting $+ vt = -z$ in the first of these equations, and $+ l + vt = -z$ in the second, we obtain

$$f(z) = -f(-z) \qquad (5),$$

and $$f(2l + z) = -f(-z) \qquad (6),$$

whence $$f(2l + z) = f(z) \qquad (7).$$

Thus, equation (5) shows that the amplitude changes sign with change of sign of x, and (7) shows that the function is periodic in length $2l$. Hence, for a stretched string originally displaced in any manner, but without velocity, we may construct the subsequent motion as follows :—

Describe a curve of displacements for the length of the string, the abscissæ denoting lengths along the string, but the ordinates being only *half* the actual displacements at the corresponding points. Beyond the string's length describe a curve obtained from the foregoing by revolving a half turn first about the axis of x, and then about that of y. We have thus described curves for the length $2l$, *i.e.* for twice the length of the string. This forms one complete pattern of the curve required, and needs repeating indefinitely right and left. This curve must now be taken to represent, at the instant $t = 0$, *two* sets of component wave trains which have, at that instant, identical displacements. One of these trains is to move to the right, the other to the

left, each with speed v. The actual displacement and
motion of the string at time t are to be found as the
resultants of those corresponding to the parts of the two
component wave trains which are, at that instant, between
the limits $x = 0$ and $x = l$.

To avoid obtaining any resultant outside the limits
occupied by the string, the component wave trains must
be regarded as having no real existence outside these limits,
but as being, while there, convenient but wholly abstract
mathematical conceptions which give birth to the corresponding physical realities only when passing inside the
limits $x = 0$ and $x = l$.

This construction should be compared with that for
reflection at a fixed end (art. 137 and Fig. 46), which was
a rather simpler example of the same essential principles.

141. Plucked String.—Suppose now the initial displacement to be produced by " plucking," that is, by pulling
a point of the string aside and letting it go. Let the co-
ordinates of the plucked point when let go be $(a, 2b)$.

Then, for $\qquad a > x > 0, f(x) = bx/a \qquad$ (8),

and for $\qquad l > x > a, f(x) = \dfrac{b}{l - a}(l - x) \qquad$ (9).

Further, in constructing the component wave trains for
$t = 0$, we shall have

$$y = 0 \text{ for } x = \pm nl \qquad (10),$$

where n is any integer ;

$$y = + b \text{ for } x = a \pm 2nl \qquad (11),$$

and finally $\qquad y = - b \text{ for } x = - a \pm 2nl \qquad$ (12).

The points determined by (11) and (12) joined by
straight lines give the required component wave trains at
$t = 0$, equation (10) serving as a check. Fig. 47 shows
these components and the resultant for a number of
positions. It will be seen that the resultant form of the

vibrating string consists always of two or three straight lines. The component wave trains outside the limits of the string are shown in broken lines to indicate that they must not be taken as actually existing. The components inside the limits are shown by fine continuous lines, the resultant by a bold line.

EXPT. 24.—These phenomena can easily be illustrated by an india-rubber cord about a centimetre in diameter and ten metres long, fastened at each end and plucked by the hand.

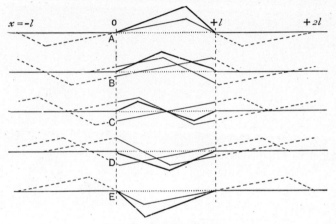

FIG. 47.—PLUCKED STRING.

142. Alternative Method for Vibrating String.—Let the string as before extend from $x = 0$ to $x = l$, the ends being fixed. And let its differential equation of motion be

$$\frac{d^2y}{dt^2} = v^2\frac{d^2y}{dx^2} \qquad (1).$$

Then the terminal conditions are represented by

At $x = 0$, and at $x = l$, $y = 0$ for all values of t (2).

The most general integral of (1) which fulfils (2), and corresponds to a periodic motion of the string, may be written

$$y = \sin \frac{\pi x}{l}(a_1 \cos pt + b_1 \sin pt)$$

$$+ \sin \frac{2\pi x}{l}(a_2 \cos 2pt + b_2 \sin 2pt) + \ldots + \ldots$$

$$+ \sin \frac{n\pi x}{l}(a_n \cos npt + b_n \sin npt) + \ldots + \ldots \quad (3).$$

Now suppose that the initial conditions are given by

At $t = 0$, $y = F(x)$ and $\dot{y} = 0$ from $x = 0$ to $x = l$ (4).

Then, we have by (4) in (3),

$$F(x) = a_1 \sin \frac{\pi x}{l} + a_2 \sin \frac{2\pi x}{l} + \ldots + a_n \sin \frac{n\pi x}{l} + \ldots (5).$$

Again, by differentiating (3) with respect to time to obtain $\dot{y}$, and equating to zero according to (4), we obtain

$$0 = b_1 p \sin \frac{\pi x}{l} + b_2 2p \sin \frac{2\pi x}{l} + \ldots + b_n np \sin \frac{n\pi x}{l} + \ldots (6),$$

which is satisfied if the b's are all zero.

Further, the values of the coefficients in (5) may be determined as shown when treating Fourier's theorem (see equation (18) of article 54). Thus, multiplying both sides of (5) by $\sin \frac{n\pi x}{l} dx$ and integrating from $x = 0$ to $x = l$, we obtain

$$a_n = \frac{2}{l} \int_0^l F(x) \sin \frac{n\pi x}{l} dx \qquad (7).$$

Hence equation (3) may be rewritten as a final solution in the form

$$y = a_1 \sin \frac{\pi x}{l} \cos pt + a_2 \sin \frac{2\pi x}{l} \cos 2pt + \ldots$$

$$+ a_n \sin \frac{n\pi x}{l} \cos npt + \ldots (8),$$

the values of the a's being given by (7).

The treatment of the vibrations of stretched membranes is reserved for Chapter V.

143. Plucked String by Second Method.—Let us now treat the case of the plucked string by this second method. Let the co-ordinates of the point when plucked be (h, k), the string as before extending from $x = 0$ to $x = l$. Then equations (4) and (5) of the previous article break into two parts each,

since
$$F(x) = kx/h \text{ for } h > x > 0 \quad\left.\vphantom{\frac{k(l-x)}{l-h}}\right\}$$

and
$$F(x) = \frac{k(l - x)}{l - h} \text{ for } l > x > h \quad\left.\vphantom{\frac{k(l-x)}{l-h}}\right\} \qquad (9).$$

Equation (7) accordingly becomes

$$a_n = \frac{2}{l} \int_0^h \frac{kx}{h} \sin \frac{n\pi x}{l} dx + \frac{2}{l} \int_h^l \frac{k(l - x)}{l - h} \sin \frac{n\pi x}{l} dx \quad (10).$$

This, when evaluated, gives

$$a_n = \frac{2kl^2}{n^2\pi^2 h(l - h)} \sin \frac{n\pi h}{l} \qquad (11).$$

Hence, equation (8), with the values of the a's substituted from (11), gives the solution for the plucked string under consideration, viz.

$$y = \frac{2kl^2}{\pi^2 h(l - h)}\left(\sin \frac{\pi h}{l} \sin \frac{\pi x}{l} \cos pt + \ldots \right.$$

$$\left. + \frac{1}{n^2} \sin \frac{n\pi h}{l} \sin \frac{n\pi x}{l} \cos npt + \ldots \right) \quad (12).$$

We see from this equation that the nth tone will disappear when $\sin n\pi h/l = 0$, *i.e.* when nh/l is any integer, m say, or, we may say that the nth tone disappears when $h = ml/n$. Thus, if we divide the string into n equal parts and pluck it exactly at any one of the points of this division the nth tone is absent, and this is the tone whose nodes fall upon the points in question. But a node for the nth tone is

also a node for the $2n$th, $3n$th, etc., tones; hence all these
higher tones are absent also in the case under discussion.
We also see from equation (11), that the expression for a_n
has n^2 in the denominator. Hence the series in (12),
though infinite, is usually quickly convergent. But its
convergence does not depend simply upon the values of the
a's. For, as shown in (12), the amplitude of each component is affected by the fluctuating factor $\sin n\pi h/l$, whose
values depend upon the co-ordinate h of the point plucked.
The amplitudes of the partials in any given case may easily
be exhibited graphically as follows. From O in a horizontal
base line OX, draw a series of radii making with it the
angles $\pi h/l$, $2\pi h/l$, $\ldots$ $n\pi h/l$, $\ldots$ etc. Mark off on them
lengths proportional to 1, $1/2^2$, $1/3^2$, $\ldots$ $1/n^2$, $\ldots$ Call
these points so found on the radii P_1, P_2, $\ldots$ P_n, $\ldots$ etc.
Then the projections on the axis of y (at right angles to the
axis OX) of these radii OP_1, OP_2, $\ldots$ OP_n, $\ldots$ etc., show
the series of amplitudes required. The relative intensities
of the partials is, of course, found by taking for each the
square of the amplitude multiplied by the square of the
frequency.

The above investigation is strictly valid only for a very
thin flexible string whose possible tones form the harmonic
series. If, owing to stiffness, the tones natural to the string
form an inharmonic series, there is nothing in the act of
plucking to coerce them. Hence the motion cannot be
expressed by a Fourier series whose components are always
of commensurate periods, for the higher partial tones
produced will be all slightly sharper than the corresponding
tones of the harmonic or commensurate series. Also, it
must be remembered that, owing to various losses of energy
in friction and sound radiation, all the tones of a plucked
string die away, and probably each one of the various components at its own rate differing from those of the others.

The approximate application of this theory to the harp
and kindred instruments will be found in Chapter VIII.

144. Struck Strings.—Consider now a string extending from $x = 0$ to $x = l$, struck at the infinitesimally short region from $x = h$ to $x = h + dx$, and let the velocity instantaneously imparted there be u. Thus for $t = 0$, we have everywhere $y = 0$, and also $\dot{y} = 0$, except for the length dx at h where $\dot{y} = u$. We may thus write as the general equation for the vibration of the string—

$$y = \sin \frac{\pi x}{l} b_1 \sin pt + \sin \frac{2\pi x}{l} b_2 \sin 2pt + \ldots$$

$$+ \sin \frac{n\pi x}{l} b_n \sin npt + \ldots \qquad (13).$$

The cosine terms are all absent in order to secure $y = 0$ for $t = 0$. From (13) we find for the initial velocity

$$(\dot{y})_0 = pb_1 \sin (\pi x/l) + 2pb_2 \sin (2\pi x/l) + \ldots$$

$$+ npb_n \sin (n\pi x/l) + \ldots \qquad (14).$$

Then, applying to this Fourier expression for $(\dot{y})_0$, equations (17) and (18) of article 54, and remembering that $\lambda/2$ is here represented by l, we find

$$npb_n = \frac{2}{l} \int_0^l (\dot{y})_0 \sin \frac{n\pi x}{l} dx = \frac{2}{l} \int_h^{h+dx} u \sin \frac{n\pi x}{l} dx.$$

From this, since $p = 2\pi N$, where N is the frequency of the prime tone of the string, we obtain

$$b_n = \frac{c}{n\pi l N} \sin \frac{n\pi h}{l} \qquad (15),$$

where c is written for udx. Substituting these values of the b's in (13) we find as the solution sought—

$$y = \frac{c}{\pi l N} \left(\sin \frac{\pi h}{l} \sin \frac{\pi x}{l} \sin pt + \ldots + \ldots \right.$$

$$\left. + \frac{1}{n} \sin \frac{n\pi h}{l} \sin \frac{n\pi x}{l} \sin npt + \ldots \right) \quad (16).$$

Thus, here again if the point excited by striking be exactly at one of the nodes of a certain possible tone, that tone is not directly generated by the blow. It should be further noted that the series of tones is again infinite and convergent, yet it is more slowly convergent than that for the plucked string, since we now have in the expression for the amplitude of each component tone n itself in the denominator instead of n^2 as in the previous case when the string was plucked. The sine term is still present, producing, as before, a fluctuation of amplitude dependent on the place of excitation.

In Chapter VIII. a reference is made to an extension of this theory to the pianoforte, in which the blow is somewhat different.

In the case of the struck string, as with the plucked one, it must be noted that stiffness may make the series of tones natural to the string inharmonic, and so cause a slight departure from the above theory. Further, the component tones will all die away, and each at its own special rate. Hence the above theory strictly applies only to the commencement. If terms expressing the resistance were introduced at the outset, the corresponding damping factors would have appeared in the solution.

145. Energy of Progressive Waves.—We shall now consider the energy of wave motion, and its distribution in place and time.

Let us begin with the progressive wave represented by

$$y = a \sin \omega(t - x/v) \qquad (1),$$

and deal with unit area of cross section of the parallel beam of radiation. Let the total energy of the waves per unit volume at place x and time t be denoted by E, and its kinetic and potential portions by K and P respectively. Then, since $K = \frac{1}{2}$ mass × velocity squared, we find by differentiation of (1) and substitution,

$$K = \tfrac{1}{2}\rho a^2 \omega^2 \cos^2 \omega(t - x/v) \qquad (2),$$

where ρ is the density of the medium, which we may suppose to be a gas. But the sum of the kinetic an potential energies of a vibrating point is a constant, and when one form of energy is at its maximum value the other form is zero. Thus the maximum value of K furnishes us with the value of the constant sum of the variables K and P. Hence we have

$$E = K_{\text{max.}} = \tfrac{1}{2}\rho a^2 \omega^2 \qquad (3).$$

Accordingly

$$P = E - K = \tfrac{1}{2}\rho a^2 \omega^2 [1 - \cos^2 \omega(t - x/v)] \qquad (4).$$

Further, on multiplying (3) by λ we have

Total energy of the progressive wave motion per wave length

$$= \tfrac{1}{2}\rho \lambda a^2 \omega^2 \qquad (5).$$

146. Energy Current.—But this is the length passed over in time τ, the period of the vibration. Hence the rate of flow of energy per unit time per unit cross section, passing along the line of advance of the wave, or the *energy current* per unit area, is given by

$$C = \tfrac{1}{2}\rho \lambda a^2 \omega^2 / \tau = \tfrac{1}{2}\rho v a^2 \omega^2 \qquad (6).$$

It should be noted that though K and P vary with x and t, yet E and C are each independent of both x and t.

If we wish to compare the energy currents in two gases of different densities, we must remember that v changes also, and in a manner related to the change in ρ. For it has been shown that in a gas $v = \sqrt{\gamma p / \rho}$. Hence $v\rho = \gamma p / v = \sqrt{\gamma p \rho}$. Thus equation (6) may be written

$$C = \tfrac{1}{2}a^2 \omega^2 \gamma p / v = \tfrac{1}{2}a^2 \omega^2 \sqrt{\gamma p \rho} \qquad (7).$$

Thus, if γ, the ratio of the specific heats, is the same for each of the two gases, and ω and p are constant, we have

$$C \propto a^2 / v \ \text{or} \ C \propto a^2 \sqrt{\rho} \qquad (8).$$

147. Let us now ascertain how the energy throughout the wave length is distributed in the two forms of kinetic and potential. To do this we may slightly transform equation (2), and then integrate it with respect to x from x to $x + \lambda$. We thus obtain

Kinetic energy of the motion per wave length

$$= \tfrac{1}{2}\rho a^2\omega^2 \int_x^{x+\lambda} \cos^2 \left\{ 2\pi \left(\frac{t}{\tau} - \frac{x}{\lambda} \right) dx = \tfrac{1}{4}\rho\lambda a^2\omega^2 \quad (9).$$

Dealing in the same way with equation (4), we find

Potential energy of the motion per wave length

$$= \tfrac{1}{4}\rho\lambda a^2\omega^2 \quad\quad\quad\quad (10).$$

Hence the energy of a progressive wave motion over any exact number of wave lengths is, at every instant, half kinetic and half potential.

To apply the above to waves along a cord or rope of linear density σ, it is obvious that σ then replaces the volume density ρ of the preceding equations, and that other modifications are needed.

Let us, for example, find the energy current in rope waves. Then $v = \sqrt{F/\sigma}$ where F is the tensile force and σ the linear density. Accordingly, $v\sigma = F/v = \sqrt{F\sigma}$, and we have

$$C = \tfrac{1}{2}a^2\omega^2 F/v = \tfrac{1}{2}a^2\omega^2 \sqrt{F\sigma} \quad\quad (11).$$

Thus, for ω and F constant, we see that

$$C \propto a^2/v \text{ or } C \propto a^2 \sqrt{\sigma} \quad\quad\quad (12).$$

148. Energy of Stationary Waves.—Taking now the energy of stationary waves, we shall represent the motion in question by

$$y = 2a \sin (2\pi x/\lambda) \sin \omega t \quad\quad\quad (1),$$

and use E', K', P', and C' to correspond with the respective unaccented letters of the last article. By differentiating (1) to t we have $\dot{y} = 2a\omega \sin (2\pi x/\lambda) \cos \omega t$, hence the kinetic energy per unit volume is given by

$$K' = 2\rho a^2\omega^2 \sin^2 (2\pi x/\lambda) \cos^2 \omega t \quad\quad (2).$$

Also $E' = K'_{max.} = 2\rho a^2\omega^2 \sin^2 (2\pi x/\lambda) \quad\quad (3),$

where $K'_{max.}$ denotes the maximum value of K' at place x. Equation (3) shows that E' varies with x, and fluctuates between the values zero and $4E$. (See equation (3) of preceding article.) Again, we have for the potential energy

$$P' = E' - K' = 2\rho a^2 \omega^2 (1 - \cos^2 \omega t) \sin^2 (2\pi x/\lambda) \quad (4).$$

From equation (3), by integration with respect to x from x to $x + \lambda$, we obtain

Total energy of the stationary waves per wave length

$$= \rho \lambda a^2 \omega^2 \qquad (5).$$

On comparing this with equation (5) of the last article, we see that this value is double that for the progressive waves. This should be the case, seeing that the waves now under consideration are compounded of two sets, each like that in the last article, except that one is reversed in direction of propagation. But in the stationary waves, as the name implies, there is no advance of this wave energy in either direction. Hence the flux of energy is zero, or

$$C' = 0 \qquad (6).$$

In other words, the value of C' here is the algebraic sum of the values of the C's, the energy currents, in the two oppositely-travelling progressive waves, of which the stationary waves may be built up. But these two energy currents are equal and opposite, so the resultant C' is zero.

It may be noted here that while K' and P' each vary with x and t, E' varies with x only, while C' is invariably zero. This statement may be compared with the corresponding one on progressive waves just after equation (6) of the preceding article.

Let us now integrate equations (2) and (4) with respect to x from x to $x + \lambda$. We thus find how the kinetic and potential energies are distributed throughout the wave length. The results are—

Kinetic energy of the stationary waves throughout a wave length $\qquad = \rho \lambda a^2 \omega^2 \cos^2 \omega t \qquad (7),$

and Potential energy of same per wave length

$$= \rho \lambda a^2 \omega^2 (1 - \cos^2 \omega t) \qquad (8).$$

It is thus seen that the energy of stationary waves over any number of wave lengths is divided between the forms kinetic and potential in a way which varies from instant to instant, but is independent of place. Thus the energy is all kinetic everywhere when $\cos \omega t = \pm 1$, and all potential everywhere for $\cos \omega t = 0$. Contrast this with the corresponding statement for progressive waves at the end of the previous article.

149. Spherical Radiation in Air.—We now pass to the treatment of wave motions in air, or other gases, without restriction to the case of plane waves. We shall simplify the matter, as far as possible, by making at the outset the following assumptions [1] :—

(1) That the action of gravity upon the medium in question is negligible.

(2) That the effect of viscosity in the medium is negligible.

(3) That the motion is devoid of rotations, and is a vibratory one.

(4) That the vibrations are small, so that writing the density $\rho = \rho_0 (1 + s)$, s is a small quantity often negligible in comparison with unity.

(5) That the velocities and accelerations of the medium are small quantities whose squares and products are negligible.

This last assumption introduces an important simplification in the method of estimating the accelerations. In thinking of the accelerations of a fluid, two views may be taken. Thus, we may follow in thought an individual particle, and note how much *its* velocity is increased per second. Or, secondly, we may note what is the increase

[1] See the author's article on "Spherical Radiation," etc., *Phil. Mag.*, January 1908.

per second of the velocity of those particles whichever they
are that, at the time in question, occupy a given fixed
position.　In other words, the first method notes the
increase of speed of an individual in a procession, the
second method notes the increase of speed of each part
of the procession in turn at the instant when it passes a
given point fixed on the route.　In our use of acceleration
the first of these methods should, in strictness, be taken.
But with the assumption (5) the distinction drops, as the
difference between the two is of the second order of
quantities which it has been agreed to consider small.
Under these restrictions the problem, though sufficiently
general for our purpose, is comparatively simple.　Especially
so when, following Riemann, we use the condensation s as
the final single dependent variable, and avoid using velocity
potential, the conception of which might prove an unnecessary difficulty to some readers.　The plan of procedure
is to derive the differential equation of the wave motion
of the medium, to solve it, and apply the solution to the
various cases of interest.　The differential equation is itself
based upon the so-called equation of continuity, and the
equation of motion.　These we take in order.

150. Equation of Continuity.—The so-called equation
of continuity is simply the mathematical form of the statement that no matter is created or annihilated in the interior
of the fluid.　Take a rectangular parallelopiped, whose
edges dx, dy, dz are parallel to the respective co-ordinate
axes, and one corner is at the origin.　Then the excess of
matter escaping over that entering through its faces in
the time dt must equal the diminution of stuff inside the
parallelopiped during this time.　Let the velocity components of the fluid parallel to the axes of x, y, and z be
u, v, and w respectively.　Then the matter entering the
face in the y-z plane is given by $u\,dt \cdot dy\,dz \cdot \rho$; for $u\,dt$
is the length passed over in time dt, multiplying by the
area $dy\,dz$ of the face we get the volume which is passed

in, finally the density being introduced gives the mass required. Similarly that passing out during time dt at the opposite face, parallel to the y-z plane, but distant dx from it, is given by

$$\left(\rho u + \frac{d(\rho u)}{dx} dx \right) dy\ dz\ dt.$$

Hence the excess passing out of the parallelopiped by the pair of faces in question is

$$\frac{d(\rho u)}{dx} dx\ dy\ dz\ dt.$$

By considering the other velocity components v and w, and the faces to which they are respectively normal, we obtain like expressions. Thus the total mass lost by the parallelopiped in time dt is

$$\left\{ \frac{d(\rho u)}{dx} + \frac{d(\rho v)}{dy} + \frac{d(\rho w)}{dz} \right\} dx\ dy\ dz\ dt.$$

But obviously the mass lost may also be expressed as

$$- \frac{d\rho}{dt} dx\ dy\ dz\ dt.$$

Thus, equating these two forms we obtain

$$\frac{d\rho}{dt} + \frac{d(\rho u)}{dx} + \frac{d(\rho v)}{dy} + \frac{d(\rho w)}{dz} = 0 \qquad (1).$$

This is the equation of continuity in its general form. Now $\dfrac{d\rho}{dt} = \rho_0 \dfrac{ds}{dt}$, and for our purpose, by the initial assumptions,

$$\frac{d(\rho u)}{dx} = \rho_0 (1 + s) \frac{du}{dx} + u \frac{d\rho}{dx} = \rho_0 \frac{du}{dx} \text{ nearly,}$$

the product of the two small quantities u and $d\rho/dx$ being negligible. And the like simplifications apply to the other terms. Hence we may replace equation (1) by

$$\frac{ds}{dt} + \frac{du}{dx} + \frac{dv}{dy} + \frac{dw}{dz} = 0 \qquad (2).$$

And this is the form of the equation of continuity suitable for small oscillations of an elastic fluid whose weight is negligible in comparison with the elastic forces.

151. Equations of Motion.—We have now to express, for the fluid in our parallelopiped, the condition that the product of its mass into the acceleration equals the moving force to which it is subjected. The product, mass into acceleration parallel to the x axis, is $(dx\,dy\,dz)\rho\ du/dt$. The moving force, parallel to the axis of x, is the excess of that due to normal pressure p on the y-z face behind over that due to the pressure $p + dp$ on the parallel face in front. Or, in symbols, the moving force in question is

$$p\,dy\,dz - \left(p + \frac{dp}{dx}dx\right)dy\,dz = -\frac{dp}{dx}dx\,dy\,dz.$$

Hence, equating these two, we find

$$-\frac{dp}{dx} = \rho\frac{du}{dt} \text{ or } \frac{1}{\rho}\frac{dp}{dx} = -\frac{du}{dt} \qquad (3).$$

But p is some function of ρ, and whatever the form of the curve co-ordinating p and ρ, the small portion with which we are concerned may be regarded as straight. Hence, for our small vibrations we may write

$$\frac{dp}{d\rho} = a^2, \text{ a constant} \qquad (4).$$

It should be noted that we are not entitled to integrate equation (4), and draw from the result of that process any conclusions about the general relation between p and ρ. On the other hand, the relation between p and ρ must be determined independently, and the general value of $dp/d\rho$ derived from it. Then the value of a^2 applicable to our case can easily be chosen. This point will be referred to again later.

From equation (4) we have

$$\frac{dp}{\rho} = a^2\frac{d\rho}{\rho} = \frac{a^2\rho_0 ds}{\rho_0(1+s)} = a^2\,ds \text{ nearly} \qquad (5).$$

Then the substitution of equation (5) in (3) gives the following equation (6), from which (7) and (8) are written by symmetry.

$$a^2\frac{ds}{dx} = -\frac{du}{dt} \qquad (6),$$

$$a^2\frac{ds}{dy} = -\frac{dv}{dt} \qquad (7),$$

$$a^2\frac{ds}{dz} = -\frac{dw}{dt} \qquad (8).$$

These are the required equations of motion.

152. General Differential Equation.—We have to deal with equations (2), (6), (7), and (8). These involve not only the dependent variable s which we wish to retain, but also u, v, and w. These last three we must eliminate. This is easily performed as follows. First differentiate (2) with respect to t. The result of this may be written—

$$-\frac{d^2s}{dt^2} = \frac{d^2u}{dx\,dt} + \frac{d^2v}{dy\,dt} + \frac{d^2w}{dz\,dt} \qquad (9).$$

Next, differentiate equation (6) with respect to x, (7) to y, and (8) to z, and add the three equations so obtained. Their sum may be written in the following form :—

$$-a^2\left(\frac{d^2s}{dx^2} + \frac{d^2s}{dy^2} + \frac{d^2s}{dz^2}\right) = \frac{d^2u}{dt\,dx} + \frac{d^2v}{dt\,dy} + \frac{d^2w}{dt\,dz} \quad (10).$$

But, since the order of partial differentiation is indifferent, the right sides of (9) and (10) are equal. We may accordingly equate their left sides, thus obtaining

$$\frac{d^2s}{dt^2} = a^2\nabla^2 s \qquad (11),$$

where $\nabla^2 s$ is written for $\dfrac{d^2s}{dx^2} + \dfrac{d^2s}{dy^2} + \dfrac{d^2s}{dz^2}$. ($\nabla$ is pronounced "nabla"). Equation (11) is the general form applicable to small vibratory disturbances of a light compressible medium in space of three dimensions.

As a check, let us reduce it to the form for representing plane waves advancing along the axis of x. Under these circumstances s will be a function of t and x only, being independent of y and z. For the wave fronts will always be parallel to the yz plane, and at every point in a wave front the condensation s has the same value. In this case $\nabla^2 s$ reduces to $\dfrac{d^2s}{dx^2}$, and equation (11) is replaced by

$$\frac{d^2s}{dt^2} = a^2 \frac{d^2s}{dx^2} \qquad (12).$$

Now this equation is of the form already obtained (see article 127). And the two can be identified if the a^2 here has the value of v^2 in the previous case. We therefore now proceed to examine this point. And first let us obtain another expression for $dp/d\rho$. Denote by U the specific volume. Then $\rho = 1/U$ and $d\rho = -\dfrac{1}{U^2}\,dU$, hence

$$a^2 = \frac{dp}{d\rho} = -\left[\frac{dp}{dU/U}\right]U = EU = E/\rho = \gamma p/\rho \qquad (13).$$

We thus see that a^2 has the value, elasticity divided by density, and is accordingly identical with the value of v^2 in article 127. For to our order of approximation subscripts to p and ρ may be retained or dropped at our option.

153. Solution for Spherical Waves.—Let us now pass to the case of spherical wave motion. For this we must transform our cartesian co-ordinates to polar co-ordinates in space of three dimensions.

The relation of the two sets of co-ordinates is illustrated in Fig. 48 and expressed in the following equations, the co-ordinates of P in cartesians being (x, y, z), and in polars $(r,\ \theta,\ \phi)$:—

$$x = r \sin \theta \cos \phi,\ y = r \sin \theta \sin \phi,\ z = r \cos \theta \quad (14).$$

With this transformation of the co-ordinates, it is shown in text-books on the Differential Calculus (see *e.g.* Williamson's) that

$$\nabla^2 s = \frac{d^2 s}{dr^2} + \frac{2}{r}\frac{ds}{dr} + \frac{1}{r^2 \sin \theta}\frac{d}{d\theta}\left(\sin \theta\ \frac{ds}{d\theta}\right) + \frac{1}{r^2 \sin^2 \theta}\frac{d^2 s}{d\phi^2} \quad (15).$$

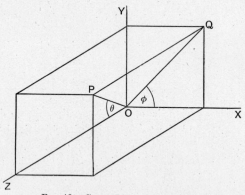

Fig. 48.—Solid Polar Co-ordinates.

Now suppose we have spherical symmetry about the centre of the system at the origin of co-ordinates. That is, all the successive wave fronts are concentric spheres, where common centre is the origin, and s will be a function of r only and independent of θ and ϕ. With this simplification (15) reduces to

$$\nabla^2 s = \frac{d^2 s}{dr^2} + \frac{2}{r}\frac{ds}{dr} = \frac{1}{r}\frac{d^2}{dr^2}(rs) \quad (16).$$

And, with this substitution, the general equation (11) is replaced by

$$a^2 \frac{d^2(rs)}{dr^2} = \frac{d^2(rs)}{dt^2} \quad (17).$$

The general solution of this equation may be written—

$$rs = f_1(r - at) + f_2(r + at) \qquad (18),$$

where f_1 and f_2 denote arbitrary functions.

154. The solution denotes both diverging and converging spherical waves of any type whatever, but travelling with speed a. If we now restrict ourselves to diverging waves of simple harmonic type, we may write the solution as follows :—

$$s = \frac{c}{r} \cos k(r - at) \qquad (19),$$

where c and k are arbitrary constants. To obtain the speed of the gas along the radius r, denote this speed by u, and we then derive from equations (6) and (19)

$$-\frac{du}{dt} = a^2 \frac{ds}{dr} = \frac{a^2 c}{r} \left\{ -k \sin k(r - at) - \frac{1}{r} \cos k(r - at) \right\} \quad (20)$$

Thus

$$u = -a^2 \int \frac{ds}{dr} dt = \frac{ca}{r} \left\{ \cos k(r - at) - \frac{1}{kr} \sin k(r - at) \right\} \quad (21).$$

And if the displacement along r be denoted by ξ, we have, by another integration $\xi = \int u dt$, or,

$$\xi = -\frac{c}{kr} \left\{ \sin k(r - at) + \frac{1}{kr} \cos k(r - at) \right\} \quad (22).$$

Let us now compare equations (19), (21), and (22). We thus see that the condensation s has only the ordinary phase change inseparably associated with the advance of a progressive wave. Its amplitude, however, suffers diminution by varying inversely as r. But, owing to this diminution or attenuation with advance, we have in the other equations the factors $\frac{1}{r}$ and *also* $\frac{1}{r^2}$, one applying to a sine and the other to a cosine function. Thus the speed u and the displacement ξ each exhibit, during advance, an additional slight change in phase beyond that always present in a progressive wave. But at such distances as make $\dfrac{1}{kr}$ a negligibly small quantity, equations (21) and (22) reduce to the simple approximate equations

$$u = \frac{ca}{r} \cos k\,(r - at) \text{ nearly} \qquad (23),$$

$$\text{and } \xi = -\frac{c}{kr} \sin k\,(r - at) \text{ nearly} \qquad (24).$$

Now the activity of the wave motion per unit area being proportional to the square of the amplitude is thus seen to vary inversely as r^2. But the area affected by the spherical radiation varies directly as r^2. Thus the activity of the whole wave front remains constant, as would be anticipated.

It is pointed out by Lord Rayleigh (*Theory of Sound*, vol. ii. pp. 127-128) that for cylindrical radiation between two parallel reflecting planes, the intensity falls off inversely as the first power of the distance. It should be noted that the attenuations here referred to are those due simply to the spreading of the waves during radiation. Anything of the nature of frictional resistance to be overcome in the passage of the waves through the medium would produce a further enfeeblement.

155. Reflection at Pole.—Let us now regard the two spherical waves represented by equation (18) as a converging one and a diverging one, to which the other gives rise by reflection at the pole or centre of the system. And let it be required to determine the relation between f_1 and f_2 thereby resulting. The total current across the surface of a sphere of radius r is $4\pi r^2 u$, and for $r = 0$ this current must vanish, since all is symmetrical round the origin or pole. That is, u cannot be infinite and make $r^2 u$ finite for $r = 0$. But, if $4\pi r^2 u$ is to vanish for all values of t, so also will $4\pi r^2 du/dt$. And this condition is easier to obtain analytically. Thus we have from (6) and (18)

$$4\pi r^2 \frac{du}{dt} = -4\pi a^2 r^2 \frac{ds}{dr} = 4\pi a^2 \{f_1(r-at) + f_2(r+at)\}$$
$$-4\pi a^2 r \{f_1'(r-at) + f_2'(r+at)\}.$$

Hence, putting $du/dt = 0$ for $r = 0$, we have

$$0 = f_1(-at) + f_2(at) \qquad (25)$$

as the relation between f_1 and f_2.

But we see from (18) that the right side of (25) is the value of rs for $r = 0$. Hence we may write as the condition at the pole

$$rs = 0 \text{ for } r = 0 \qquad (26);$$

or, rs must vanish with r.

Thus, at the pole, a condensation is reflected as a *rarefaction* and *vice versa*, somewhat as in the case of reflection at the *open* end of a parallel pipe! Hence if an initial disturbance occurs at the surface of a sphere of radius r_0, we may have two spherical waves originating thence, one divergent and the other convergent. But the latter, by reflection at the centre, gives rise to a second divergent wave, in which the condensation suffers reversal of algebraic sign on reflection.

156. Partial Reflection of Waves.—We shall now consider the partial reflection and transmission of waves on encountering an abrupt change of density of the medium in which they are travelling. The waves in question may be of the transverse type, along a cord or rope which suddenly changes to another more or less massive rope, the tensile force being, of course, the same throughout both its sections. Or, the waves may be sound waves in a gas which suddenly gives place to a second gas of a different density, but having the same value for γ, the ratio of the two specific heats. A thin membrane of negligible thickness, mass, and elasticity may be supposed to divide the two gases. The case of longitudinal waves in a solid rod will be dealt with separately.

For the sake of simplicity we shall first adopt a treatment which, where it fails in rigour, is founded upon an assumption that is almost axiomatic. We shall afterwards pass to the more complete and rigorous discussion of the problem. The assumption just referred to is that no change of phase occurs in the act of reflection and transmission other than can be represented by a change in the algebraic sign of the amplitude. In other words, we assume that the phase of a derived wave is the same or opposite to that of the parent wave, hence the ratio of displacement is constant and equals that of the amplitudes. The justification or ground of this assumption is that any other phase relation involves a varying ratio of displacements which in turn entails a temporary accumulation of energy at the junction. But for this there is no provision, as the junction is a point or a plane, and has no volume.

It now suffices to use the energy equations and the equation of continuity of displacements at the junction. This method is similar to that adopted by Fresnel for the analogous problem in optics. Let the amplitudes of the incident, reflected, and transmitted waves be respectively a, b, and c, and let v_1 be the velocity of propagation in the first medium, v_2 that in the second.

157. Transverse Rope Waves or Sound in Gases.— By the conservation of energy, the energy current in the incident waves must equal the sum of those for the reflected and transmitted waves. In the case of gases, we shall suppose the incidence to be normal, and may take the energy currents per unit cross section. In the case of the waves along a rope or string, the cross section may vary suddenly at the junction, but the energy currents must, of course, apply to the total energy throughout the cross section for the wave in question. These energy currents are given in equations (8) and (12) of articles 146-147, and the result for our problem when γ for each gas has the same value, is the same for both cases, viz.

$$\frac{a^2 - b^2}{v_1{}^2} = \frac{c^2}{v_2{}^2} \text{ or } a^2 - b^2 = \mu c^2 \qquad (1),$$

where $\qquad\qquad \mu = v_1/v_2.$

The equation of continuity of displacements at the junction gives $\qquad\qquad a + b = c \qquad\qquad (2)$, since we have assumed the phases to be like or opposite. These are our two equations from which to determine b/a and c/a. Equation (1) divided by (2) gives

$$a - b = \mu c \qquad (3).$$

Also $(3) \div (2)$ gives $\qquad \dfrac{a - b}{a + b} = \mu,$

whence $\qquad\qquad b/a = -\dfrac{\mu - 1}{\mu + 1} \qquad (4).$

Again, $\qquad (2) + (3)$ yields $c/a = \dfrac{2}{\mu + 1} \qquad (5).$

These results are identical with those obtained by Young for light incident normally and analogous to those by the author for electrical waves along a pair of wires.[1]

158. Longitudinal Waves in Bars.—For the partial reflection of longitudinal waves in solid rods or bars, the conditions and results are somewhat different. Thus the energy currents per unit cross section of the incident wave of amplitude a is $\frac{1}{2}a^2\omega^2\rho_1 v_1$ or $\frac{1}{2}a^2\omega^2 q_1/v_1$, the vibrations being expressed by $\sin \omega t$. Hence, if the cross sections of the rods before and after the junction are s_1 and s_2, our previous energy equation (1) is replaced by

$$(a^2 - b^2)s_1 q_1/v_1 = c^2 s_2 q_2/v_2 \qquad (6),$$

the q's denoting the values of Young's modulus for each part of the rod. This may be written

$$a^2 - b^2 = \mu' c^2 \qquad (7)$$

[1] See *Proc. Roy. Soc.*, vol. liv., 1893; *Ann. der Physik*, Bd. 53, 1894.

where
$$\mu' = \frac{v_1}{v_2} \cdot \frac{s_2 q_2}{s_1 q_1} = \frac{s_2 \rho_2 v_2}{s_1 \rho_1 v_1} \qquad (8).$$

But we still have, as before, $a + b = c$. Thus using this and (7) instead of (2) and (1) we obtain a result of the same form, but in which μ is replaced by μ' defined by (8). Hence, for our present case

$$b/a = -\frac{\mu' - 1}{\mu' + 1} \qquad (9),$$

and
$$c/a = \frac{2}{\mu' + 1} \qquad (10).$$

These results are in agreement with those found by Lord Rayleigh, who used the equality of tensions at the junction instead of that of the energies given and received as here done.

159. Alternative Method for Partial Reflections.— Let us now attack the problem more fully, providing for possible changes of phase, but restricting ourselves to rope waves or sound in gases. Let the waves be

Incident train, $\quad y = a \sin \omega(t - x/v_1)$.
Reflected train, $\quad y = b \sin \{\omega(t + x/v_1) + \beta\}$.
Transmitted train, $y = c \sin \{\omega(t - x/v_2) + \gamma\}$.

Then the continuity of displacement at the junction, $x = 0$, gives $a \sin \omega t + b \sin (\omega t + \beta) = c \sin (\omega t + \gamma)$. But this holds for all the values of t. Hence, on expanding and equating to zero the coefficients of $\sin \omega t$ and of $\cos \omega t$ respectively, we obtain

$$a + b \cos \beta - c \cos \gamma = 0 \qquad (1)$$
and
$$b \sin \beta - c \sin \gamma = 0 \qquad (2).$$

We have thus two equations out of the four necessary to determine the two amplitudes and the two phases. We accordingly require two more. Now the relation derived from consideration of energy would furnish us with only a single equation, for the energy current is independent of

x and t, and therefore of β and γ also. Let us therefore make use of the condition that at the junction there must be continuity of dy/dx. For a sudden change anywhere in the value of dy/dx would involve a finite force acting upon an indefinitely small mass, and accordingly produce an infinite acceleration, which is not present in the waves under consideration. Hence, we first differentiate with respect to x the expressions for the three waves, next put $x = 0$ in the results, and, finally, equate the sum of the expressions so found for the incident and reflected waves to that for the transmitted wave. These operations give

$$- a \cos \omega t + b \cos (\omega t + \beta) = - \mu c \cos (\omega t + \gamma),$$

where, as before, μ denotes v_1/v_2. Now this equation holds for all values of t, and therefore, on expansion, gives us the two further relations required, viz.

$$a - b \cos \beta - \mu c \cos \gamma = 0 \qquad (3),$$

and $$b \sin \beta + \mu c \sin \gamma = 0 \qquad (4).$$

By substituting (2) in (4) we obtain

$$(\mu + 1)c \sin \gamma = 0,$$

which is satisfied by $\gamma = 0$. Then both (2) and (4) are satisfied by $\beta = 0$. Thus $\cos \beta$ and $\cos \gamma$ are each equal to unity, and equations (1) and (3) reduce respectively to equations (2) and (3) of article 157. Thus the results are

$$\beta = \gamma = 0$$
$$b/a = - \frac{\mu - 1}{\mu + 1}, \quad c/a = \frac{2}{\mu + 1} \left.\right\} \qquad (5).$$

They are accordingly in agreement with the results found by simpler means.

160. Partial Reflections by Imaginary Analysis.— By introducing imaginary quantities the above working may be shortened a little. Thus, let the incident, reflected

and transmitted waves be represented respectively by the
real parts of

$$ae^{\,i\omega(t-x/v_1)}, \quad be^{\,i\omega(t+x/v_1)} \quad \text{and} \quad ce^{\,i\omega(t-x/v_2)}$$

in which i denotes $\sqrt{-1}$. If the three coefficients a, b,
and c are all real this will correspond to like or opposite
phases; but if, while a is real, b or c is partly imaginary,
that would indicate a change of phase in the corresponding
wave train. Thus if $\dfrac{b}{a} = \dfrac{1+i}{\sqrt{2}}$ we should have a change of
phase of $\pi/4$ in the reflected waves.

The condition of continuity of displacement at the
junction $x = 0$ gives

$$a + b = c \qquad\qquad (6).$$

Similarly the condition of continuity of dy/dx at $x = 0$,
yields

$$a - b = \mu c \qquad\qquad (7).$$

These two equations give the entirely real ratios,

$$\frac{b}{a} = -\frac{\mu-1}{\mu+1} \quad \text{and} \quad \frac{c}{a} = \frac{2}{\mu+1} \qquad (8),$$

as found before, and thereby show that there is no change
of phase calling for trigonometrical expression. The above,
of course, applies to either rope waves or sound in gases.
But the boundary conditions used are not the only ones
which could be chosen.

161. Alternative Method for Gases.—To illustrate
this point let us now find the reflected and transmitted
waves for gases. We shall take, as before, the continuity
of displacement for one boundary condition and the equality
of pressures at every instant for the other. Let the
incident, reflected and transmitted waves be represented
respectively by

$$\xi_1 = ae^{\,i\omega(t-x/v_1)},$$
$$\xi' = be^{\,i\omega(t+x/v_1)},$$
and
$$\xi_2 = ce^{\,i\omega(t-x/v_2)}.$$

Then the continuity of displacement, at $x = 0$, gives

$$a + b = c \qquad (1).$$

The adiabatic relation may be written $p = k\rho^\gamma$ where k is a constant and γ the ratio of the specific beats. Then, since the increase of density $d\rho$ is represented by $-\rho d\xi/dx$, the corresponding change of pressure is given by

$$dp = d(k\rho^\gamma) = k\gamma\rho^{\gamma-1}(-\rho d\xi/dx) = -\gamma p d\xi/dx.$$

Hence, for equality of pressures at the junction at every instant, the sum of pressure increments for the incident and reflected waves must equal that for the transmitted wave. Thus, we find

$$-\gamma p\left(-\frac{i\omega}{v_1}\xi_1 + \frac{i\omega}{v_2}\xi'\right) = -\gamma p\left(-\frac{i\omega}{v_2}\xi_2\right),$$

or

$$\frac{\xi_1 - \xi'}{v_1} = \frac{\xi_2}{v_2}.$$

And for $x = 0$ this becomes $a - b = \mu c$ $\qquad$ (2), where $\mu = v_1/v_2$ as before.

But equations (1) and (2) here are respectively like equations (1) and (3) previously obtained for the same problem, and so lead to the same results, viz.

$$b/a = -\frac{\mu - 1}{\mu + 1} \text{ and } c/a = \frac{2}{\mu + 1}.$$

In applying these formulæ to a numerical case it must be remembered that the activity or energy currents of the waves reflected or transmitted are proportional to $\rho v \times$ amplitude^2, or, if the γ's are the same, to $\sqrt{\rho} \times$ amplitude^2. (See equation (6) of article 146.) Thus for waves incident normally from hydrogen to oxygen, we have

$$\rho_1/\rho_2 = 1/16, \ \mu = v_1/v_2 = 4.$$

Hence $\qquad b/a = -3/5 \text{ and } c/a = +2/5.$

Thus the energy reflected is $9/25$ of that incident, and the energy transmitted is $\sqrt{16} \times (c/a)^2 = 16/25$ of the incident. If the waves had originated in the oxygen, then still b/a has the same numerical value but of opposite sign which disappears on squaring, so the energy reflected is, as before, $9/25$ of that incident. The transmitted *amplitude* is now $8/5$ of the incident! But the energy transmitted is measured by one-quarter of the square of this amplitude, owing to the density being one-sixteenth. Thus the fraction of incident energy in the transmitted wave is, as before, $16/25$; being now $1/4$ of $64/25$. Facts of this kind can be best illustrated by rope waves as in the following experiment:—

162. EXPT. 25. *Partial Reflection of Rope Waves.* —· The phenomena of partial reflections may be suitably illustrated by the use of an india-rubber cord about 8 or 10 metres long, fixed at each end. One part, say about half the total length, may be 5 or 6 mm. diameter, the other part just double that diameter. Then the linear densities of the two parts would be in the ratio $1 : 4$, corresponding to wave speeds as $2 : 1$. In other words, waves from the thin to the thick part have an index $\mu = 2$.

Hence $\qquad b/a = -1/3$ and $c/a = +2/3$.

Let the thin cord, near its fixed end, be struck by the hand so as to produce a displacement of about 30 cm. Then a wave may be seen travelling along to the junction, from which point a reflected wave of reversed displacement and amplitude about 10 cm. will be seen returning. At the same instant a transmitted wave of direct amplitude of about 20 cm. will pass on from the junction along the thick cord.

Suppose now that waves are originated in the thick part of the cord by a blow of the hand as before. In this case μ is clearly of the value $1/2$, hence

$$b/a = +1/3 \text{ and } c/a = +4/3!$$

Thus we obtain visibly the somewhat surprising result, that the partial wave transmitted in the thin cord not only travels twice as fast, but has an amplitude exceeding that of the original wave, part of whose energy is spent in producing a reflected wave. But though the amplitude and speed are greater, the energy current, owing to the smaller linear density, is less than that of the original wave. Indeed, the energies associated with the reflected and transmitted waves are easily seen to be respectively 1/9 and 8/9 of that of the incident wave.

163. Physical Characteristics of Wave Motion.—We may now fitly summarise some of the chief physical characteristics of wave motion, and with this we close the present chapter.

1. An elastic medium is required for the propagation of wave motion.

2. The speed of propagation is finite and differs for different media.

3. Reflection usually occurs when waves reach an abrupt termination of the medium.

4. Refraction, accompanied by partial reflection, occurs at a junction of two different elastic media.

5. Diffraction occurs when the waves reach an opening or obstacle very small compared with the wave length.

6. Rectilinear propagation occurs, forming sharp geometrical shadows when openings or obstacles are encountered which are very large compared with the wave length.

7. Interference phenomena may occur under special conditions, say, when reflection gives rise to a virtual second source.

8. Stationary waves may be formed by reflection of a train of progressive waves.

9. Energy is flowing along the line of advance of waves, hence for their maintenance we need a source of energy at the source of the waves.

10. Attenuation of waves is involved by their divergence apart altogether from any dissipation of energy which may occur owing to frictional resistances on the way.

11. Pressure is exerted upon an absorbing or reflecting surface by wave motion incident upon it (see articles 594-601).

12. Momentum also is sometimes associated with wave motion (see articles 602-606).

CHAPTER V

VIBRATING SYSTEMS

164. Types of Vibrating Systems.—Having dwelt sufficiently on the mathematical side of acoustics, we pass now to its physical aspect. In the present chapter we shall deal with the more important vibrating bodies or systems, concerning ourselves chiefly with the frequencies of the various natural tones proper to each system, and its division into the appropriate segments while executing them. When two or more of these free vibrations or proper simple tones are simultaneously elicited, they are called the partials of the compound tone then produced. The lowest of the partials is called the prime tone or fundamental, and the others the upper partials or overtones. The nominal pitch of the compound tone is usually that of its fundamental, an exception occurring in the case of bells. We defer to Chapter VIII. the consideration of the various qualities of compound tone due to the relative intensities of these partials in any particular case. And we shall there also examine the dependence of these relative intensities on the details of the system and the means by which its vibrations are excited.

The various types of vibrating systems may be divided into the following three classes:—The systems whose possible tones (1) form the full harmonic series; (2) form the odd harmonic series; (3) are inharmonic. In other words, the relative frequencies of the partials in the first and second classes are represented respectively by 1, 2, 3, 4, 5, 6, etc., and 1, 3, 5, 7, etc.; while those in the third class cannot be expressed by any small whole numbers. The compound tones which may be elicited from these systems require, as we shall see later, a more extended classification than the systems themselves. We now take the different systems beginning with strings.

165. Strings vibrating transversely.—Let us consider the transverse vibrations of a string of linear density σ gms. per cm., stretched by a force F dynes, and fixed at two points l cm. apart. We have to find the pitch of the prime and the relation borne to it by the other possible tones. We have as the general relation,

$$N = v/\lambda \qquad (1),$$

where N is the frequency of any wave, λ its length, and v its speed of propagation. In order, then, to determine N we require v and λ.

But for the present case (see article 117)

$$v = \sqrt{F/\sigma} \qquad (2).$$

Lastly, λ must be found from its relation to l when both ends are fixed. This is obtained from article 39, Figs. 20 and 21. Whence we see that the longest waves admissible in this case, namely, those giving stationary waves with nodes l apart, satisfy the relation

$$\lambda_1 = 2l \qquad (3).$$

We see, by (1), that the greatest wave length λ_1 corresponds to the smallest value of N. Thus, denoting this by N_1, we have from (1), (2), and (3),

$$N_1 = \frac{1}{2l} \sqrt{F/\sigma} \qquad (4),$$

giving the frequency of the prime tone or fundamental. For the other tones, we may write in place of equation (3), a generalised one for all possible λ's, namely

$$2l = \lambda_1 = 2\lambda_2 = 3\lambda_3 = \ldots = n\lambda_n \qquad (5),$$

where n is any integer. This is obtained by noting the condition that we must have nodes at the ends of the string, no other conditions being imposed on the remaining parts of it. By equations (1), (2), (4), and (5), we see that

$$N_n = \frac{n}{2l}\sqrt{F/\sigma} = nN_1 \qquad (6).$$

Or, in other words, the possible tones form the full harmonic series, thus putting the string in type 1 of article 164. This second result is apparent in equation (3) of article 142. The first result as to frequency of prime may also be deduced from it, affording perhaps a better way for those familiar with the calculus.

166. EXPT. 26. *Vibrations of Strings.*—The above results may be roughly verified by simple experiments on the monochord. Let the length between the bridges be one metre, and use for the "string" a steel piano wire of say 0·6 mm. diameter. We could find the density of the wire by weighing a given length of it; suppose it is 8 gm. per cc. Next, tune the wire to $N_1 = 128$ per second, using a standard fork to compare it with, and adjusting the tension by weights until, on exciting the fork and plucking the string, the beats finally disappear. Then to test the result with the theoretical formula, let us write equation (4) in the form

$$N_1 = \frac{1}{2l}\sqrt{Mg/\pi r^2 \rho} \qquad (7),$$

where M is the mass in grams of the weights used to produce the tension, g is the acceleration (in cm. per sec^2) due to gravity, r is the radius of the wire in cm., and ρ is its density in gm. per cc. For our present case equation (7) gives $M = 15$ kilograms nearly.

To test the theoretical relation of the pitches of the other tones possible to the string, leave the tension the same, but touch the middle of the string lightly with the finger, bow it at about 5 or 6 cm. from one end, and compare the tone thus elicited with a 256 fork. It will be found that the two are practically in unison. Similarly, touch the string at one of its points of trisection, bow it at about 3 cm. from one end, and compare the tone with a 384 fork. Proceeding in this way, it will be found that equation (6) is practically correct. It may further be verified that simultaneously reducing the tension to one-quarter, and the length to one-half, has no effect on the pitch, which again is in accordance with equations (4), (6), and (7).

167. Stiffness of Strings.—If, instead of the rough lecture experiments just described, the vibrations of strings are examined with great care, deviations from the equations (4) and (6) of article 165 may be observed. This is partly owing to the stiffness of the strings. An investigation of this disturbance was carried out by Savart, who found a result that may be expressed as follows :—

$$N'^2 = N^2 + N_0^2 \qquad (1),$$

where N' is the true observed frequency, N that given by equation (4), and N_0 is the frequency with which the string would vibrate, in virtue of its own stiffness, without any tension whatever. Duhamel sought to give a simple explanation of this result by likening the effect of the string's stiffness to a constant increase, F_0 say, of the tension. Thus, if instead of the actual tension F we wrote in equation (4) of article 165 the value $F + F_0$, we should obtain Savart's equation. It was shown by August Seebeck (1846-47) that this was only an approximation, and that to be more correct we must write

$$N' = N(1 + c) \qquad (2),$$

where, the N's having the previous meanings, c is a correcting factor. Now this factor increases with increasing values of the radius of the string or the Young's modulus of its material. But it decreases with increasing values of the length of the string or the tension to which it is subjected. Lord Rayleigh also finds similar results. Thus, if we keep to the same string we are concerned with the second remark only. Hence, if we raise the pitch by increasing the tension, we approach closer and closer to the case where $c = 0$, and therefore $N' \div N = 1$. If, however, we raise the pitch by taking smaller lengths of the string at the given tension, we increase c and make $(N' \div N)$ become greater and greater. But this latter is the case when, beginning at the prime, we elicit in succession the various possible tones of a given string. Hence, when the stiffness of the string is taken into account, we see that not only is the prime tone sharpened, but that the others are sharpened still more, and accordingly no longer form with it an harmonic series. With the strings employed in music these facts, however, are practically inappreciable.

168. Yielding of Bridges.—The modification in the vibrations of strings, due to the yielding of the bridges at their ends, has been mathematically investigated by Lord Rayleigh. The result may be stated thus:—(1) Let the end supports have a negligible mass, but a very large spring or restoring force μ. Then, to the order of approximation used, the possible tones do not cease to form an harmonic series, but the pitches of all are slightly lowered. The effect of the yielding is the same as that due to an increase in the length of the string by an amount inversely proportional to μ. (2) Let the end supports have a negligible spring, but very large mass M. The effect is then equivalent to shortening the string to an extent depending on the pitch of the tone. There is consequently a rise in pitch, and this rise is greater the lower the component tone. Thus, the harmonic series is here violated.

169. Longitudinal Vibrations in Rods. CASE I. *Both Ends fixed.*—In dealing with the longitudinal vibrations of bars, we shall follow the plan adopted for the transverse vibrations of strings. Our two general equations are accordingly as follows:—

$$N = v/\lambda \qquad\qquad (1),$$

and
$$v = \sqrt{q/\rho} \qquad (2).$$

Our third equation, for both ends fixed, may be written

$$2l = \lambda_1 = 2\lambda_2 = \ldots = n\lambda_n = \ldots \qquad (3),$$

since, as in the case of vibrating strings, we must here have a node at each end. We thus obtain

$$N_1 = \frac{1}{2l} \sqrt{q/\rho} \qquad (4),$$

and
$$N_n = nN_1 \qquad (5),$$

in which N_n is the frequency of the nth tone, l is the length of the bar, q and ρ the Young's modulus and density of the material. Thus, the pitches of the possible tones is obtained, and they are seen to constitute the full harmonic series. It should be noted that this result will apply equally to a wire or string, provided it be made to vibrate longitudinally and not transversely, as is also possible to it. It is also noteworthy that the pitch for longitudinal vibrations is, to our present approximation, independent of the cross-section of the rod or wire and of the tension, if any is applied. Further, since the value of v for longitudinal waves exceeds that possible for transverse ones in a thin wire (equations (6) and (7) of article 123), the pitch for longitudinal vibrations is higher than any possible for transverse ones from the same wire.

170. EXPT. 27. *Longitudinal Vibrations.* — The various points embodied in equations (4) and (5), and just enlarged upon, admit of easy experimental illustration as follows :— Take a steel wire about 5 or 10 metres long, and say a millimetre in diameter. Let one end be coiled round a wrest pin firmly fixed in a heavy bench. The other end of the wire is to be firmly attached to the centre of a wooden tray or board, say 70 cm. by 50, which is itself fastened to a bench or table. The attachments of the board to the wire and to the bench must be so related as to leave the board capable of vibration, and yet enable it to withstand the pull of the wire. Strain the wire by turning the wrest pin until all appearance of looseness or kinks is removed, and then rub it longitudinally with a rosined wash-leather. It will then be found to emit a musical tone. If the wire be plucked or bowed so as to excite transverse vibrations, the pitch of the tone thus produced will be found much lower, no matter how much it is sharpened by increasing the tension. The tone given by the longitudinal vibrations, on the other hand, will be found practically the same in pitch, whatever the tension, provided both ends of the wire are really fixed.

To illustrate equation (5), nip the wire at its middle between the finger and thumb, and rub one of its halves so as to make it vibrate longitudinally in two equal segments. The tone so produced is found to be the octave of the prime. Similarly, if nipped at one of the points of trisection and rubbed elsewhere, it gives the twelfth of its fundamental. Again, making a node at the quarter length, rubbing excites the double-octave of the prime, and so forth in accordance with equation (5). Now, let the length available for vibrations be altered by clipping the wire at some intermediate point very firmly on to a heavy block, say a 56 lb. weight. Then the dependence of frequency on length may be shown to follow the law contained in equation (4). By changing to a thicker or thinner wire of the same length and material, we find there is no change in the pitch of the longitudinal vibrations. This is in accordance with (4), since diameter does not occur in the equation. Now let us change from a steel wire to a brass one of the same length. We thus leave the density practically unaltered, while reducing the value of Young's modulus to about a half. As seen from equation (4), this should cause a lowering of the frequency to $\dfrac{1}{\sqrt{2}}$, or 0·707 of its former value. The musical interval in question is thus of the order half an octave (or three whole tones on the tempered scale), for its ratio is the square root of that defining the octave, and hence its logarithm is one-half. Again, we may note from (4) that the alteration in material may be compensated by changing the length to 0·707 of its former value. Both these views of the matter will be found in agreement with the results of the experiment. It is much better, of course, for the sake of comparison of different materials, to have the two wires simultaneously in use, each with its own board and means of adjusting the length. It may then be shown that about 7 metres of brass wire gives longitudinal vibrations in unison with those from 10 metres of steel wire, the tones being of the same quality facilitates comparison and tuning.

The longitudinal vibrations of a rubbed string have been examined in an elaborate series of experiments by H. N. Davis (*Amer. Academy*, May 1906). He finds a general accord between these vibrations and the transverse ones of which the string is capable.

171. CASE II. *Rods fixed at one End.*—For the case of a bar vibrating longitudinally with one end fixed and one free, it is clear that the general equations, (1) and (2) of article 169, still hold good. Equation (3), however, is now replaced by

$$4l = \lambda_1 = 3\lambda_2 = 5\lambda_3 = \ldots = (2n-1)\lambda_n \quad (6).$$

For the fixed end must be a node, and the free end must be an antinode of the stationary waves set up in the rod. Thus, as may be seen by reference to Fig. 21, the length of the rod must contain an odd number of quarter wave-lengths. And this fact is mathematically stated in (6). On substituting from equations (6) and (2) of article 169 in (1) we obtain

$$N_1 = \sqrt{q/\rho}/4l \quad (7),$$

and

$$N_n = (2n-1)N_1 \quad (8).$$

We have in this case, therefore, the odd harmonic series illustrated.

172. CASE III. *Rods fixed at the Middle.*—It is obvious that this case is equivalent to two rods each of half the length, placed end to end, fixed where they meet and free elsewhere. Thus the possible tones will again compose the odd harmonic series as in the case of rods fixed at one end just considered. The pitch of the prime tone, however, will be raised an octave by changing the fixed point from one end to the middle. In other words, the pitch of the prime

returns to that of the first case with both ends fixed.
Using as before the two general equations (1) and (2) from
article 169 we have as our third equation for this case

$$2l = \lambda_1 = 3\lambda_2 = \ldots = (2n - 1)\lambda_n \qquad (9).$$

Thus, by substitution, we obtain

$$N_1 = \sqrt{q/\rho}/2l \qquad (10),$$

and $\qquad\qquad N_n = (2n - 1)N_1 \qquad\qquad (11).$

This case presents an important practical advantage over
the other two methods of fixing. For when the rod is
vibrating longitudinally with its middle fixed, any two points
symmetrically placed along it are always moving at equal
speeds, but in opposite directions. Thus the whole vibration is balanced and a very slight constraint is sufficient to
start and maintain this fixedness of the middle point. For
example, when using a wood rod a metre long and a centimetre in diameter, holding at the middle with thumb and
finger is sufficient to fix it so that rubbing it with a rosined
leather near the end excites the prime tone. In the other
cases previously considered very massive or rigid supports
would be necessary to impose the fixedness theoretically
contemplated.

In connection with the present case it should be noted
that it is the fixture of the middle and not the freedom of
the ends which suppresses the evenly-numbered tones of
the full harmonic series. Thus if, while the ends of the
bar were free, the middle were alternately fixed and free,
the bar would then yield all the tones, odd and even, of the
full harmonic series.

173. Torsional Vibrations of Rods.—A cylindrical rod
of circular section, whether solid or hollow, may be twisted
by couples in such a manner that each transverse section
remains in its own plane and unchanged in shape. The
forces by which the twist is resisted depend upon the elastic
constant termed rigidity. This has been dealt with in

R

Chapter III., and was there denoted by the symbol n. To form our differential equation let us consider a cylindrical tube of radius r and thickness dr, with axis coinciding with the axis of x. Let it have a free end at the origin, extend along the positive direction of the x axis, being fixed at some distant place. Now suppose the tube to be in equilibrium under the following conditions. At the origin let a couple K act about the axis, and along the tube imagine couples to be continuously distributed of amount k per unit length. Then at the point x the couple will be $K + kx$. Let the value of the angular displacement at x be θ, then at radius r this involves a tangential displacement $r\theta$. But θ decreases with increasing x, hence the amount of the shear at x is $-d(r\theta)/dx$ or $-rd\theta/dx$. In Chapter III. this quantity was denoted by χ; it may be regarded as the tangent or the circular measure of the change of angle between the sides of an elementary cube. Now, by definition, rigidity is the tangential force per unit area divided by the amount of shear. Hence, in the present case, the force per unit area is $-nrd\theta/dx$. And, for the whole ring, the force is $2\pi r dr$ times this. Lastly, the moment of the force is r times the product of these two quantities. Hence, equating this expression to the couples producing the state of twist in equation, we have

$$- 2\pi nr^3 dr d\theta/dx = K + kx \qquad (1).$$

But this involves K and x, and we wish to obtain an equation which takes cognisance only of the state of things at a point. Hence, differentiate (1) to x, and we have

$$- 2\pi nr^3 dr d^2\theta/dx^2 = k \qquad (2),$$

an equation confined to the point under consideration, and therefore independent of any special conditions which were adopted to obtain it, except the vital one that at x the *total couple* increases at the *rate* k per unit length. Now the slice of the tube of length dx situated at x is in equilibrium under the action of the external couple kdx and the reactions of the neighbouring portions of the tube. Hence, if the external couple be removed the slice would be acted upon by the couple $-kdx$. Accordingly this quantity may be equated to the product of the moment of inertia of the slice into its angular acceleration. Now the radius of gyration of the slice is r, and its mass is $2\pi r dr dx \rho$, where ρ is the density. We thus obtain

$$2\pi r^3 dr dx \rho \, d^2\theta/dt^2 = -kdx \qquad (3).$$

Comparing (2) and (3) we have

$$\frac{d^2\theta}{dt^2} = v^2\frac{d^2\theta}{dx^2} \qquad (4),$$

where

$$v^2 = n/\rho \qquad (5).$$

These equations being independent of r apply equally well to a tube of finite thickness or a solid rod.

174. Torsional Vibrations compared with Longitudinal.—We thus see that the differential equation for the propagation of torsional vibrations is identical in form with those obtained in Chapter IV. for the transverse disturbances of stretched strings, bars vibrating longitudinally, and the propagation of sound in gases. Hence, torsional waves may be propagated in either direction with speed $v = \sqrt{n/\rho}$. For a fixed end the condition is obviously $\theta = 0$. For a free end, as seen by putting K and $x = 0$ in equation (1), we have $d\theta/dx = 0$. Or, in other words, we have a node at the fixed end and an antinode at the free end. Hence the whole theory of rods vibrating torsionally is like that for rods vibrating longitudinally. The speed of propagation and the frequency of any tone in any case being obtained by substituting n for q in the appropriate formulæ. In article 78, Table V. shows that $q/n = 2(1 + \sigma)$, hence

$$N/N' = v/v' = \sqrt{q/n} = \sqrt{2(1 + \sigma)} \qquad (6),$$

where the dashes denote the quantities applying to torsional vibrations and the others those for longitudinal ones.

Moreover the values of σ for all solids lie between 0 and $1/2$. Hence $\sqrt{q/n}$ lies between $\sqrt{2}$ and $\sqrt{3}$, *i.e.* between $1.414 \ldots$ and $1.732 \ldots$. For an ordinary value of σ, say $1/3$, we have $\sqrt{q/n} = \sqrt{8/3} = 1.63$ or $5/3$ nearly. Thus, we may say roughly that torsional vibrations under any given conditions are of the order a major sixth lower in pitch than the corresponding longitudinal vibrations.

> EXPT. 28. *Torsional Vibrations.*—In the production of torsional vibrations the rods should be well polished, and then, if round, excited by a rosined leather turned round right or left. If the rod is not round, two bows may be used simultaneously crosswise and in opposite directions; for example, one up and one down at the ends of a horizontal diameter. If only one bow is available care must be taken to avoid producing the transverse vibrations. By comparing the frequencies of the longitudinal and torsional vibrations, and using equation (6), the value of Poisson's ratio might be determined for the material of the rod.

175. Parallel Pipes.—We pass now to the elementary theory of columns of air or other gases vibrating in parallel pipes, open or stopped. Owing to the parallelism of the pipes we may assume the motion at any instant to be the same at each point in any one cross-section. Hence the methods of the previous articles apply here also. We may therefore write as follows for the frequency and speed of waves:—

$$N = v/\lambda \qquad (1),$$

and
$$v = \sqrt{\gamma P U} = v_0 \sqrt{1 + at} \qquad (2),$$

where γ is the ratio of the elasticities and specific heats, P is the pressure in absolute units, U the specific volume, v_0 is the speed of propagation at $0°$ C., a is the coefficient of expansion, and t the temperature in degrees cent.

CASE I. *Open Pipes.* — For pipes open at both ends, since motion is possible there, and change of pressure a vanishing quantity, each end must be an antinode of the stationary vibration. Again, the middle of the pipe may be either a node or an antinode. Hence we have, where l is the length of the pipe and λ the wave length,

$$2l = \lambda_1 = 2\lambda_2 = 3\lambda_3 = \ldots = n\lambda_n \qquad (3).$$

We thus obtain for the pitch of the fundamental,

$$N_1 = v_0 \sqrt{1 + at}/2l = \sqrt{\gamma PU}/2l \qquad (4),$$

and for the series of over-tones natural to the pipe,

$$N_n = nN_1 \qquad (5).$$

It is thus seen that equations (1) and (3) are independent of the gas used for the pipe, but that (2) (and hence (4) also) depends both on the gas and its temperature. Obviously the pitch is raised by rise of temperature. It should also be noted, as shown by (4), that the pitch of a given pipe does not depend simply on the *density* of the gas used, as so often implied in text-books, but upon the value of γ also. Thus, if we change from oxygen to hydrogen, since both have two atoms in the molecule, the values of γ are practically identical, and so for this case we have velocities and frequencies inversely proportional to the square roots of the densities. But if the comparison is made between hydrogen and carbon-dioxide, then the value of γ changes from about $1\cdot4$ for the hydrogen to about $1\cdot25$ for the tri-atomic carbon-dioxide. And this change must be taken into account as well as that of the densities.

An alternative method of deriving equation (4) is as follows :—Let a condensation start from the mouth of the pipe and arrive at the open end. It is there reflected as a rarefaction, and again traverses the length of the pipe to the mouth. It is here again changed by reflection, and so becomes a condensation as at first. Consequently, any state of density and motion completes its full cycle of possible changes by twice traversing the length of the pipe. Hence, the frequency of the tone in question will be the number of times that the double-length of the pipe can be traversed by the wave motion per second. In other words, the frequency is the quotient $v/2l$, and this is what (4) expresses.

176. CASE II. *Stopped Pipes.* — For stopped pipes equations (1) and (2) still hold, while (3) is replaced by

$$4l = \lambda_1 = 3\lambda_2 = 5\lambda_3 = \ . \ . \ . \ = (2n-1)\lambda_n = \ . \ . \ . \ = (6),$$

since we must always have a node at the stopped end and an antinode at the mouth. We accordingly obtain the following solution for this case :—

$$N_1 = v_0 \sqrt{1 + at}/4l \qquad (7),$$

and

$$N_n = (2n - 1)N_1 \qquad (8).$$

Here again it is instructive to derive (7) by the alternative method as used for (4). Thus, a condensation starting from the mouth traverses the pipe to the stopped end, where it is reflected as a condensation and again reaches the mouth as such. It is here changed by reflection into a rarefaction, and again passes to the stopped end and back without further change of its nature. Then, by the second reflection at the mouth it is changed into a condensation as at the outset. This completes its cycle of possible changes and involves traversing the length of the pipe *four* times. Accordingly the frequency of the prime is $v/4l$ as stated by equation (7).

177. EXPT. 29. *Vibrations in Organ Pipes.*—The actual state of things inside a pipe when sounding may be experimentally illustrated by the following two methods. First, a little fine dry sand may be scattered upon a small imitation tambourine about 2 or 3 cm. diameter. This is then suspended by a thread at various positions within the pipe when sounding as shown in Fig. 49. If it is hung at the open top of the pipe, the sand will always be agitated, no matter what tone the pipe is made to produce. For, as shown by the letter A, the top is always an antinode whatever tone is being produced. The same result would follow if the tambourine were lowered to the mouth of the pipe. If, however, it be suspended at the middle of the pipe

the effect will vary with the tone produced.   Thus, as stated
in the first column headed prime tone, we have a node at
the middle for this tone, consequently the sand will remain
at rest there while the pipe speaks its prime.   The same
remark applies to the third tone possible to the pipe as shown
in the third column.   Whereas for the second tone we have
an antinode at the middle, thus the sand would be agitated

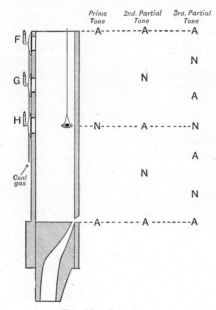

Fig. 49.—Open Pipe

there when the pipe speaks the octave of the prime, as it may
easily be made to do by overblowing.   If, now, the tambourine be again supplied with sand and placed one-quarter
or three-quarters down the pipe while the octave is sounding,
it will remain at rest, indicating nodes at these places as
marked in the second column on the figure.

The second method of illustration is that by Koenig's
manometric flames.   This is of great importance, and we
shall have occasion to make further reference to it.   The
manometric capsules F, G, and H have coal gas supplied to

them by the pipe shown, and the jets are lit.   They are each
divided from the interior of the pipe by their membranes.
Hence, when the pipe is sounding, a capsule at the place of
maximum change of pressure will have its membrane
agitated.   And this effect is rendered visible by the
flickering of the corresponding jet.   On the other hand, a
capsule at a place of no change of pressure for a given tone
will remain steady while that tone is sounded, provided the
pipe is not simultaneously producing one of its other tones.
Now the places of maximum change of pressure are those of
minimum displacement, *i.e.* nodes.   Similarly, the places of
no change of pressure are those of greatest change of displacement, or antinodes.   Hence, for any tone producible by
the pipe the flame at F might be expected to be quiet.   As
a matter of fact, since it cannot be quite at the end, and this
method is extremely sensitive, it will always flicker a little.
The jet at H, on the other hand, will flicker very much and
be extinguished when the prime tone is sounded.   The jet
G will behave in an intermediate manner for the prime tone.
But when, by overblowing, the second tone, or octave of the
prime, is produced, the jet G may be extinguished while H
is only slightly affected.   In conjunction with the manometric flames a rotating mirror is often used, but for the
present purpose it reveals a distinct flickering in the flames
under all circumstances.   The special flickering of the jet
when at a node can be seen quite well enough without the
mirror.   It is therefore better to dispense with it for this
experiment.

It was shown by K. Marbe[1] that on passing a paper
rapidly through a smoky König's flame a record could be
obtained indicating the frequency and quality of the sound
thus examined.

178. Expt. 30. *Pipe Vibrations illustrated by Projection
Model.*—The stationary vibrations in an open or closed pipe
may also be illustrated by the optical lantern and the working
model devised by the writer and shown in Fig. 50.   In this
model, which is used as a lantern slide, three wires are
provided, each capable of rotating in concert, being coupled
by wheels as illustrated in the photograph.   One of these
wires is a right-hand screw whose projection is a sine graph ;

---

[1] *Phys. Zeitschr.*, Aug. 1, 1906.

on turning this wire by the handle provided, its projection represents a progressive wave moving, say, in the positive direction. At the same time, a second wire in the form of a left-hand screw gives a projection representing a negatively progressing wave. The third wire being itself in one plane and in the form of a sine graph yields, on turning, a projection representing a stationary wave. And the model is so arranged, that at any position the stationary wave repre-

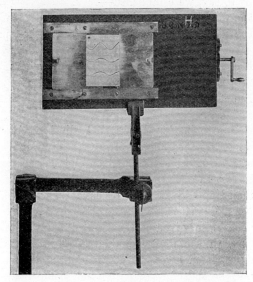

Fig. 50.—Projection Model for Stationary Vibrations.

sented by this third wire is that which is formed by compounding the progressive waves represented by the other two. Further, the brass plates at the ends are movable, and may be so adjusted that each end represents an " open end," or so that one end is open and the other a "stopped end." It thus illustrates graphically on the screen the vibrations of an open or a stopped pipe.

179. Corrections for Open Ends.—By the elementary theory of parallel pipes advanced in article 175, the various proper or natural tones were determined. And in accordance with that theory their relative frequencies for open and stopped pipes of a given length may be represented as follows :—

Open pipe— 2, 4, 6, 8, 10, 12, etc.

Stopped pipe ⎱
of same length⎰ —1, 3, 5, 7, 9, 11, etc.

That is to say, we established—
(1) The pitches of the prime tones.
(2) The simple octave relation between the open and stopped pipes of same length.
(3) The frequencies inversely as the lengths of the pipes of either class, open or stopped, and
(4) The strictness of the harmonic series for each class of pipe.

A closer examination shows that all these four points are subject to modification, and traces these modifications to the phenomena occurring at the open ends of the pipes.

The correct theory of the open organ pipe was discovered by Helmholtz, and given in his classical memoir of 1859 (*Theory of Air Vibrations in Open-ended Tubes*). Lord Rayleigh has also given a theory, and his results are in agreement with those of Helmholtz. These theories are, however, restricted by two assumptions : first, that the diameter of the end of the pipe is small compared with the wave length ; and second, that it is fitted into an infinite plane flange to which the axis of the pipe is perpendicular. No theoretical solution of the problem of an unflanged open pipe seems yet to have been given. Under the above restrictions, the correction for an open end to be added to the length of the pipe was determined by Helmholtz in certain cases to be $\frac{\pi}{4}R$, while Lord Rayleigh obtained the value $0\cdot82R$, where R is the radius of the end. As the unflanged end was not amenable to theory, Rayleigh sought to determine the effect of the flange experimentally. The

result was that $0\cdot2R$ was that part of the correction due
to the flange, or, when repeated by Mr. Bosanquet, $0\cdot25R$.
Thus, subtracting the mean of these two values from the
full theoretical correction, we obtain $0\cdot6R$ as the correction for an unflanged open end, small in comparison
with the wave length. Direct experiment by D. J. Blaikley
on the correction for an unflanged open end, the tube
being of thin brass about two inches diameter, gave values
varying between $0\cdot564R$ and $0\cdot595R$, the mean correction
being $0\cdot576R$ (for details see article 531 in Chap. X).
Helmholtz has shown that the correction for the open end
is a function of λ, and that for very short λ the correction
tends to vanish. Rayleigh has also shown that for certain
cases the correction for an open end is a function of the
length L of the neck, and that the correction is $\dfrac{\pi}{4}R$ when
L vanishes; and approaches, but cannot reach $\dfrac{8}{3\pi}R$ for L
infinite.

The mathematical theories of the phenomena occurring
at the open end are too abstruse for introduction here
either wholly or in part. A simple consideration will,
however, suffice to show that the elementary theory
previously developed needs supplementing. Thus, in dealing with the reflection at an open end (articles 138 and 175),
it was assumed that the particles at the end were quite free,
and that the change of pressure and density were negligible.
But obviously these assumptions are not strictly correct.
The air outside the end is not devoid of inertia. Hence,
the vibrations extend beyond the actual end of the pipe.
Let us note the consequences of this extension.

    (1) There is communication of sound to the external
          air. Hence the sound of the pipe may be heard.
          Thus, near the open end, we have *inside* the pipe
          stationary plane waves, and *outside* it *progressive
          spherical* waves.

(2) The intensity of the waves reflected from the open end is less than that of the incident waves, since some energy escapes. Thus the sound of an organ pipe very quickly dies away unless the blast is maintained to supply the energy thus dissipated.

(3) The virtual length of the pipe is increased, and thus the pitch is lowered.

180. It is with the third of these consequences that we are now concerned. The theories and experiments hitherto mentioned give $0.6R$ as the correction for the upper open end of an organ pipe. But if this end needs correction on account of lack of openness, the mouth of the pipe, being far less open, must need a still greater correction. According to Cavaillé-Coll, the whole correction required for both ends is $3\frac{1}{3}R$. This leaves about $2.7R$ as the correction for the mouth alone. Observations by Rayleigh confirm the necessity for a very large correction for the mouth. Let us now apply these results to a stopped and an open pipe of equal lengths and diameters. Then we see that the stopped pipe needs the correction for the mouth only, while the open one needs the additional correction for the upper open end. Thus, not only are both lowered in pitch by this correction of the elementary theory, but the simple octave relation between them is destroyed. In other words, to produce a given tone the stopped pipe must be shorter than the elementary theory gives, and to produce the exact octave of this the open pipe of same diameter must be shortened still more from the length given by the simple theory.

Or, to put the matter in symbols, equations (4) and (7) of articles 175 and 176 will now need replacing by the following:—

For open pipes, $$N_1 = \frac{v_0\sqrt{1+at}}{2(l+c+c')} \qquad (1),$$

For stopped pipes, $$N_1 = \frac{v_0\sqrt{1+at}}{4(l+c)} \qquad (2),$$

where c is the correction for the mouth of the order $2 \cdot 7R$, and $c' = 0 \cdot 6R$ nearly is the correction for the open end. These end corrections, while considered as fractions of the radius of the pipe and independent of wave length, have no disturbing influence on the harmonic series of tones for each pipe. These are accordingly represented to this approximation by equations (5) and (8) of articles 175 and 176, the values of N_1, from this article being now used in them. But this view of the matter is valid only while the assumption of the theory is fulfilled, viz. that the wave length is large in comparison with the diameter of the pipe. Thus for narrow pipes and the lower tones we have practically the harmonic series. But for wide pipes the proper or natural tones distinctly depart from the harmonic series. Thus Helmholtz says, "for wide open pipes the adjacent proper tones of the pipe are all somewhat sharper than the corresponding harmonic tones of the prime."

Thus to summarise :—

(1) The elementary theory gives the first rough approximation to the pitches of the various tones natural to open and stopped pipes.

(2) The introduction of an end correction as a fraction of the radius of the pipe gives the second approximation. This lowers the pitches of all tones, and destroys the simple octave relation between the open and stopped pipes of given length and diameter, but leaves the harmonic series undisturbed.

(3) While, lastly, the recognition that the end correction depends slightly upon the wave length also disturbs the harmonic series for each pipe, specially so if they are wide.

It should be carefully noted by the student that throughout this chapter we are discussing the natural tones, or tones proper to each system vibrating freely. That is, in the case of pipes, we are speaking of the tones which could be most easily and powerfully excited in them. Other tones slightly different in pitch may be elicited under the influence of forcing. When the tones of an organ pipe are produced and maintained by the blast in the usual way, that is an example of forcing for any tones lying off the harmonic series, because the whole motion must then be strictly periodic. Hence all the components that speak must constitute an exact harmonic series. The question as to what are the frequencies of the free vibrations is still, however, of the utmost importance. For evidently upon this depends the presence and relative intensity of the various tones simultaneously elicited under the influence of forcing.

181. Helmholtz has shown that a cylindrical pipe may be constructed with an end so formed as to require no end correction. The end in question is slightly widened and of trumpet form. The curvature of its longitudinal section is everywhere convex to the inside. The radius of curvature of this section decreases continually from the cylindrical part till at the mouth it is infinitesimal. The form of the section and that of the stream lines inside are confocal hyperbolæ. The area of the mouth is twice that of the cross section of the cylindrical part. Or, in other words, the radius of the mouth is $\sqrt{2}$ times that of the cylindrical part of the pipe.

182. Conical Pipes.—In the discussion of parallel pipes we had only plane waves to deal with whose treatment was possible by elementary methods. In the present case of conical pipes we have to consider spherical waves,[1] and must therefore use the more general theory developed in articles 149 to 155. We commence with equation (17) in article 153, viz.

$$a^2\frac{d^2(rs)}{dr^2} = \frac{d^2(rs)}{dt^2} \qquad (1),$$

where a is the speed of propagation of the wave motion,

[1] See the author's article on "Vibrations in Conical Pipes," etc., *Phil. Mag.*, January 1908.

s the condensation, and r the radius vector from the centre of disturbance. To apply this to conical pipes we must use the form of solution corresponding to stationary waves. Thus, let rs be everywhere proportional to $\cos kat$. Then

$$d^2(rs)/dt^2 = -k^2a^2(rs),$$

and equation (1) transforms into

$$\frac{d^2(rs)}{dr^2} + k^2(rs) = 0 \qquad (2).$$

The general solution of this may be written

$$rs = (A \cos kr + B \sin kr) \cos kat \qquad (3),$$

where A and B are arbitrary constants. These are to be determined for each case by the position and nature of the ends of the pipe. There will, accordingly, be a number of separate cases to consider.

183. CASE I. *Open Ends.*—First, let both ends of the conical pipe be open. Then obviously the condition at each end is approximately $s = 0$. For at the ideal open end there can be neither condensation nor rarefaction. Let the co-ordinates of the ends of the pipe be r_1 and r_2, measured, of course, from the vertex of the cone produced. Then we have from (3) for the terminal conditions,

$$A \cos kr_1 + B \sin kr_1 = 0, \text{ and } A \cos kr_2 + B \sin kr_2 = 0.$$

Whence, by the elimination of A/B, we obtain

$$\sin k(r_2 - r_1) = 0, \text{ or } k(r_2 - r_1) = n\pi.$$

This may be written

$$r_2 - r_1 = n\lambda_n/2, \text{ or } N_n = \frac{na}{2(r_2 - r_1)} \qquad (4),$$

where n is an integer; for, since s is proportional to $\cos kat$, $k = 2\pi N/a = 2\pi/\lambda$, N being the frequency and λ the wave length of the motion. Thus, for a conical pipe with open ends the pitch of the prime tone and the form of the series of the other natural tones are like those for an open-ended parallel pipe. . This might have been anticipated from the similarity of the differential equations, and the conditions for the open ends in each case. There is, however, this slight difference, that $r_2 - r_1$ is the *slant* length of the conical pipe and not its length parallel to the axis. But if the conicality is slight, this involves only the second order of small quantities. Lord Rayleigh has also shown that the conicality of the pipe affects the wave length only to the second order of small quantities, *Theory of Sound*, vol. ii. p. 115. As to the segments into which the pipe is divided when emitting its higher natural tones, it follows from equation (4) that the antinodes are equidistant. It will be seen from Case II. that this simplicity does not extend to the nodes.

184. CASE II. *Closed Ends.*—The condition at closed ends is obviously $u = 0$. Consequently $du/dt = 0$ there also. But by equation (6) of article 151 $du/dt = -a^2 ds/dr$ if u denotes the velocity along r. We may thus write as our condition for a closed end $ds/dr = 0$. Applying this to equation (3) of article 182, we obtain

$$A(\cos kr_1 + kr_1 \sin kr_1) = B(kr_1 \cos kr_1 - \sin kr_1),$$

and $A(\cos kr_2 + kr_2 \sin kr_2) = B(kr_2 \cos kr_2 - \sin kr_2).$

On dividing out by the cosines and writing $\tan \theta_1$ and $\tan \theta_2$ for kr_1 and kr_2 we may eliminate A/B between these equations, the results being written in the forms

$$\frac{A}{B} = \frac{\tan \theta_1 - \tan kr_1}{1 + \tan \theta_1 \tan kr_1} = \tan (\theta_1 - kr_1) = \tan (\theta_2 - kr_2),$$

or $kr_2 - \tan^{-1} kr_2 = kr_1 - \tan^{-1} kr_1$ (5).

Here again, it may be shown (Rayleigh's *Sound*, vol. ii. p. 115) that a slight conicality has only a second-order influence on the pitch. The complicated form of equation (5) shows that in a conical pipe the nodes will not be equidistant. We shall presently determine where they are situated in the important case of a complete cone with open base.

185. CASE III. *Closed Cone.*—To treat the case of a cone continued to the vertex and with the base closed, we have simply to write $r_1 = 0$ in equation (5), and R the slant length of the cone for r_2. This gives

$$\tan kR = kR \qquad (6).$$

To solve this equation, which we may regard as $\tan x = x$, we may proceed graphically. Thus plot the two graphs $y = x$ and $y = \tan x$. Then their intersections will give the roots required. See Fig. 51 as an illustration of this. The equation may also be solved by successive approximations. Proceeding thus, Rayleigh finds (*Theory of Sound*, vol. i. p. 334)—

$$\frac{kR}{\pi} = \frac{x}{\pi} = 0,\ 1\cdot 4303,\ 2\cdot 4590,\ 3\cdot 4709,\ 4\cdot 4747,\ 5\cdot 4818,$$

$$= \theta_1, \qquad \theta_2, \qquad \theta_3, \qquad \theta_4, \qquad \theta_5, \qquad \theta_6,$$

$$6\cdot 4844,\ \text{etc.}$$

$$\theta_7,\ \text{say} \qquad (7).$$

Thus these quantities, each multiplied by π, give the first seven values of kR in equation (6). Now, since $\theta_1 = 0$, we may write $(k_n R) = \pi\theta_{n+1}$. But we also have as the general relation $k_n = 2\pi N_n / a$. Hence, we may write for the frequency of the nth tone natural to the closed cone

$$N_n = \frac{a}{2R}\theta_{n+1} \qquad (8).$$

Thus the frequencies are directly proportional to the speed of sound, inversely proportional to the slant length of the cone, and the relation of the various possible tones in the series follows that of the roots given in equation (7).

186. CASE IV. *Open Cone.*—We now consider the case of a complete cone with base open. At the open base, as in article 183, we have the condition $rs = 0$. And it was shown in article 155, equation (26), that at the pole of spherical waves $rs = 0$; this, accordingly, is our condition for the vertex also. So that although one end is open and the other end closed, we have the apparent anomaly that the same condition applies to each. Hence if R is the co-ordinate of the base, *i.e.* is the slant length of the cone, we have from (4)

$$R = m\lambda_m/2, \text{ or } N_m = ma/2R \qquad (9),$$

where N_m is the frequency of the mth natural tone, λ_m its wave length, and a the speed of sound. Thus, we have the strange phenomenon of a tube open at one end and stopped at the other, in the form of a complete cone, giving practically the *same fundamental* and the same *full* harmonic series of other natural tones as are obtainable from a parallel pipe of the same length open at both ends.

EXPT. 30*a*. *Conical Resonators.*—That this is the case may be easily verified experimentally by a cone of zinc and a set of tuning-forks of relative frequencies 1, 2, 3, etc. Apart from end corrections, the cone must be of the same length as a parallel pipe open at both ends, whose prime is in resonance with the lowest fork. This cone will then respond to each of these forks, thus verifying the surprising relations in question.

187. We see from the first form of (9) that the wave length is inversely as the order of the tone produced, hence the antinodes are all equidistant. This, however, does not apply to the nodes. To determine the positions of the nodes we must refer to equations (6), (7), and (8). Now, equation (8) gives in terms of θ the various values of N for a closed cone of *fixed* slant length R. Let us, however, substitute the *variable* r for the constant R, and, dropping the subscript of N, rewrite this equation as follows :—

$$2Nr/a = \theta_1, \theta_2, \theta_3, \theta_4, \theta_5, \theta_6 \text{ or } \theta_7, \text{ etc.} \qquad (10).$$

We may now regard both N and r as variables which must satisfy equation (10), r being the slant length of a closed cone. Again, equation (9) gives the frequencies of the various tones natural to the open cone. Let us rewrite it, dropping from N its subscript, and writing for m on the right side the series of natural numbers which it represents. We thus obtain

$$2NR/a = 1,\ 2,\ 3,\ 4,\ 5,\ 6 \text{ or } 7, \text{ etc.} \qquad (11).$$

Here we consider the slant length R of our open cone as a constant, and N to vary in accordance with the numbers on the right side of the equation. Now by dividing equation (10) by (11) we eliminate the variable N, and obtain the required relations between r and R, viz.

$$\left.\begin{array}{l} \dfrac{r}{R} = \dfrac{\theta_1}{1},\ \dfrac{\theta_1,\text{ or }\theta_2}{2},\ \dfrac{\theta_1,\ \theta_2,\text{ or }\theta_3}{3},\ \dfrac{\theta_1,\ \theta_2,\ \theta_3,\text{ or }\theta_4}{4}, \\[3mm] \dfrac{\theta_1,\ \theta_2,\ \theta_3,\ \theta_4,\text{ or }\theta_5}{5},\ \dfrac{\theta_1,\ \theta_2,\ \theta_3,\ \theta_4,\ \theta_5,\text{ or }\theta_6}{6},\ \text{or} \\[3mm] \dfrac{\theta_1,\ \theta_2,\ \theta_3,\ \theta_4,\ \theta_5,\ \theta_6,\text{ or }\theta_7}{7},\ \text{etc.} \end{array}\right\} (12).$$

188. It is necessary to cross combine the right sides of (10) and (11) in this way to obtain all the values sought. The denominator of any one of the fractions on the right of (12) shows the order of the tone being emitted by the pipe, while the various values of r/R obtained by taking the various θ's in the numerator of that fraction locate the nodes for the tones in question. The series of θ's in each numerator is finite, being limited by the obvious fact that r/R cannot exceed unity. The first few nodal positions are given in Table VIII. They are also exhibited graphically together with the positions of the antinodes in Fig. 51. In this diagram the graph $y = x$ is shown by a full line, and the branches of $y = \tan x$ by broken lines. The abscissæ of their intersections show the values of the roots of the equation $\tan x = x$. To show the segments of one pipe of fixed lengths, when emitting its various tones as expressed by equation (12) with R constant, a number of such diagrams would be needed. To

TABLE VIII.—NODAL POSITIONS OF AN OPEN CONE

Order m. of Natural Tone, i.e. Denominator of Fractions in Equation (12).	Nodal Positions, i.e. Values of $r/R = \theta/m$ in Equation (12).						
1	0						
2	0	0·7152					
3	0	0·4768	0·8197				
4	0	0·3576	0·6148	0·8677			
5	0	0·2861	0·4918	0·6942	0·8949		
6	0	0·2384	0·4098	0·5785	0·7458	0·9136	
7	0	0·2043	0·3513	0·4958	0·6392	0·7831	0·9263
Values of θ's in Numerator of Fractions in Equation (12).	θ_1 0	θ_2 1·4303	θ_3 2·4590	θ_4 3·4709	θ_5 4·4747	θ_6 5·4818	θ_7 6·4844

avoid this repetition, a series of pipes is shown in the upper part of the diagram. These are of various lengths, so that the longest at the top is shown with the segments corresponding to its seventh natural tone. Passing down the series we reach the last pipe, the shortest of all, with one segment only as when emitting its fundamental. The antinodes are indicated by small circles, and the nodes by crosses. The equidistant positions midway between the antinodes are shown by dots. Experiments by D. J. Blaikley have shown the existence of these nodes in positions slightly displaced from equidistances, each node being moved towards the vertex from the corresponding equidistant position. Further, it was found by Blaikley that the displacement was the greater for those nodes which are nearer the vertex. Or, in other words, the nodes in the cone are at increasing distances apart, reckoning from the open end, and at the apex of the cone is a node common to all the notes. These nodal positions were established by Blaikley with an experimental bugle made in sections. On

taking this to pieces, thin metal diaphragms were inserted
at the positions of the nodes for a certain note, and their

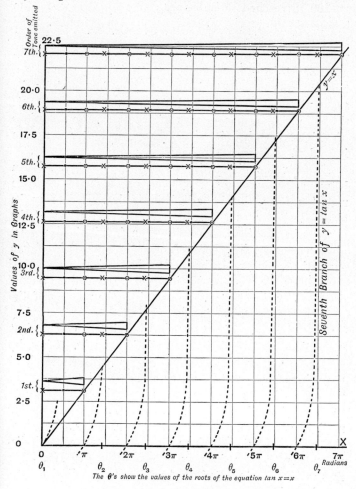

Fig. 51.—Vibrations in Open Cones.

presence was found not to prevent the production of the
note in question. The diaphragms had each a few small

holes to admit the passage of the player's breath, but prevented all free vibration at the place.

189. Stretched Membranes.—We pass now to the treatment of the vibration of stretched membranes. The theoretical membrane of acoustics is an infinitely thin and perfectly flexible solid sheet of uniform material and thickness. It is stretched in all directions in its plane by a tension great enough to be not sensibly increased by the small displacements supposed to occur. The problem is therefore very similar to that of the transverse vibrations of strings, but the vibrations now extend over a surface instead of, as before, only along a line.

To form the differential equation we need a relation between the curvature of an element of surface and the restoring force thereby called into play. This may be obtained simply as follows:—Imagine each point of the element in question to experience an infinitesimal normal displacement. Then the work done is susceptible of two expressions. First, it is the product of the excess of pressure on the concave side into the increment of volume described by the element. Second, it is the product of the tension of the surface into the increment of area acquired by the element. Then on equating the two equivalent expressions we can derive the relation sought. Thus, let the plane of xy be tangential to the surface. And, at the point of contact, take as the element an infinitely small rectangle of sides a and β. Let these sides be parallel to the axes of x and y respectively, and let the corresponding radii of curvature of the surfaces be r_1 and r_2. Then, as the curvature is everywhere very small, the normal displacement of each point may be denoted by dz. Hence our first expression for the work of a small normal displacement may be written

$$dW = pa\beta dz \qquad (1),$$

where p is the excess of pressure on the concave side of the surface. To obtain the increment of the surface in consequence of the displacement, we need an expression for the increase of each side of the rectangle. Thus

$$\frac{a}{r_1} = \frac{a+da}{r_1+dz} = \frac{da}{dz},$$

since each of these expressions is the circular measure of the angle subtended by the side of length a at the centre of its curvature. Hence

$$da = \frac{a}{r_1}dz, \text{ similarly } d\beta = \frac{\beta}{r_2}dz.$$

190. Thus, if T is the tension of the membrane, our second expression for the work of the small displacement may be written

$$dW = Td(a\beta) = T(\beta da + a d\beta) = Ta\beta dz\left(\frac{1}{r_1} + \frac{1}{r_2}\right) \quad (2).$$

Equating these two expressions for the work, we obtain

$$p = T\left(\frac{1}{r_1} + \frac{1}{r_2}\right) \qquad\qquad (3).$$

The restoring forces called into play by the curvature is, of course, equal and opposite to p, and may be equated to the product mass of the element into its acceleration. Let the equilibrium position of the membrane be taken as the plane of xy, and let displacement parallel to the axis of z be denoted by w. Then, as all the displacements and curvatures are small, $\frac{1}{r_1}$ may be replaced, to the required approximation, by $\frac{d^2w}{dx^2}$, the divisor $\left\{1 + \left(\frac{dw}{dx}\right)^2\right\}^{3/2}$ in the expression for curvature being practically equal to unity. A similar remark applies to $\frac{1}{r_2}$, which is accordingly replaced by d^2w/dy^2.

Thus the restoring force on the element of surface is

$$T\left(\frac{d^2w}{dx^2} + \frac{d^2w}{dy^2}\right)a\beta.$$

Again, the product mass of element into its acceleration is $a\beta\sigma\ddot{w}$, σ denoting the surface density of the membrane. Hence the differential equation for the vibrations of the membrane may be written

$$\frac{d^2w}{dt^2} = c^2\left(\frac{d^2w}{dx^2} + \frac{d^2w}{dy^2}\right) \tag{4},$$

where $c = \sqrt{T/\sigma}$ and is of the nature of a velocity.

191. Rectangular Membrane.—Let now a particular case be taken, in which the membrane is rectangular, extending in the plane of xy between the co-ordinate axes and the lines $x = a$ and $y = b$. For every point in the area equation (4) must be satisfied, and for every point along the boundary we must have in addition $w = 0$ for all values of t. Both conditions are satisfied by the equations—

$$\left.\begin{array}{l} w = \sin\dfrac{m\pi x}{a} \sin\dfrac{n\pi y}{b} \cos pt \\[2mm] p^2 = c^2\pi^2\left(\dfrac{m^2}{a^2} + \dfrac{n^2}{b^2}\right) \end{array}\right\} \tag{5},$$

where

and m and n are any integers.

These may easily be verified by examination and differentiation. This, therefore, constitutes a particular integral. The substitution of $\sin pt$ for $\cos pt$ gives another particular integral, the addition of both would give another. Following this method the general solution is found, and may be written as follows :—

$$w = \sum_{m=1}^{m=\infty} \sum_{n=1}^{n=\infty} \sin\frac{m\pi x}{a}\sin\frac{n\pi y}{b}\left\{A_{mn}\cos pt + B_{mn}\sin pt\right\} \tag{6},$$

where the A's and B's are a series of arbitrary constants for each value of m and n, which must be chosen to suit any given initial conditions.

192. *Initial Conditions.*—Now let the initial displacement and velocity of the membrane be specified as follows :—

For $\qquad t = 0$, let $w_0 = f_1(x, y)$ $\qquad$ (7),

and $\qquad\qquad\qquad \dot{w}_0 = f_2(x, y)$ $\qquad\qquad$ (8).

Then we must so choose the constants in equation (6) as to satisfy equations (7) and (8). By putting $t = 0$ in (6) and equating to (7), we have

$$w_0 = f_1(x, y) = \sum_{m=1}^{m=\infty} \sum_{n=1}^{n=\infty} \sin \frac{m \pi x}{a} \sin \frac{n \pi y}{b} A_{mn} \quad (9).$$

And from equation (26) of article 55 we obtain

$$A_{mn} = \frac{4}{ab} \int_0^a \int_0^b w_0 \sin \frac{m \pi x}{a} \sin \frac{n \pi y}{b} dx \, dy \quad (10).$$

Also, by differentiating (6) to t, then putting $t = 0$ in the result, and equating to (8), we have

$$\dot{w}_0 = f_2(x, y) = \sum_{m=1}^{m=\infty} \sum_{n=1}^{n=\infty} \sin \frac{m \pi x}{a} \sin \frac{n \pi y}{b} p B_{mn} \quad (11),$$

where, by analogy from (10),

$$B_{mn} = \frac{4}{abp} \int_0^a \int_0^b \dot{w}_0 \sin \frac{m \pi x}{a} \sin \frac{n \pi y}{b} dx \, dy \quad (12).$$

Nodal Lines.—When either m or n is greater than unity, nodal lines will occur in the membrane, *i.e.* lines for which $w = 0$. Their positions are evidently given by

$$\left. \begin{array}{l} x = \dfrac{a}{m}, \dfrac{2a}{m}, \ . \ . \ . \ \dfrac{m-1}{m} a, \\[2mm] y = \dfrac{b}{n}, \dfrac{2b}{n}, \ . \ . \ . \ \dfrac{n-1}{n} b \end{array} \right\} \quad (13).$$

The nodal system therefore divides the rectangle into mn equal parts, in each of which the numerical values of w recur.

Frequency.—From equation (5) we see that the frequencies of the vibrations natural to the membrane are given by the following equation :—

$$N_{mn} = \frac{p}{2\pi} = \frac{c}{2} \sqrt{\frac{m^2}{a^2} + \frac{n^2}{b^2}} = \frac{1}{2} \sqrt{\frac{T}{\sigma} \left(\frac{m^2}{a^2} + \frac{n^2}{b^2} \right)} \quad (14).$$

In this any integral values may be ascribed to m and n.

193. Square Membranes.—To treat the case of square membranes, we have simply to write $b = a$ in the preceding equations. We may then find the frequencies and nodal lines by giving different values to m and n. This we shall do for a few of the simpler cases. For further particulars the works of Lord Rayleigh and of Riemann should be consulted. Thus the equation of motion may be written

$$w = \sin \frac{m\pi x}{a} \sin \frac{n\pi y}{a} \cos pt \qquad (15).$$

The frequencies are accordingly given by

$$N_{mn} = \frac{p}{2\pi} = \frac{c}{2a} \sqrt{m^2 + n^2} \qquad (16).$$

Prime Tone.—$m = n = 1$. The lowest tone, or fundamental, is given by putting $m = n = 1$. In this case we have

$$w = \sin \frac{\pi x}{a} \sin \frac{\pi y}{a} \cos pt \qquad (17),$$

and

$$N_{11} = \frac{c}{2a} \sqrt{2} \qquad (18),$$

where the subscripts of N denote the values of m and n. The lines which are always at rest are readily found by putting $w = 0$ for all values of t. Hence, for the present case, we obtain from (17)

$$\sin \frac{\pi x}{a} \sin \frac{\pi y}{a} = 0 \qquad (19).$$

This splits into $\sin \pi x/a = 0$ or $\sin \pi y/a = 0$. Hence equation (19) gives the lines whose equations are $x = 0$, $x = a$, $y = 0$, $y = a$; *i.e.* the sides of the square in question. Thus, as must be the case, there are no other nodal lines for the prime tone.

Second Tone.—The next higher tone is obtained by putting $m = 1$ and $n = 2$, or *vice versa*. In either case it is evident from (16) that the frequency is the same, and given by

$$N_{12} = N_{21} = \frac{c}{2a} \sqrt{5} \qquad (20).$$

Thus two distinct vibrations are possible whose periods are the same. If these two coexist, nodal lines will be obtained, provided the vibrations are of the same phase. For we may now represent the whole motion by the equation

$$w = \left\{ C \sin \frac{2\pi x}{a} \sin \frac{\pi y}{a} + D \sin \frac{\pi x}{a} \sin \frac{2\pi y}{a} \right\} \cos pt \quad (21).$$

To find the nodal lines put $w = 0$. We thus obtain

$$\sin \frac{\pi x}{a} \sin \frac{\pi y}{a} \left\{ C \cos \frac{\pi x}{a} + D \cos \frac{\pi y}{a} \right\} = 0 \qquad (22).$$

This expression vanishes for $\sin \dfrac{\pi x}{a} = 0$ or $\sin \dfrac{\pi y}{a} = 0$,

which give the edges of the membrane which must be nodal. On equating to zero the factor in the brackets, we obtain, in general, a curved line, which, however, always passes through the centre of the square. In special cases this reduces to a diameter or diagonal of the square. These are easily found by writing successively in (22), $C = 0$, $D = 0$, $C + D = 0$, $C = D$. For representations of the nodal lines see Table IX., which illustrates all the cases dealt with.

194. *Third Tone.*—The next case in order of pitch occurs when we write $m = n = 2$. The motion may be represented by

$$w = \sin \frac{2\pi x}{a} \sin \frac{2\pi y}{a} \cos pt \qquad (23).$$

And, in addition to the edges, the nodal lines are determined by

$$\cos \frac{\pi x}{a} \cos \frac{\pi y}{a} = 0 \text{ or } y = \frac{a}{2} \text{ and } x = \frac{a}{2} \qquad (24).$$

They are accordingly the two diameters. The frequency is expressed by

$$N_{22} = \frac{c}{2a} \sqrt{8} \qquad (25).$$

Fourth Tone.—Let us now write $m = 3$ and $n = 1$, or *vice versa.* The frequency is then given by

$$N_{13} = N_{31} = \frac{c}{2a} \sqrt{10} \qquad (26).$$

When the two vibrations coexist in the same phase, the whole motion may be written

$$w = \left\{ C \sin \frac{3\pi x}{a} \sin \frac{\pi y}{a} + D \sin \frac{\pi x}{a} \sin \frac{3\pi y}{a} \right\} \cos pt \quad (27).$$

From this, rejecting the factors $\sin \dfrac{\pi x}{a} \sin \dfrac{\pi y}{a}$, which correspond to the edges, we have for the internal nodal lines

$$C\left(4 \cos^2 \frac{\pi x}{a} - 1 \right) + D\left(4 \cos^2 \frac{\pi y}{a} - 1 \right) = 0 \quad (28).$$

From this equation we see that for any ratio of C/D, the curve passes through the four points given by $x = a/3$ or $2a/3$ and $y = a/3$ or $2a/3$. For $C = 0$ we have the two lines $y = a/3$ and $y = 2a/3$ as the nodal lines, for $D = 0$ we have instead $x = a/3$ and $x = 2a/3$. For $C + D = 0$ we obtain the two diagonals of the square $y = x$ and $y = a - x$. Lastly, for $C = D$ the equation of the nodal curve is

$$\cos^2 \frac{\pi x}{a} + \cos^2 \frac{\pi y}{a} = \frac{1}{2} \qquad (29).$$

This is a closed curve resembling a circle. Its diameters parallel to the sides of the square are $a/2$, while those along the diagonals are only $a\sqrt{2}/3$, *i.e.* $0\cdot4714$ instead of $0\cdot5$ of a. By giving to C/D different values any number of intermediate forms could be obtained.　Some of these

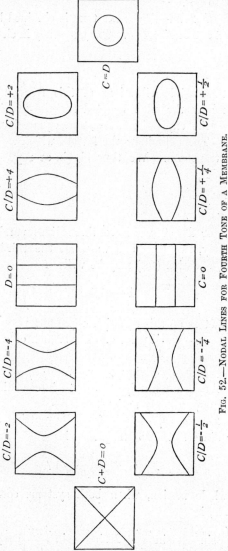

FIG. 52.—NODAL LINES FOR FOURTH TONE OF A MEMBRANE.

together with those noted above, are shown in Fig. 52,

which should be followed round by taking the lower line from right to left.

195. *Fifth Tone.*—The next tone is obtained by putting $m = 2$ and $n = 3$ or *vice versa*. The frequency in either case is

$$N_{23} = N_{32} = \frac{c}{2a} \sqrt{13} \qquad (30).$$

When both possible vibrations of this frequency coexist, we may follow the plan adopted for the previous tones. Thus, write the expression for w, and equate it to zero for the nodes. Then eliminate the factors which represent the edges and transform. We thus obtain as representing the internal nodes,

$$C\left(4 \cos^2 \frac{\pi x}{a} - 1 \right) \cos \frac{\pi y}{a} + D \cos \frac{\pi x}{a}\left(4 \cos^2 \frac{\pi y}{a} - 1 \right) = 0 \ (31).$$

For $C = 0$ or $D = 0$ we have three lines parallel to the edges, namely, two lines one way and the third across it. For $C = D$, equation (31) may be written

$$\left(\cos \frac{\pi x}{a} + \cos \frac{\pi y}{a} \right) \left(4 \cos \frac{\pi x}{a} \cos \frac{\pi y}{a} - 1 \right) = 0 \qquad (32).$$

The two factors of this equation represent respectively the diagonal $y = a - x$ and parts of each branch of a hyperbolic curve. For $C = -D$ we have the same pattern about the diagonal $y = x$. By giving to the ratio C/D other values, we could obtain any number of curves intermediate between the simple ones already noticed.

Sixth Tone.—This is obtained by putting $m = 1$ and $n = 4$, or *vice versa*. The frequency is

$$N_{14} = N_{41} = \frac{c}{2a} \sqrt{17} \qquad (33).$$

The whole motion, when both systems coexist in the same phase, is

$$w = \left\{ c \sin \frac{4\pi x}{a} \sin \frac{\pi y}{a} + D \sin \frac{\pi x}{a} \sin \frac{4\pi y}{a} \right\} \cos pt \quad (34).$$

The nodal system is given by equating to zero the quantity in the brackets. Omitting the factors $\sin \dfrac{\pi x}{a}$ $\sin \dfrac{\pi y}{a}$, which represent the edges, this reduces to

$$C \cos \frac{\pi x}{a} \cos \frac{2\pi x}{a} + D \cos \frac{\pi y}{a} \cos \frac{2\pi y}{a} = 0 \quad (35).$$

For $C = 0$, this gives three equidistant lines parallel to the axis of x. For $D = 0$, the corresponding system parallel to the axis of y is obtained. Take, thirdly, the case of $C = D$. It is then convenient to transform $\cos \dfrac{\pi x}{a} \cos \dfrac{2\pi x}{a}$ to $2 \cos^3 \dfrac{\pi x}{a} - \cos \dfrac{\pi x}{a}$, and the same with the factors involving y. Collecting like powers of the cosines, equation (35) then becomes

$$2\left(\cos^3 \frac{\pi x}{a} + \cos^3 \frac{\pi y}{a}\right) - \left(\cos \frac{\pi x}{a} + \cos \frac{\pi y}{a}\right) = 0,$$

or,

$$\left(\cos \frac{\pi x}{a} + \cos \frac{\pi y}{a}\right) \times$$

$$\left(1 + 2 \cos \frac{\pi x}{a} \cos \frac{\pi y}{a} - 2 \cos^2 \frac{\pi x}{a} - 2 \cos^2 \frac{\pi y}{a}\right) = 0 \quad (36).$$

The first factor, equated to zero, gives the diagonal $y = a - x$. The second factor gives a closed curve passing through the points

$$\left(\frac{a}{2}, \frac{a}{4}\right), \left(\frac{a}{4}, \frac{a}{4}\right), \left(\frac{a}{4}, \frac{a}{2}\right), \left(\frac{a}{2}, \frac{3}{4}a\right), \left(\frac{3}{4}a, \frac{3}{4}a\right), \text{ and } \left(\frac{3}{4}a, \frac{a}{2}\right).$$

For $C = -D$, the same system is obtained about the other diagonal $y = x$.

Seventh Tone.—The last tone we shall notice is that obtained by writing $m = n = 3$. The frequency is given by

$$N_{33} = \frac{c}{2a} \sqrt{18} \quad (37).$$

As m and n are equal no variety can be effected by their interchange. It is evident also, without writing the equation, that the single pattern of internal nodal lines is a set of four straight lines, namely, two equidistant with the edges parallel to the axis of x, and two others similarly situated with respect to the axis of y.

196. Summary of the Various Cases.—The relative frequencies, values of m and n, and typical diagrams of the nodal lines for a square membrane, are collected together in Table IX. It thus serves as a compact summary of all the chief cases hitherto discussed. The relative frequencies in the first column are the values of $\sqrt{m^2 + n^2} \div \sqrt{1^2 + 1^2}$, and so give the ratio of frequency of each tone to that of the prime for the same membrane.

197. Circular Membranes.—The mathematical treatment of circular membranes is far more difficult than that of rectangular ones, and cannot be given here. It is fully discussed by Rayleigh. The nodal lines are shown to be either concentric circles or diameters, the ends of the latter being equidistant. The prime tone has, of course, no nodal line except the boundary itself. In the order of ascending frequencies the nodal patterns of the other tones are as follows:—One diameter, two diameters, one circle, radius 0·436 that of the membrane, three diameters, one diameter and one circle, of radius 0·546, four diameters, two diameters and one circle, of radii 0·601, two circles, of radii 0·278 and 0·638, five diameters, three diameters and one circle, of radius 0·654, six diameters, etc. The relative frequencies of the corresponding tones, including the prime, are 1, 1·594, 2·136, 2·296, 2·653, 2·918, 3·156, 3·501, 3·600, 3·652, 4·060, and 4·154.

Experimental researches upon the vibrations of membranes have been made by a number of physicists, and have given results which, in their main features, are in harmony with theory. Many discrepancies have, however, been detected owing to various disturbing causes not allowed

TABLE IX.—VIBRATIONS OF SQUARE MEMBRANES

Tones and their Relative Frequencies	Values of Constants		Diagrams of Typical Nodal Lines
	m	n	
Prime, 1	1	1	
Second, 1·58	1	2	$C=0$ $D=0$ $C+D=0$ $C=D$ $D=-2C$
	2	1	
	1 2	2 1	
Third, 2	2	2	
Fourth, 2·24	1	3	$C=0$ $D=0$ $C+D=0$ $C=D$
	3 1 3	1 3 1	
Fifth, 2·55	2	3	$C=0$ $D=0$ $C+D=0$ $C=D$
	3	2	
	2 3	3 2	
Sixth, 2·98	1	4	$C=0$ $D=0$ $C+D=0$ $C=D$
	4 1 4	1 4 1	
Seventh, 3	3	3	

for in the theory. Membranes have been tried made of paper wetted and glued to wood rings. Drum-skins have been used and even soap films also. In the case of soap films, the nodal lines have been detected by interference of light. With the solid membranes sand is used to indicate the nodes. The performance of any of these experiments, however, appears to be a matter of considerable difficulty.

198. Transverse Vibrations of Bars.—Anything like a full treatment of bars vibrating transversely is beyond the scope of this work. For that the reader is referred to Lord Rayleigh's *Theory of Sound*, to which the writer is so much indebted for what follows. We shall restrict ourselves to the case of a bar of uniform section, not subject to tension, and straight when left at rest free from external forces. We shall further suppose that the curvatures are so small as to be represented by d^2y/dx^2, and to leave the lengths along the bar and along the axis of x practically equal. We shall neglect gravity in comparison with the elastic forces, and, finally, shall take the rotatory inertia of the bar as negligible in comparison with the inertia due to translation. This is practically the case for thin bars, since the inertia of translation varies as the thickness simply, while the inertia of rotation varies as the cube of the thickness. In other words, the two inertias in question vary as the section and as its moment of inertia respectively. Before proceeding to derive the differential equation of motion, some preliminary steps must be taken. These are dealt with in order.

Bending Moment.—In attacking the problem we need, at the outset, an expression for the bending moment or couple required to bend a bar to a given curvature of radius R say. Let the bar be bent in the plane of xy, then there is in it, perpendicular to this plane, a *neutral surface* which is neither extended nor contracted. Outside this neutral surface extension occurs, inside it contraction. Consider an element of the bar of length x, distant η radially from the neutral surface. Then, by the bending of the bar to the radius R, the length of this element becomes $x + dx$ where $\dfrac{x + dx}{R + \eta} = \dfrac{x}{R} = \dfrac{dx}{\eta}$. Thus, the fractional elongation of the element is given by $dx/x = \eta/R$. Hence, by definition of Young's modulus, here denoted by q, the tensile force on this element of cross section dS is $q\eta dS/R$. The bending moment is, of course, found by multiplying this expression by η the distance from the neutral surface, and integrating over the whole cross section of area ω say. Then, writing κ for the radius of gyration of the cross section about its intersection with the neutral surface, we obtain for the bending moment

$$M = \int q\eta^2 dS/R = q\omega\kappa^2/R = q\omega\kappa^2 d^2y/dx^2 \qquad (1).$$

199. Bending Moments and Forces on a Bar at Rest.—Laying aside all attempt at complete generality, let us take the next step in the problem by finding a relation between the bending moment, the shearing forces, and the applied forces on a bar by the following method. Consider the bar bent in the plane of xy, and in equilibrium under given forces. Let it have a free end at the origin of co-ordinates and lie almost along the axis of x, the further end being maintained at rest by clamps or any other convenient arrangements (see Fig. 53). Then suppose, first, an isolated

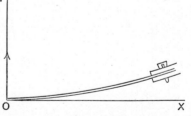

FIG. 53.—BAR BENT BY FORCE AT END.

force f_1 to act at the origin along the axis of y. The shearing force in the bar is accordingly f_1 at every point up to where it is clamped, but the bending moment at x is $f_1 x$. That is, the bending moment is zero at the origin, and increases with x at the rate f_1 per unit length along x. Thus, if M denotes the bending moment, we have $M = f_1 x$ and $dM/dx = f_1$. Or, if M be plotted as a graph,

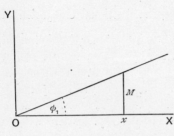

FIG. 54.—BENDING MOMENT OF BAR WITH FORCE AT ORIGIN.

we obtain a straight line through the origin at an angle ϕ_1 with the axis of x, where $\tan \phi_1 = f_1$ (see Fig. 54). Next, at x_2, between the origin and x, let a second force f_2 act together with, and parallel to, the force f_1 at the origin. Then the graph for M consists of two straight lines, their junction occurring over the point x_2 where the second force is applied. The bending moment at x, where $x > x_2$, is now given by $M = f_1 x + f_2(x - x_2)$, and is thus dependent on x_2, the place of application of the second force. But, as seen from the equation or the graph shown in Fig. 55, the *rate of increase* of M is independent of x_2 and depends only on the *sum of the forces*.

Thus, for values of x exceeding x_2, $dM/dx = f_1 + f_2$. Or,

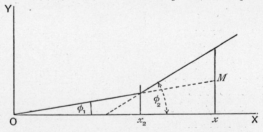

FIG. 55.—BENDING MOMENTS DUE TO TWO FORCES.

if the angle of the final part of the graph is ϕ_2, then $\tan \phi_2 = f_1 + f_2$. Hence, for any number of isolated forces applied along the bar between the origin and x, we have

$$dM/dx = f_1 + f_2 + f_3 + \ldots = F \text{ say} \qquad (2).$$

In other words, if the magnitudes of the forces are specified, the space rate of increase of M is determinate and equals their sum, although the actual value of M is unknown unless the positions of all the forces are given also. It is obvious that this sum F of all forces, applied between the origin and x, is also the shearing force on the bar at x.

200. Now, suppose forces to be continuously applied between the origin and x, and beyond x also. Then, the broken straight-line graph gives place to a continuous curve, and F becomes the integral of the forces acting between the origin and x. But we still have $dM/dx = F$, and, since F is now itself a continuous function of x, we may differentiate it and so obtain

$$d^2M/dx^2 = dF/dx = f \text{ say} \qquad (3).$$

Further, this rate of increase of F per unit length of x, denoted by f, is obviously the value per unit length at x of the impressed forces to whose sum that shearing force F is due. Hence, though the bending moment itself depends upon the magnitudes and positions of forces acting elsewhere, and the first derivative of the bending moment equals the sum of all the forces acting up to that point, the second derivative of the bending moment at any point equals the applied force per unit length acting there, and is independent of all other considerations. This is the important relation sought, for the equation of motion is a relation between displacement and acceleration, and the latter is proportional to the force on the element. Thus we need to express the force in terms of the displacement, and by means of the bending moment this is now possible.

201. But, before passing to the differential equation, some readers may prefer to illustrate and check the relations just obtained. This may be suitably done by taking, as the impressed force, any simple characteristic function of the length. Then, by integration, find F and M, whence by differentiation the original function is returned to as the value of the impressed force.   To find M it is advisable to find first M_0 for x_0, and then drop the subscript.

Example I.—Let the force f per unit length be px^n.

Then
$$F = \int_0^x px^n dx = \frac{px^{n+1}}{n+1}.$$

Also, for the bending moment, we have

$$M_0 = \int_0^{x_0} px^n(x_0 - x)dx = \frac{px_0^{n+2}}{(n+1)(n+2)}, \text{ whence } M.$$

Then, by differentiating, we find

$$dM/dx = \frac{px^{n+1}}{n+1} = F,$$

and $$d^2M/dx^2 = dF/dx = px^n = f.$$

Example II.—Let the force f per unit length be $p \sin x$.

Then $$F = \int_0^x p \sin x dx = p(1 - \cos x),$$

and $$M_0 = p \int_0^{x_0} \sin x(x_0 - x)dx = p(x_0 - \sin x_0), \text{ whence } M.$$

Thus $$dM/dx = p(1 - \cos x) = F,$$

and $$d^2M/dx^2 = dF/dx = p \sin x = f.$$

It should be noted that if a uniform force p per unit length were taken, then the final result p would be ambiguous.   For, though p is truly the force at x, it is not characteristic of that point only, but is also the force anywhere and the mean of the forces everywhere.   The above two examples were so chosen as to avoid any such uncertainty.

202. Differential Equation of Motion.—We have now seen, for a bent bar in equilibrium, what relation holds between the impressed force f per unit length at a point, and the bending moment there. Suppose now that all the impressed forces are suddenly removed, then, at each point x there will be an acceleration proportional to the reverse force $-f$, due to the difference of shearing forces in the element and which previously balanced the impressed force on the same element.

We may thus write

$$\omega\rho\, d^2y/dt^2 = -f \tag{4},$$

where ρ is the density of the material.

Then equations (1), (3), and (4) give

$$\frac{d^2y}{dt^2} + \kappa^2 b^2 \frac{d^4y}{dx^4} = 0 \tag{5},$$

where $b = \sqrt{q/\rho}$ is the speed of longitudinal waves in the bar. This equation is identical with that obtained by Lord Rayleigh from the full equation after discarding the rotatory inertia. Thus, reviewing the argument, its steps may be summarised as follows:—Considering any point in the bar, (1) The acceleration there is proportional and opposite to the force which must be applied to keep it at rest in its then bent state. (2) This force is the first derivative of the shearing force and the second derivative of the bending moment, both with respect to x. (3) The bending moment is proportional to the second derivative, with respect to x, of the displacement y. (4) Thus, the displacement being taken as the dependent variable, its second derivative, with respect to t, is proportional to its fourth derivative with respect to x, or

$$d^2y/dt^2 \propto d^4y/dx^4.$$

And it is this relation that, with the correct coefficient inserted, constitutes the differential coefficient of motion of the bar, which must be satisfied at every point and at every instant. We need in addition other equations for the ends of the bar.

203. Conditions at Ends.—The ends may be fixed, free

or "supported." At a fixed end it is clear that we have, for all values of t,

(*Fixed End*) $\qquad y = 0$ and $dy/dx = 0 \qquad\qquad$ (6).

At a free end, on the contrary, y and dy/dx are arbitrary. But, as there is nothing beyond to produce a couple or transmit force, there can be at the end neither bending moment nor shearing force. Thus it follows from equations (1) and (2) that we have always at a

(*Free End*) $\qquad \dfrac{d^2y}{dx^2} = 0$ and $\dfrac{d^3y}{dx^3} = 0 \qquad\qquad$ (7).

We may also consider what is called a supported end, that is, an end in which no displacement is allowed, but any slope whatever may be assumed. In this case the only external force added by the constraint is applied at the end and consequently has no moment there. Thus there can be no curvature at the supported end. Hence we have the conditions

(*Supported End*) $\quad y = 0$ and $\dfrac{d^2y}{dx^2} = 0 \qquad\qquad$ (8).

Since each end of the bar may be of any one of these three types, we have six cases in all. These may be classed as follows :—

(1) Both ends fixed. (2) Both ends free. (3) Both ends supported. (4) One end fixed and one free. (5) One end free and one supported. (6) One end supported and one fixed.

204. Solution of Equations.—The full working of the solution of these equations (5)-(8) is somewhat beyond the scope of this work. But, following the method of Lord Rayleigh, we shall establish the essential features of the problem, and quote some of the other more important results which have been obtained. Assume first that the motion is harmonic. Then y may be expressed as a sine or cosine function of the time. Thus, let us put

$$y = u \cos \left(\frac{\kappa b}{l^2} m^2 t \right) \qquad (9),$$

where l is the length of the bar and m is an abstract number to be determined afterwards. Substituting from (9) in (5) we find

$$\frac{d^4 u}{dx^4} = \frac{m^4 u}{l^4} \qquad (10).$$

Suppose $u = e^{pmx/l}$ is a solution of this. Then, on differentiating, we find $p^4 = 1$, *i.e.*, $p = \pm \sqrt{-1}$ or ± 1. Thus u can be represented as the sum of four terms each involving one of the values of p and an arbitrary coefficient. Accordingly, after a little transformation, we may write

$$u = A \cos \frac{mx}{l} + B \sin \frac{mx}{l} + Ce^{mx/l} + De^{-mx/l} \quad (11).$$

This, with (9), is a solution of (5). Before proceeding to fit it to equations (6), (7), and (8), let us discuss it a little. The simplest case is when the motion is strictly periodic with respect to x. Then C and D vanish, and if the wave length, period, and frequency are denoted respectively by λ, τ, and N, we have the following results :—

$$2\pi/\lambda = m/l \text{ or } \lambda = 2\pi l/m \qquad (12),$$

$$2\pi/\tau = \kappa b m^2/l^2 \text{ or } \tau = 2\pi l^2/\kappa b m^2 = \lambda^2/2\pi\kappa b \quad (13),$$

$$\text{and } N = \frac{\kappa b m^2}{2\pi l^2} = m^2 \frac{\kappa}{2\pi l^2} \sqrt{q/\rho} \qquad (14).$$

205. The first of these three equations shows that the wave length varies directly as the length of the bar, and inversely as m. While the last of the three shows that the frequency of any given tone, in the series possible, varies—

(1) Directly as the radius of gyration, and therefore as the thickness of the bar for a given shape of section.

(2) Directly as the square root of the Young's modulus for the material.

(3) Inversely as the square of the length of the bar.

(4) Inversely as the square root of the density of the material.

Whereas the frequencies of the various tones in the series for a given bar vary directly as the square of m.

Reverting now to equations (6), (7), and (8), if the rod extends from $x = 0$ to $x = l$, we see that the terminal conditions afford us four equations, two for each end of the rod. To complete the solution, the constants in (11) must satisfy these four equations. We may thus obtain the three ratios $A : B : C : D$ and derive in addition an equation which must be satisfied by m. The roots of this last equation give the values of m which are alone admissible. And, for each m so found, the corresponding u is determined in everything save a constant multiplier which must be fixed by the initial state.

206. Initial Conditions.—Now the initial conditions of the bar may be specified by the displacement and velocity of each point at $t = 0$. These two conditions would give the coefficient or amplitude of each component of the motion and also its phase. Or, if the motion were represented as the sum of sine and cosine terms, these two conditions would give the values of the two sets of coefficients.

Thus, if we write the general value of y as follows :—

$$y = u_1\left(A_1 \cos \frac{\kappa b}{l^2}m_1^2 t + B_1 \sin \frac{\kappa b}{l^2}m_1^2 t\right)$$

$$+ u_2\left(A_2 \cos \frac{\kappa b}{l^2}m_2^2 t + B_2 \sin \frac{\kappa b}{l^2}m_2^2 t\right)$$

$$+ \ldots + \ldots + \ldots \tag{15},$$

we should have initially

$$y_0 = A_1 u_1 + A_2 u_2 + \ldots + \ldots \qquad (16),$$

$$\text{and } \dot{y}_0 = \frac{\kappa b}{l^2} \left\{ m_1{}^2 B_1 u_1 + m_2{}^2 B_2 u_2 + \ldots + \ldots \right\} \quad (17).$$

And, it may be shown (Rayleigh's *Theory of Sound*, vol. i. §§ 164–168) that, multiplying these equations by u_r and integrating over the length of the bar,

$$\int u_r u_s dx = 0, \text{ and therefore}$$

$$\int y_0 u_r dx = A_r \int u_r{}^2 dx \qquad (18).$$

Similarly, from (17)

$$\frac{l^2}{\kappa b} \int \dot{y}_0 u_r dx = m_r{}^2 B_r \int u_r{}^2 dx \qquad (19).$$

These two equations, (18) and (19), serve to determine the arbitrary constants A_r and B_r to fit any given initial conditions defined by y_0 and $\dot{y}_0$ in the left sides of (16) and (17). They accordingly finish the solution except for the examination of the equations which determine the series of values of m and the ratios $A : B : C : D$. These depend upon the conditions at the ends, of which there are six cases as enumerated at the end of article 203. Of these six we shall work in detail two cases only, viz. that with both ends fixed and that with one end fixed and one free.

207. Free-Free Bar.—Beginning with the bar free at each end, let us rewrite equation (11) as follows, x' denoting mx/l :—

$$u = A \cos x' + B \sin x' + C(\cosh x' + \sinh x')$$
$$+ D(\cosh x' - \sinh x')$$

or, $u = P(\cos x' + \cosh x') + Q(\cos x' - \cosh x')$
$$+ R(\sin x' + \sinh x') + S(\sin x' - \sinh x') \qquad (20).$$

This is identical with (11) provided that

$$2P = A + C + D, \ 2Q = A - C - D, \ 2R = B + C - D$$
$$\text{and } 2S = B - C + D.$$

The advantage of the form of expression used in (20), as pointed out by Lord Rayleigh, is that the four quantities in the brackets repeat themselves on differentiation and vanish with x' except $\cos x' + \cosh x'$ which equals 2 for $x' = 0$. It must be borne in mind that $\cosh x = \frac{1}{2}(e^x + e^{-x})$ and $\sinh x = \frac{1}{2}(e^x - e^{-x})$, and that accordingly $\frac{d}{dx} \cosh x = \sinh x$ and $\frac{d}{dx} \sinh x = \cosh x$.

Now, for the bar free at both ends and extending from $x = 0$ to $x = l$, we have to apply at each end the two conditions given in equation (7). Thus, for the end at the origin, we must differentiate equation (20) twice with respect to x, put $x = 0$, and equate the result to zero. And similarly for the second condition in (7), differentiating this time thrice with respect to x. These operations give

$$Q = 0, \text{ and } S = 0 \qquad (21).$$

We have now to follow the same method for the other end, but can omit to begin with the terms involving the constants Q and S, already shown to be each zero. Hence we have

$$u = P(\cos x' + \cosh x') + R(\sin x' + \sinh x') \quad (22).$$

Differentiating this twice and thrice respectively, and putting $x = l$, *i.e.* $x' = m$, and equating to zero, we obtain

$$P(-\cos m + \cosh m) + R(-\sin m + \sinh m) = 0 \left.\right\}$$
$$\text{and } P(\sin m + \sinh m) + R(-\cos m + \cosh m) = 0 \quad \left.\right\} \ (23).$$

These two equations give two expressions for the ratio $P : R$, and enable us by equating them to find m. Thus, omitting a constant multiplier, we may write from the second form of (23),

$$u = (\cos m - \cosh m)(\cos x' + \cosh x')$$
$$+ (\sin m + \sinh m)(\sin x' + \sinh x')\quad(24),$$

or a corresponding and equivalent expression from the first form of the same equation.

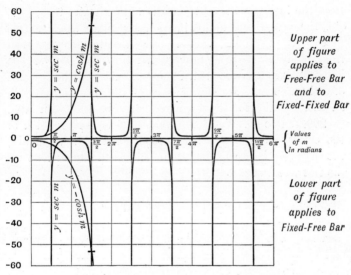

Fig. 56.—Graphical Solution of $\sec m = \pm \cosh m$.

The simple harmonic component of this type may be denoted by

$$y = Ku \cos\left(\frac{\kappa b}{l^2} m^2 t + \epsilon\right)\quad(25),$$

in which, when m is known, the K and ϵ are easily expressible in terms of the A's and B's of equation (15).

208. Series of Tones.—We further derive from the two equations (23) the following relation :—

$$\left.\begin{array}{l}\cos m \cosh m = 1, \\ \sec m = \cosh m\end{array}\right\}\quad(26).$$

or,

This may be solved by the aid of tables of hyperbolic cosines, or by a method of expansions and successive approximations. It may also be solved graphically as follows :—Take the second form of (26) and plot the graphs $y = \cosh m$ and $y = \sec m$. Then the values of m at their intersections will give the roots of m sought. It will be seen from the upper part of Fig. 56 that, apart from the first value zero, the series approximates to 3, 5, 7, etc., times $\pi/2$, the approximation becoming closer as we proceed to the higher values. Now the frequency, as seen from equation (25), is proportional to m^2, hence for the higher values the frequencies approximate to the squares of odd numbers. The lower part of the diagram refers to another equation for the fixed-free bar to be dealt with later.

209. Table X. gives the values of m, the relation of the corresponding frequencies proportional to m^2, and also the intervals between the prime and each higher tone for the free-free bar.

TABLE X.—TONES FOR FREE-FREE BAR (*or Fixed-Fixed Bar*)

Values of m.	Relative Frequencies, $(N/N_1) \propto m^2$.	Intervals from Prime to each Higher Tone.	Approximate Notes.
		Octaves, Equal Semitones	
$m_0 = 0$	...		...
$m_1 = 4\cdot73$	1	...	C
$m_2 = 7\cdot85$	2·756	1 and 5·52	F′♯
$m_3 = 10\cdot996$	5·404	2 and 5·23	F″
$m_4 = 14\cdot137$	8·933	3 and 1·91	D‴
$m_5 = 17\cdot279$	13·345	3 and 8·86	A‴

The first column of Table X. is from Rayleigh's *Sound*, the values being obtained by computation. The second column is derived from the first by squaring and reducing the prime tone to unity. To reduce relative frequencies to equal semitones, in order to obtain the third column, we may write

$$s = k \log (N'/N),$$

where s is the number of mean semitones in the interval between the tones whose frequencies are N' and N and k, some constant. Then, obviously, we have $12 = k \log 2$. Whence

$$s = \frac{12 \log (N'/N)}{\log 2} \qquad (27).$$

This gives the third column of the table from which the fourth easily follows, the accents representing successive higher octaves, though the letters must not be taken as denoting any absolute pitch, but are all relative only. It is thus seen that the series of tones rises much more rapidly than those of either an open organ pipe or a stretched string fixed at the ends. Further, they depart utterly from the simple relation constituting the harmonic series. From equations (14) and (25) and the table above for the values of the m's, we can obtain the actual frequency of any tone for a given bar. Thus, let the prime tone be required for a free-free bar of steel of rectangular section of thickness a cm., and length l cm., then $\kappa = a/\sqrt{12}$, $\sqrt{q/\rho} = 523,700$ cm./sec $= b$, whence $N_1 = 538,400 \ (a/l^2)$ per second. Multiplying this value by the other numbers in column 2 of Table X., we obtain at once the other tones for the same bar.

Fixed-Fixed Bar.—On applying the proper conditions, equation (6), article 203, for a bar fixed at each end, it will be found that the same series of tones is obtained as for one free at each end.

210. Nodes for Free-Free Bar.—By inserting any one value of m in equations (24) and (25), the displacement curve at any instant may be obtained for that type of vibration. Hence, also, the nodes or points of no displacement can be found. The work is, however, somewhat long, and will not be reproduced here. It must suffice to quote the results as to position of nodes found by Rayleigh for the free-free bar. The theoretical distances of the nodes from one end in fractions of the bar's length are—

TABLE XI.—THEORETICAL NODAL POSITIONS

First tone .	0·2242	...	...	0·7758
Second tone .	0·1321	0·5	...	0·8679
Third tone .	0·0944	0·3558	0·6442	0·9056
The nth tone	$\left\{\dfrac{1\cdot3222}{4n+2}\right.$	$\dfrac{4\cdot9820}{4n+2}$	$\dfrac{9\cdot0007}{4n+2}$	$\dfrac{4j-3}{4n+2}$

The last term in the last line indicates the position of the j-th node from the end when the bar is producing the n-th tone. This does not apply to the few nodes near the end.

EXPT. 31. *Vibrations of Free-Free Bar.*—These phenomena can be suitably illustrated by means of a steel bar supported at one pair of nodes by little pads of india-rubber. The one used at Nottingham was supplied by Mr. Joseph Goold, and is 29 inches long, $1\frac{1}{4}$ inch wide, and $\frac{1}{2}$ inch thick. It may be excited by an ordinary bow, or by the special generators designed by Mr. Goold and described in the next chapter. The presence and positions of the nodes are best indicated by chalk grated upon the bar by a sharp-edged stick or by carbonate of magnesia. The bar should be kept vaselined when out of use. Before use it must be scrupulously cleaned, the last trace of grease being removed by india-rubber. The closeness of the agreement between experimental and theoretical results for this bar is shown in the accompanying Table XII.

[TABLE

TABLE XII.—ACTUAL FREE-FREE BAR COMPARED WITH THEORY

No. of Tone.	Actual Frequencies.		Relative Theoretical Frequencies.	Distance of Nodes from nearer End according to Theory (Actual Values in Brackets).			
	Per Second.	Relative.					
1	126[1]	1	1	0·2242 (0·224 and 0·223)			
2	350	2·7777	2·756	0·1321 (0·134 and 0·13)	0·5 (·504 and ·496)		
3	686	5·4444	5·404	0·0944 (0·095) (0·091)	0·3558 (0·359) (0·349)		
4	1134	9·0000	8·933	0·0734 (0·0759) (0·718)	0·277 (0·2812) (0·293)	0·5 (·507)	
5	1696	13·4603	13·345	0·0601 (0·063) (0·0596)	0·2265 (0·232) (0·222)	0·4091 (0·4146) (0·4037)	
6	2366	18·7777	18·63	0·0509 (0·053) (0·0504)	0·192 (0·1951) (0·1885)	0·3462 (0·351) (0·3416)	0·5 (0·505)
7	3150	25·0000	24·24	0·0441 (0·046) (0·0438)	0·1661 (0·1684) (0·163)	0·3002 (0·306) (0·294)	0·4333 (0·438) (0·426)

211. Fixed-Free Bar.—Let the bar be fixed at $x = 0$ and free at $x = l$. Then we have to determine the constants in equations (20) consistently with equation (6) for $x = 0$, and equation (7) for $x = l$. Thus for $y = 0$ at $x = 0$ we

[1] The theoretical frequency of the prime as determined by equations (25) and (26) is 126·03 per second.

find $P = 0$. Again for $dy/dx = 0$ at $x = 0$ we find $R = 0$. Thus, equation (20) reduces to

$$u = Q (\cos x' - \cosh x') + S (\sin x' - \sinh x') \quad (28).$$

This has now to be made to satisfy $d^2y/dx^2 = 0$, and $d^3y/dx^3 = 0$ for $x = l$, *i.e.* for $x' = m$.

These conditions give

$$\left.\begin{array}{l} Q (\cos m + \cosh m) + S (\sin m + \sinh m) = 0, \\ \text{and } Q (- \sin m + \sinh m) + S (\cos m + \cosh m) = 0 \end{array}\right\} \quad (29).$$

From these we have two expressions for the ratio Q/S. Hence, omitting a constant multiplier, we may write

$$\begin{aligned} u = &(\cos m + \cosh m) (\cos x' - \cosh x') \\ &+ (\sin m - \sinh m) (\sin x' - \sinh x') \end{aligned} \quad (30),$$

from the second equation of (29), or a similar equation from the first. Further, by equating the two expressions for Q/S from (29), we find an equation to determine m, viz.

$$\left.\begin{array}{l} \cos m \cosh m + 1 = 0, \\ \text{or, } \qquad \sec m = - \cosh m \end{array}\right\} \quad (31).$$

The second form of (31) is convenient for graphical solution and is illustrated in the lower half of Fig. 56. From this it is seen that the values of m are approximately as the odd values of $\pi/2$, the approximation at first being somewhat rough, but rapidly becoming very close with higher values. The frequencies of the possible tones are as the squares of these numbers. Table XIII. gives the values of m obtained by Rayleigh, together with the intervals, also the odd values of $\pi/2$ for comparison with the m's.

[TABLE

TABLE XIII.—TONES FOR FIXED-FREE BAR

Odd Values of $\pi/2$.	Values of m.	Relative Frequencies. $N \propto m^2$.	Intervals from Prime to each Higher Tone.	Approximate Notes.
1·571	$m_1 = 1\cdot875$	1	Octaves, Equal Semitones	C
4·712	$m_2 = 4\cdot694$	6·267	2 and 7·77	$G''\sharp$
7·854	$m_3 = 7\cdot855$	17·55	4 and 1·60	D^{iv}
10·996	$m_4 = 10\cdot996$	34·39	5 and 1·24	$D^{v}\flat$
14·137	$m_5 = 14\cdot137$	56·85	5 and 9·95	$B^{v}\flat$
17·279	$m_6 = 17\cdot279$	84·93	6 and 4·90	F^{vi}

212. Nodes for Fixed-Free Bar.—The distances of the nodes from the free end of a bar fixed at the other end, as found by Seebeck and by Donkin, are as follows :—

> *Second tone,* 0·2261
> *Third tone,* 0·1321, 0·4999
> *Fourth tone,* 0·0944, 0·3558, 0·6439
> *nth tone,* $\dfrac{1\cdot322}{4n-2}$, $\dfrac{4\cdot9820}{4n-2}$, $\dfrac{9\cdot0007}{4n-2}$ . . .

$$\frac{4j-3}{4n-2}, \quad \cdots \quad \frac{4n-10\cdot9993}{4n-2}, \quad \frac{4n-7\cdot0175}{4n-2}.$$

For the nth tone, the first three nodes and the last two are given numerically, that involving j being the general term for a jth node intermediate between the other two sets.

EXPT. 32. *Nodes on Large Tuning-Fork.*—It is interesting to compare the theoretical results with the positions found for the nodes of a tuning-fork when higher tones are elicited. For this purpose the fork should be taken out of its resonance box which encourages the fundamental tone and that only. It may be laid with its stalk on a massive table and there held by the hands of an assistant, the prongs projecting horizontally from the edge of the table, one being exactly over the other. The fork should now be bowed at the end while a finger is lightly applied to the prong at various distances from the end. In this way higher tones may be elicited, and the positions of the nodes shown by chalk dust scattered on the prong. An UT_2 fork of 128 per second was examined by this method. Its prongs were $10\frac{15}{16}$ inches long to the inside of the hollow between them, or say 11 inches to the point which would remain at rest. Then, with the second tone, a node was found $2\frac{3}{8}$ inches from the end, *i.e.* 0·216 of its length, which compares well with the theoretical value 0·2261. On placing two fingers in the right positions as found by trial and bowing suitably, the third tone was elicited. The nodes were at 1·5 and 5·5 inches respectively from the end. This gives 0·136 and 0·5 of the length of the prong, which again are close to the theoretical values of 0·1321 and 0·4999.

If it is only desired to elicit and hear the higher partials of a tuning-fork, this may be effected as follows without removing from its resonance box :—Touch one prong lightly with the edge of a piece of cork at a node and tap the same prong at an antinode with a padded hammer.

213. Simpler Methods for Fixed-Free Bar.—In his *Theory of Sound*, Rayleigh has shown that the dependence of the frequency of a fixed-free bar upon its material and dimensions may be established by a simpler method, and even the absolute value of the frequency closely approximated. The method consists in supposing that the vibration curve of the bar is that in which the bar would dispose itself if statically deflected by a force applied at its free extremity or some other point along it. The expressions for the potential and kinetic energies of the bar are then quoted from a former article where they were obtained by the calculus of variations. It is thus found that the frequency varies as $\kappa b/l^2$, the symbols having their previous meanings. Further, if the bar be supposed pulled aside at the free end and at one-quarter its length from the free end respectively, the corresponding periods thus calculated have the values 0·98556 and 0·9977 of the true value calculated by the fuller theory. In other words, the pitches found by the approximate methods are too sharp. Rayleigh points out that the bar when vibrating cannot really assume the curve of one deflected by a force at the end, since this curve

violates one of the conditions for a free end, viz.—
$d^3y/dx^3 = 0$.

214. In 1904, C. A. B. Garrett gave to this theory a
still more elementary form, and also found experimentally
for a particular bar the best place for the deflecting force.
The experimental part consisted of two portions—one photo-
graphical, the other microscopical. The bar was set
vibrating and then instantaneously photographed. It was
next deflected with the same *end* displacement and photographed at rest, the camera occupying the same position as
at first. This was done with the deflecting force at the
end, one-tenth, one-fifth, and three-tenths from the end
respectively. The photographs showed the best agreement
for the force at one-fifth. The second method of examination was based on the following consideration :—If the bar
when deflected by a force at a certain place assumed the
form it had when vibrating so as to give its prime tone,
then as the vibrations died away the amplitudes at any
place, say the middle of the bar, would die away continuously. If, however, the bar, when held pulled aside,
assumed a curve distinctly different from that when
vibrating for its fundamental, then the vibrations from that
time will consist of the prime *plus* certain upper partials or
overtones. And these higher forms of vibration would be
of periods incommensurate with the prime, and would,
accordingly, alternately increase and diminish the apparent
amplitude of the middle of the bar. Thus if curves are
plotted with the displacements of the middle as ordinates,
and time as abscissae, we should have a wavy curve when
the bar is pulled at a wrong place, and a curve showing
simple subsidence, or nearly so, when the bar is pulled aside
at the best place. By observing the amplitudes microscopically, the best place of pulling was determined as one-fifth
the bar's length from the free end, thus agreeing with the
result found from the photographs.

215. Garrett's theory may be given in our notation as

follows :—For a bar of length l fixed at the origin and pulled aside by a force F at the end the equation may be written

$$y = \frac{F}{6q\omega\kappa^2}(3lx^2 - x^3).$$

Thus the displacement y_1 at the free end is

$$y_1 = \frac{Fl^3}{3q\omega\kappa^2}, \text{ or } y/y_1 = (3lx^2 - x^3)/2l^3 = \ddot{y}/\ddot{y}_1,$$

where the dots denote differentiations with respect to time. Thus the moment about the origin of the forces producing the motion of the bar is given by

$$M = \int_0^l x\ddot{y}\rho\omega dx = \frac{11}{40}\rho\omega l^2 \ddot{y}_1.$$

But the bending moment at O, if the shape remains as when pulled, is Fl for the initial displacement, and remains proportional to that displacement. Or it may be obtained from the value of d^2y/dx^2 at the origin. In either case, we have

$$M = 3q\omega\kappa^2 y_1/l^2.$$

Equating these two expressions for M we obtain

$$\ddot{y}_1 = -\left(\frac{120}{11} \cdot \frac{q}{\rho} \cdot \frac{\kappa^2}{l^4}\right)y_1.$$

Thus the motion is simple harmonic of frequency

$$N_1 = \frac{1}{2\pi}\sqrt{-\ddot{y}_1/y_1} = 0\cdot 525\kappa b/l^2.$$

Garrett next finds that if the bar be pulled aside at a point pl from the fixed origin, its frequency would be on this method of computation

$$N_2 = N_1\sqrt{\frac{11}{p(p^3 - 10p + 20)}}.$$

216. A still simpler way than Garrett's is available to suggest the dependence of frequency on material and size

of the bar.   Thus, suppose the inertia of the bar when
vibrating may be replaced by that of a smaller mass at its
free end, the rotatory inertia of this mass being neglected.
And let the deflecting force F be applied at the free end
and produce the deflection y_1 there.   Then the force per
unit displacement at the free end is

$$F/y_1 = 3\omega\kappa^2 q/l^3.$$

And let the hypothetical mass replacing that of the bar be
$j\omega\rho l$, where j is some proper fraction.   Then for the
equation of motion at the end we have

$$j\omega\rho l\ddot{y} = -\left(\frac{3\omega\kappa^2 q}{l^3}\right)y.$$

Hence, the motion is simple harmonic, of frequency given by

$$N_3 = \frac{\sqrt{3/j}}{2\pi}\kappa b/l^2.$$

That is, the frequency is directly proportional to the thickness of the rod and to the speed b of longitudinal waves in
it, and inversely proportional to the square of the length.

It is obvious that Garrett's theory may be regarded as a
method of evaluating the quantity j.

217. Remaining Cases of Vibrating Bars.—The bar
vibrating with one end free and the other supported is like
half of a free-free bar when vibrating with a node in the
middle.   For, at the central node $y = 0$, and it can be seen
from symmetry that $d^2y/dx^2 = 0$ also.   But these are the conditions for a supported end.   Again, the vibrations of a rod
fixed at one end and supported at the other are like those
of one-half of a rod with both ends fixed and vibrating with
a central node.

We have now to treat very briefly the sixth and only
remaining case, namely, that with both ends supported.
Referring to equations (20) and the conditions (8) we find
that at $x = 0$, $y = 0$ gives $P = 0$, and $d^2y/dx^2 = 0$ gives $Q = 0$.
Again, at $x = l$, i.e. $x' = m$, we find $y = 0$ gives $R - S = 0$ and

$d^2y/dx^2 = 0$ gives $\sin m = 0$, *i.e.* $m = n\pi$, where n is any integer. Thus, in equation (20), P and Q having vanished, and the sinh x' having disappeared also in virtue of the equality of

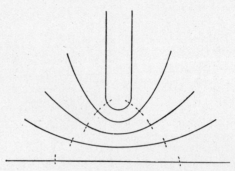

Fig. 57.—Approach of Nodes in a Bent Bar.

R and S, the expression reduces to a single term, viz. that involving $\sin x'$. We may accordingly write

$$y = K \sin \frac{n\pi x}{l} \cos \left(\frac{\kappa b n^2 \pi^2}{l^2} t + \epsilon \right) \qquad (32),$$

where K and ϵ are arbitrary constants to be chosen to satisfy the initial conditions. It is thus seen that the

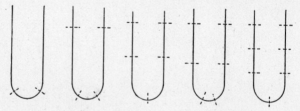

Fig. 58.—Nodes for U-shaped Bar.

segments of the rod in this case are like those of a string fixed at the ends. The frequencies of the possible tones, however, are quite different. For, in this case of the rod, the frequency of any tone is proportional to n^2 instead of to n simply as for a string. The frequency of the nth tone for the rod is evidently given by

$$N_n = \frac{\kappa b n^2 \pi}{2l^2} = n^2 N_1 \qquad (33).$$

218. Bent Bar vibrating Transversely. — Chladni experimented on the transverse vibrations of a bent bar free at each end, and showed that as the bar deviated more and more from the straight form the two nodes of the fundamental vibration approached each other more and more closely. This gradual approach of the nodes from the case of a straight bar to that of a bar bent with its two limbs parallel is shown in Fig. 57, taken from Chladni's diagram.

As the bar was bent more and more, Chladni found it more and more difficult to elicit the vibration with three nodes. Until in the final U-shape with parallel limbs, this mode of vibration was quite impossible. The other modes with 4, 5, 6, 7, and 8 nodes respectively were, however, all obtained. The nodes are shown in Fig. 58, and the approximate pitches in Table XIV., both taken from Chladni's celebrated work. The bars were excited by a violin bow, and each node rendered visible by arranging that part horizontal and scattering a little sand on it.

TABLE XIV.—VIBRATIONS OF U-SHAPED BAR

No. of Nodes	2	3	4	5	6	7	8
Approximate Pitches	c	Missing	$g''\sharp$	$f'''\sharp$	d^{iv}	$g^{iv}\sharp$	d^v
Numbers whose squares give approximate relative frequencies	(2)		(5) 3	4	5	6	7

219. Tuning-Forks.—The behaviour of the U-shaped bars just dealt with approximates to that of tuning-forks. But the vibration of tuning-forks is usually further complicated by the presence of an additional block at the centre of the bend and the stem attached thereto. Indeed, it may be a nearer approximation to regard each prong as a straight bar fixed at the end near the stem and free at the other end. On this supposition, let us calculate the pitch of the prime tone of a prong of steel of thickness a cm. and length l cm., the section being rectangular. From equation (14) of article 204 we have

$$N = \frac{m^2 \kappa}{2\pi l^2} \sqrt{q/\rho} \qquad (1).$$

Here $\kappa = a/\sqrt{12}$, and for steel we may write $\sqrt{q/\rho} = 523,700$ cm./sec. Further, we see from Table XIII., article 211, that $m_1 = 1\cdot875$. Whence, for the fundamental vibration, we have

$$N = 84,590 \; a/l^2 \text{ nearly} \qquad (2).$$

220. Temperature Variation of Pitch.—To show the effect on a tuning-fork of change of temperature we may proceed as follows :—By a rise of temperature $t°$ C. let the value of Young's modulus be affected by the factor $(1 - yt)$, and the linear dimensions by the factor $(1 + zt)$. In other words, let z be the coefficient of linear expansion and y the co-efficient of *decrease* of Young's modulus with rise of temperature. Then, since yt and zt are small, we may use the approximate binomial expansion $(1 + h)^n = 1 + nh$, where h is small compared with unity. Then, writing N_t for the frequency when the temperature is raised $t°$ C. from that where the frequency was N, we have

$$N_t = \frac{m^2}{2\pi} \frac{a(1 + zt)}{\sqrt{12}} \frac{\sqrt{q(1 - yt)}}{l^2(1 + 2zt)\sqrt{\rho(1 - 3zt)}}$$

$$= \frac{m^2 a \sqrt{q/\rho}}{2\pi l^2 \sqrt{12}} \left(1 - \frac{y - z}{2}t\right),$$

or, $$N_t = N\left(1 - \frac{y-z}{2}t\right) \qquad (3).$$

But, in the absence of any better determination of y, we had perhaps better take the value of $(y - z)$ from the direct experiments on a fork. Thus, Koenig found that the temperature coefficient of a fork was 0.000112. This, then, is the value to be ascribed to $(y - z)/2$ in equation (3). From this, since $z = 0.000012$ nearly, we obtain $y = 0.000236$.

221. Vibrations of a Ring.—A complete ring of elastic material may be made to exhibit either longitudinal or flexural vibrations. The latter were experimentally studied by Chladni as early as 1787. Chladni recommends that the ring be placed horizontally, resting on three supports of cork or other soft material at the nodes. A vibrating segment should project beyond the table and be excited by a violin bow, the ring being meanwhile held in place by the tips of two fingers over the nodal supports. Chladni states that the vibrations are most easily excited if the bow is used vertically. It would appear, therefore, that the vibrations chiefly contemplated by Chladni were flexural ones perpendicular to the plane of the ring. It is obvious that flexural vibrations in the plane of the ring are also possible. Chladni obtained the following vibrations:—

Number of nodes—   4, 6, 8, 10, 12, 14.

Numbers whose squares are proportional to the frequencies of the corresponding tones— } 3, 5, 7,   9, 11, 13.

The subject has been treated mathematically by Hoppe, by Michell, and by Lord Rayleigh. The results are briefly as follows:—Let the ring be circular of radius a and of circular cross section of radius c, small compared with a. Suppose its material to be of density ρ and Young's modulus q. Lastly, let it vibrate so as to have s periods (or complete wave lengths of the stationary vibration) in its circumference. Then, for flexural vibrations in the plane of the ring Hoppe (1871) and Lord Rayleigh found that the frequency may be expressed by

$$N_1 = \frac{1}{4\pi} \cdot \frac{s(s^2 - 1)}{\sqrt{1 + s^2}} \cdot \frac{c}{a^2} \sqrt{\frac{q}{\rho}} \qquad (1).$$

For flexural vibrations perpendicular to the plane of the ring, Michell (1889) found

$$N_2 = \frac{1}{4\pi} \frac{s(s^2 - 1)}{\sqrt{1 + \sigma + s^2}} \cdot \frac{c}{a^2} \cdot \sqrt{\frac{q}{\rho}} \qquad (2),$$

in which σ denotes the value of Poisson's ratio for the material of the ring.

In each of the above vibrations the circular axis of the ring is supposed to remain unextended. For the other class of vibrations, in which the ring remains in its own plane, but suffers alternate extension and contraction, Hoppe found

$$N_3 = \frac{\sqrt{1 + s^2}}{2\pi} \cdot \frac{1}{a} \sqrt{\frac{q}{\rho}} \qquad (3).$$

222. In equation (3), if $s = 0$, we have the solution for vibrations which are purely radial. In other words, the ring contracts and expands alternately, always remaining a circle and in the same plane.

For the flexural vibrations s cannot be less than two, in which case we have the gravest tone with four nodes. For $s = 1$ we should have a translation of the ring as a whole in its own plane but without deformation.

The sequences of tones found from either (1) or (2) agree fairly well with those experimentally observed by Chladni.

The vibrations of a ring are mentioned here, not so much for their own sake, but rather because they form the first step towards the very complicated phenomena presented by the vibrations of bells. It should be carefully noted that the motions in the general flexural vibrations here contemplated are not purely radial. For that would be inconsistent with the supposition that no extension occurs. Thus, when $s = 2$, and the number of nodes is 4, the deformed ring is elliptical, cutting the equilibrium circle in 4 points which are nodes for the radial motion, but are places of maximum tangential motion. Conversely, the places of maximum radial motion are nodes with respect to the tangential motion.

223. Vibrations of Plates.—We have already seen that, in passing from the theory of the ideal *one*-dimensional stretched string of acoustics to the *two*-dimensional stretched membrane, the complication is much increased. The same remark holds good if we pass from the flexible string to the *elastic* bar. If, therefore, we attempt to deal with the vibrations of a plate, a system at once *two*-dimensional and *elastic*, we may expect to encounter still greater difficulties. And such is the case. Indeed, the problem in its generality seems not to have been solved. Fortunately, the experimental methods of treatment are as easy as the theory is difficult.

The vibration of plates with free edges was approached from the experimental side by Chladni, and his first results published in 1787. The systems of nodal lines so obtained are still called Chladni's figures.

The mathematical treatment of this subject lies beyond the scope of this work; it may, however, be desirable to quote a few of the chief results which have been obtained.

224. Fundamental Equations.—Let the plate, when at rest, be in the plane of xy, have thickness $2h$, volume density ρ, Young's modulus q, and Poisson's ratio σ. Let w be a small displacement perpendicular to the plane of the plate at the point (x, y), and at time t. Suppose the vibrations to be flexural only, *i.e.* of the type which involves no extension or contraction of the middle sheet of the plate.

Then it may be shown (Rayleigh's *Sound*, §§ 215-217) that the differential equation is

$$d^2w/dt^2 + c^4\nabla^4 w = 0 \qquad (1),$$

where

$$c^4 = \frac{qh^2}{3\rho(1-\sigma^2)} \qquad (2),$$

and

$$\nabla^2 = \frac{d^2}{dx^2} + \frac{d^2}{dy^2} \qquad (3).$$

If we assume that $w \propto \cos(pt - \epsilon)$, equation (1) becomes

$$(\nabla^4 - k^4)w = 0 \qquad (4),$$

where

$$k^4 = p^2/c^4 \qquad (5).$$

225. Boundary Conditions.—For the boundary conditions of the edges parallel to the axis of y, we have the following scheme of equations applying as shown at right and left :—

$$\frac{d}{dx}\left\{\frac{d^2w}{dx^2} + (2-\sigma)\frac{d^2w}{dy^2}\right\} = 0 \qquad (6)$$

$$\text{Supported edges.}\quad\begin{cases}\dfrac{d^2w}{dx^2} + \sigma\dfrac{d^2w}{dy^2} = 0 & (7)\end{cases}$$

Free edges.

$$dw = 0 \qquad (8)$$

$$\frac{d}{dx}dw = 0 \qquad (9)$$

Fixed edges.

Of these four equations (6)-(9), as indicated by the words near the braces, the first pair apply to a free edge, the last pair to a fixed edge, and the middle pair to a supported edge. To express the conditions for an edge parallel to x, the letters x and y in the above equations need to be interchanged. In equations (8) and (9) dw denotes the increment of w consequent upon a change in the form of the function which gives w in terms of x and y ; or it may be regarded as denoting an arbitrary displacement consistent with the nature of the system.

226. Supported Rectangular Plate.—Consider the case

of a rectangular plate extending between the co-ordinate axes and $x = a$, $y = b$. And let its edges be supported. Then the solution of the necessary equations, namely (4), (7), and (8), may be written

$$w = \sin\frac{m\pi x}{a}\sin\frac{n\pi y}{b}\cos pt \qquad (10).$$

This form insures that at all points of the boundary

$$w = 0,\ \frac{d^2 w}{dx^2} = 0\ \text{and}\ \frac{d^2 w}{dy^2} = 0,$$

which fulfils (7) and (8).

Further, on introducing (10) in (4), we find that it is satisfied provided that $p^2 w = c^2 \nabla^2 w$, i.e. if

$$p = c^2 \pi^2\left(\frac{m^2}{a^2} + \frac{n^2}{b^2}\right) \qquad (11).$$

Equation (10) shows that the vibrational segments of a "supported" rectangular plate are like those of a stretched membrane of the same shape. Equation (11), however, shows that the analogy does not extend to the sequence of tones. The same kind of partial analogy was seen to occur between a bar with supported ends and a string, the vibration segments of the bar being like those of the string, but the tones being inharmonic for the bar and harmonic for the string.

227. Plates with Free Edges. Chladni's Figures.— The problem of rectangular plates with free edges is one of great theoretical difficulty which is only partly removed by making the plate square. We shall therefore entirely omit its mathematical treatment, and pass to the experimental methods introduced by Chladni. To produce each type of vibration of a plate and render visible the corresponding nodal lines, we must proceed generally as follows:—Hold it at one or more points on nodal lines, sprinkle a little sand on it, and excite with a violin bow a part of the edge between two nodal lines. The sand is then thrown off by the vibrating portions and accumulates on the nodal lines. To this general instruction we may now add various details which will facilitate the success of the experiment. The plates may be of glass, or of any sufficiently sonorous metal, for example steel or copper. Wood yields irregular figures on account of the varying elasticity in different directions. Chladni preferred glass plates as they are easily obtained to order, and their transparency permits of the fingers being used underneath at points which are shown to be nodal by the sand above. Small plates up to six inches diameter will serve quite well for simple figures, larger ones are better for the more complicated figures. The edges of the plate must be filed or ground smooth so as not to injure the hairs of the bow. It is desirable to hold the plate where two nodal lines intersect. The plate may be held between the thumb and finger, or be clamped between the rounded ends of a stud and an opposing screw. Or, the plate may have a hole through it and be fitted on the screwed stalk of a stand and fastened down with a nut. In this case leather washers may be introduced above and below the plate to leave it as free as possible to take any direction in the neighbourhood of the part held. In addition to the place where the plate is held, it is desirable and usually imperative to touch it at another place with a finger of the left hand while bowing with the right. This place may be at the edge of the plate, or away from the edge either above or below. It is usually best to bow at an antinode rather near to the nodal line thus touched. If the desired figure appears but imperfectly, shift the place of touch slightly. To reproduce any particular figure, mark the places of touching and bowing that were found satisfactory. To exclude undesired figures touch with a finger at a second place which is also nodal for the desired figure, but *not* nodal for the figure which it is sought to exclude. In general simple figures correspond to grave tones, and are more easily produced by the hard pressure of a slack bow moved slowly. The compli-cated figures, on the other hand, usually correspond to high tones, and are more easily produced by the light pressure of a tight bow moved quickly. It is also here desirable to remove the bow from the plate at each end of its stroke. If several tones seem to be struggling together and the sound fluctuates, it may usually be found which tone corresponds to the figure desired, and further what sort of bowing encourages it to the exclusion of the other. When

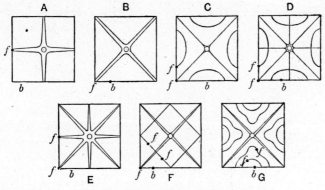

FIG. 59.—TYPICAL CHLADNI'S FIGURES.

this is ascertained, persevere in the right bowing till the desired figure is clearly produced and the corresponding tone heard alone.

228. EXPT. 33. *Chladni's Figures on a Square Plate.*—Observing the precautions just enumerated, produce with a square metal plate of about 30 cm. side and 2 mm. thick the following seven typical figures of Fig. 59. The plate is to be held throughout in the centre, touched with the fingers where marked f, and bowed where marked b.

The figures A, B, E, and F are examples of exact agree-ment with forms fairly easy to predict theoretically. The seven shown in Fig. 59 are but typical of a large number possible. Chladni's original work gives illustrations of 52 figures obtained with a square plate.

229. Circular Plates. — To apply the theory to a circular plate, it is necessary to transform to polar coordinates the fundamental equation and boundary conditions. The complete solution may then be expressed in a Fourier series. But, as the analysis is rather long and involves Bessel functions, it must suffice here to quote some of the results. The nodal system for a circular plate with free edges may have n diameters symmetrically distributed round the centre but otherwise arbitrary. It may also have n' circular nodes. Lord Rayleigh points out that theory confirms the discovery by Chladni " that the frequencies corresponding to figures with a given number of nodal diameters are, with the exception of the lowest, approximately proportional to the squares of consecutive even or uneven numbers, according as the number of diameters is itself even or odd." Further, within certain limits, " the pitch is approximately unaltered, when any number is subtracted from n', provided twice that number be added to n." In other words, each nodal circle has about twice the effect in raising the pitch possessed by a nodal diameter. For the radii of the circular nodes Table XV. presents a comparison between calculation and observation. The observations are throughout by Strehlke, while the calculations are due to Poisson or based upon the theory of Kirchhoff. The radii are given in fractions of that of the disc.

[TABLE

TABLE XV.

RADII OF CIRCULAR NODES ON DISC WITH FREE EDGE

Number of Nodal Diameters. n.	Number of Nodal Circles. n'.	Radii of Nodal Circles.	
		Observation.	Calculation.
0	1	0·678	0·681
0	2	$\begin{cases} 0·391 \\ 0·841 \end{cases}$	$\left. \begin{array}{c} 0·392 \\ 0·842 \end{array} \right\}$
0	3	$\begin{cases} 0·256 \\ 0·591 \\ 0·894 \end{cases}$	$\left. \begin{array}{c} 0·257 \\ 0·591 \\ 0·894 \end{array} \right\}$
1	1	0·781 to 0·783	0·781
2	1	0·79 to 0·82	0·823
3	1	0·838 to 0·842	0·847
1	2	$\begin{cases} 0·488 \text{ to } 0·497 \\ 0·869 \end{cases}$	$\left. \begin{array}{c} 0·497 \\ 0·870 \end{array} \right\}$

It should be noted that the circular disc in a telephone is clamped round its edge. The theory of this case has been developed by Lord Rayleigh (*Theory of Sound*, vol. i. pp. 366-367).

Number and Varieties of Chladni's Figures.—The number of Chladni's figures obtainable is practically unlimited. For example, beside the 52 figures for a square plate already mentioned, Chladni gives illustrations of 43 figures with a circular plate, 30 with an hexagonal plate, 52 with a rectangular plate, 26 with elliptical plates, 15 with semicircular plates, and 25 with triangular plates.

230. Simple Derivation of Chladni's Figures. — We

may often obtain a clue to the formation of a Chladni figure by noting that it is due to the coexistence of two simple vibrations of the same period. This coexistence was shown to occur in the case of membranes when treating them analytically (see Fig. 52, art. 194), and can now be applied here even in the absence of the full theory of which it is a natural result. For example, take the case of a square plate vibrating with three nodal lines parallel to one edge and the axis of x. It will have the same period if

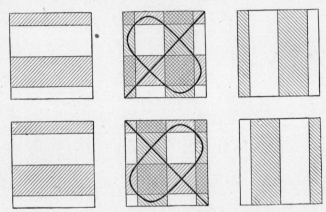

Fig. 60.—Derivation of Chladni's Figures.

vibrating with three nodal lines parallel to the axis of y. Hence the two vibrations may, and usually will, coexist. The phases may be the same or opposite, and their composition will produce different figures in the two cases. In Fig. 60 let the shaded portions represent the parts of the plate which are down at a given instant, the unshaded portions those which are up at the same time. Then, the first and third figures in the upper line represent the component vibrations just referred to. The middle figure in the upper line shows the two sets of shading superposed, and therefore represents the coexistence of the corresponding kinds of vibration. In this case it is clear that the nodal lines must lie in the once shaded portions, those portions doubly shaded being displaced down by each vibration, and therefore doubly down, the unshaded portions in like manner being doubly displaced up. The nodal lines are accordingly as shown in the middle figure of the upper line. Both analysis and Chladni's experiments confirm the result thus simply obtained. The three figures in the lower line show the composition of the same vibrations, but with the right hand one reversed in phase. It is seen, as might be expected, that the resultant figure is now formed about the other diagonal, but is in other respects like the first.

This simple method of derivation may be applied to obtain the figures of the nodal lines in vibrating membranes also, or as a check on results analytically derived.

231. Vibrations of a Cylindrical Shell.—The problem of the flexural vibrations of a thin cylindrical shell has been attacked by several mathematicians. For the case of a long cylinder which suffers no extension or contraction of the middle surface, Lord Rayleigh's theory furnishes the following expression for the frequency :—

$$N = \frac{s(s^2 - 1)}{\pi \sqrt{s^2 + 1}} \cdot \frac{h}{a^2} \sqrt{\frac{\left(k + \dfrac{n}{3}\right)n}{(3k + 4n)\rho}} \qquad (1).$$

Here s is the number of periods, or wave lengths, into which the circumference is divided, so $2s$ will be the number of nodal lines, $2h$ is the thickness of the shell, a its radius, k is the volume elasticity of the material of the shell, n its rigidity, and ρ its volume density. Thus, for a given material and number of nodes, we have from equation (1) that

$$N \propto h/a^2 \qquad (2).$$

This relation has been confirmed by Fenkner (1879) in his experiments on thin metallic cylinders open at one end. And as it was shown by this physicist that the pitch is

almost independent of the length, we have evidence that
the vibrations may be regarded as approximately two-
dimensional as assumed in Rayleigh's theory. As to the
sequence of tones, Fenkner found the relative frequencies to
be as *one*, 2·67, 5·00, 8·00, 12·00. The agreement with
(1) would be improved if these figures were raised by about
one-twelfth part, *i.e.* the prime relatively lowered. When
$s = 1$, it is seen from equation (1) that the frequency is zero,
as might have been expected, the motion being then one of
the shell as a whole and not a deformation. The principal
mode of vibration corresponds to $s = 2$. In this case there
are four nodes a right angle apart. Here again, as in the
case of the ring, it should be noted that these nodes are not
places of absolute rest, but of *maximum tangential* motion.
For this tone the maximum tangential motion is half of the
maximum normal motion. And generally for the sth term,
the maximum normal motion is s-times the maximum
tangential motion, each such maximum motion occurring at
the nodes of the other. The existence of the tangential
motion for an air-pump receiver has been verified by Lord
Rayleigh. "A small chip in the rim, reflecting the light of
a candle, gave a bright spot whose motion could be observed
with a Coddington lens suitably fixed." It was found "that
the spot moved tangentially when the bell was excited
(tangentially) at points distant therefrom 0, 90, 180, or
270 degrees; and normally when the friction was applied
at the intermediate points."

232. Bells.—Just as a tuning-fork is like a bent and
loaded bar, so a bell may be regarded as derived from a disc
curved and loaded near the middle. Or we may think of
it as a modified cylinder open at one end. In either case
we may expect a bell to exhibit nodal meridians, and, by
the analogy of the disc, we may also anticipate nodal
"parallels of latitude." Both surmises are borne out by
experiments on actual bells.

English bell-founders seem to recognise five chief tones

in the sound of a bell. Beginning from the highest, these are called, for a church bell, the "nominal," the "fifth," the "tierce," the "fundamental," and the "hum-note." It is thus remarkable that the highest tone is here that from which the pitch is reckoned, and not the lowest as in practice for other cases in which a set of tones is simultaneously produced by the same vibrating source. Lord Rayleigh experimented upon two church bells, of 6 cwt. and 4 cwt. respectively, and found the various tones produced as follows :—*Gravest tone,* 4 nodal meridians, no nodal circle ; *next higher tone,* 4 nodal meridians, one nodal circle ; *third tone,* 6 nodal meridians, sound best produced when the blow was delivered on the lower thick part termed the "sound bow" where the clapper strikes ; *next tone,* 6 nodal meridians, best elicited by striking about half-way up ; *highest tone of the five,* 8 nodal meridians. The pitches of the 4 cwt. bell, which was by the Taylors of Loughborough, were compared with a harmonium and found to be as follows in Table XVI. :—

TABLE XVI.
TONES OF BELL BY TAYLORS OF LOUGHBOROUGH

Names of Tones	Hum-note	Fundamental	Tierce	Fifth	Nominal
Pitches of Tones	$e'\flat - 2$	$d'' - 6$	$f'' + 4$	$b''\flat$ to b''	d'''
Nodal meridians and circles	(4)	(4/1)	(6)	(6)	(8)

In this statement of pitch the numerals indicate approximately the number of beats per second between the tone in question and the harmonium. Thus $e'\flat - 2$ means that this tone on the bell was two vibrations per second flatter than the $e'\flat$ on the harmonium, $f'' + 4$ means that tone of the bell was four vibrations per second sharper than the f'' on the harmonium. The next tone was about midway between $b''\flat$ and b''. The single numbers in brackets refer to the number of nodal meridians, and where two numbers occur the second refers to the number of nodal circles.

The highest tone of the five seems to be taken by the English bell-founders as the nominal, because just after striking it is the most prominent of the five. Hence for tuning and naming the bells of a set to be used in quick succession this must be taken as defining the pitch.

233. The endeavour of bell-founders seems to be to make the "hum-note," "fundamental," and "nominal" successive octaves; the "fifth" and "tierce" being respectively the major fifth and a major or minor third above the so-called "fundamental." This, however, seems never to be attained. The great aim is to make the nominal and fundamental a true octave apart, the others being of less importance. In the example given above, accepting the nominal as the standard, we see (1) that the fundamental is 6 per second flat, (2) that the hum-note is nearly a semitone sharp, (3) that the tierce is 4 per second too sharp for a minor third, (4) that the fifth is about $\frac{3}{4}$ of a tone sharp.

To any one at all familiar with the rules of harmony it might appear incredible that such tones as these five could be heard together with pleasure. But it must be remembered that each tone of the bell is itself *simple*, and not an ordinary musical tone, which is usually compound. Thus, for example, sounding the bell referred to, and striking simultaneously five keys on a piano tuned to the above pitches, the effects in the two cases would be widely different. The bell, with its *simple* though inharmonic tones, gives a subtle delight. The discordant effect on the piano from the mistuned *compound* tones would be distressingly painful. The reasons for this will be seen in the chapter on concord and discord.

234. Cause of Beats in Bells.—Very often, on listening

to a bell, whether a large church bell or a hand bell, beats
may be observed, and indeed often several sets are heard
simultaneously.   Their production is explained by Lord
Rayleigh as follows :—" If there be a small load at any
point of the circumference a slight augmentation of period
ensues, which is different according as the loaded point
coincides with a node of the normal or of the tangential
motion, being greater in the latter case than in the former.
The sound produced depends, therefore, on the place of
excitation ; in general both tones are heard, and by interference give rise to beats, whose frequency is equal to the
difference between the frequencies of the two tones."

CHAPTER VI

235. Order of Treatment.—In this chapter we shall be concerned chiefly with experiments which illustrate either (1) the phenomena of resonance, (2) the maintenance of vibrations, or (3) some other action on the part of a sensitive apparatus in response to an external periodic impulse. All the cases treated here will be of the acoustic order of frequency. The term resonance, or resounding, refers, of course, to the production of a second sound by the stimulus of a first. We shall not restrict the use of the term to the ideal case in which both sounds are of precisely the same pitch. Maintenance, on the other hand, refers to the continuance of a vibration with undiminished vigour, owing to the application of some external periodic force. In both cases we may call the first sound or other active agency the driver, and the second sound or vibration evoked or maintained the driven. This leads to another distinction between resonance and maintenance. In the former both driver and driven are sounds, while the term maintenance we restrict to cases in which one or other is not a sound. In all the cases of resonance with which we shall deal, and in some of the cases of maintenance, the driver and the driven have each their own definite natural periods, not necessarily alike. Here, therefore, the theory of forced vibrations developed in Chap. III. strictly applies. And,

314

consequently, the closer the tuning between driver and driven, the fuller is the resonance, or the more efficient is the maintenance. In other cases of maintenance, the driver has no perfectly definite period of its own, or it may be no period whatever, yet, by the reaction of the driven, assisted perhaps by the care of the experimenter, the driver's action becomes periodic and of a suitable frequency. Hence, in this case also, the theory of forced vibrations applies, or, at any rate, affords a valuable clue. The period to be ascribed to the driver is, of course, that which the reaction of the driven awakens in it, and is nearly, though not of necessity precisely, the natural period of the driven. The starting of these actions is somewhat uncertain, but once started they are stable. Lastly, we have a class of cases in which the stimulus is periodic and the response to it on the part of some sensitive apparatus continues while the stimulus lasts. The theory of such will be indicated in connection with each. The various cases to be dealt with are classified on the foregoing plan in Table XVII. For completeness' sake this table includes a few important examples whose consideration is wholly or partially deferred to the next chapter. In each such case a reference to the explanatory article is given in the table. The remaining contents of the four columns will be taken downwards in order. It will be noticed that the side headings on the left indicate a subdivision of each column into several rows or sections, according to whether the driver and driven are respectively solid and fluid, both solid, etc.

[TABLE

TABLE XVII.

EXAMPLES OF RESONANCE AND ALLIED PHENOMENA

Nature of Driver and Driven respectively.	Resonance	Maintenance.		Other Responsive Actions.
		Period of Driver Definite.	Period of Driver wholly or partially induced by Driven.	
Solid Fluid	1. Tuning Fork near Air Resonator 2. Adjustable Resonator 3. Helmholtz Resonators (see also ch. viii.)			
Solid Solid	4. Helmholtz's Experiment ...	7. Melde's Expt. ...	10. Goold's Generators and Bars 11. Violin Bow and String, Fork or Plate 12. Trevelyan's Rocker	
Fluid Fluid	5. Voice and Air Resonator ...	... ...	13. Singing Flames 14. Organ Pipes (chap. viii.)	16. Sensitive Flames of various kinds
Fluid Solid	6. One Fork responding to another at a distance ...	8. Erskine-Murray's Phonoscope ... 9. Human Ear	... ...	17. Setting of Disc 18. Kundt's Dust Figures 19. Striations same
Magnetic Field Solid	...	...	15. Electrically-driven Tuning-Fork	

236. EXPT. 34. *Tuning-Fork and Simple Air Resonators.*—
Perhaps the simplest experiment on resonance is that with a

tuning-fork and a tumbler or bottle. If the natural tone of the cavity of the vessel is too flat to correspond with the fork, it may be raised by pouring in water. If, on the other hand, the pitch of the cavity is too sharp, it may be flattened by shading the mouth. The necessary adjustment can usually be effected in a few minutes. Some clue to dimensions will be afforded by the following particulars of an actual case. Here the necessary adjustments were made in a few minutes, although only the homeliest materials were available. The fork used was an ordinary musician's philharmonic a' (say 454 per second). The tumbler used was almost cylindrical in shape, $2\frac{1}{2}$ inches diameter at the top, and $4\frac{1}{4}$ inches high. Its natural tone when empty, as ascertained by gently blowing across the top, was higher than the fork. Hence it needing shading. A closely-fitting glass plate is perhaps best for this purpose; but a small pamphlet answered well enough. The best resonance was obtained when the pamphlet covered about three-quarters of the diameter of the tumbler's mouth perpendicular to the edge of the pamphlet. Even the hand put over the tumbler's mouth answered almost as well, the necessary adjustment being quite possible during a single sounding of the fork. As an example of a second resonator initially too low, the case of a bottle may be noticed, the same fork being still used. The body of the bottle was nearly cylindrical, about $3\frac{3}{4}$ inches high, and $1\frac{3}{4}$ inches diameter inside. Its nearly cylindrical neck, 3 inches high, was $\frac{3}{4}$ of an inch diameter at the bottom, but had a short constriction to $\frac{3}{8}$ of an inch diameter near the top. To tune this bottle as a resonator to the fork, it was necessary to pour in water to the height of $3\frac{1}{4}$ inches, thus leaving only $\frac{1}{2}$ inch of its body occupied by air. A sensitive method of detecting the fault when too much water is in, consists in placing a finger so as to partially shade the mouth of the neck while the fork is sounding. When too much water is in and the natural tone of the bottle is in consequence too sharp, the shading flattens its pitch and thus improves it as a resonator, which is shown by an increased volume of sound. The fact that the first two articles which came to hand were readily tuned to the only fork then available, shows how simple this process is. If it is desired to tune a vessel more permanently to a given sound, instead of water, oil or melted wax should be poured into a vessel naturally too flat. Or the glass plate used to shade the mouth of a vessel naturally too sharp may be fastened on with wax.

The mounting of tuning-forks on resonance boxes is another application of the principle just dealt with.

237. EXPT. 35. *Use of Adjustable Resonator.*—The principle of partially occupying the air cavity with water to

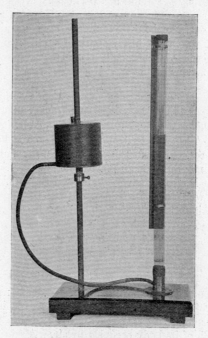

FIG. 61.—ADJUSTABLE RESONATOR.

raise the pitch to correspondence with any given sound receives a more elaborate application in the apparatus now to be described. It consists essentially of a tall cylindrical glass jar connected at the base by an india-rubber tube to a reservoir of water which is adjustable to various heights on a wooden upright. The reservoir may be clamped at any desired height by means of a screw. The jar may have a graduated scale attached to it for reading the depths below its mouth corresponding to best resonance with any given forks or other sources of sound. One form of this simple but very useful piece of apparatus is shown in Fig. 61.

This apparatus may be very rapidly and silently adjusted by raising or lowering the reservoir. Thus, the position for maximum resonance with a fork may be obtained *while it is sounding*. If a simple jar is used, it is usual to tune by *successive* trials of the water level. But this makes it hard to decide precisely which level is best. An improvement with the simple jar is the use of a stick thrust into the water and adjusted with one hand while the other holds the fork. But the apparatus shown above is much more convenient and yields better results ; about 20 inches is a convenient height for the resonating column. As an example of its use let us determine the relation between the prime tone of a fork and that with four nodes, that is, one near the end of each prong in addition to the usual two near the stem. As already seen in the theory of the lateral vibration of bars (art. 211), the ratio of the frequencies of the second tone and prime for a fixed-free bar is about 6·3. For a series of tuning-forks examined by Helmholtz this ratio was found to vary between 5·8 and 6·6. Let a c' fork be used, of frequency 256 per second. And suppose 12·67 inches to be the measure of the column of air above the water for the best resonance, with its prime tone obtained by bowing or by striking on a soft pad. Then by striking on a hard surface find the resonance position for the first upper partial. Let this distance be 1·73 inch. Suppose the internal diameter of the cylinder to be 1·5 inch. Then, by article 179, each of the above lengths needs increasing by the end correction 0·6 R which is here ·6 × ·75 = 0·45 inch. The two corrected lengths are accordingly 13·12 and 2·18 inches respectively. Hence, the ratio of the frequencies is the ratio of these lengths, that is 13·12/2·18. And this equals 6·02. Other uses can be made of this apparatus, as we shall see later.

238. Theory of Resonators.—Having noticed some simple preliminary experiments, we now pass to another and very important class of resonators, namely, those whose openings to the external air are small in comparison with the enclosed cavity. These are used to respond to particular tones as fully and precisely as possible. They thus indicate the presence of those tones even when very weak, and also serve to ascertain their pitch with great nicety. These qualities are due to the fact that the small opening allows of only a small dissipation, and hence a vibration once started in them persists for a considerable number of periods. Now, it was shown in articles 94-96, on forced vibrations, that the smaller the damping possessed by a vibrating system, the greater is the vibration forced upon it and the more sensitive is it to exact tuning. Hence the advantage of the form under notice and the necessity for a theory concerning it. They are included here because they were used so extensively by Helmholtz to respond to tuning-forks close to their mouths. They thus afford an example of the driver being a solid body, and the driven or responsive substance a gas, viz. the air. It is obvious, however, that they can be used also to respond to the voice or other sounds originating in the air and not produced by the vibration of a solid body. The full theory, as given by Helmholtz and others, is beyond the scope of this work. We can, however, follow the simple method given by Lord Rayleigh for the pitch of the prime tone of such resonators.

239. Imagine first the case of a stopped cylinder in which a piston moves without friction. Let the piston move to and fro very slowly. Then, as an approximation, we may suppose the pressure of the air inside to be everywhere the same, namely, that due to the momentary position of the piston. Now, if the mass of the piston were considerable in comparison with that of the air in the cylinder, the natural vibrations of the system would occur slowly and almost as if the air had no inertia. Thus, in calculating the period, it would be possible (1) to consider the kinetic energy as resident wholly in the piston, and (2) to treat the potential energy of the enclosed air as if its rarefactions and condensations were uniform. Thus, the air inside acts as a spring and the form of the containing vessel is immaterial, the period for a given piston remaining the same provided the capacity is unchanged.

When we pass from the case just described to an actual resonator of the type to be dealt with, the approximation becomes less close.   For here the piston is represented simply by the air in and near the opening, and its mass cannot be great.   But, since its velocity may be very great in comparison with that of the air well within the chamber, we may still regard the kinetic energy as resident chiefly in this air "piston," and write our equations accordingly. The results obtained by this elementary method afford an instructive view of the subject, and often give a fair value for the pitch of the prime tone or fundamental.   They must not, however, be supposed to correspond to a rigorous treatment of the subject.

240. We have already seen (arts. 84-85) that, if a mass is urged by a restoring force proportional to its displacement, it executes simple harmonic motion of period expressed by

$$\tau = 2\pi \sqrt{\text{mass} \div \text{spring factor}} \qquad (1).$$

We have, accordingly, to express for our present problem the values of mass and spring factor and substitute in (1). Let the cross sectional area of the neck, its length and the density of the gas in it, be denoted respectively by A, L, and ρ'.   Then, for the "piston" with which we are concerned, we have obviously

$$\text{mass} = AL\rho' \qquad (2).$$

Let S be the volume of the chamber of the resonator and ρ the density of the gas within it (not necessarily the same gas as that in the neck).   Then the spring factor or force per unit displacement may be denoted by Adp.

But it was seen (in art. 152) that

$$v^2 = \frac{dp}{d\rho} = \gamma p / \rho \qquad (3),$$

v being the average speed of sound in the gas occupying the chamber, and p the pressure.

Y

Thus $$dp = \gamma p \, d\rho / \rho \qquad (4).$$

Also, by the geometry of the case for a displacement of unit length in the neck,

$$S(\rho + d\rho) = (S + A)\rho,$$

whence $$d\rho / \rho = A / S \qquad (5).$$

Thus, from equations (4) and (5) we obtain for the spring factor

$$A \, dp = A \gamma p \, d\rho / \rho = A^2 \gamma p / S \qquad (6).$$

Hence, substituting from (2) and (6) in (1), we have

$$\tau = 2\pi \sqrt{L S \rho' / A \gamma p} \qquad (7),$$

or, $$\tau = 2\pi \sqrt{S \rho' / c \gamma p} \qquad (8),$$

where c is written in place of A/L, and by electrical analogy may be called the "conductivity of the neck." The frequency is given by

$$N = \frac{\sqrt{c \gamma p / S \rho'}}{2\pi} \qquad (9).$$

241. We thus see that the pitch is dependent on the density of the gas in the neck, but is independent of the nature of the gas in the chamber except for the small possible variation due to a change in the value of γ. If, now, we suppose the gas to be the same throughout the chamber and neck, we have from equations (3) and (8),

$$\lambda = v\tau = 2\pi \sqrt{S/c} \qquad (10).$$

Hence, in this case, the wave length is independent of the gas used, and depends only on the size and shape of the resonator itself. Again, if the gas is the same throughout, (9) may be rewritten

$$N = \frac{v}{2\pi} \sqrt{c/S} \qquad (11).$$

It may be noted here that the introduction of the conductivity c of the neck not only affords a more compact expression of the results of the simple theory, but may be

used to express also the frequency obtained by the more
complete treatment. In the latter case, however, c is no
longer the quotient A/L merely, but the value of the
conductivity determined by higher analysis.

242. Comparison with Experiments.—From experiments on flasks with long necks, Sondhauss found

$$N = 4,670 \cdot 5 \sqrt{A/LS} \qquad (12),$$

which corresponds in form with (11), but gives the pitch
about a tone flatter than that obtained by the simple theory
putting $v = 33,200$ cm./sec. For the case of resonators
without necks, Sondhauss gave the formula

$$N = 5,240 A^{\frac{1}{4}}/S^{\frac{1}{2}} \qquad (13).$$

The theory of such a resonator has been developed by
Helmholtz, who found

$$N = \frac{v}{\sqrt[4]{4\pi^5}} A^{\frac{1}{4}}/S^{\frac{1}{2}} = v(A/4\pi^5 S^2)^{\frac{1}{4}} \qquad (14).$$

Putting $v = 33,200$ cm./sec, this gives $N = 5,617 A^{\frac{1}{4}}/S^{\frac{1}{2}}$
nearly. The theoretically determined pitch is again sharper
than the observed, but this time the discrepancy is only of
the order a semitone. Helmholtz's theory is developed on
the assumption that all dimensions of the chamber are
vanishingly small compared to the wave length of the air,
and the air opening vanishingly small in comparison with
that of the chamber walls.

But, in actual practice, the necks are not usually so long
that end correction is unnecessary as assumed in the simple
theory developed in the last article. Neither are they
usually so short as to be themselves negligible as assumed
in the theory leading to equation (14). We have already
seen, in connection with organ pipes (articles 179, 180), that
we may represent the end correction by an addition to the
length. Further, this quantity is to a first approximation
independent of the length of the neck L and of the wave
length λ. As previously noticed in connection with pipes,

the value of the end correction depends on whether at the open end there is an infinite flange. But for our present purpose the value $\frac{\pi}{4}R$, where R is the radius of the neck, will be near enough. For this is the value theoretically found when the infinite flange is present, and when the neck is short this condition almost represents the fact, and when the neck is long the correction is itself of small account. Hence, in place of equation (11) we may write

$$N = \frac{v}{2\pi}\sqrt{\frac{A}{S(L + \frac{\pi}{4}R)}} = \frac{v}{2\pi}\sqrt{\frac{A}{S(L + \frac{1}{4}\sqrt{\pi A})}} \quad (15).$$

The second form being more convenient if the opening is nearly but not quite circular.

It must be clearly understood that the methods spoken of refer only to the pitch of the prime or gravest tone of the resonators in question. The overtones are relatively very high, and to determine them it would not be legitimate to neglect the inertia of the air in the chamber. The experimental use of resonators of this class will be sufficiently exemplified in the next chapter.

243. EXPT. 36. *Helmholtz's Resonance Experiment.*—Tune the wire of a monochord exactly in unison with a good fork having a frequency of 128 per second. Prepare a number of riders of white paper each about 2 cm. long and 2 mm. broad, and bent to an L-shape. Place several riders anywhere upon the wire. Then bow the fork and immediately place it with the stem on the wire just where it passes over one of the bridges. If all has been properly performed, the wire should be set into vibration in its gravest mode as shown by its almost instantaneous rejection of all the riders. Next, place only three riders on the wire, and at the points 1/4, 1/2, and 3/4 of its length from one end. Bow a fork of frequency 256 per second, and place its stem on the bridge as before. This time the first and third riders should be kicked off the wire while the second remains, thus showing that the vibration has two segments appropriate to the first overtone, as might be anticipated. The experiment may be repeated with a fork of 384 per second, riders placed at 1/3 and 2/3 along the string remaining, while riders at 1/6, 1/2, and 5/6 should be jerked off by the vibration of the string in three segments. Again, with a fork of 512 per second, riders placed at 1/4, 1/2, and 3/4 along the wire should remain, others at 1/8, 3/8, 5/8, and 7/8 along being thrown off. The higher the pitch of the fork, the harder it becomes to elicit from the wire vibrations of sufficient amplitude to dislodge the riders. To be successful the tuning must be very exact, and the bowing of the fork as vigorous as possible, It may also be found desirable to roughen or notch the end of the tuning-fork stem, and it sometimes acts better if placed not quite over the bridge, but a little (say 1 or 2 mm.) from the bridge towards the middle of the wire. If, however, the stem needs moving any considerable distance from the bridge before the response occurs, it is proof that the string is too flat.

In all these cases the riders are for indicating to the distant members of a class that the string has responded ; those very near may hear the resonance if the experiment is well executed.

244. EXPT. 37. *Air Resonators responding to the Voice.*—The response to the voice of a simple air resonator such as a bottle, flask, or vase may be demonstrated as follows :—Blow across the mouth of the vessel to ascertain its pitch, then sing powerfully into the vessel a vowel at that pitch. Immediately on ceasing to sing, apply the mouth of the resonator to the ear, when the response will be heard, and with some vessels lasts a second or two. If a Helmholtz resonator is available, an observer may have its nozzle applied to his ear while a tone of the right pitch is sung at some distance by another person. The reinforcement due to the resonator will then be clearly perceived.

EXPT. 38. *One Fork responding to Another.*—For this experiment two very good tuning-forks are required of *precisely* the same pitch, and each mounted on a suitable resonance box. One fork is vigorously bowed, and the two held for a few seconds with the mouths of their resonance boxes near together. Then, on stopping the first fork with the finger, the other will be heard distinctly sounding. This is classed in the table as a case of a fluid vibration driving a solid body, because it is the air in the resonance box of the first fork which starts that in the box of the second fork, and *this* in turn appears to be chiefly instrumental in generating the vibrations of the *fork* itself.

This concludes our notice of resonance proper.

245. Melde's Experiments.—In this illustration of the maintenance of vibrations, a thread is set in regular periodic motion by a tuning-fork. The thread extends from a fixed point to one prong of the fork, and when matters are properly adjusted responds to the fork's motion. There are two chief modes of the experiment to consider, which may be called the transverse and the longitudinal positions or modes respectively. In the transverse position the length of the thread is placed at right angles to the path described by the tip of the prong to which it is attached. In the longitudinal position the thread and the path described by the tip of the prong are in the same straight line. In the former position the nature of the action is quite simple, the latter, however, requires a special examination.

Transverse Arrangements.—Here we may regard the stationary waves in the thread as formed by the composition of the direct waves sent from the fork, and those reflected from the fixed point at the far end. Hence, the ordinary equation for vibrating strings will apply. Thus, for the vibration of the thread in one segment we have (see equation (4), article 165)

$$N = \frac{1}{2L} \sqrt{F/\sigma} \qquad (1),$$

where N is the frequency of vibration of the thread, L is its length, F the stretching force, and σ the mass of the thread per unit length. If this vibration is to be caused by a fork of frequency N, then L, F, and σ must be chosen so as to satisfy (1). If, however, we wish the same length of thread to vibrate in two segments, keeping to the same fork, we must tune the thread down an octave by reducing the stretching force to one-quarter of its previous value. Then the fork, though still exciting a vibration synchronous with its own, elicits, not the prime, but the second vibration of which the thread is capable. So generally, if we require n segments excited in the thread by the same fork, we must tune the string down so that its prime has a frequency N/n. In other words, keeping N, L, and σ constant, we must so choose F_n the stretching force for n segments, as to satisfy the equation

$$F_n = F/n^2 \qquad (2),$$

F being defined by (1). For values of F see Table XVIII.

246. *Longitudinal Arrangements.*—For the longitudinal form of Melde's experiment, suppose the thread to be horizontal, and the fork with its prongs upwards vibrating horizontally in the vertical plane through the thread. And, in considering the nature of the action involved, begin with the prongs apart and the thread consequently slack as shown in the upper line A of Fig. 62.

We suppose here that the fork and the thread are each at the full extent of their excursions and have for the instant no velocity. This fact is indicated by the small circles near the prongs and the thread. Now let the prongs approach each other till their nearest position is reached, and let the thread at the same time be just straight and horizontal. Then the prongs, as before, are at the pause for an instant. The thread, however, is now moving upwards. This state of things is represented by the second line B of Fig. 62, in which the circles indicate rest and the arrows motion. Now, let the prongs separate again to their fullest extent. The thread having liberty will naturally move to its position of maximum displacement. But, owing to its upward momentum when horizontal, its displacement this time will be upwards. This position is represented in the lowest line C of Fig. 62, the circles again indicating rest. Now from the position shown in line A to that shown by C, the *whole* period of the fork elapses, but only *half* a period of the thread's vibration. Hence for the vibration of the thread in one segment as shown we must have it tuned an octave below the fork. In other words, the action of the driver depends upon the position of the driven, and by the momentum of the driven that position and action are reversed in each succeeding period of the driver. Hence, in its effect upon the driven, two periods of the driver are

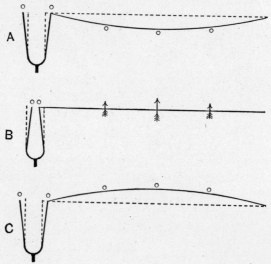

Fig. 62.—Longitudinal Arrangement of Melde's Experiment.

required to complete the cycle of operations. Thus, if the frequency of the fork be N as before, and the stretching force of the thread be F', we have

$$\frac{N}{2} = \frac{1}{2L} \sqrt{F'/\sigma} \qquad (3).$$

So
$$F' = F/4 \qquad (4),$$

where F is the force in the transverse form of the experiment for one segment.

Suppose now we require n vibrating segments in the

thread when excited longitudinally. Then we have the tension expressed by

$$F'_n = F'/n^2 \qquad (5).$$

For lecture illustration a large fork of 64 per second and a thread about 2·5 metres long have been found convenient. The thread may be of silk and about 16 metres to the gram. The corresponding stretching forces in a set of lecture experiments were then as shown in Table XVIII.

TABLE XVIII.—MELDE'S EXPERIMENT WITH A 64 FORK.

No. of Segments in Thread, n.	Transverse Mode.		Longitudinal Mode.	
	Frequency of Thread.	Stretching Force, F_n.	Frequency of Thread.	Stretching Force F'_n.
1	64	640	32	160
2	32	160	16	40
4	16	40	8	10
8	8	10		

247. EXPT. 39. *Melde's Experiment.*—This experiment may be carried out on a variety of scales and in different ways according to the object in view. For a large audience the thread may be horizontal and illuminated by the beam from an arc lantern. Another method is to steep the thread in sulphate of quinine and expose it to the violet rays of the arc light as suggested by Tyndall, the string then exhibiting a brilliant greenish-blue fluorescence. In this case it is better if the fork is electrically driven (see article 278).

But where these elaborations are not needed or cannot be attempted, the experiment may be performed in the following simple way in a laboratory, or for audiences up to a hundred :—Clamp the fork so as to project horizontally from the top of a stool, and let the thread, about a metre or more long, hang vertically from it with its weight at the bottom. The right adjustment of length and stretching force may be found either by calculation or by a preliminary experiment with the thread horizontal and passing over a pulley. This being done for one segment with the transverse mode of the experiment, the key is obtained to the whole set of forces required for any other number of segments of that mode or of the longitudinal mode. Then the proper weights being hung on, a single stroke of the bow sets the fork and the thread into the desired vibration. Thus, for the thread previously mentioned, but now $1\frac{1}{4}$ metre

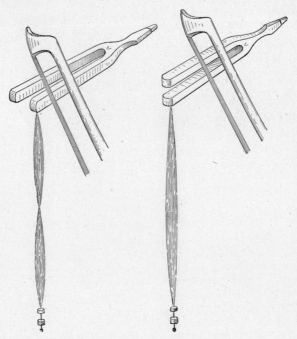

FIG. 63.—SIMPLE FORM OF MELDE'S EXPERIMENT.

long and used on a fork of 128 per second, the series of weights given in Table XVIII. will apply. The simple turning of the fork in the clamp through 90° about its own axis serves to effect the change from the transverse to the longitudinal mode of the experiment. Both modes are shown in Fig. 63.

248. Theory of Longitudinal Form of Melde's Experiment.—The somewhat unusual character of the

maintenance by a driver of double frequency met with in the longitudinal form of Melde's experiment has been treated mathematically by Lord Rayleigh, whose method we follow here. The motion of the fork produces a variation of the tension of the string, and hence, if the adjustments are right and if by any means a vibration is started, then it is maintained. Let us therefore suppose the steady motion to be in existence, and examine the conditions necessary to continue it. Now, a variation in the tension produces a corresponding variation in the restoring force acting on any displaced portion of the string. Thus, limiting our consideration to a single vibrating point we may represent the effect of the driver by a periodic variation of the spring factor. We may thus, with our previous notation, write as follows a sufficiently representative equation of the motion:—

$$m\ddot{y} + r\dot{y} + (s - 2ma \sin 2pt)y = 0.$$

Or, if $r/m = \kappa$ and $s/m = n^2$, we obtain as our working expression,

$$\ddot{y} + \kappa\dot{y} + (n^2 - 2a \sin 2pt)y = 0 \qquad (1).$$

Try as a solution

$$\begin{aligned} y = &A_1 \sin pt + B_1 \cos pt \\ &+ A_3 \sin 3pt + B_3 \cos 3pt \\ &+ A_5 \sin 5pt + B_5 \cos 5pt + \ \ldots \quad (2), \end{aligned}$$

terms involving an even multiple of pt being unnecessary. Substituting in equation (1) and equating to zero the coefficients of the sines and cosines of pt, $3pt$, $5pt$, etc., we find

$$\left. \begin{aligned} A_1(n^2 - p^2) - aB_1 - \kappa pB_1 - aB_3 = 0 \\ B_1(n^2 - p^2) - aA_1 + \kappa pA_1 - aA_3 = 0 \end{aligned} \right\} \quad (3),$$

$$\left. \begin{aligned} A_3(n^2 - 9p^2) - aB_1 - 3\kappa pB_3 - aB_5 = 0 \\ B_3(n^2 - 9p^2) + aA_1 + 3\kappa pA_3 - aA_5 = 0 \end{aligned} \right\} \quad (4),$$

$$\left. \begin{aligned} A_5(n^2 - 25p^2) - aB_3 - 5\kappa pB_5 \ \ldots \ = 0 \\ B_5(n^2 - 25p^2) + aA_3 + 5\kappa pA_5 \ \ldots \ = 0 \end{aligned} \right\} \quad (5).$$

Equations (4) show that A_3 and B_3 are of the order a times

A_1 and B_1. Similarly equations (5) show that A_5 and B_5 are of the order a times A_3 and B_3. Thus, if from (3) we omit A_3 and B_3, we have as a first approximation

$$
\left.
\begin{aligned}
A_1(n^2 - p^2) = B_1(a + \kappa p) \\
B_1(n^2 - p^2) = A_1(a - \kappa p)
\end{aligned}
\right\} \tag{6}.
$$

Whence $\qquad \dfrac{B_1}{A_1} = \dfrac{n^2 - p^2}{a + \kappa p} = \dfrac{a - \kappa p}{n^2 - p^2} = \dfrac{\sqrt{a - \kappa p}}{\sqrt{a + \kappa p}} \qquad (7),$

and $\qquad\qquad (n^2 - p^2)^2 = a^2 - \kappa^2 p^2 \qquad (8).$

249. Thus, if a be given, the value of p necessary for a steady motion is definite. And if p has this value, we have to our approximation by omission from (2) of A_3, B_3, etc., $y = A_1 \sin pt + B_1 \sin pt$, or,

$$
y = P \sin (pt + \epsilon) \tag{9},
$$

where $\qquad P^2 = A_1^2 + B_1^2$, and $\tan \epsilon = B_1 / A_1 \qquad (10),$

in which, therefore, ϵ is definite also. Hence the period and phase are fixed. But there is nothing as yet to determine P, the absolute amplitude, whose value, therefore, depends upon other circumstances.

Equation (8) shows that, for regular motion, a must be not less than κp. If $a = \kappa p$, we then have $p = n$ by equation (8), and from equations (7) and (10) we see that $\epsilon = 0$. Hence (9) becomes

$$
y = P \sin nt \tag{11},
$$

when $a = \kappa p$, or in words, this is the case of ideal adjustment considered in the elementary view of the matter, and in which the frequency of the driver is just double that of the driven, supposing friction to be absent.

If a were less than κp, the motion would not be maintained. But if a were greater than κp, then the energy available for supply would be greater than needed. But the balance between energy actually supplied and that dissipated could be attained by an alteration of the phase relation. Equations (10) and (7) show that ϵ may have either algebraic sign.   If the sign is taken positive, then by (8), p is given by

$$p^2 = n^2 - \sqrt{a^2 - \kappa^2 p^2} \qquad (12).$$

It thus appears from the equations that the adjustment of frequencies by the experimenter must be perfect in order to secure the maintenance of the motion.   This is, however, subject to modification in the actual experiment.   For, with the thread used, the value of n is to a slight extent dependent on amplitude.   Hence the steady state may be automatically attained by the assumption of a large and determinate amplitude which secures the necessary adjustment of frequencies.

250. Dr. Erskine - Murray's Phonoscope. — For the graphical exhibition to an audience of the vibrations constituting sounds produced in their hearing, very similar arrangements seem to have been independently devised at about the same time by Professor J. G. M'Kendrick and by Dr. J. Erskine-Murray.   The one here described was first publicly exhibited at Nottingham in 1901.   Its action will be easily understood from Fig. 64, which shows the essentials of the device.   The exciting sound is produced close to the large open end AD of the conical tube ABCD.   The small end BC of this tube is covered with a thin membrane left rather slack.   Near the middle of this end a small mirror E is hinged upon a wire F.   The mirror is also connected near its axle by a light support (of aluminium foil, say) to a point G near the middle of the membrane.   Thus every flutter of the membrane rocks the mirror about its horizontal axis.   A beam of light HE from an arc lantern is passed through a small hole in a diaphragm and arranged to fall upon the mirror E.   It is thus reflected to a set of mirrors J capable of rotation about a vertical axis. From the mirror J the light passes to a point K, say, on a large distant screen KL, upon which the light is focused by a lens not shown in the diagram.   If the mirror J is at

rest and the sound directed into the open mouth AD, the
membrane BC flutters, the mirror E rocks about its
horizontal axis, and the vertical line MN is described by the
spot of light on the screen. If, on the other hand, without
any sound being produced the mirror J is rotated about its
vertical axis, we should have the horizontal line KL
described by the spot of light on the screen. When, however, the sound is directed into the instrument, and the set
of mirrors at J is simultaneously rotated, we have, from the
composition of the two motions, a periodic curve such as
KPQRL described on the screen. In making this phono-

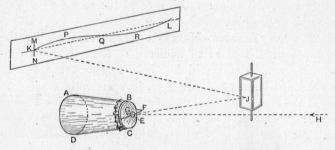

FIG. 64.—DR. ERSKINE-MURRAY'S PHONOSCOPE.

scope, it is of the utmost importance that the mirror E
should be very light and quite free to move, but without
shake, and that the membrane should be somewhat slack.
The diameter of the membrane must also be chosen with
reference to the pitch of the sounds for which it is to
be used.

251. EXPT. 40. *Phonoscope responding to Organ Pipe Tones.*
—Place an organ pipe with its *mouth* close to AD, switch
on the lantern, adjust and focus. One operator should now
rotate the mirror J while another sounds the prime tone of
the organ pipe. The sine graph is immediately described
on the screen by the spot of light. Next, suddenly place
on the open end of the organ pipe, a padded board. This
converts it into a stopped pipe, and therefore lowers the pitch

about an octave. Immediately the pitch is heard to fall the sine graph on the screen is observed to change its wave length to about double its former value. A third experiment with the same pipe is as follows :—Elicit the prime tone of the open pipe as at first, and then suddenly "over-blow" it so as to make it speak its first overtone. This is an octave higher than the prime, and is recorded on the screen by a sine graph of half the previous wave length. A fourth variation may be made by blowing so as to elicit simultaneously the prime and the first overtone. Both sounds may be heard with care, and the beautiful curve characteristic of this compound tone at the same time appears on the screen. It is difficult to maintain this state of things for long, and indeed requires some little address to obtain at all. A fifth experiment may be made by obtaining the first overtone of the same pipe when stopped. This, as shown theoretically, will be heard and seen to be the twelfth of the corresponding prime. Sixthly, the prime and first overtone of the stopped pipe may be obtained together, and the curve showing the composition of frequencies 3:1 exhibited on the screen.

Other uses of the phonoscope of still greater interest and importance may be made in the case of vowels and consonants uttered by the voice.

252. The Human Ear.—For anything approaching full details of the human ear, the various anatomical and physiological works should be consulted. Nothing can be attempted here beyond what is needed for understanding the physics of the phenomena with which we are concerned. And, for this purpose, it must suffice to give a bare outline of the disposition and action of the more essential parts. Starting from the outside, we have first the external ear (*pinna*), from which extends the ear passage (*external auditory meatus*). This ends at the drum-skin (*membrana tympani*), usually, though improperly, spoken of as the drum. Beyond this lies the cavity which is properly called the drum (*tympanum*). From the drum the Eustachian tube proceeds to the pharynx. This tube is usually closed, but opens each time swallowing occurs. This occasional opening of the tube for an instant effects, when necessary, the equalisation of the pressure of the air inside the drum with that of the external atmosphere. In other words, it relieves the drum-skin of any tension due to a difference of air pressures on its inner and outer sides. The drum is bridged across by a train of three little bones or *ossicles*. These are called the hammer, the anvil, and the stirrup (or *malleus*, *incus*, and *stapes* respectively). One part of the hammer is in contact with the drum-skin, while another part articulates with the anvil. A process of the anvil is attached to the apex of the stirrup. The base of the stirrup is applied to a membrane which closes an oval opening (*fenestra ovalis* or *fenestra vestibuli*) in the bony wall which forms the inner or *mesial* limit of the drum. In this bony wall there is in addition a round opening (*fenestra rotunda* or *fenestra cochlea*) also closed by a membrane. Beyond this mesial side of the drum with its two windows lies the innermost part of the organ of hearing called the labyrinth. This may be subdivided according to the natures of its materials or according to the shapes of its parts. Following the first method of subdivision, we recognise, first, the bony labyrinth or hollow excavated in the bony substance itself; and, secondly, the membranous labyrinth, a similar structure enclosed in the other and of similar shape. The membranous labyrinth contains a liquid called the endolymph. It is also surrounded, wholly or partially, by another liquid called the perilymph. This fills up the space between the membranous labyrinth and the bony labyrinth. Taking now the second method of subdivision, according to shape, the labyrinth comprises the vestibule, the three semi-circular canals, and the cochlea. The vestibule is the middle portion of the labyrinth, and contains the oval window that receives the foot of the stirrup. Upward and backward from the vestibule proceed the three semi-circular canals, each of which debouches with both its ends into the vestibule. With these we are not much concerned. Forward and

downward from the vestibule we have that very important
structure, the cochlea.   This is a spiral canal in form like a

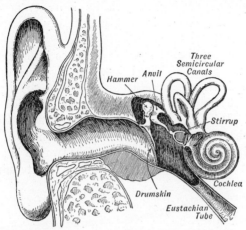

FIG. 65.—GENERAL VIEW OF HUMAN EAR.

snail shell.   At its entrance lies the round window previously referred to.

253. Let us now try to form a working conception of
these parts and their mutual relations.   A reference to
Fig. 65 will assist in this
endeavour.   But it must be
borne in mind that in a single
general diagram on a moderate
scale it is impossible to obtain
intelligibility without some
sacrifice of strict accuracy.
In this case, for example, the
labyrinth is, for clearness' sake,
drawn on a larger scale than
the rest.

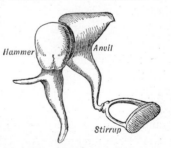

FIG. 66.—AUDITORY OSSICLES IN
POSITION.

Fig. 66 gives a larger view of the ossicles in position,
and should be examined next.

254. Let us now pass to a closer study of the cochlea.

Z

Suppose the spiral canal which forms the cochlea to be
straightened out. Then let a longitudinal section of it be
taken without cutting through its inner or membranous
portion. The result is diagrammatically represented in
Fig. 67.

We thus see that the perilymph space is, for the greater
part of the length, divided into two by a partition (the
lamina spiralis) which reaches almost to the tip of the
cochlea. The upper part in the diagram is called the *scala
vestibuli*. It begins at the oval window on which rests the foot
of the stirrup. The lower part is called the *scala tympani*
and begins at the round window. The two are in communication at the tip of the cochlea beyond the termination of

FIG. 67.—LONGITUDINAL SECTION OF COCHLEA AS IF STRAIGHT.

the lamina spiralis. It should be noted that each of these
scalæ, though here shown straightened out, is in the actual
cochlea comparable to the winding stairway of a turret,
hence their names.

255. We now pass to the consideration of a transverse
section of the spiral canal of the cochlea. This is shown in
Fig. 68.

In addition to the two perilymph spaces (scala vestibuli
and scala tympani) seen in the longitudinal section, this
shows the membranous portion of the cochlea (*canalis cochlearis*). It is thus seen that in this region the membranous
labyrinth is almost triangular in section. Its curved base
is closely applied to the corresponding portion of the bony
labyrinth instead of being separated from it by any space
filled with perilymph. The apex of the triangle meets the

partition (lamina spiralis) which completes the separation
between the scala vestibuli and the scala tympani. The
upper side of the triangle, as seen in the diagram, is known
as the membrane of Reissner. It divides the canalis cochlearis from the scala vestibuli. It is thin and simple in
character. The lower side of the triangle, on the other

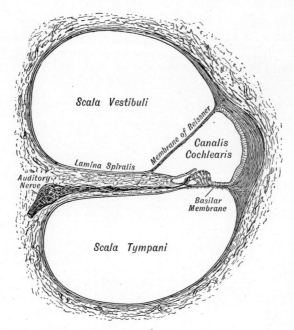

Fig. 68.—Diagram of a Transverse Section of a Whorl of the Cochlea.

hand, is very complex. Its outer part, to the right in the
figure, is formed by the basilar membrane. Its inner
portion (to the left) is composed of a projecting part of the
lamina spiralis, which here terminates in two lips (the
labium vestibulare and the *labium tympani*). Just beyond
these lips we have the organ of Corti. This comprises a
number of inner and outer rods of Corti (somewhat like
rafters of a roof), and various other minute structures.

This organ rests upon the centre part of the basilar membrane, which is thin and not highly specialised. The outer portion of the basilar membrane, which is free from other structures, is itself thicker and more highly specialised. It is found to be composed of radial fibres lying side by side and embedded in the homogeneous ground substance of different nature.

The auditory, cochlear nerve passes up the axis of the cochlea. As it ascends it gives off fibres passing outwards in a spiral manner into the lamina spiralis. The fibres pass into and become connected with the auditory epithelium of the organ of Corti.

256. The Act of Hearing.—Having sketched the chief parts of the human ear, we are now prepared to trace the contributions made by each to that complicated train of phenomena which constitutes the act of hearing. Suppose we have a simple tone produced at any external source in the neighbourhood, then waves of sound pass from that source to the ear. The atmosphere at the entrance to the ear is consequently vibrating in a simple harmonic manner. As the air waves fall upon the drum-skin, they force it into approximately corresponding vibrations. For the drum-skin is of such size and tension as to readily respond to any vibrations between certain wide limits. These vibrations then pass through the train of three ossicles. For the motion of the drum-skin is imparted to that process of the hammer in contact with it, by means of its articulation the hammer then passes the motion on to the anvil, and this in turn moves the stirrup bone. The base of the stirrup is applied to the membranous covering of the oval window, and so hands on its motion to the perilymph beyond, which occupies the scala vestibuli. This vibratory motion of the perilymph appears to affect the endolymph in the canalis cochlearis, the two liquids being separated only by the thin membrane of Reissner. Thus, the organ of Corti and the basilar membrane are exposed throughout the length of the cochlea to vibrations synchronous with those originating at the external source in the atmosphere. From the base of the cochlea to its tip these structures are graduated in size. They seem, therefore, designed to respond sympathetically to vibrations of all different frequencies throughout the range of audition. Formerly it was supposed that the rods of Corti played this part. But that view was abandoned as untenable. The *rôle* of sympathetic vibrations has since been ascribed to the basilar membrane. For it is loose longitudinally, that is, from base to tip of the spiral of the cochlea, but tense radially. Hence, it may be considered as consisting of a number of parallel strings somewhat like those of a harp. The radial dimensions of the basilar membrane are found to increase from the base to the tip of the cochlea. According to this view, then, as any simple vibration sweeps along the cochlea, it throws into sympathetic vibration just that part of the basilar membrane which is tuned to respond to motions of that particular frequency. The vibration thus excited in the membrane in turn so affects the overlying structures that auditory impulses are generated in a particular group of fibrils of the auditory nerve. These auditory impulses reaching the brain give rise to the corresponding sensation of a sound of that particular pitch, loudness, and duration.

257. Compound Tones.—Suppose now that two or more simple tones proceed from the same or different sources. We then have the corresponding number of simple harmonic vibrations produced at the external ear. Or we may regard the motion there as one compound vibration. This compound motion travels like the simple one through the drum-skin and chain of ossicles, arriving at the perilymph and endolymph in the cochlea. Then, as the composite vibration sweeps along the basilar membrane, we suppose it to excite sympathetic vibrations in certain parts of it, and in those only. Further, the parts

in question are those which are tuned to respond to the
particular frequencies which characterise the simple tones
of which the compound sound may be regarded as composed.
But this view of the case as to the function of the basilar
membrane must be taken only as a hypothesis. The
dimensions of the membrane seem scarcely adequate to
confirm it. In man the whole width of the membrane
has been found to vary between 0·21 mm. at the base of
the cochlea, to 0·36 mm. at the tip. The dimensions of the
outer specially-modified part show a similar range, being
0·075 mm. at the base to 0·126 mm. at the tip. The
estimated number of the radial fibres is 24,000. Thus,
even the physics of hearing is very complicated, and part
of it not clearly established. It is thus impossible strictly
to classify the ear along with the comparatively simple
physical experiments. It has been treated in this place
because the action of the drum-skin, which is perhaps best
understood, is certainly an example of the maintenance of
vibrations.

According, then, to the hypothesis just developed, we
may regard as follows the perception of those features
which characterise any musical sound, namely, pitch, loudness, and quality. The perception of pitch of a simple
tone is fixed by the part of the basilar membrane excited,
its loudness by the degree to which that part is excited,
while the perception of quality of a compound tone
depends upon the relation of pitch and loudness which
subsists between the different simple tones into which, by
the ear, we suppose the compound tone to have been
analysed. For we have already seen (see articles 12,
31, 51, and 164) that the quality of a tone depends upon
the number of partials of which it is composed, their
relative frequencies and intensities. (See also Chap. VIII.)

258. Vibrations modified by Aural Mechanism.—We
are not, however, to suppose that, in the act of hearing,
each part repeats and hands on with absolute fidelity the

type of vibration received by it. Indeed, that this is highly improbable a moment's reflection will show. For the vibration originally in the air has to be copied in turn by an elastic membrane, a chain of three rigid solids, a second membrane, a liquid, a third membrane, a second liquid, and, finally, those minute elastic structures in connection with the auditory nerve. Further, that first elastic membrane, namely, the drum-skin, is not flat, but has a point near its middle drawn inwards. From this point radial fibres proceed which are themselves convex outwards, see Fig. 69.

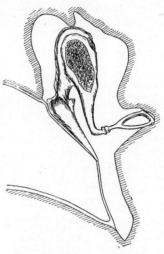

Hence the drum-skin is under asymmetrical conditions as regards motions inwards and motions outwards. It

FIG. 69.—EDGE VIEW OF DRUM-SKIN OF THE EAR AND OSSICLES.

may thus be expected to display all the complication which we have previously found to characterise the behaviour of such systems when under the action of periodic forces (see articles 115 and 116). Next, in the chain of ossicles it is found that an asymmetry results from their manner of articulation. Hence all aural sensations need careful interpretation, or, in various cases, we may be led astray. This subject will be referred to again later (see article 304).

259. Goold's Generators and Bars.—Having sufficiently considered cases of maintenance in which the period of the driver is quite definite, we now pass to those cases in which the periodic action of the driver is wholly or partially induced by the reaction of the driven whose period is definite. The first example we take is that furnished by bars vibrating transversely under the stimulus of a cane or other elastic rod passed in an oblique position over their surface. This method of eliciting the tones of bars, plates, etc., is due to Mr. Joseph Goold of Nottingham. It is illustrated in Fig. 70.

The motion of the generator seems like that of a walking-stick (say of Malacca or other cane) when grasped firmly by the handle and pushed along with its point on a smooth pavement. The stick then executes a number of vibrations which cause its point to move along by a series of short leaps or bounds. A smart blow is thus struck on the ground after each leap. Similarly a Goold's generator, when grasped in the hand and moved along the bar, seems

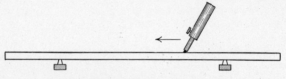

Fig. 70.—Action of Goold's Generator.

to give the bar a number of taps. Now if these are roughly in tune with the bar (say within a major third), then by slightly altering the inclination of the generator or the pressure of the fingers, or both, the tuning may be brought sufficiently near to elicit the tone of the bar by transverse vibrations. Thus in this case the driver acquires the correct period not solely by the direct automatic reaction of the driven, much of the adjustment being due to the intelligence and dexterity of the operator directed by suggestions derived from the driven.

The simplest form of generator adopted by Mr. Goold is that shown in Fig. 70. It consists of a piece of round cane fitted into a metal tube provided with a set screw for fixing the cane in the position found best for the purpose in view. The tip of the cane is simply rounded off. Some generators for rather low tones are tipped with leather.

Others, designed for eliciting low tones of 100 to 200 per second, have the elastic part of wire fitted into a massive iron handle. These are provided with a tip of india-rubber for contact with the bar.

260. EXPT. 41. *To elicit a given Partial from a Bar by a Goold's Generator.*—First obtain a rectangular bar of tool steel, say 70 to 80 cm. long, and about 3 cm. by 1 cm. cross section. Then, find from the theory of transverse vibrations of bars (article 210) the positions of the nodes for the particular vibration desired, and mark these positions on the bar. At two of these nodes the bar should be supported on india-rubber. Mr. Goold makes these supports by putting three or four short pieces of round rubber, about 5 mm. diameter, into a base of wood so that the ends of the rubber just stand up in a millimetre or two, and are in a straight row. This row of rubbers forms the support for one node ; a precisely similar arrangement supports the other node. If the bar has been prepared for this experiment some-time previously, and greased to preserve it from rust, it must be cleaned as perfectly as possible before use. It is desirable to remove the last trace of grease with india-rubber. Place the bar so that it is supported on the rubber at two of the nodes for the required vibration. Now it is important to have evidence when the bar is beginning to vibrate in the mode desired, so dust of some kind must be scattered on the bar. Sand, however, should be avoided, as a single grain of it interferes with the action of the generator. Use, in preference, flakes of chalk. But even this should not be present where the generator is to be used, say a region half the width of the bar and extending from near a node to the next antinode. So cover that portion of the bar with a card or slip of wood, and then scatter over the whole the dust or flakes obtained by grating a piece of chalk with the sharpened edge of a wood stick or dry gum brush (not a knife blade). Carbonate of magnesia scattered from a pepper-box is still better than chalk. Remove the covering from the part where the generator is to be used. Then stroke this part gently with a suitable generator. Listen for the sound, and watch whether the chalk flakes move towards the nodes. The pitch of the sound could be obtained by theory, or more simply by giving

the bar, when properly supported, a tap with a padded
mallet or even with the knuckle. If the desired sound is
not at first obtained, lengthen or shorten the projecting part
of the cane or other elastic substance of the generator. Also
change its inclination to the bar when in use. But do not
press hard or in any way use great force. That is useless.
But when the right length of cane is found, and the proper
inclination, these must be strictly preserved in use. Indeed,
the manipulation is much like that used with a glazier's
diamond, when the adjustments are perfect a gentle touch
suffices. Much time may be occupied in finding the right
length of cane for a given pitch on the first occasion. The
cane should then be marked and preserved in that position for
future use for the given pitch. On repetition with all duly
prepared, the experiment is very striking and beautiful, and
well repays the time originally spent upon it.

261. Action of Violin Bow.—In the case of Goold's
generators just considered, if the driver is sufficiently near
being in tune with the driven, the reaction of the latter
seems to complete the tuning and make the experiment
succeed. But some approximate tuning is first needed.
The striking peculiarity in the action of the violin bow is
that practically no tuning of the driver is needed. The
driver in this case has no period whatever proper to itself.
Indeed, it has no periodic motion of its own at all. Still
it readily excites and maintains vibrations in any string,
fork, bow, or plate capable of vibrating in the direction of
the bow's motion. How, then, does it act ? Consider first
its construction. A good violin bow when newly haired
contains about one hundred hairs from the tail of a white
horse, about half their number being directed one way, and
the rest the opposite way. The hairs are then rosined to
enable them to attack the strings well. Let a string,
initially at rest, have a bow drawn across it. The string
begins to vibrate, and that vibration may be maintained till
the end of the bow is reached. Thus while the bow moves
continuously in one direction, the part of the string under

it moves to and fro. Hence the motion of the string is alternately with and against that of the bow. Thus the speed of the bow relative to the string is alternately less and more than its own actual speed. But the tangential frictional force called into play between unlubricated solids is greater with a low relative speed than with a high one. Hence the urging effect of the bow when the string is moving with it is greater than its retarding effect when the string is moving against it. Thus there is, in the action of the bow, an outstanding excess of energy supplied to the string over that withdrawn. And it is this excess which is able to increase the vibrations of the string or maintain them in spite of dissipative forces. Moreover, the vibrations of the string, although thus maintained, are practically free as regards the naturalness of their frequencies. For, as we have just seen, it is the motion of the string itself which imparts periodicity to the action of the bow. The bow, as previously mentioned, has no periodicity in its own motion.

Suppose a horizontal string is bowed at a point nearer the right end than the left, and that the bow moves downward. Then, it appears from the experimental investigations of Helmholtz that the place on the string bowed, for the greater part of the period, moves down with a constant but comparatively low speed. Then it suddenly flies up, this high speed being also constant. It is then caught by another part of the bow and again moves slowly down. Its speed of descent is probably about that of the bow.

262. EXPT. 42. *Vibrations started and maintained by continuous Motion.*—An interesting illustration of the maintenance of vibrations by alternate bite and release is afforded by the following arrangement :—Set up in bearings a horizontal shaft of rough wood about 2 cm. diameter provided with a small handle. From this shaft hang a little bob of lead by a thread about a metre long. The loop of the thread round the shaft should be quite slack. Now rotate the shaft slowly and steadily in one direction. The pendulum will soon be seen to be vibrating, and the vibrations may be maintained indefinitely by the continuous rotation of the shaft. This illustrates on a cruder and more visible scale the type of action involved in the use of the bow.

263. Trevelyan's Rocker.

263. Trevelyan's Rocker.—We now pass to the first example of a vibration maintained by the periodic communication of heat and the consequent expansion. The experiment is due to Trevelyan, and is usually referred to as Trevelyan's rocker. The rocker consists of a prism of brass almost triangular in section, but one edge is taken

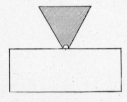

FIG. 71.
SECTION OF TREVELYAN'S
ROCKER.

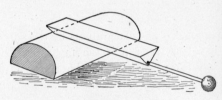

FIG. 72.
TREVELYAN'S ROCKER.

away and a groove made in the small flat thus produced, see Fig. 71. When working this prism rests with its groove downwards on a block of lead with a rounded top. The end of the rocker is carried by a rod terminating in a ball which rests on the counter, see Fig. 72.

264. EXPT. 43. *To produce Various Tones by Trevelyan's Rocker.*—Clean the rounded top of a lead block with a steel scraper, or burnish it with a smooth steel rod. Avoid using sand-paper or emery-paper on the lead, as the gritty particles so introduced would stick in the soft lead and interfere with the good metallic contact between the lead and brass, and thus prevent the rapid heat conduction so essential for the desired action. Next, place the rocker with groove uppermost over a Bunsen burner, and leave it till the flame is tinged with green. Remove the rocker from the flame, and quickly polish with fine emery the two narrow faces separated by the groove. Then immediately place it groove downwards on the lead block. The brass of the rocker is hard enough to bear the use of emery without detriment though the lead block is too soft for such handling. The rocker may spontaneously emit a musical sound immediately it is placed on the lead, or it may require a slight tap to start it rocking. Or, at first attempt, it may be too hot or too cold to work properly. But when, after a little trial, matters are rightly adjusted, it will rock rapidly and emit a humming sound. The pitch of this sound may be sharpened at will by pressing on the rod of the rocker near the ball with a round-ended rod, say a pen-holder. Also, by alternately increasing and decreasing the pressure so applied the sound emitted will rise and fall like the soughing of the wind.

The explanation of the maintenance of vibrations in this case is simple. The metallic surfaces being quite clean, very rapid communication of heat is possible. Thus, when the rocker is placed on the lead with one of its narrow faces in contact, the heat is communicated to the lead, and by the consequent expansion a slight hump is raised on the lead. This tilts the rocker over on to its other face, where the operations are repeated, and the rocker thereby returned to its original position. In order to account for the maintenance, we must introduce the idea of a slight lag between contact and expansion, or the approach of the rocker would be checked, and the motion discouraged to an extent equal to its encouragement in its return motion. The slight lag decreases the discouraging effect and increases the encouraging effect of the expansion, and thus there is an outstanding excess of encouragement which accounts for the maintenance of the vibration.

265. Singing Flames.—We now deal with a still more interesting though more complicated class of examples, in which vibrations are maintained by heat, namely, those in which the vibrating body is gaseous, and the heat is supplied by a small flame which vibrates in the process and so emits a musical sound. Hence the term singing flames. The vibrating body is the mixture of air and other gases contained in the tube or chamber into which the flame is introduced. To prevent deterioration of the air in this chamber it must evidently be open both above and below, but its form may be cylindrical or bulbous, like a lamp chimney. The gas used for the flame may be the ordinary coal gas, or be hydrogen evolved in the usual way from granulated zinc and hydrochloric acid in a flask with the jet tube mounted at the top. Let us first consider the matter from the experimental side, and notice the conditions requisite for success. We shall then be in a better position to examine in detail the hypotheses which have been advanced to account for these somewhat obscure phenomena.

266. Expt. 44. *Simple Form of Singing Flames.*—In a horizontal gas-pipe, about half an inch diameter, fasten an upright supply pipe about 10 cm. high with a pinhole burner at the top. Cut off from glass tubing about 1·5 cm. diameter a piece 30 cm. long. Light the jet and place the glass tube over it supported by a clip stand so that the jet is about 7 or 8 cm. from the lower end of the tube. The flame may perhaps spontaneously "sing." If not, it must be coaxed by adjusting its position or its size, or both ; or it may be that it will start if one sounds in the vicinity the note proper to the tube, found previously by blowing across its end. Usually the "singing" of the flame may be most easily started as follows :—Begin with the jet fairly large, and very slowly turn the gas lower until the flame begins to sing. It may then be turned much larger again without danger of losing the musical sound thus started.

Next try, with the same supply pipe and jet, a sound tube 15 cm. long and the same bore as before. Probably no coaxing will make the flame sing in this tube. The sound tube may be raised and lowered, moved sideways so as to bring the jet near its wall or back to the middle, and the gas turned lower, but probably all in vain. The reason for this we shall discuss later. It may easily be ascertained whether the luminous part of the flame is intermittent by moving the head rapidly from side to side. The same fact may be more conveniently demonstrated to an audience by the use of a rotating mirror.

If several singing flames are desired to sing simultaneously, a number of equal supply tubes and jets may be arranged on the same horizontal gas-pipe, and a singing tube placed in the right position over each, the whole being mounted on a simple wooden frame. If the lengths of the singing tubes vary they will emit sounds of correspondingly different pitches. Thus, if the sounding tubes are 60, 48, 40, and 30 cm. long, their internal diameters being graduated from 3 cm. to 1·5 cm., we should obtain the major chord and octave. If the lengths or diameters are not exact, and therefore the tones a little out of tune, the needed tuning may be effected by rings of paper sliding on the tops of the tubes. Raising this paper slider lengthens the tube and lowers its tone.

267. Phase of Heat-Supply.—In the case of the forced vibration of a point, we have already seen that the best effect in encouraging the kinetic energy of the vibration occurs if the impressed force is at a maximum when the displacement is zero (see arts. 91-96). Thus if the equation of motion is

$$\ddot{y} + 2\kappa\dot{y} + p^2 y = f \sin nt \qquad (1),$$

the forced vibration is expressible by

$$y_1 = \frac{f \sin \delta}{2\kappa n} \sin (nt - \delta) \qquad (2),$$

where

$$\tan \delta = \frac{2\kappa n}{p^2 - n^2} \qquad (3).$$

And, for the kinetic energy to be a maximum, we must have sin δ a maximum, i.e. $\delta = \pi/2$.

Hence by (3) we see that for this case $n = p$ (4).

Accordingly (2) becomes,

$$y_1 = -\frac{f}{2\kappa p} \cos pt \qquad (5),$$

where the impressed force is $f \sin pt$.

But, for vibrations maintained by heat, Lord Rayleigh has shown that the vibrations are best encouraged when the heat is given at the phase of greatest condensation and abstracted at the instant of greatest rarefaction. And, in stationary waves, the *states* of greatest condensation and rarefaction (at *places between nodes and antinodes*) occur when the particles are at their maximum displacement. So, at first sight, this may seem contradictory to what we have said above as to forced vibrations. However, it is not so, as we shall find presently.

268. The communication of heat may be regarded either (1) as replacing the impressed force of a forced vibration, or (2) as altering the zero position of the vibrating point, and consequently the value of the restoring forces throughout the time until the next abstraction or communication of heat. Now, if the heat were supplied and withdrawn according to a sine function of the time, the first view of the matter and an analytical treatment might be most convenient. But if, as we suppose, the heat is given somewhat suddenly, the second view of the matter and a graphical treatment seem more convenient. The vibrations of these gaseous particles and their maintenance by heat are comparable to the vibrations of a simple pendulum, and their maintenance by a periodic shift of its point of suspension. It will therefore probably facilitate a thorough understanding of the essential features of the case if we consider the two sets of conditions side by side.

269. Thus, suppose we have a simple pendulum of length l, the bob having unit mass and the point of suspension moving horizontally in the plane of vibration. Then, if the vibrations are small, so that the tension of the thread may be equated to the weight of the bob, we have the restoring force represented by $\frac{g}{l}(y - y_0)$, where y is the horizontal displacement of the bob, and y_0 that of the point of suspension. Hence, the equation of motion may be written

$$\ddot{y} + 2\kappa\dot{y} + \frac{g}{l}(y - y_0) = 0 \qquad (1).$$

Now, if $y_0 \propto \sin nt$, we may easily retain the analytical method and obtain the ordinary equation of forced vibration, namely,

$$\ddot{y} + 2\kappa\dot{y} + p^2 y = f \sin nt \qquad (2),$$

p^2 here denoting g/l. If, however, y_0 is susceptible to sudden changes only, instead of varying harmonically, it seems simpler to adopt a graphical representation corresponding to equation (1). Thus let the amplitude of the vibration be a and let y_0 be alternately zero and k. Thus, let y_0 be zero till the displacement is at its full negative value $-a$, when y_0 suddenly becomes k. It is evident that the amplitude is thereby virtually changed to $a + k$, and that all the restoring forces are altered accordingly so long as y_0 retains its value k. The bob therefore swings in the next half-period, from the position $-a$, about the displaced centre of suspension k, to the other end of its swing, viz. $a + 2k$. If, at this instant, the point of suspension returns suddenly to the zero position, *i.e.* $y_0 = 0$, it is evident that the amplitude is thereby made equal to the displacement $a + 2k$. Thus, each time the displacement of the centre of suspension is suddenly changed at the right instant and in the right direction, the amplitude is increased by k, the same amount as the shift. If, in the meantime, due to the frictional resistances, the amplitude had diminished by that amount, then the dissipative forces would be just balanced and the vibrations maintained.

270. Turn now to the gaseous vibrations, and let us consider first a pipe stopped at one end E, and with an antinode at or near O, see Fig. 73. Let the amplitude of the vibrations at O be a. Then, when the particles are displaced their full amplitude from O to A, let heat be

2 A

given to the portion EO, and increase its pressure so that, on the pressure falling to its normal value, O is shifted to O′, where $OO' = k$. Then, by the first of the two views of the matter previously mentioned, we could say that the impressed force is acting to urge the particles from A towards O in addition to the ordinary restoring force. But, taking the second view of the matter, which is here more convenient, we can say that the zero position of the particles is suddenly shifted from O to O′, and that the amplitude is accordingly $a + k$ instead of a only. Half a period later the particles will be at B, where $O'B = O'A = a + k$. If, at this instant, heat be suddenly abstracted so that O′ is brought back to O, then the amplitude is $OB = a + 2k$.

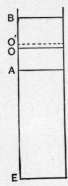

FIG. 73.

THEORY OF SINGING FLAMES.

271. To determine whether the period is unaltered, we must examine if the restoring forces bear to the displacement the same relation as before. Now, the heat communicated causes expansion from O to O′ under constant pressure, and the elasticity of a gas is proportional to the pressure. Hence the elasticities with zeros at O and O′ must be equal. Let the increments of pressure for displacement y be respectively p and p' with zeros at O and O′. Then, since the volumes concerned are proportional to the lengths of the columns, we have

$$\frac{p}{y/\text{EO}} = \frac{p'}{(y+k)/\text{EO}'}, \text{ or } \frac{p}{y} : \frac{p'}{y+k} = \text{EO}' : \text{EO} \quad (3),$$

that is, forces per unit displacement with zeros at O and O′ are in the ratio EO′ to EO. Thus, if $OO' = k$ be negligible in comparison with EO, we have

$$\frac{p}{y} = \frac{p'}{y+k} \text{ nearly} \qquad (4).$$

And to this approximation the periods are equal.

272. Let us now examine the slight effect on the period when OO' is not neglected. The period of a simple harmonic motion is given by

$$\tau = 2\pi/\omega \text{ where } \omega = \sqrt{\frac{\text{force per unit displacement}}{\text{mass}}}.$$

Thus, the ratio τ/τ' of the periods with zeros at O and O' is given by

$$\tau/\tau' = \omega'/\omega = \sqrt{EO/EO'} \tag{5}.$$

Or, in words, the period is slightly increased by the shift of zero due to heating.

Another way of obtaining the same result is to note that, for the stationary waves in question,

$$\tau = \frac{\lambda}{v} = \frac{\lambda_0(1+at)}{v_0\sqrt{1+at}} = \frac{\lambda_0}{v_0}\sqrt{1+at} \tag{6},$$

where λ and v denote wave length and speed of propagation at temperature t; λ_0 and v_0 those at $0°$ C., and a the co-efficient of expansion. Thus, if, on the supply of heat and consequent expansion from O to O' at constant pressure, the temperature rises from t to t', we have $\tau/\tau' = \dfrac{\sqrt{1+at}}{\sqrt{1+at'}}$; or, since the volume EO is proportional to the factor $1+at$,

$$\tau/\tau' = \sqrt{EO/EO'} \tag{7},$$

which agrees with (5).

If, in contrast to the above cases, heat were given when the particles were passing from O' to O, it is obvious that the period would be slightly shortened, for the zero position would come out to meet them. On the other hand, if heat were given half a period later, when the particles were passing from O to O', the period would be slightly lengthened. In either of these cases the amplitude would not be much changed, because near the equilibrium position the restoring forces are very small, hence the speed is about the same at

O or O′, and therefore the amplitude about the same with respect to one zero position or the other.

273. Graphical Treatment of the Problem.—Let us now illustrate graphically a forced vibration, the impressed force being harmonic, in contrast with vibrations maintained by heat suddenly supplied and withdrawn. The first state of things is shown in Fig. 74, and the second in the two following figures.

HARMONIC AND IMPULSIVE FORCES.

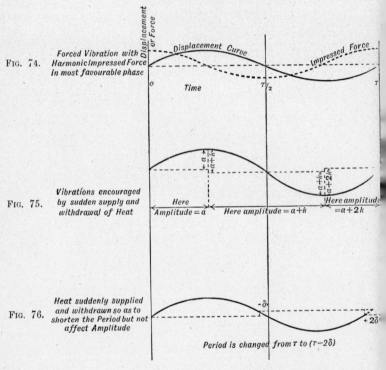

FIG. 74. Forced Vibration with Harmonic Impressed Force in most favourable phase

FIG. 75. Vibrations encouraged by sudden supply and withdrawal of Heat

FIG. 76. Heat suddenly supplied and withdrawn so as to shorten the Period but not affect Amplitude

Thus, we may summarise as follows:—(1) If heat is supplied at the instant of greatest condensation (the particles then having their maximum displacement) or abstracted at the instant of greatest rarefaction, or both, the vibration is encouraged and the period not much changed. (2) If the heat is supplied and abstracted when the vibrating particles are not displaced, and consequently the gas at the normal density, the amplitude is not much changed, but the period is. (3) Thus, the period is shortened if the heat is supplied a quarter of a period before the phase of greatest condensation, and the period is lengthened if the heat is supplied a quarter of a period after the phase of greatest condensation. (4) If, in the general case, heat is supplied at intermediate times, then it will produce effects both on the amplitude and the period.

These statements should be verified by the reader from the figures and the general theory applicable to them and already adduced. The comparison of Figs. 74 and 75 will also solve the paradox that for the best encouragement of the vibrations a harmonic force must be at its maximum when the displacement is zero, but the sudden supply or withdrawal of heat should occur when the displacement has its maximum value.

274. Place of Heat-Supply.—In considering the phase of heat-supply and its effects upon the vibrations, we have so far supposed the heat to be diffused along the quarter wave length from a node to an antinode. Let us now examine the consequences of restricting the region, and of changing its position with respect to the stationary waves in question. And, first, let the heat be supplied near a node. Then it may be seen that the effects above described will be produced however near to the node the place of heat-supply may be. In other words, heat supplied near a node alters the restoring force or spring, and is like shifting the point of suspension of the pendulum. It thus changes the zero position of the vibrations, and either their amplitude or period according to the phase of supply. If, however, the heat be supplied near an antinode, the spring is practically unaltered. In Fig. 77 let E be a node, O an antinode, A the particles at their maximum displacement downwards from O, and let heat be supplied in the thin layer between C and A. Then the portion CA may be expanded to CA′ and the zero shifted from O to O′, where AA′ = OO′. But the amplitude is not thereby altered, although the heat was supplied in the most favourable phase, for A′O′ = AO. Or reverting again to the pendulum, the introduction of heat in CA may be compared to shifting simultaneously and by equal amounts both the point of suspension and the bob itself.

FIG. 77.—PLACE OF HEAT-SUPPLY.

We have thus ascertained not only the phase, but also the place of heat-supply to best encourage the vibrations. In what follows we can, therefore, dispense with the restriction of a stopped end, replacing it by any node of the stationary waves. We are accordingly now in a position to consider the maintenance by heat of vibrations in a tube open at both ends like those used in the experiment No. 44.

275. Length of Supply Tube.—We have now finally to consider under what conditions the heat may be supplied at the right place and times to encourage the vibrations, and thus explain the experimental facts of singing flames. It might at first sight seem probable that the greatest issue of gas would occur at the phase of least pressure in the sounding tube, and that the greatest heating effect would occur at the instant of greatest issue. If these things were so the flame would be unable to maintain the vibrations, but would discourage them, the circumstances being the reverse of what we have seen (in articles 270-274) to be requisite for encouragement. But both the above suppositions are incorrect. Lord Rayleigh has pointed out that there are

really stationary or approximately stationary waves, not
only in the larger or singing tube, but also in the smaller
or supply tube.   And at the jet or tip of the supply-tube
we must have the condition that the pressures in large
and small tubes are equal.   Hence for equality of pressures
it is evident that the pressures in both tubes must be
increasing or decreasing simultaneously.   Now in stationary
waves the amplitudes and velocities increase with distance
from a node.   Thus, when there is motion from a node the
pressures are decreasing, because more gas is being lost
by the higher velocities at places remote from the node
than is being received by the lower velocities at places
nearer the node.   Hence, both in the singing and supply
tubes, the motions at any instant must be either both to
or both from their respective nodes.

276. Consider now a supply tube, whose length, from
the jet to the longer pipe below, into which it opens, is
a little less than a quarter of a wave length for the gas
being burnt and the frequency produced in the sounding
tube.   Let the jet be well inside the sounding tube, as
in our Expt. 44.   Then in the supply tube we have an
antinode at the bottom where it opens into the larger pipe,
and a node a little above its top.   In the sounding tube
we have an antinode at the bottom and a node at the
middle.   Thus, at any given instant we may have the
motions in the two tubes near the jet either both up or
both down.   For, with motions up in each tube, they will
be towards a node in each, and consequently the pressure
will be increasing in each, and this makes it possible for
the pressures to remain equal at the jet in the small tube
and the large one.   If, on the other hand, the motions are
both down, the pressures at the jet are decreasing in each
tube, which again allows them to remain equal as required.
In Fig. 78 the motions in the two cases are indicated by
arrows drawn in full lines and dotted lines respectively.
The node and antinode for the supply tube are denoted by

N_1 and A_1, and those for the singing tube by N_2 and A_2 respectively.

Thus we shall have gas coming out of the jet best when the air in the singing tube is condensing at N_2. Hence we might obtain the greatest heating effect at the instant of greatest condensation if we could account for a lag in that effect behind the instant of. freest emission of gas from the jet. That such a lag must exist is evident from the fact that time is required for combustion and heat production, and also for sending out the air previously sucked in at the jet.

277. Thus we have the conditions required by theory for the maintenance of the vibrations, and the phenomena of the singing flames are, in the main, explained.

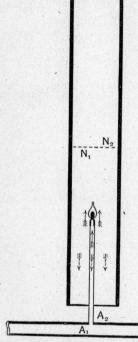

FIG. 78.—SIMULTANEOUS MOTIONS IN SINGING AND SUPPLY TUBES.

If the supply tube is made more than $\lambda/2$, but less than $3/4\lambda$, it will again encourage the vibrations and give a singing flame. If, however, the length of the supply tube is made more than $\lambda/4$ and less than $\lambda/2$, we should have the vibrations discouraged, and no coaxing would make the flame sing. (This is the explanation of the failure of the 15 cm. tube in Expt. 44.) It must be remembered that the λ here used is that corresponding to the gas supplied to the jet, and to the frequency of the note emitted by the singing tube. This frequency in turn depends on the length of the singing tube and on the nature and temperature of the gases in it. There is thus no simple geometrical relation between the λ above mentioned and the length of the sounding tube. The lengths of the supply tube and the effects of the corresponding jets in the vibrations may be thus exhibited—

Lengths of Supply Tube	o	$\lambda/4$	$\lambda/2$	$3\lambda/4$
Vibrations of Singing Tube	encouraged	discouraged	encouraged	

If the length of the supply tube were made exactly $\lambda/4$ the vibration would be neither encouraged nor discouraged, for the jet would be at a node, and no variation in the flow could occur there.

What we have discussed simply concerns the maintenance of a vibration already started. Such vibrations may or may not start spontaneously. Hence, in the actual experiment it is sometimes necessary to start the sound by making a sound of the right pitch near the tube.

278. Electrically-Driven Tuning - Fork. — Another good example of the maintenance of vibrations is that afforded by a tuning-fork fitted with an electro-magnet between its prongs. The current may be derived from one or two storage cells, and is interrupted by the

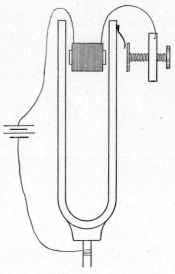

Fig. 79.—Diagram of Electrically-Driven Tuning-Fork.

vibrations of the fork itself. The interruption may be accomplished by a platinum wire dipping into a cup of mercury, as advised by Helmholtz. Or it may be due simply to a platinum wire on the prong and an adjustable screw on the framework, which alternately make and break contact as the fork vibrates. This arrangement is shown diagrammatically in Fig. 79. To set the fork going it is only necessary to put on the current, tap the fork with

the finger to obtain a slight initial vibration, and then adjust
the screw contact until the vibrations are increased and
vigorously maintained.

It is interesting to examine why the current is competent
to maintain this vibration. If the end of the prong and
contact wire were quite rigid, and the magnetic field and
current followed their motions instantaneously, then no
encouragement of the vibrations would be possible. For
in that case the magnet's attraction on the prongs assisting
their closing motion would be exactly counterbalanced by
its equal and equally-long exerted attraction opposing their
opening motion. There would thus be no balance carried
over to compensate for dissipation. But owing to self-
induction there is a lag in the establishment of the magnetic
field and current, and also in the annulling of the field
again. And thus, for both reasons, the prongs of the fork
will be more assisted in closing than resisted in opening.
Hence the encouragement of the vibrations is explained.
Here, of course (as shown by the theory of forced vibration,
see art. 96), the maximum effect on energy of vibrations
and the minimum disturbance of period will be secured
only if the maximum of impressed force occurs at the
instant of no displacement of the prongs.

279. Sensitive Jets and Flames.—Having sufficiently
treated the maintenance of vibrations, we now pass to the
consideration of various pieces of sensitive apparatus which
undergo some change in response to a sound, and thus
serve as indicators of its presence and reception. We begin
with what are called sensitive flames. The term sensitive
flame is usually applied to specially arranged flames which
burn steadily of a given size and shape when no sound
reaches them, but shorten and roar when excited by the
receipt of appropriate sounds. But Tyndall has shown
experimentally that the seat of the sensitiveness lies, not
in the flame itself, but in the jet of gas issuing from the
burner. Thus the term "sensitive jet" is really more

correct. The flame is a mere indicator of the behaviour of the really sensitive portion of the unignited gas.

The problem of sensitive jets has been dealt with mathematically by Lord Rayleigh. But the analysis is unsuited for introduction here. It must suffice to quote the results as follows :—When the fluid jet is launched into still air a steady motion may satisfy the dynamical conditions, and so be in a sense possible. But under certain conditions the smallest departure from such ideal steady motion tends to increase, and often very rapidly. Thus any impressed force, however feeble, provided it is of suitable frequency and reaches the jet at the right place, produces a departure from the normal motion, which departure is quickly exaggerated and made evident by the consequent behaviour of the flame.

Many types of sensitive flame have been devised. We shall deal here with three illustrative types, namely, Tyndall's vowel flame, Lord Rayleigh's enclosed jet, and an ordinary bunsen burner made sensitive.

280. EXPT. 45. *Tyndall's Vowel Flame.*—This is a high-pressure flame sensitive to sounds of very high pitch. The gas issues from the single orifice of a Sugg's steatite pinhole burner, and the flame reaches a height of about 24 inches. The gas may be derived from a weighted gas bag or a steel cylinder of compressed gas. In either case the pressure must be adjusted till the flame is as tall as possible without flaring. Tyndall, in his *Lectures on Sound* (p. 260), describes its sensitiveness as follows :—"The slightest tap on a distant anvil reduces its height to 7 inches. When a bunch of keys is shaken the flame is violently agitated, and emits a loud roar. The dropping of a sixpence into a hand already containing coin, at a distance of 20 yards, knocks the flame down. It is not possible to walk across the floor without agitating the flame, the creaking of boots sets it in violent motion. The crumpling or tearing of paper, or the rustle of a silk dress, does the same. It is startled by the patter of a rain-drop. I hold a watch near the flame : nobody hears its ticks ; but you all see their effect upon the flame. At

every tick it falls and roars. The winding up of the watch
also produces tumult. The twitter of a distant sparrow
shakes the flame down; the note of a cricket would do the
same. A chirrup from a distance of 30 yards causes it to
fall and roar." . . . "To distinguish it from the others I
have called this the 'vowel flame,' because the different
vowel sounds affect it differently. A loud and sonorous
U does not move the flame; on changing the sound to O
the flame quivers; when E is sounded the flame is strongly
affected. I utter the words *boot, boat,* and *beat* in succession.
To the first there is no response; to the second the flame
starts; by the third it is thrown into greater commotion.
The sound *Ah !* is still more powerful."

We shall see in Chapter VIII. that the different vowels
have components of certain definite frequencies specially
favoured. Hence the flame responds best to those vowels
which contain prominent components near the pitch to
which it is most sensitive.

281. Expt. 46. *Rayleigh's Sensitive Flame.*—Lord Rayleigh's
enclosed jet is sensitive to sounds of ordinary pitches, say
those throughout the compass of the pianoforte, and possesses
the great advantage of working off the ordinary gas-supply.
A jet of coal gas rises from a steatite pinhole burner placed
in the interior of a chamber. It then passes through a
vertical tube $\frac{7}{8}$ inch inside diameter and $6\frac{1}{4}$ inches long,
mounted on the chamber, and, on reaching the top, burns
in the open air. The front of the chamber is formed of
tissue paper; on this flexible membrane the sounds are
allowed to impinge, and so affect the jet just after leaving
the burner. A stout rod of copper, covered with asbestos,
may with advantage pass from the top of the tube, where
the combustion commences, down to the supply tube, as near
as possible to the burner. This rod, by conduction of heat,
prevents the formation of dew on the steatite pinhole
burner. The dew is to be avoided, because it would interfere with the proper working of the apparatus.

To adjust the flame to sensitiveness, begin with the full
pressure of the ordinary gas-supply. The flame then presents
the appearance of a Bunsen flame when air is excluded.
Next lower the gas pressure very slowly and watch the
flame. When a certain pressure is reached the flame suddenly
assumes a fluttering and lop-sided appearance, being at one

side drawn down into the tube a little. Lower the pressure
a little more until, though still lop-sided, the flame is steady.
The flame is then right for use, and will be found sensitive
to the crumpling of paper and to the sound of walking
across a boarded floor, to the clapping of hands, and to the
notes of the pianoforte. Its recovery after excitation is
rather slow.

282. EXPT. 47. *Sensitive Flame from a Bunsen Burner.*—
Select a Bunsen burner whose upright tube is of brass,
5 inches high and 3/8 inch in bore, and of the pattern which
possesses only *one* side hole for the admission of air, and
which is *perfectly* closed by a *half*-turn of the sleeve provided
for that purpose. To obtain the sensitive state, exclude
the air completely by the half-turn of the sleeve, and then
reduce the pressure of the gas-supply until the flame becomes
lop-sided but quiet. The maximum pressure subject to
these conditions seems to give the best results. The
flame is then about 4 inches high, that side of its base
next the supply tube being detached from the lip of
the upright tube and extending downwards into it about
a third of an inch. The burner is not, however, "lit
back."

When responding to suitable sounds, the flame falls from
its usual height of 4 inches to a height of about $1\frac{1}{2}$ inch.
This form of flame is insensitive to the crumpling of paper
and the jingling of keys, but responds promptly to clapping
the hands, shuffling the feet on a boarded floor, coughing,
speaking, whistling, or singing. The flame, after responding
to any sound, quickly resumes its sensitive state ready to
receive and respond to another sound. Hence it is possible
to whistle a slow staccato passage, each note being acknow-
ledged by a "duck" or curtsy of the flame, and each rest
by a recovery to its usual height and form.

283. Suspended Disc.—When a light disc is suspended
so as to be capable of rotating freely about a vertical axis,
it shows a tendency to set normally to the direction of flow
of the medium in which it is placed. The rigid proof of
this and the evaluation of the couple experienced are
beyond the scope of this work, but Lord Rayleigh gives a
simple qualitative explanation as follows :—

"That a flat obstacle tends to turn its flat side to the stream may be inferred from the general character of the lines of flow round it. The pressures at the various points of the surface BC (Fig. 80) depend upon the velocities of

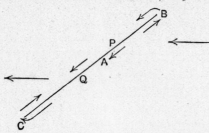

the fluid there obtaining. The full pressure due to the complete stoppage of the stream is to be found at two points where the current divides. It is pretty evident that upon the up-stream side this lies (P) on

FIG. 80.—EXPLANATION OF COUPLE ON DISC.

AB, and upon the down-stream side upon AC at the corresponding point Q. The resultant of the pressures thus tends to turn AB so as to face the stream."

For the quantitative solution of the problem, the reader is referred to an article by König.[1] In the case of a thin circular disc, whose normal makes the angle θ with the direction of the undisturbed stream, the moment M of the couple tending to diminish θ is given by

$$M = \frac{4}{3}\rho a^3 W^2 \sin 2\theta,$$

ρ being the density of the medium streaming with velocity W, and a being the radius of the disc. If the stream be alternating instead of steady, the mean value of W^2 must be employed. It is seen that the equation supports the view that might have been inferred from the elementary consideration of stream lines, viz. that the moment is a maximum for $\theta = 45°$.

EXPT. 48. *Setting of Suspended Disc.*—In front of the mouth of the resonance box of a tuning-fork of (say) 128

[1] *Wied. Ann.*, xliii. p. 51, 1891.

vibrations per second, suspend by a cocoon fibre a disc of thin card about 1 cm. in radius. Adjust the fibre so that the equilibrium position of the disc is at an angle of about 45° with the mouth of the resonator. Then, on bowing the fork, the disc will promptly set itself approximately across the mouth. In order to demonstrate the effect to an audience, replace the disc by a small mirror, which reflects a beam of light on to a distant screen. Then, on bowing the fork, the spot of light will sharply move across the screen. The same response may also be elicited by powerfully singing the same note to the vowel ōō in front of the resonator.

Prof. C. V. Boys, by an arrangement of double resonators, has exalted in a remarkable degree the sensitiveness of an instrument constructed on this principle.[1]

284. Kundt's Dust Figures.—To make evident the stationary waves in a horizontal glass tube and mark their length, Kundt devised the method of strewing its interior with lycopodium seed or other dust. This dust is promptly thrown into a recurring pattern when the waves are excited with sufficient vigour. The experiment was performed in several ways by Kundt himself, and further applications of the principle have been made by others. Some of these uses of the experiment will be noticed in the chapter on acoustical determinations, a brief description of one simple form sufficing here as an introduction of the method. In this form the stationary waves in the tube are excited by the longitudinal vibrations of a rod.

285. EXPT. 49. *Simple Form of Kundt's Dust-Figures.*— Select a glass tube about 60 to 100 cm. long and 5 cm. internal diameter. This is to form what is called the *wave tube* in which the stationary vibrations are to be set up. They in turn, under proper conditions, produce the dust figures by which the vibrations are recognised and measured. To start and maintain the stationary waves, choose a brass rod about a metre long and a centimetre diameter. This may be called the sounding rod. One end of this rod must

---

[1] *Phil. Mag.*, vol. xiv. p. 186, 1882.

be provided with a disc, preferably of ebonite. This disc
must be small enough to enter without touching the wave
tube, but so large as to only just clear it.

The sounding rod needs firmly clamping exactly in the
middle of its length, and the wave tube must be supported
so that the axis of rod and tube are in the same line, the
disc of the rod being within the tube. The far end of the
tube must also be closed by· a cork or rubber bung. A
simple and convenient way of effecting these arrangements
is shown in Fig. 81, in which it will be noticed that the
bases of the supports for rod and tube are separate and fit
together so as to allow of a sliding motion endwise. When
these arrangements are made, the *modus operandi* is briefly as
follows :—A very little lycopodium having been introduced
into the wave tube and spread about it, stroke the rod with
a rosined leather so as to elicit its longitudinal vibrations.

FIG. 81.—APPARATUS FOR KUNDT'S DUST FIGURES.

This may set up stationary waves in the tube and so lead to
the formation of the dust figures which mark their presence
and length. Thus the actions of the rosined leather on the
rod, and of the rod on the air in the tube, are examples of
maintenance. But the formation of the dust figures, with
which we are here principally concerned, is an example of a
sensitive arrangement which passes from one state to another
in response to a wave motion. Hence the inclusion of the
experiment in this subdivision of the chapter.

But in order to make the experiment succeed, several
practical details need careful attention. For the rod will
not "speak" freely if clamped anywhere. Neither will the
stationary waves be set up in the wave tube unless the
length between its stopped end and the disc on the rod is a
multiple of the half-wave in air (or other gas in the wave
tube) of the vibration executed by the rod. And, finally, the
stationary waves, when set up, will not give the desired dust
figures if either the tube or dust is wet or too much dust is
present. So we summarise as follows :—(1) Wipe the wave

tube out with a "mop" of cotton wool on the end of a stick, and then dry it thoroughly over a Bunsen flame (use no liquid in the tube). (2) Dry the lycopodium in a desiccating chamber or in a porcelain bowl over a small flame. (3) Use only as much lycopodium as will cover a strip the length of the wave tube and about 2 mm. wide. (4) When the wave tube is in place, tap it smartly with a metal rod or pencil to bring the lycopodium into a line along the bottom of the tube, then rotate the tube about its axis through 45° or even 60° till the lycopodium is just on the point of slipping down. (5) Take care that the sounding rod is clamped exactly at the middle so that it can "speak" freely. (6) Adjust the length in the wave tube between its stopped end and the disc on the rod, by steps of about a

FIG. 82.—PLAN OF KUNDT'S DUST FIGURES, FIRST STAGE.

FIG. 83.—PLAN OF KUNDT'S DUST FIGURES, FINAL STAGE.

centimetre. Stroke the rod with the rosined leather after each such adjustment until the pattern of the dust figures appears. Their first appearance will probably be due to the lycopodium remaining stationary at the nodes, and falling at the ventral segments or spaces between the nodes as shown in Fig. 82. This state is all that is required for purposes of lecture demonstration to show that the waves are present and can move the dust. It is not, however, very suitable for purposes of exact measurement. So, if this is required, (7) make the disc fit the tube as perfectly as possible by putting, if necessary, a thin paper round it till it is as large as may be without touching the tube. By a continued sounding of the rod's note, by stroking it, the dust figures should then change slowly by a motion in the ventral segments, from the disc towards the stopped end of the wave tube, until the dust is in little heaps at the nodes. This state, which is somewhat difficult to obtain, is shown in Fig. 83.

The length of the sounding rod is half the wave length in

that material of the tone it emits, also the distance between
the nodes in the wave tube is half the wave length of that
same tone in the air or other gas occupying the wave tube.
Further, the wave lengths for a given tone are proportional
to speed of propagation. Hence the experiment gives
directly a comparison between the speed of sound in the
material of the sounding rod and in the gas occupying the
wave tube. Thus by using rods of different material and
filling the tube with gases a variety of experiments is
possible. These will be dealt with in the chapter on
acoustical determinations.

286. Striations in Dust Figures.—As shown in Fig.
82, Kundt's dust figures not only exhibit the pattern
with which we are mainly concerned, and whose length is
half the wave length of the stationary vibrations in the tube,
but show also a much smaller pattern or *striation*. And
this too is of interest, being closely connected with the
phenomenon of rotation of a suspended disc when exposed
to vibrations or a steady current. We saw in article 283
that a suspended disc was subject to a couple, and that the
couple would be experienced by any flattened or elongated
body. But the lycopodium seeds are approximately spheres,
and a sphere exposed to a stream could have no tendency
to turn. Further, an isolated sphere exposed to a stream
would have the flow symmetrical on the up-stream and
down-stream sides, and consequently the main pressures
would balance one another. Thus a sphere would
experience neither force nor couple in an ideally perfect
fluid. But a close examination of the dust figures in a
Kundt's tube show that, while the vibrations are in
progress, a rib-like structure obtains, the lycopodium grains
being at places heaped up, and the tube in the intervening
spaces being nearly bare. When the vibrations cease,
much of this striation is lost, but evidence of it still
remains. The presence of these striations has been explained by A. König.[1] Although a single spherical obstacle

[1] *Wied. Ann.*, vol. xlii. pp. 353 and 549, 1891.

experiences no force nor couple from an alternating current, each of a pair of spheres at a moderate distance apart may do. First, let us note that where the velocity of the stream is greater the pressure must be less, for it is accelerated in passing from a space of greater pressure to one of less pressure. Now consider two spheres, one ahead of the other in the alternating stream. Each screens the other, so the stream speed between them will be less than outside, hence the pressure between them is greater than outside, and the spheres repel each other. Again, consider two spheres side by side in the alternating stream. It is easy to see that the stream speed between them is greater than normally, and accordingly the pressure is less than normally, hence attraction follows. The result of these forces is a tendency to aggregation in laminæ across the stream. König has also calculated the direction and magnitude of the forces operative on two spheres which are not too close together. From this it appears that when the spheres are oblique the direction of the forces does not coincide with the line of centres. If the spheres are rigidly connected, the forces on them reduce to a couple, tending to increase θ, whose moment is given by

$$G = \frac{3\pi\rho a_1{}^3 a_2{}^3 W^2}{r^3} \sin 2\theta,$$

where ρ is the density and W the speed of the fluid, $a_1\ a_2$ the radii of the spheres and r their distance asunder, and θ is the angle between the line of centres and the direction of the current. When the current is alternating the mean value of W^2 is to be taken.

287. Maintenance of Compound Vibration.—Suppose we have a system capable of simultaneous vibrations of periods nearly or quite commensurate. And let it be acted upon by a periodic impressed force almost in tune with the primary free vibrations. Then it may be shown that each

harmonic component of the force produces in the system a
harmonic motion of the same period as that of the force,
provided that the squares of the displacements and velocities
may be neglected.[1]　But, if the whole force impressed is
strictly periodic, it may be regarded as consisting of a
number of *commensurate* harmonic forces as shown by
Fourier's theorem (see article 51).　Hence, the compound
vibrations maintained in the system will consist wholly
of *commensurate* harmonic motions, although the periods of
the free vibrations natural to that system may differ slightly
from the harmonic series.

But, if these periods natural to the system do not form
a harmonic series, this fact is not without effect on the
character of the vibrations maintained.　For although the
periods are forced to be commensurate, the amplitudes are
greater the closer the tuning between the vibrations natural
to the system and those forced upon it.　Hence the closer
the period of any of the free vibrations lies to that of the
corresponding vibrations in the strict harmonic series, the
more fully will that component vibration be elicited and
maintained by the impressed force.　Those lying farther
out of tune with the corresponding tones of the harmonic
series being less powerfully brought forth (see also arts.
97 and 98).

This fact has an important bearing in connection with
the maintenance of vibration in strings and organ pipes.
For both these systems are capable, as we have already
seen, of a number of vibrations whose periods are almost
but not quite a harmonic series.　When exciting free
vibrations in such systems (say by plucking a string), this
departure from the harmonic series would be preserved.
When, however, the string is bowed or the pipe blown, the
vibrations are maintained by a periodic force, and the
periods are forced into the strict harmonic series.　Accord-

---

[1] Rayleigh's *Sound*, vol. i. p. 147 ; compare also article 116 of the present
work.

ingly, in view of what we have just seen, those partials are most favoured which lie closest to the strict harmonic series, and those are feeblest heard which depart more widely from that strict series. The effect of this will be discussed further in Chapter VIII.

CHAPTER VII

INTERFERENCE AND COMBINATIONAL TONES

288. Interference.—In dealing with the kinematics of the subject (articles 28 and 43) we saw that the composition of two vibrations of equal period and amplitude but opposite phases yielded a zero resultant. Or, in other words, two such vibrations destroy one another. This is the typical case which is often referred to as an example of interference. The term interference is used in acoustics and optics to denote the phenomena of alternate additive and subtractive character which occur, under suitable conditions, when radiations from two sources mingle. Thus, as shown in any treatise of physical optics, two sources of light may produce on a given screen equidistant bright and dark bands, the effects of the two sources being additive in the bright and subtractive in the dark bands. These phenomena are not only of importance as showing that the radiation concerned is a wave motion, but they also enable us to measure the wave length. For evidently in passing from a bright to the next dark band we pass from a place where the vibrations from the two sources are in the same phase to a place where they are in opposite phases. Suppose the two sources to be in the same phase, and that the bright band in question were equidistant from these sources. Then the neighbouring dark bands would be at distances from the two sources differing by a half-wave

374

length. Or, generally, if the difference of distances from the two sources of any bright band is $2n$ half-wave lengths, the difference of distances of the contiguous dark bands from the two sources must be $(2n \pm 1)\lambda/2$.

289. Reserving quantitative applications of this principle to the tenth chapter, we shall now deal with the experimental illustrations suitable to demonstrate its reality in the domain of acoustics. It should be observed at the outset that, in dealing with the actual vibrations of material bodies, it does not follow, as a matter of course, that the simple kinematical rules developed in Chap. II. will always hold. They certainly will when the displacements are indefinitely small. And throughout the first part of this chapter, dealing with interference, we shall suppose that condition to hold good. Later, under the heading of combinational tones, we shall study what happens when the above condition of very small displacements is violated.

The phenomena of interference may sometimes be noticed when a fairly regular swell is running on the sea near a pier, embankment, or sea-wall. The waves rolling towards the wall are then met by those reflected from it. At certain places crest meets crest, and a specially high crest is there formed in consequence. At other places crest meets trough, and the usual undisturbed level is scarcely departed from. This is, in fact, the extension to space of two dimensions of stationary waves which we first studied along space of one dimension, viz. a string or rope. These effects may be imitated and systematised on the small scale in a "ripple tank" (see art. 50), but are somewhat difficult to produce and observe. They have been, however, very successfully produced and photographed by Dr. J. H. Vincent.[1] Tuning-forks were used to periodically disturb the surface of mercury, and the effects obtained were rendered permanent by instantaneous photography. Two of the many beautiful plates so obtained are reproduced in Figs. 84 and 85.

[1] *Phil. Mag.*, 46, 1898, pp. 290-296.

FIG. 85.

FIG. 84.

290. EXPT. 50. *Interference from Tuning-Fork.*—Perhaps the simplest illustration of interference accessible to everyone is that afforded by a tuning-fork. When the prongs are separating it is evident that a compression starts from the outer surface of each and proceeds in the direction of separation. But, at the same time, it is equally clear that a rarefaction starts from the place between the prongs and proceeds in the direction perpendicular to that before mentioned. Hence if the fork stands with its prongs upright, while compressions are starting from it and going say north and south, rarefactions will be starting from it and travelling east and west. Hence, in directions about intermediate between the cardinal points of the compass we shall have destructive interference, for the vibrations being in opposite phases and of equal amplitudes destroy each other. Hence if the ear can pass quickly across these regions we shall lose and regain the sound repeatedly. This is most easily effected by moving the fork and its associated alternating regions of fullest sound and zero effects. Thus, strike or bow a small fork, hold it by the stem to the ear and twirl it round, and the sound will be intermittent, being quite lost four times in each revolution.

If it be wished to demonstrate this effect to an audience, bow and then turn a large fork in front of its own resonance box. Better still, if a whirling table be available, mount the fork upon it, place the resonance box with its mouth near the prongs and facing the audience. Then bow the fork and rotate it at any suitable speed.

It should be noticed that in this experiment the alternations of sound and silence occur primarily in regions fixed relatively to the fork. They are only made to succeed one another at a given place, viz. the ear of an observer, by the device of turning the fork. Thus, as the fork may be turned at various speeds, there is no one constant frequency of the alternating effects characteristic of the given fork. In the case of beats, with which we deal shortly, it is just the reverse.

291. EXPT. 51. *Interference from Chladni's Plate.* — The same effect may be very strikingly shown by means of a Chladni's plate. Use, say, a square plate mounted at its centre on a stand, touch and bow it so as to elicit one of the simpler figures with large segments, say that with the diagonals as nodal lines. While the plate is vibrating pass the ear rapidly over the nodal lines, shown by sand, in the usual way. The sound will be lost and regained at each passage of the ear over a nodal line.

To render the effect appreciable to an audience, have a wood or metal plate made to cover alternate vibrating segments. Strew the plate with sand, set it vibrating in the manner to which the cover corresponds, then bring the cover close down upon the plate and raise it again promptly. At each approach of the cover, although half the plate is thereby screened off from the audience, the sound will be noticed to be much louder, and at each removal of the cover the sound is again enfeebled. This shows conclusively that, under the ordinary conditions, the sound heard is much enfeebled, though not destroyed, by interference between those waves or radiations which proceed from the alternate segments.

292. Expt. 52. *Interference from an Organ Pipe.*—A very interesting illustration of interference may be sometimes obtained from a bass organ pipe in a church or other large building. The interference is obtained between the direct waves proceeding from the pipe and those reflected from a distant wall which must be large and fairly unbroken. For this purpose a single pipe must be sounded, say a 16 foot wide open pipe giving C, about 34 per second. Or the effect may perhaps be obtained from an 8 foot stopped pipe giving the same note. In either case the waves are of the order 32 feet long; hence, if the direct and reflected waves are along the same straight line, the quarter-wave length separating a node from an antinode is about 8 feet. It is not in every church, or other building containing an organ, that a sufficiently large and unbroken surface is available for reflection and in the right position relative to the organ. But the test for this may usually be made and the experiment tried when an organ is being tuned or under repair. When all the circumstances are favourable the effect is very striking, the silences of the nodes being almost perfect when a wide pipe is used whose overtones are scarcely audible.

293. Beats.—When the two interfering sources are of precisely the same frequency the opposite effects, additive and subtractive, are exhibited at certain places, but remain the same at these while the sounds are maintained. If, however, we have two sounds of nearly, but not quite, the same frequency, a different state of things is produced. For evidently we shall now have, at every place reached by the two sounds, additive and subtractive effects succeeding each other as one sound gains half a vibration on the other. This periodic waxing and waning of intensity constitutes the phenomenon of *beats*. In other words, with sounds of the same pitch we have *throughout time, places* of maximum and minimum effects; whereas with sounds of slightly different pitch we have *throughout space, times* of maximum and minimum effects. The former case is usually intended by the term interference, the latter being always meant by the term beats.

The kinematics of beats has already been given in articles 29 and 31, and graphically illustrated in Fig. 13. We there saw that two vibrations, $a \sin (m+n)t$ and $a \sin(m-n)t$ give a resultant which may be represented by

$$y = 2a \cos nt \sin mt \qquad (1).$$

Hence, if the difference of frequencies is very small, we may regard the sound as an approximately simple harmonic motion expressed by $\sin mt$, whose amplitude, however, changes slowly from $2a$ to zero as expressed by $2a \cos nt$. Or, if the frequencies of the two component tones are N_1 and N_2, we have approximately a tone of frequency $\dfrac{N_1 + N_2}{2}$ whose amplitude waxes and wanes in cycles of frequency given by

$$B = N_1 \sim N_2 \qquad (2),$$

B denoting the number of beats per second. Thus the difference of frequencies is known when the beats can be observed and timed. The following selection of experiments affords instructive examples of beats :—

294. EXPT. 53. *Beats from Sonometer.*—Fit two strings or wires on the sonometer and tune one to a low note, say 100 per second. Then tune the other till beats of about four per second are heard between them. In order to bring out the beats plainly the strings should be plucked and let go. Or, they may be both very vigorously bowed simultaneously and then let go. The beats cannot be heard to advantage while the strings are being bowed. This is because bowing on a crude instrument like a sonometer usually introduces from time to time sudden changes in the phase of the vibrations. Hence the even flow of each tone and the consequent regular succession of beats is, in that case, prevented. On the violin, with a good bow well handled, the beats may be heard while the bow is still on the strings. In any case it will probably be noticed that absolute silence is not attained at the minimum. Two reasons for this may easily be seen as follows :—*First,* the primes may not be equal in intensity. Hence to make the beats as perfect as possible we must endeavour to produce primes of equal amplitude both at first and all through. Plucking carefully nearly secures this. *Second,* suppose the prime tones in question are 100 and 104 per second. Then each string may yield also the octave of its prime of frequencies 200 and 208 respectively. Hence we should have not only 4 beats per second between the primes, but also 8 beats per second between the first over-tones. Further, suppose a maximum of these quicker beats to be coincident with a maximum of the slower. Then the quicker beats would also have a maximum coincident with a minimum of the slower beats. And this prevents absolute silence being attained even when the primes are equal. To reduce this disturbance to a minimum choose rather thick strings and pluck near the middle.

295. EXPT. 54. *Beats from Two Singing Flames.*—Mount two singing flames side by side, the tubes being the same length, but one fitted with a stout paper slider to tune it. Set the two flames going, but then put them out of unison by raising the slider on the tube fitted with it. They will then produce beats. The frequency of the beats can be adjusted to any requisite nicety by corresponding movement of the slider.

EXPT. 55. *Beats Audible and Visible.*—If two open organ

pipes and a Helmholtz resonator, all of the same pitch, are available, the phenomena of beats may be strikingly exhibited to an audience as follows :—Mount the two organ pipes on a wind chest with their mouths side by side, and both facing the mouth of the resonator. Fit the nipple of the resonator into a manometric capsule and light its jet. Now sound the pipes and, by shading the upper end of one of them with the hand, put it out of unison with the other. We then have the beats not only audible, but also made visible by the manometric flame throbbing to the pulsations of pressure in the capsule. The audible and visible effects, of course, keep exact time. For a large audience it is well to use acetylene gas for the flame, and to project it with a lens on to a distant screen. It should be specially noted that a rotating mirror is both useless and detrimental for this experiment, for it analyses too much, and by showing us the separate vibrations, with which we are not concerned, masks the very beats we are wishing to observe. If, instead of the hand placed over one pipe, a lead shade is fixed, the tuning may be made whatever is desired, and so left producing permanently, say 4 beats per second.

296. EXPT. 56. *Frequency of Beats by a Helmholtz Siren.* —By means of a Helmholtz siren we can not only produce beats, but demonstrate that their frequency is the difference of frequencies of the generating tones. The double siren in question, shown in Fig. 86, was evolved by Helmholtz from the single siren due to Dove. Dove's siren had a single chest with several circles of holes and a corresponding disc rotating over it. Any one or more of these circles can be thrown into use by means of separate "hit and miss" rings of holes. Helmholtz arranged two chests on the same vertical axis with one spindle carrying the two discs required for the two chests. The circles in the lower disc contain respectively 8, 10, 12, and 18 holes, while those in the upper disc contain respectively 9, 12, 15, and 16 holes. Or, calling the tone obtained from the circle of 8 holes c, the lower disc gives the tones c, e, g, and d', and the upper gives d, g, b, and c'.

Hence we cannot get the characteristic effect of beats by using any of these tones in their ordinary way, that is, with the chests stationary and the discs rotating. For, when the disc was spinning fast enough to produce audible tones, the beats between them would be too quick for easy counting. But, to produce beats, Helmholtz has added a special device by which the upper chest, usually stationary while the disc

Fig. 86.—Helmholtz Siren.

revolves, is itself capable of a slow rotation by means of a handle and pair of wheels seen in the figure at the right hand top corner. If we use the circles of 12 holes in each chest, and do not turn the handle, we obtain tones of the same pitch for each chest. But if, while the siren is sounding, the handle is turned, then the tone from the upper chest is sharpened or flattened and beats are heard. Further, for every complete turn of the handle the upper chest is turned through one-third of a revolution, and this corresponds to 4 holes out of the circle of 12. Thus, according to the direction of turning the handle, the tone from the upper chest has $12n + 4$ or $12n - 4$ vibrations while that from the lower has $12n$ simply, where n is the number of turns of the spindle to one of the handle. And it is found that one turn of the handle always produces 4 beats, whether the discs are turning slowly or quickly. That is, the number of beats per second is the difference of the frequencies of the generating tones, and is constant for a constant difference no matter how great or small those frequencies may be.

297. Combinational Tones.—We now turn from the case in which the amplitudes of the component vibrations are very small, and the resultant is the simple sum of the components to the case in which the amplitudes are large enough to render invalid the process of simple addition which has just been followed in the preceding articles. That is, we pass from the cases of comparatively feeble sounds, in which the law of simple superposition of small vibrations is valid and the phenomena of interference are produced, to examples of louder sounds, well sustained, which generate new tones differing in pitch from their generators. We have already dealt mathematically with one case in which new tones are thus produced (see article 115). Let us now regard the matter from the historical and experimental standpoints. One example of combinational tones, as they are now called, was first discovered in 1745 by Sorge, a German organist. They were afterwards generally known through the Italian violinist Tartini, and from him they were called Tartini's tones. Helmholtz further examined the matter very fully. He gave the name *differential tones* to those known to Sorge and Tartini, because their frequency is the difference of the frequencies of the generating tones. A second class of combinational tones was discovered by Helmholtz himself, and by him called *summational tones,* because their frequency is the sum of the frequencies of their generators.

To render these combinational tones audible their generators must be loud and should be sustained. Further, it is desirable to choose the pitches of the generators so as to bring the combinational tone fairly near the middle of the compass, say somewhere on the bass staff. Thus, to hear a differential tone, the generators should be high in pitch and preferably near together, so that the differential is quite distinct in pitch from either of the generating tones. To obtain the summational, which is more difficult to hear, low notes should be used, and the interval between them may be as much as a major fifth. For either differential or summational, it is well to sound first that generator which lies nearer in pitch to the combinational tone to be produced, and then let the more distant generator join the other. This order of procedure makes the third tone stand out more distinctly. The following experiments will sufficiently illustrate these facts :—

298. Expt. 57. *Differential Tone from a Double Whistle.*— A type of whistle consisting of two "stopped pipes" side by side has had a considerable vogue in various forms. It has been used by policemen, tram-conductors, and cyclists, also by referees at football and water polo. The type is therefore probably well known to many who have never examined the principles of its action. Whistles of this class depend for their efficiency upon the differential tone which they generate with great intensity when the two pipes are simultaneously blown in the usual manner. In some forms of the whistle the two pipes give notes whose interval is a minor third, in others the interval between the generators is a semitone only. In either case, piercing as the generators are, they sink into insignificance in comparison with the differential tone generated by them. And it is this differential tone which gives the whistle its value. This can be illustrated by covering one of the two

separate pipes successively with a finger so as to sound the
other pipe alone, and then, while one is sounding, remove
the finger and let it be accompanied by the other. The
effect is very striking, and can be appreciated by an audience
of five hundred or more. Either generator alone is a feeble,
high-pitched note of whistle quality, whereas the two
together generate the deep boom so characteristic of this
type of whistle.

299. Expt. 58. *Differential Tone from Two Flageolet Fifes.*
—A yet more striking method of producing a powerful
differential tone is that by the use of two flageolet fifes as
mentioned by the late Mr. A. J. Ellis, the translator of
Helmholtz. For this purpose, two precisely similar instruments in G are to be preferred. On these, one performer
should produce e^{iv}, f^{iv}, $f^{iv}\sharp$ as loudly as possible, and then
the other player should join in with the note g^{iv}, or, the
e^{iv}, f^{iv}, $f^{iv}\sharp$, and g^{iv} may be sounded successively by
one player while the other holds g^{iv}. The fingerings for
these notes and a few others on the G fife, are shown in
Table XIX., in which ○ denotes an open hole, and ● a
hole closed by a finger. To produce the higher notes
somewhat forcible blowing is needed. The differential tones
produced by any of the above-mentioned combinations may
be calculated from the law of their formation or seen by
reference to Table XX.

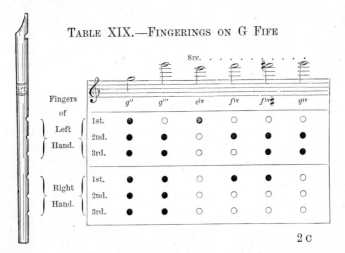

TABLE XIX.—Fingerings on G Fife

		g''	g'''	e^{iv}	f^{iv}	$f^{iv}\sharp$	g^{iv}
Fingers of Left Hand.	1st.	●	○	●	○	○	○
	2nd.	●	●	○	●	●	●
	3rd.	●	●	○	○	●	●
Right Hand.	1st.	●	●	○	●	●	○
	2nd.	●	●	○	○	○	○
	3rd.	●	●	○	○	○	○

2 c

300. EXPT. 59. *Differential Tones from Two Organ Pipes.*— For this purpose two open pipes should be selected to give two high notes about a semitone apart, say $f^{iv}\sharp$ and g^{iv} respectively. It is better for these pipes to be upon a wind chest and fed with air of the right pressure, namely, that for which they were "voiced" by the organ-builder supplying them. By shading the $f^{iv}\sharp$ pipe with the finger its tone may be flattened to f^{iv} or e^{iv}, which causes the differential generated by it and the g^{iv} pipe to rise; or by shading the g^{iv}, so as to flatten it to $f^{iv}\sharp$, the differential tone may be flattened below the range of audition. This experiment when properly performed is very effective, and may be appreciated by a large audience. As in the case of the fifes it is well to sound the two notes singly, then sound the lower one alone, and after its tone is well asserted let it be joined by the higher one, when the deep, boom of the differential is immediately heard.

301. EXPT. 60. *Combinational Tones from a Harmonium or Pianoforte.*—To produce and detect the differential tone, sound as loudly as possible on a harmonium the a' followed almost immediately by c'' (both in the treble staff). These produce quite plainly the F (just below the bass staff). It is perhaps advisable to sound this F faintly before the a' and c'', so as to be prepared to recognise it when present. Further, if the a' and c'' are not strictly of frequencies as $5:6$, the differential produced by them may be slightly out of unison with the F on the instrument. If so, it will give beats with the F if sounded along with the a' and c''. If, on the other hand, the differential should chance to be quite in tune with the F on the instrument, then slightly flatten the F by only partly depressing the digital. Beats will then be heard between it and the differential.

This differential may also be heard, by a careful observer, on sounding the same two notes very loudly on a pianoforte.

The pairs of notes in Table XX. at the intervals of a fifth, a fourth, and a major third respectively, may also be used to obtain the differentials on a harmonium, but, being less striking in their effects, it may be difficult to hear the differentials from them on the pianoforte.

To obtain a summational, use by preference the harmonium, and commence by sounding the c (in the bass staff), followed by the accompaniment of the F (just below the bass staff).

As soon as the F is sounded along with the c, the a (at the top of the bass staff) is heard completing the chord. Here again the a produced as a summational can be the easier recognised if it has been just faintly sounded previous to the c and F.

To obtain proof of this summational on the piano, use the same generators, but proceed as follows :—Without sounding the a, hold down the digital with a finger of the right hand, so as to lift the damper off the string. Then, with the left hand, strike simultaneously the c and F as vigorously as possible, sustain the notes a little, and then raise the left hand so as to stop the generators. The a will then be heard singing, its note having been started in response to the summational in unison with it. This affords another interesting example of sympathetic resonance. It should be noted that this a is not an upper partial of either the F or the c which were used as its generators, so the effect cannot be spurious and due to an overtone of either generator.

The above method must not be applied to detect a differential on the piano. For, suppose the two notes named above a' and c'' were used. Their frequencies are as $5 : 6$. Then although they would evoke the vibrations of the F whose relative frequency is represented by unity, they would also evoke, and far more strongly, those upper partials of that string which are in unison with the generating tones a' and c''. And whatever simply related generators are used, they or their upper partials are themselves upper partials of the differential which they can produce. Thus, if the generators are as $4 : 5$, they are both upper partials of the differential tone represented by 1. If, again, the generators are as $3 : 5$, their upper partials 6, 12, etc., from the 3, and 10, 20, etc., from the 5, are all upper partials of the differential represented by 2.

It should be noted that these experiments with the harmonium, and still more those on differentials with the piano, can only be appreciated by a small group gathered closely round the instrument. They are quite unsuitable for demonstration to a larger audience. The resonance experiment on the piano for demonstrating the summational may, however, be heard by an audience of a hundred or more. The summationals may be produced on the harmonium also from generators at the interval of an octave, a fourth, etc., as given in Table XXI.

302. Pitches of Combinational Tones.—Tables XX. and XXI. give respectively the differential and summational tones produced by different pairs of generators. Their pitches are in all cases chosen so as to be fairly suitable for demonstrating the effects sought. They may, however, be changed an octave or in other ways modified with advantage, when using any special instrument or apparatus. The table for the differentials begins with the case of two generators an octave apart, although, if the interval were perfect the differential would be lost in the lower generator. But, if the interval is not perfect, the differential gives beats with the lower generator, hence the importance of this case and its inclusion in Table XX.

TABLE XX.—DIFFERENTIAL TONES

Intervals of Generators—

	Octave.	Fifth.	Fourth.	Major Third.	Minor Third.	Whole Tone.	Semitone.
Relative Frequencies of all Tones	$2-1=1$	$3-2=1$	$4-3=1$	$5-4=1$	$6-5=1$	$9-8=1$	$16-15=1$

TABLE XXI.—SUMMATIONAL TONES

	Octave.	Fifth.	Fourth.	Major Third.	Minor Third.
Intervals of Generators					
Relative Frequencies of all Tones	$1+2=3$	$2+3=5$	$3+4=7$	$4+5=9$	$5+6=11$

* Really flatter than $b\flat$.   † Really between f' and $f'\sharp$

303. Have Combinational Tones Objective Reality?
—The foregoing experiments have been chosen as seeming most generally suitable to demonstrate combinational tones to others, but by no means exhaust the list of possibilities in this direction. For example, combinational tones may be obtained from the violin or the concertina, while Helmholtz himself for this purpose used his double siren. He also asserted that combinational tones sometimes have an objective existence, whereas formerly it had been believed that they were purely subjective. At that time only the differential tones were known, and they were connected with the phenomena of beats. It was thought that when these beats occurred with sufficient rapidity, the waxings and wanings of intensity would produce the sensation of a new tone of frequency equal to that of the beats. But this, in the first place, leaves the summational tones entirely un-explained; and, secondly, this supposition cannot be reconciled with the experimental law that the only tones which the ear hears correspond to pendular vibrations of the air. Lastly, Helmholtz showed " that under certain conditions the combinational tones existed objectively, independently of the ear, which would have had to gather the beats into a new tone." He showed that the condition for the generation of combinational tones is that the same mass of air should be violently agitated by two simple tones simultaneously. This occurs in his double siren if the tones are produced by two series of holes blown upon simultaneously from the *same* wind chest. In this case Helmholtz asserts that the combinational tones are almost as powerful as the generators. Of the objective existence of the combinational tones, Helmholtz assured himself by the sympathetic resonance of membranes tuned in unison with them. He also used his air resonators, which were more sensitive than the membranes. Helmholtz experimented also upon the harmonium as to its power of producing combinational tones. When two notes were sounded from the same

source of air pressure, the combinational tones were clearly reinforced by resonators tuned in unison with them. Yet, in this case, it was found that the greater part of the intensity of the combinational tone was generated in the ear itself. This was shown by the following method :—One of the generating notes was sounded by air from the bellows moved below by the foot, and the other was blown by the reserve bellows, which was first pumped full, and then cut off by drawing out the so-called expression stop. It was then found that the combinational tones were not much weaker than before, but the objective portion which resonators reinforce was much weaker. Again, Helmholtz found that " when the places in which the two tones are struck are entirely separate and have no mechanical connection, as, for example, if they come from two singers, two separate wind instruments, or two violins, the reinforcement of the combinational tones by resonators is small and dubious. Here, then, there does not exist in the air any clearly sensible pendular vibration corresponding to the combinational tone, and we must conclude that such tones, which are often powerfully audible, are really produced in the ear itself."

304. Mathematical Examination of Combinational Tones.—In article 115 we treated an asymmetrical system subject to double forcing. It was there shown that, given such circumstances, differential and summational tones are produced in addition to those in unison with the impressed forces. Let us now regard the drum-skin of the ear as the system under forcing. Now we have already seen (art. 258) that the drum-skin is differently related to displacements inward and outward, and is therefore an asymmetrical system of the type contemplated. Hence the subjective existence of differential and summational tones is accounted for. Let us also examine, in a little more detail, the quantitative results of the theory. Looking at equation (5), article 115, we see, by the numerators of the coefficients of the terms in question, that the amplitudes of the combinational tones are proportional to the products of those of the impressed forces, which are due to the generating tones. This shows why, in the experiments, it was essential to have loud generating tones. Again, the frequency of the natural vibration of the drum-skin and its attached ossicles is small. Everett states it to be about ten per second.[1] Accordingly, it may be almost neglected in comparison with the frequencies of the generating tones. Hence, from the denominators of the coefficients in equation (5) of article 115, we find the following result:—The amplitude of the differential is to that of the summational almost as the square of the fraction : sum of frequencies of generators divided by their difference. Or, in symbols,

$$\frac{D}{S} = \left(\frac{N_1 + N_2}{N_1 \sim N_2}\right)^2 \text{nearly,}$$

where D and S are the respective amplitudes of the differential and summational tones produced by generators of frequencies N_1 and N_2. This explains, what any experimenter soon finds, namely, that the summational tones are harder to hear and demonstrate than the differentials.

Lastly, note in the equation (5), article 115, that all the combinational tones have as a factor the coefficient a, which expresses that the displacement is not simply proportional to the force producing it. Hence, if a vanishes *absolutely*, then all the combinational tones vanish also.

305. But the above theory is not limited in its application to the human ear. We may have, outside the ear altogether, systems in which the restoring force is not simply proportional to the displacement, but requires for its exact expression higher powers of that displacement. Where, *e.g.*, the cube of the displacement comes into account, it might be shown that results apply similar to those deduced in article 115, where the square of the

[1] *Phys. Soc. of London,* vol. xiv. p. 94, 1896.

displacement occurred.   Instead, however, of developing
the matter further along these lines, take the following
simple illustration.   Suppose we have a system in which a
force f producing a displacement y is represented by

$$f = ay + by^2 + cy^3 + \ldots \tag{1},$$

and let two forces f_1 and f_2, when acting alone, produce the
displacements y_1 and y_2 respectively.   Then we have

$$\left. \begin{aligned} f_1 &= ay_1 + by_1^2 + cy_1^3 + \ldots \\ \text{and } f_2 &= ay_2 + by_2^2 + cy_2^3 + \ldots \end{aligned} \right\} \tag{2}.$$

Now let these two forces act simultaneously and produce
the displacement Y.   Then by (1) we have

$$f_1 + f_2 = aY + bY^2 + cY^3 + \ldots \tag{3}.$$

But, from (2) by addition we obtain

$$\left. \begin{aligned} f_1 + f_2 = a(y_1 + y_2) &+ b(y_1 + y_2)^2 + c(y_1 + y_2)^3 + \ldots \\ &- 2by_1y_2 - 3cy_1y_2(y_1 + y_2) - \ldots \end{aligned} \right\} \tag{4}.$$

And, on comparison of (3) and (4), we see that

$$Y \neq y_1 + y_2 \tag{5}.$$

306.   Or, in words, when the relation between force
and displacement is *not linear*, the displacement due to the
simultaneous action of two forces is *not the simple sum* of
those due to the forces acting separately.   Now, in actual
practice, this condition of linear relation, or simple proportionality between force and displacement, is scarcely
ever rigorously fulfilled.   But, usually, the coefficients of
the squares and higher powers of the displacements are
small.   Thus when, in addition, the displacements themselves are very small, the terms in equation (1), involving
the squares and higher powers, are often quite negligible.
It is under these circumstances that the coefficients b and c
in equations (1) to (4) are ignored, or in other words that
the principle of the *superposition of small motions* is con-

sidered legitimate. The equations (1) to (4) in that case reduce to

$$f = ay, f_1 = ay_1, f_2 = ay_2, f_1 + f_2 = aY = a(y_1 + y_2) \quad (6),$$

and (5) becomes $\qquad Y = y_1 + y_2 \qquad\qquad (7).$

But, as soon as the displacements are large instead of small, the terms involving their squares and higher powers become paramount instead of negligible. And then, small as the coefficients b and c may be, the terms involving them are important, and combinational tones are produced. Hence, whenever we have such a system with such displacements, *outside* the ear, the combinational tones may be expected to have *objective* reality.

307. Upper Partials from a Loud Simple Tone.— Continuing the line of thought of the preceding article, we may show that a system which admits of combinational tones being formed in it from two generators of different pitches, admits even of higher tones being formed in it by a vigorous single simple tone acting as the impressed force! This was pointed out by Helmholtz, who remarks that the effect is as though the tone formed summational tones with itself. We may reason the matter out as follows, taking the asymmetrical and symmetrical cases separately.

Asymmetrical Case.—Take first the case in which the restoring force changes numerical value as well as sign when the displacement is reversed simply. Then the expression for the restoring force involves, say, the first and second powers of the displacement. Let the system be acted upon by a harmonic impressed force to represent the single simple tone. Then the equation of motion may be written

$$\ddot{y} + p^2 y + ay^2 = f \cos nt \qquad (1).$$

To obtain the first approximate solution, suppose that a is negligible. Then the equation reduces to $\ddot{y} + p^2 y = f \cos nt$ and is satisfied by

$$y = \frac{f}{p^2 - n^2} \cos nt \qquad (2).$$

Put this approximate value of y in equation (1). After a little transformation, it may then be written

$$\ddot{y} + p^2 y = \frac{-af^2}{2(p^2 - n^2)^2} + f \cos nt - \frac{af^2}{2(p^2 - n^2)^2} \cos 2nt \quad (3).$$

Try as a solution,

$$y = A + B \cos nt + C \cos 2nt \quad (4).$$

We thus find that this satisfies (3), provided that

$$A = \frac{-af^2}{2p^2(p^2 - n^2)^2}, \quad B = \frac{f}{p^2 - n^2}, \text{ and}$$

$$C = \frac{-af^2}{2(p^2 - n^2)^2(p^2 - 4n^2)} \quad (5).$$

Thus, to this degree of approximation, the objective existence of the *octave* is established when a body vibrates with sufficient amplitude in a medium in which the *squares* of the displacements are involved in the expression for the restoring force. This is shown by the presence of a in equations (5) and (1), and the significance of C in (4).

308. Symmetrical Case.—Take now the case in which the restoring force involves the first and third powers of the displacement, and let the system be acted upon by a simple tone as the impressed force. Then we may write the equation of motion as follows :—

$$\ddot{y} + p^2 y + \beta y^3 = f \cos nt \quad (6).$$

Proceeding as before, we obtain the first approximate solution by ignoring β. Thus

$$y = \frac{f}{p^2 - n^2} \cos nt \text{ nearly} \quad (7).$$

And this value, put in the y^3 term of (6), gives

$$\ddot{y} + p^2 y = f \cos nt - \frac{\beta f^3}{(p^2 - n^2)^3} \cos^3 nt ;$$

or, since $\cos^3\theta = \frac{1}{4}(3\cos\theta + \cos 3\theta)$, we may write

$$\ddot{y} + p^2 y = \left[f - \frac{3\beta f^3}{4(p^2 - n^2)^3} \right] \cos nt - \frac{\beta f^3}{4(p^2 - n^2)^3} \cos 3nt \quad (8).$$

Now, trying as a solution, $y = B\cos nt + D\cos 3nt$ (9),

we find that this satisfies (8) provided that

$$B = \frac{f - \dfrac{3\beta f^3}{4(p^2 - n^2)^3}}{p^2 - n^2} \quad \text{and} \quad D = \frac{+\beta f^3}{4(p^2 - n^2)^3(9n^2 - p^2)} \quad (10).$$

Thus we see that in the symmetrical case, in which, however, the *cube* of the displacement is involved in the expression for the restoring force, the *twelfth* and not the octave will be elicited when the prime tone is the impressed force.

309. Octave from Tuning - Fork and Resonator.

EXPT. 61.—In the light of the theory just developed, it is instructive to consider an experiment in which the octave is elicited when a tuning-fork is vigorously bowed and placed near a suitable resonator. For this purpose select a large tuning-fork, say c', 256 per second, and a narrow jar about 18 inches high, or preferably the adjustable water resonator (see article 237). Adjust the level of the water in the jar or other resonator, so as to give the strongest resonance to the prime tone of the fork, and note that it *is* the prime tone that is thus reinforced. Next raise the level of the water till the resonant air column above it is about half its former length, and adjust so as to give best response to a fork an octave higher than that first used. Then bow the large fork very vigorously and hold over the resonator. When the adjustment is properly made and the bowing vigorous enough, the octave of the fork's prime tone may be distinctly heard by the operator and a small class of say a score.

310. Discussion of Result.—Let us now discuss this

result and see where and how the octave may be generated. To this inquiry it is difficult to give any decisive answer.

Probably the octave arises or is strengthened at several points in the chain of phenomena. Let us note the following considerations :—

(1) The fork cannot itself produce the octave by dividing into segments as a string or open pipe can. For we have already seen (arts. 211 and 237) that the first overtone of a clamped-free bar, to which the prong of a fork may be assimilated, has a frequency about 6·3 times that of the prime. In other words, its pitch is rather more than two octaves and a musical fifth above the prime.

(2) But we have seen that in the large free vibrations of an asymmetrical system the prime is accompanied by the octave feebly sounded (see arts. 112 and 113). Now the prongs of a tuning-fork are rather differently conditioned for displacements inwards and outwards. Hence the fork itself may give the octave. This has been pointed out by Lord Rayleigh, who says : " A trained ear can generally perceive the octave in the sound of a tuning-fork caused to vibrate strongly by means of a bow."

(3) Or we may regard the fork as giving the prime tone only, and the air around it as a system unable accurately to follow this simple harmonic motion when the displacements are large. This view of the matter has been maintained by Helmholtz. He used a C fork (64 per second) and an amplitude of almost a centimetre. He remarks that " when a sharp-edged body, such as the prong of a tuning-fork, makes vibrations of such a length, vortical motions, differing sensibly from the law of simple vibrations, must arise in the surrounding air. On the other hand, as the sound of the fork fades, these upper partials vanish long before their prime, which is itself only very weakly audible. This agrees with our hypothesis that these partials arise from disturbances depending on the size of the amplitude."

(4) The drum-skin of the human ear is certainly an asymmetrical system, and may further increase the effect

in question of producing the octave. But since, to many observers, the octave is scarcely audible without a resonator, and is so distinctly heard with it, it seems probable that very little of the effect heard has its origin in the ear itself.

(5) We are then naturally led to ask if the effect in part arises in the resonating air column. That is, should we regard the fork as supplying a simple harmonic impressed force, and the resonating air column as an elastic system which in response gives the octave as well as the prime? We have just seen (art. 113) that, in order to give the octave under simple harmonic forcing, the system acted upon must be asymmetrical. The matter thus turns upon the question whether the air column of the water resonator is an asymmetrical system. The following line of reasoning leads us to infer that it is.

311. The resonator consists of a cylindrical pipe stopped at the lower end by the surface of the water, and open at the upper end, the space of its interior being occupied by air. And the question whether the air column in it is an asymmetrical system may be attacked by examining if the frequency for small vibrations changes when the equilibrium position of the particles changes. That is to say, would the period be changed if particles which formerly vibrated at the mouth were compelled, by greater pressure, to penetrate the tube a little and execute their vibrations about a displaced zero. Now the frequency about such a displaced zero depends upon the rate of change of displacing force with respect to displacement at that position. But this space rate of change of displacing force is the differential coefficient of the original function which expresses the force in terms of the displacement. Thus, let the displacing force f on a particle of unit mass, in terms of the displacement y, be supposed given by the somewhat general expression

$$f = ay + by^2 + cy^3 \qquad (1).$$

Then $\dfrac{df}{dy} = a + 2by + 3cy^2$ (2).

But for small vibrations the frequency N is given by

$$2\pi N = \sqrt{\text{acceleration/displacement}}$$

$$= \sqrt{\text{force per unit mass/displacement}};$$

or $\qquad 4\pi^2 N^2 = df/dy = a + 2by + 3cy^2$ (3).

Now equation (3) expresses the frequency N for small vibrations, but these may be about any zero, the value of df/dy being inserted accordingly, in which y defines the zero.

312. Thus we see that if N changes, when the sign and not the numerical value of y changes, b must be present in (3) and (2), that is, the term involving y^2 must be present in (1). But, when y^2 is present in (1), the restoring force changes numerical value as well as sign when the sign only of y changes. That is, the system would be asymmetrical, and the octave produced in it from the fork's prime.

On the other hand, it may be seen that if N is unchanged in value by a reversal of sign of y, then c may be present, but *not* b, the vibrating system is symmetrical and the octave is not heard, but the twelfth is if c is present.

Hence we have now to inquire how N changes with y. For this purpose suppose we have originally the ordinary air pressure and small vibrations, and consider the particles oscillating at the mouth of the resonator. Let the corrected length of the vibrating air column be L, and the frequency N, then we have

$$N = \frac{v}{\lambda} = \frac{v}{4L}$$ (4).

313. Now, to determine the frequency for small vibrations about a displaced zero, let a large vibration be made inwards, and then imagine the particles vibrating about this new displaced zero. They would vibrate in the same time as all the others, since we have stationary waves. Further, because the large vibration was made under the ordinary acoustical conditions, the compression was adiabatic. Hence the temperature was raised, and therefore the value of v, the velocity of sound, correspondingly increased. But L has remained constant, hence N must be increased. Similarly with an expansion, or outward displacement of the zero, N would be decreased, for there would be a cooling and a consequent decrease of v. Thus in the expression for N in equation (3) the coefficient b must appear. It must therefore be retained in equation (1), giving the force in terms of the displacement. That is, the system is asymmetrical, and may itself produce the octave under the action of the prime as the impressed force.

314. Thus, so far as the present experiment goes, all we can say is, *first*, that the fork does not produce the octave by subdivision of itself, as in the case of a vibrating string or organ-pipe; and, *second*, that the part played by the mechanism of the ear in producing the octave is probably very slight.

The octave may be produced at any of the other points in the apparatus concerned in the phenomena, namely, by the fork itself as an asymmetrical vibrator, by the vortical motion of the air immediately round the prongs, or by the resonator as an asymmetrical system under simple harmonic forcing. Probably the relative portions of the effect produced at each point would depend upon the proportions and disposition of the apparatus.

315. Researches of Koenig and Bosanquet: Beat Notes. — The subject of combinational tones has been experimentally treated both by R. Koenig [1] and by R. H. M. Bosanquet.[2] The experimental results of these independent

---

[1] *Ann. der Physik*, 1881.   [2] *Phys. Soc. of London*, 1880-81.

workers are summarised as follows by Mr. Ellis in his
translation of Hemholtz, p. 529 :—

"If two simple tones of either very slightly or greatly
different pitches, called generators, be sounded together,
then the upper pitch number necessarily lies between two
multiples of the lower pitch number, one smaller and the
other greater, and the differences between these multiples
of the pitch number of the lower generator and the pitch
number of the upper generator give two numbers which
either determine the frequency of the two sets of beats
which may be heard, or the pitch of the two beat-notes
which may be heard in their place.   The term ' beat-notes '
is here used *without any theory as to the origin of such tones*,
but only to show that they are tones having the same
frequency as the beats, which are sometimes heard simultaneously."

In certain cases the beat-notes arising from the lower
multiple of the lower generator is heard alone, in other
cases that from the upper multiple is heard alone, while in
intermediate cases both beat-notes may be heard giving
secondary beats or beat-notes with each other.

316. The experiments of such able physicists must be
received with all respect and accorded the full weight due
to them.   As to the possible presence of upper partials in
the generators, Koenig took especial pains that his tones
should be as simple as he could make them.   He says,
"The forks that I used with resonators had no recognisable
harmonic upper partials at all.   The occurrence of harmonic
upper partials in tuning-forks depends not so much on the
lowness of their pitch and the amplitude of their vibrations
as on the relation of the amplitude to the thickness of the
prongs." [1]

On the question of the objective or subjective existence of combinational tones and beat-notes, Koenig [2] says :
" Neither these combinational tones nor the beat-notes

---

[1] Ellis's *Translation of Helmholtz*, p. 528.   *Ibid.* p. 531.

already described are reinforced by resonators." Bosanquet made an improved resonator, by means of which he could completely block up both ears against any sound but that coming from a resonance jar. He then says,[1] " By means of these arrangements I some time ago examined the nature of the ordinary first difference-tone, and convinced myself that it is not capable of exciting a resonator. In short, the difference-tone of Helmholtz or first beat-note of Koenig, as ordinarily heard, is not objective in its character.

" When the nipples of the resonator-attachment fitted tightly into the ears, nothing reached the ear but the uniform vibrations of the resonator sounding C. But if there was the slightest looseness between the nipple and the passage of either ear, the second note (c) of the combination got in, and gave rise to the subjective difference-tone (first beat-note of Koenig), by the interference of which with the C I explain the beats on that note. *These beats are therefore subjective.*"

Thus, as to the nature of these combinational tones, *i.e.* as to whether they are partly objective or wholly subjective, Koenig and Bosanquet seem in conflict with Helmholtz. But the views of these physicists do not close the matter, as we shall see in the following article.

317. Objectivity of Combinational Tones. *Rücker and Edser's Work.*—In a paper read before the Physical Society of London, March 1895,[2] Professor A. W. Rücker and E. Edser gave an account of experiments undertaken to test the question of the " Objective Reality of Combination Tones."

To produce the generating tones, a siren of the Helmholtz pattern was used almost throughout. The resonator to respond to the combinational tone was usually a tuning-fork of 64 per second. Now the tuning-fork is relatively difficult to excite by resonance, and it was accordingly necessary to use a very delicate method of

---

[1] Ellis's *Translation of Helmholtz*, p. 531.   [2] See vol. xiii. pp. 412-439.

detecting its motion if present. The method adopted was to attach a mirror to a prong so as to make it one of a system by which were produced Michelson's interference bands (see any text-book on Physical Optics). " A movement of the prong amounting to half a wave length of light (say 1/80,000 of an inch) would alter the length of the path of one of the interfering rays by a wave length. A periodic vibration of this amplitude would cause the bands to disappear." The difficulty as to the possible untrustworthiness of the apparatus because of its sensitiveness to accidental disturbances was entirely overcome. Precautions were also taken to insure that the disturbance ascribed to the joint action of two notes was not produced by either note when acting alone.

318. In Table XXII. are summarised the results of their experiments made with generating tones produced on the siren, the fork and interference bands being the detector of the combinational tones.

TABLE XXII.—COMBINATIONAL TONES DETECTED BY
FORK AND MICHELSON'S BANDS

Number of Holes in Siren.	Musical Interval between Generating Tones.	Frequencies of Generating Tones.	Frequency of Combinational Tone detected by Fork, etc.		Frequency of Koenig's Beat Note.
12 and 10	Minor third	384 and 320	64		64
15 and 12	Major Third	320 and 256	64	Differential Tones	64
15 and 9	Major Sixth	160 and 96	64		32
18 and 8	Major Ninth	115·2 and 51·2	64		12·8
10 and 8	Major Third	35·5 and 28·4	64	Summational Tones	
12 and 9	Major Fourth	36·57 and 27·43	64		

In Table XXIII. are given the results of experiments in which the siren was again used to produce the generating tones, but the detector was the specially sensitive mirror resonator constructed by Prof. C. V. Boys (see art. 283). In these experiments the summational tone of 576 was dealt with, the resonator being tuned to respond to this.

TABLE XXIII.—SUMMATIONAL TONES DETECTED BY BOYS' MIRROR RESONATOR.

Number of Holes in Siren.	Musical Interval between the two Generating Tones.	Frequencies of the Generating Tones.	Frequencies of the Summational Tones detected by Resonator.
15 and 12	Major Third	320 and 256	576
16 and 12	Fourth	329·15 and 246·85	576
16 and 9	Major Sixth	360 and 216	576

The authors say (p. 427), " We attach great importance to this corroboration of our results by an instrument of a totally different construction from that first employed." They further say among their concluding remarks, " We think, then, that our experiments prove that von Helmholtz was correct in stating that the siren produces two objective notes the frequencies of which are respectively equal to the sum and difference of the frequencies of the fundamentals."

319. *Rayleigh's View.*—We may further mention here that Lord Rayleigh, after reviewing evidence for and against the objective existence of combinational tones, says, " My own observations have been made upon the harmonium, and leave me at a loss to understand how two opinions are possible. The resonator is held with its mouth as near as may be to the reeds which sound the generating notes, and is put in and out of tune to the difference-tone by slight movements of the finger. When the tuning is good the difference-tone swells out with considerable strength, but a slight mistuning (probably of the order of a semitone) reduces it almost to silence."

320. *Waetzmann's Experiments.*—In the *Ann. d. Physik*

for July 1906, E. Waetzmann describes experiments in which he detects a difference-tone by the beats arising between it and another tone of a slightly different pitch. The sensitive apparatus is a film of glycerine soap solution over the opening of a Koenig resonator. Near this are sounded three tuning-forks of frequencies n, m, and $n - m \pm \delta$ respectively, where δ varies between 1 and 10. The film is seen to throb in time with the beats heard, but if any one of the forks was stopped the appearance and sound of the beats immediately stopped also. Waetzmann attaches great importance to the fact that the beats are thus rendered visible, so that their existence is known independently of the mechanism of the human ear. Also he calls attention to the fact that the combination tone thus detected has arisen from *separate* generators, namely, the two forks of frequencies n and m, and not from the same wind chest as in siren experiments.

321. Everett's Theory of Resultant Tones.—In 1896 Prof. J. D. Everett [1] advanced a new view as to the formation of combinational or *resultant* tones. He says, "The view which I desire to put forward is closely connected with the well-known theorem of Fourier, that every periodic variation can be resolved in one definite way into harmonic constituents, whose frequencies will be as 1, 2, 3, 4, etc.

"In the majority of cases, when this analysis is carried out, the fundamental constituent represented by 1 in the above list is the largest, or among the largest; but in the case of a variation compounded of two simple tones with frequencies in the ratio of two integers, neither being a multiple of the other, the fundamental will be absent, and the Fourier series will consist of only two terms, which in the language of acoustics are harmonics of the fundamental." "The point on which I wish to insist is, that if a curve representing the superposition of two harmonics of the

---

[1] *Phys. Soc. of London*, vol. xiv. p. 93.

fundamental is in the first instance very accurately drawn, but is then inaccurately copied in such a way that all successive waves are treated alike, the inaccuracy is morally certain to introduce the fundamental."

Applying this view to the experiments of Rücker and Edser, Prof. Everett contends that the fundamental may be introduced in the pulsations of the air rushing out of the chest in which two rows of holes are open. He thus regards the difference-tone of generators in the ratios 3 : 4, 4 : 5, and 5 : 6 as being in part, at any rate, the supplied fundamental. Everett further objects to the ordinary theory treating " the reaction of the drum-skin against the air as a definite function of the displacement of the drum-skin from a certain fixed position, whereas this reaction depends also on the position and motion of the further end of the hammer at the time."

CHAPTER VIII

MUSICAL INSTRUMENTS

322. General Survey.—In this chapter we propose to consider the production and character of the sounds given by some typical musical instruments. Nothing like exhaustive completeness, as understood by a musician, can be here attempted. Further, as befits the present work, the treatment, so far as it extends, will be always from a scientific rather than a musical standpoint.

The instruments now at the disposal of musicians have been originated at widely different times, and some of them have been slowly developed to their present high standard of excellence. Their improvement has sometimes resulted from the application of theory, where simple enough to be known. But, in the many cases where the problems involved have resisted theoretical attack, progress has been made empirically and that to an astounding degree. Yet, none the less, the results obtained, by whatever means, will well repay a careful scientific examination. The action of the instruments often affords very valuable illustrations and confirmations of acoustic theory already known, and sometimes it gives an incentive to pursue the theory further in order to explain results obtained fortuitously. Indeed, in glancing over what has been accomplished by the perseverance and ingenuity of the instrument-makers, the physicist has good cause to be grateful for the wealth of illustration

406

thus placed at his disposal. He can but seldom pose as a critic of what has been accomplished, or even as a suggester of lines for further advance; so far, in this department, has practice outstripped theory.

323. Many musical instruments, though not all, require, as parts essential for their use, portions of the performer himself in conjunction with the instrument proper on which he is said to play. Thus, for example, a flute requires the lips and lungs of the performer, though, on the other hand, in the flute or flue stops of the organ, to answer the same purpose, lips and bellows are provided in the instrument itself. We shall accordingly, where necessary, treat these essential parts of the performer himself together with the instrument proper, so as to deal with the complete musical instrument in the scientific sense. Taking this broader view of the matter, it will often be found convenient to consider a musical instrument as made up of three chief divisions, viz. (1) The exciter, or means of producing vibrations; (2) The vibrating system; (3) The manipulative mechanism for the production of the various notes of the scale, for expression, etc. Thus, in the flute and the requisite portions of the performer, the lungs, breath, and lips of the player produce a suitable air blast which acts as the exciter; the blade-like stream of air striking the edge of the hole, and the column of air in the tube, constitute the vibrating system; while the holes and keys are the manipulative mechanism used to produce at will the various notes of the scale within the compass of the instrument.

The vibrating system may often with advantage be sub-divided into a vibrator of definite pitch, and a resonator which reinforces and otherwise modifies the sounds produced by the vibrator. A good example of this is afforded by the violin, in which the strings are the vibrators of definite pitch, while the sound-box and contained mass of air form the resonator. In the case of the flute and some other instruments, the resonant column of air fixes the

pitch of the vibrator which is itself indefinite, or only
lies within a desired range, and could not be maintained
at any precise pitch without the tube and contained air.
These actions will be studied in detail in their proper
places.

324. Having thus briefly glanced at the production of
sounds, let us now notice, in the sounds produced, what are
the characteristics which serve to distinguish one instrument
from another. The chief are :—(1) The range of pitch or
compass of the instrument ; (2) The interval relation of the
possible notes or the *scale* of the instrument ; (3) The *power
and delicacy* of tones producible ; (4) The noises accompanying the beginning or finishing of the sounds; (5) The possible
or inevitable *change of intensity* of the sounds while they
last ; (6) The *quality* of the sound after it is completely
established, by musicians often termed tone ; (7) Lastly, the
instrument may be restricted to the production of one note
at a time, or be capable of producing simultaneously two
or more notes, *i.e.* it may be restricted to melody or capable
of harmony. As familiar examples of instruments which
may be distinguished chiefly by these several characteristics
of their sounds, without being seen by the hearer, we may
note the following : A concertina by its smaller compass
may be distinguished from a harmonium ; a bugle by its
restricted scale, consisting of the harmonic series only, from
a cornet ; a pipe organ by its greater power from a flute ;
a trumpet from the human voice by the way the notes
commence in each case ; a piano with its quickly-dying
sounds from a violin with its sustained tones ; the "strings"
of the orchestra from the "wood-wind" by the difference in
quality ; and, lastly, a clarinet from a harmonium, in that the
former is restricted to melody and the latter capable of
harmony. No doubt our sensations in all the above cases
are very mixed, and although in deciding which instrument
is heard we may be guided chiefly by the characteristic
referred to under each head, probably some of the other

elements of the case enter almost unconsciously into our consideration and assist us in the conclusion drawn.

325. As to quality proper, we may recognise an almost infinite gradation, and are accustomed, in popularly describing these shades of difference, to use such terms as rich, full, mellow, nasal, brilliant, etc. Scientifically considered we may divide the various musical tones into the following five classes :—(1) Those with the full harmonic series of partials, *i.e.* including the prime the relative frequencies are 1, 2, 3, 4, 5, 6, 7, etc.; (2) Those with harmonic partials, but forming only the odd series of natural numbers, *i.e.* the relative frequencies are 1, 3, 5, 7, etc.; (3) Tones with inharmonic partials; (4) Simple tones, usually limiting cases of the foregoing three classes in which the upper partials are indefinitely diminished or suppressed; (5) Tones with harmonic partials, but, whatever the pitch of the note, those partials near some one or more *fixed pitches* specially reinforced, the others being relatively discouraged.

The large and important question of the special tuning of each instrument, or *temperament*, cannot be advantageously dealt with until, by conversance with the construction of the typical instruments, the reader is able to appreciate the nature of the problem to be attacked.

326. Hence, reserving that subject for the next chapter, we now propose to examine the various instruments as to their construction and action, the range and nature of the sounds produced by them, and the theoretical relations thereby deducible. Table XXIV. affords a complete survey of a number of instruments, indicating their division and subdivision, also the compass of each, and sometimes further details. The notation adopted is that of Helmholtz mentioned at the outset of this work (see art. 8), and to which the staff at the head of the table forms a key. The letters along the line for any instrument show what are called the open notes, *i.e.* the notes produced by the strings or tubes (as the case may be) without modification by fingering. The lines joining these letters, or extending beyond them, indicate that, by means of fingering, the instrument in question possesses the full chromatic scale over the corresponding range. The dotted portions of the lines at the ends or elsewhere signify that the power to produce notes in the corresponding range depends on the skill of the performer, or the special provisions of the individual instrument. Letters under the ends of the lines show the limits of the compass where such definition is necessary. For the wind instruments, isolated letters in brackets indicate notes which are difficult to obtain and seldom used.

327. It should be carefully observed that the notes for each instrument in this table represent the real sounds produced by them. It is, however, customary in the music for many instruments of the orchestra to write notes different from those which it is desired to have produced. Thus, for a cornet in B♭, when c'' is written in ordinary music, $b'♭$ is produced by the performer. This is the intention of the composer, and the practice of the performer is acquired in the school for his instrument. Similarly the horn in F for a written c' would produce an f. The instruments, in writing for which this habit prevails, are termed by musicians transposing instruments. Thus, to players of such instruments the table would appear wrong, unless allowance is made for the distinction between real sounds and the notes usually written for them to be played on the so-called transposing instruments.

328. Stringed Instruments played by the Hand.— We now pass to the detailed examination of the representative instruments in Table XXIV., taking them in the order there given.

The Guitar has six strings, of which the lower three are of silk covered with silver wire, and the three upper are of catgut. In playing it, the little finger of the right hand rests upon the body of the instrument, the thumb

CLASSIFICATION AND NAMES OF INSTRUMENTS.			Compass

(Musical staff with note c'')

STRINGS	Plucked [1]	Guitar Harp Mandolin	c' -d'——— a'————-c''—
	Struck	Pianoforte	A
	Bowed	Violin Viola Violoncello Double-Bass Viola d'Amore	-d'——— a'————-e'' d'——— a'— -d'—f'♯—-a'————-d''—
WIND	Metal Reeds without Pipes.	Harmonium and American Organ Concertina	
	Metal Reeds with Pipes.	Reed Stops } of Organ	
	Pipes without Reeds.	Flute Stops } Flute (in C) Piccolo (in C)	d'———-————(d'')
	Double Cane Reeds with Conical Pipes.	Oboe English Horn Bassoon Double Bassoon	-d'————————(d'') ———————b'♭
	Single Cane Reeds with Cylindrical Pipes.	Clarinet (in B♭) Alto Clarinet (in E♭) Bass Clarinet (in B♭)	———— a'———— —————————f'''
	Hyperbolical Pipes with Cupped Mouthpieces, Human lips as Reeds.	French Horn (in F) Trumpet (in F) Alto Trombone (E♭) Tenor Trombone (B♭) Bass Trombone (G) Bass Tuba (in C) Soprano (Cornet) (E♭) Cornet (in B♭) Tenor Horn (E♭) Euphonium (B♭) Bombardon (E♭) Double Bass (B♭)	- - e'♭ f' - g'-a' - b'- c''-d''-e''♭-e''♭-f'' - - - - f' - - a' - - - c'' - - e''♭-f''-- —e'♭———g'——-b'♭————e''♭-f''-- d'—f'——-a'♭-b'♭-c''-d'' d'—f'—g' -d'-e' —e'♭———— b'♭———-e''♭—- —— f'————-b'♭—-d''——f''— —-e'♭——g'——-b'♭———e''♭ -d'——f'———-b'♭ - - - - — e'♭ - - - - -
	Human Voices, Vocal Chords as Reeds.	Soprano Contralto Tenor Bass	d'— —————————d'' - - —g' - - - - - -
Percussion Instruments of Definite Pitch.	Kettledrum		

plays the three lower strings, and the fingers the upper strings, of which the highest is played by the third finger. To obtain the different notes of the scale, the strings, at the appropriate lengths, are pressed by the fingers of the left hand against the fret or little pieces of wood which cross the finger-board. Notes called "harmonics" may also be obtained by touching the strings instead of pressing them down on to the frets. These notes will be understood from what we have seen as to the vibrations of strings. Thus, touching at the middle of a string allows it to produce its octave as though it were pressed against the fret at the same place. Touching the string at a third of its length (where hard pressure on the fret would yield the musical fifth) gives the twelfth, touching at a fourth of its length gives the double octave, and so forth.

We thus see that the thumb and three fingers of the right hand are the exciters, the six strings the vibrators, the sound-box the resonator, while the fingers of the left hand and the frets form the manipulative mechanism for production of the scale. The guitar is of feeble tone, and does not blend well with other instruments, and may be overpowered by a strong voice.

329. The Harp.—This is the important representative of the family of stringed instruments played by the hand. The double-action harp is tuned in C♭, and is provided with seven pedals. Each pedal acts upon all the strings of a given name throughout the compass of the instrument. Moreover, each pedal may be used to raise its strings a tone or a semitone at the option of the player. Thus, by the use of the pedals, the instrument may be tuned so as to provide the major scales in each of the fifteen keys from C♭ to C♯ both inclusive. The minor scales cannot be "set" by the pedals if that form is required which differs in ascending and descending passages. For this instrument that form of the minor scale is to be preferred which has the interval of an augmented second between the sixth and

seventh notes both in ascending and descending passages.
This form of the minor scale can be "set" in the twelve
keys from A♭ to C♯ inclusive, which are all that are
necessary. The octave "harmonics" are produced on the
longer strings of the harp by touching, with the fleshy part
of the palm of the hand, the centre of the string, while plucking with the thumb and two first fingers of the same hand.

Thus, in the harp, the thumbs and fingers of both hands
are the exciters, the strings the vibrators of definite pitch,
and the sound-box the resonator. Manipulative mechanism
is not needed for playing the diatonic scale in a given key
for which the instrument is set by the pedals. The pedals,
however, supply this need in the case of accidentals, also for
setting the instrument in another key.

The harp's quality of tone mingles extremely well with
the horns, trombones, and brass instruments generally.
For the relative intensity of the various partials present
in the vibrations of a plucked string see arts. 331-332.
It must be remembered, however, that this refers to
the string itself. From a musical instrument whose
vibrators are strings (whether plucked, struck, or bowed),
the actual effect on the ear depends both on the nature of the
vibrations executed by the strings and upon the modification
of the vibrations introduced by the resonator. It is,
perhaps, at this point that the technical skill and experience
of the instrument-maker play their most important part.
Experiments have been initiated by the writer to investigate
the modifications in the vibrations from a string which are
introduced by the various other parts of the instrument on
which that string is mounted (see arts. 361-363).

330. The Mandolin has four double strings, each pair
being tuned in unison. The e'' strings are of catgut, the
a' strings of steel, the d' strings of copper, and the g strings
of catgut covered with silver wire. The strings are plucked
with a plectrum (of tortoise-shell or horn), and "stopped"
upon the finger-board to produce the notes of the scale.

Berlioz states that the quality of tone of the mandolin has a keen delicacy not possible on other instruments sometimes substituted for it.

Violin played "pizzicato."—When instruments of the violin family are played "pizzicato," that is, by plucking with the fingers of the right hand instead of with the bow, they fall strictly under the present category, but call for no further comment in this place, being treated, as to their normal mode of playing, under the heading of bowed strings.

331. Quality of Tone from Plucked Strings.—We have already seen (art. 143) that a string of length l plucked at a point distant h from one end has the full harmonic series of overtones, the amplitude of the nth partial being proportional to $(1/n^2) \sin (n\pi h/l)$. Thus, as we ascend the series of partials, the factor $1/n^2$ in the amplitude quickly decreases according to a fixed law independent of where the string is plucked. But the other factor $\sin (n\pi h/l)$ obviously depends for its effect upon the value h/l, *i.e.* upon where the string is plucked. This, then, is at the option of the player in the instruments we have now under consideration. And, by exercising choice in the matter, the quality of the tone may be somewhat varied. Thus, if a string be plucked in the middle, the evenly-numbered partials are all suppressed. The tone in this case is found to be somewhat nasal. If, on the other hand, the string be plucked at one-seventh of its length from the end, the seventh partial is the first to be suppressed, and the tone is, in consequence, much pleasanter. For any specified place of plucking the relative amplitudes may be found from the theory just quoted. Further, the physical intensities of the various partials may be calculated since they are proportional to the product $n^2 a_n^2$, or the product of square of frequency into square of amplitude. Finally, we may take the intensity of the prime tone or first partial as 100, and express the others in terms of that arbitrary value. This has been done by Helmholtz for a string plucked at one-seventh of its length from an end, and the results are given in the upper line of Table XXX. If, instead of a sharp point to pluck the string as supposed in the theory, the finger or other rounded object be used, then the angle is rounded off where the string is plucked, and the series of partials is more convergent. Now, the quicker the series of upper partials dies away, the mellower is the quality of the tone produced.

Hence, in the case of the mandolin, in which the strings are plucked by a pointed plectrum, we have more prominence given to the high partials, and thus a shriller or more tinkling tone results than with the guitar or harp plucked by the fingers. Further, the high partials are formed by thin strings; hence the thicker strings used wholly or in part on any given instrument yield a softer, sweeter tone than the others which are thinner.

332. In all the instruments in which the strings are excited by plucking, the tone obviously dies away from the instant of plucking. And, further, since the different partials usually die away at different rates, the higher ones more rapidly than the lower ones, the tone, as it continues, becomes sweeter and duller. There is also a characteristic beginning of the note due to the plucking. No doubt all these effects in various degrees help us to distinguish the family of plucked stringed instruments as a whole, and also to discriminate between the individuals of the family itself. We might also note, in conclusion, that if the strings are very thick and of rigid material, the higher partials will be slightly disturbed from the harmonic relation. This again is a distinction from the instrument played with a bow which preserves strict periodicity, and therefore (by Fourier's theorem) commensurate periods of all the partials.

333. The Pianoforte.—In this instrument the only question that need detain us is the manner of exciting the vibration by the blow of the hammer and the partials thus produced. In the theory of strings (art. 144), we saw that a string of length l, excited by an instantaneous blow at a point distant h from the end, has the full series of harmonic partials.   Further, the amplitude of the nth partial is proportional to $\frac{1}{n} \sin(n\pi h/l)$.   This series, therefore, having only the *first* power of n in the denominator, converges more slowly than that for strings plucked at a point, in which case the *square* of n occurred in the denominator.   But it has, like the plucked strings, the sine factor which here expresses the dependence of quality on place struck.   Hence the necessity, on the part of the instrument-maker, for rightly choosing where the hammers shall strike the strings. Further, to prevent the formation of the long and too obtrusive series of partials which would result from a blow with a hard hammer striking at a single point, the hammer has a rounded end and is covered with an elastic pad. Thus the motion is imparted to a considerable length of the string instead of being confined to a point; also the contact between hammer and string is not instantaneous, but extends over a time which, although very short absolutely, is appreciable in comparison with the period of vibration of the string itself.   These modifications of the phenomena Helmholtz has endeavoured to introduce in his theory.   As an approximation, he writes for the pressure of the hammer $A \sin mt$, and the hammer is supposed in contact with the string for half the period defined by m. He thus finds that the amplitudes of the partials are affected by factors, one of which is a sine function, and involves the suppression of the partials which have a node at the point of impact.   There is also an algebraic factor, according to which the amplitudes of the partials decrease nearly as the inverse *cube* of n when m is finite.   When, however, m is infinite, we have returned to the perfectly hard hammer, and the amplitudes decrease inversely as the *first* power of n.   The values of the intensities of the partials for the pianoforte calculated by Helmholtz from his formula when the striking point is $\frac{1}{7}$, and the hammer is in contact for $\frac{3}{7}$ the period of the prime, are given in Table XXX., and were found to agree with the notes a little above the centre of the compass of his grand pianoforte, *i.e.* near c''.

334. It must, however, be remembered that this theory is but approximate. Ellis states that, with the ordinary pianoforte hammer, the partial tone corresponding to the node struck, though materially weakened, is not absolutely extinguished.

As to the choice of place struck, Helmholtz writes, " In pianofortes, the point struck is about $\frac{1}{7}$ to $\frac{1}{9}$ the length of the string from its extremity, for the middle part of the instrument. We must therefore assume that this place has been chosen because experience has shown it to give the finest musical tone, which is most suitable for harmonies. The selection is not due to theory. It results from attempts to meet the requirements of artistically trained ears, and from the technical experience of two centuries."

335. The effect of the soft pedal in producing the muffled or veiled quality of tone by interposing an elastic pad between the hammer and the strings is a further interesting illustration of theory afforded by the piano.

In the pianoforte, as previously in the case of the harp, we must distinguish between the quality of tone built up of the partials of the string itself, and the quality perceived by the hearer from the whole musical instrument. For, by means of the resonator, the partials of the string are reinforced and usually in a selective or preferential manner. It is perhaps here more especially that theory fails, and the experience of musicians and instrument-makers through a long period count for so much.

336. The Violin Family.—The stringed instruments played with a bow now in ordinary use are only four in number, namely, the violin, the viola, the violoncello, and the double-bass. Of the latter, two varieties exist, those with three and those with four strings. The former is more usual in England. It is generally tuned in fourths, but occasionally in fifths, the less common tuning being shown in Table XXIV. by the letters in brackets. There is another instrument of this family, the viola d'amore, which though nearly obsolete, is of scientific interest on account of its double stringing.

Berlioz describes it as follows: " It has *seven catgut strings*, the three lowest of which are covered with silver wire. Below the neck of the instrument, and passing beneath the bridge, are seven more strings *of metal*, tuned in unison with the others, so as to vibrate sympathetically with them, thereby giving to the instrument a second resonance full of sweetness and mystery."

Beyond the points just mentioned as to the double-bass and the viola d'amore, the only distinctions between the various members of the violin family which are of import-ance to us, namely, the tuning of the strings and the compass of each, are shown in the Table XXIV.

337. The remarks which follow apply primarily to the violin as the representative of the family, but, with certain modifications which may be easily inferred, they apply also to the other kindred instruments.

The bow with its rosined hairs is the exciter, the strings of catgut, bare or covered with wire, are the vibrators of definite pitch, the sound-box is the resonator, while the finger-board, *free from frets*, allows the scale to be played by the fingers of the left hand.

Note that the absence of frets on the finger-board makes it possible to " stop " the notes anywhere. Thus, as regards intonation, it gives full freedom to the highest refinements of the finished performer, but affords no aid to the novice. Further, the smooth finger-board permits the use of the grace called *portamento*, that is, the gliding of a note con-tinuously from one pitch to another.

338. The use of the fingers of the left hand to press

the string against the finger-board always, of course, sharpens the note; for it shortens the portion of the string left free to vibrate, while not materially changing its tension. Hence, the inferior limit of the compass is quite definite, being that of the lowest open string. The superior limit, on the other hand, depends upon the skill of the performer. Very often, for the sake of special effects, notes called "harmonics" are used. That is, as already mentioned in connection with the guitar, the string is *touched* by a finger of the left hand at the middle, one-third the length, one-fourth, and so on, thus producing respectively the octave, the twelfth, the double octave, etc., of the note given by the open string itself. These are called natural harmonics. For all beyond the simple octave there is obviously a choice as to which node shall be touched for the same note. Thus, the twelfth of the open string may be produced by touching at the lower or at the higher of the two points of trisection. The former is sometimes more convenient, the latter is preferred by some as giving the nobler quality of tone. In addition to the natural harmonics on the lower and upper halves of the string, we have also what are called artificial harmonics. These are produced by pressing the string firmly against the finger-board with one finger (firm stop), and touching it lightly with another finger (loose stop) at a point between the former place and the bridge. By this means very high notes can be obtained without moving the hand far up the string. Thus, let the firm stop be made one-ninth the length of the string from the lower end, and the loose stop at one-fourth up the part of the string left free to vibrate. Then the firm stop would give a note one tone above that of the open string, while the loose stop further raises the pitch a double octave. On the violin these stops can be made with the first and fourth fingers respectively without moving the hand from its place at the lower end of the string, called the first position. These artificial harmonics are, however, entirely tabooed by some eminent players of the violin, since their introduction encourages the use of thin strings which are held incompatible with the production of the noblest quality of tone.

339. The points above mentioned for the stops are the strictly theoretical ones which apply to a perfectly uniform string.   On an actual violin the strings, when well selected, are usually a little taper, hence the theoretically assigned positions are slightly departed from.   It is important in stringing a violin that the strings all taper the same way, so that the same stops on the various strings lie truly side by side.

Another displacement of the stops from their ideal positions would occur if the bridge and finger-board are so related that the string is very high above the finger-board, for then the pressing the string to the finger-board would appreciably increase its tension.   This should be avoided by cutting the bridge, so that all the strings lie near enough to the finger-board, but still have room to vibrate.

340. The resonator of the violin demands special notice. It is this which gives to the instrument its valued quality of tone, and upon which the makers have bestowed their greatest pains.   The wood, the shape, and the varnish are all of the highest importance.   The bridge and ribs are of maple, the back of maple or sycamore, and the belly of pine.   Most violins, as tested by tuning-forks held over the "*f*" holes, show one or two specially marked resonances; but some of the finest violins appear to yield an almost continuous resonance between wide limits.   Such instruments present in a high degree the justly valued quality of tone throughout their entire compass.

341. All the instruments of the violin family may be played with a *mute*, for the sake of the specially muffled or veiled quality of tone thus obtained, and the extreme pianissimo effects then possible.   The mute is a small apparatus of wood or metal which fits on the bridge, and thus deadens the sound considerably. Its use where desired is indicated in the music.

342. With ordinary players of bowed instruments there are often perceptible hissing or rustling noises at the beginning and finishing of the notes. With the finest performers this feature almost disappears. For example, if the bow is not moved perpendicularly to the strings, but allowed a small lengthwise component also, this would generate in the string longitudinal vibrations of excessively high pitch. This is one possible explanation of the whistling sounds from a violin in the hands of a careless player. These objectionable noises may also be produced by a wrong adjustment between the pressure and speed of the bow. Yet other possible causes are a roughness of the hairs of the bow or the rosin on them, and imperfections in the wood of the violin, which cause sudden changes in the phase of the vibration, thus interrupting its uniform and even flow. Some of these causes may operate at any stage of the duration of a note, but their effect is likely to be most noticeable at the beginning and ending of a note, owing to the lack of perfect technique in the player's manner of putting on and taking off the bow.

343. The use of the bow as an exciter, unlike the plucking or striking action, enables the player to sustain the notes at will, and either with the same, a diminished, or an increased intensity. As to the handling of the bow to produce these various effects, the following points may be noticed :—The part of the string bowed, the pressure of the bow on the string, the speed of the bow over the string, are all at the disposal of the player and may be varied, not only from note to note, but during the continuance of any given note. An increased pressure and speed are required for a crescendo, a decreased pressure and speed for a decrescendo. But, by bowing nearer to the bridge, as usual in forte passages, there may be also a more brilliant quality of tone produced. While when bowing nearer the finger-board, as is usual in piano passages, a rather softer, duller quality of tone is probably obtained. But these effects may be modified by the following circumstances :—The bow is normally held obliquely, so that with a light pressure only a few of the hairs at the edge touch the string, but with a greater pressure more hairs touch, and so facilitate the production of a louder note. But this more extended place of contact of bow and string would discourage the higher partials and prevent them from being unduly obtrusive. The place on the string at which the bow is applied varies, of course, with the length of the string in vibration. Thus the bow should be applied nearer the bridge for a high stop on a given string than for a low stop or the same string open, *i.e.* with the whole string in vibration. Further, the bow may approach nearer the bridge for a thin string, as the e'' or a', than for a thick one as the d' string. The position of bowing may also be chosen with a special view to the quality of tone desired. The extreme range of positions at which bowing is admissible lie between say $\frac{1}{5}$ and $\frac{1}{25}$ of the length of the string, the normal distances being about $\frac{1}{10}$ to $\frac{1}{13}$, or roughly 1 inch from the bridge for a string whose length is $12\frac{3}{4}$ or 13 inches.

344. It should also be noticed that certain passages may be taken entirely upon particular strings for the sake of the special quality of tone thus obtained. For, as previously mentioned, some of the strings are bare, and one, the g string, in the violin is covered with wire ; further, the strings differ in thickness. Hence, each string has its own character differing slightly from each of the others, and is utilised by composers accordingly.

345. Another special power possessed by instruments of the violin family is their ability to produce the embellishment called the *tremolo*. In Spohr's *Violin School* this is described as follows :—The tremolo " consists in the wavering of a stopped note, which sounds alternately a little above and a little below its just pitch, and is produced by a trembling motion of the left hand in the direction from nut to bridge. This movement, however, should be very slight, so that the deviation from the true note may not offend the ear." It is used "rapid, for intensifying passionate expression, and slow, for imparting tenderness to sustained and pathetic melody."

346. The "strings," besides being valuable in themselves, constitute the very foundation of the orchestra. Various reasons conduce to this. For example, the players of the "strings" have not to pause to take breath, they command the most delicate shades of expression, and their quality of tone is such as not to pall upon the bearer so soon as that of the wind instruments. One writer, comparing the qualities of tone in the orchestra to the colours in a picture, has likened the strings to the various shades of grey, the wood-wind and horns to colours moderately bright and rich, the trumpets and trombones to colours approaching to purple and scarlet.

347. Vibrations of Bowed Strings.— No complete mechanical theory of the bowed string seems yet to have been given. Helmholtz, however, by a skilful combination of experiment and analysis has given a solution which serves for the most important musical applications, namely, the cases in which the bow is used so as to produce a tone of fine musical quality. Something has already been said in the previous chapter as to the action of the bow. The vibration of the string is maintained by it, but is not to any appreciable extent "forced" in the sense of having its pitch thereby modified. The maintenance is here one of those examples of the action in which the "driven" selects for itself, as it were, the periodicity of the influence under which it shall come. To discover something as to the nature of the motion executed by a bowed string, Helmholtz proceeded as follows :—The a' string of a violin was placed in a vertical position and tuned up to $b'\flat$, the part of it to

be observed was blackened with ink, when dry rubbed over
with wax, and then powdered with starch so that a few
grains remained sticking on the string. ˙A starch grain,
when illuminated, formed the point to be observed through
a microscope whose objective was carried by one prong of a
tuning-fork placed horizontally, but so that its vibrations
occurred vertically. The fork was B♭, exactly two octaves
below the string, and was electrically driven. The string
was excited by drawing the bow across it parallel to the
prongs of the fork. The figure presented in the field of
view by a luminous point, when both fork and string were
vibrating, was evidently that resulting from the two
vibrations, that of the fork vertically and that of the string
horizontally. But since that of the fork is known to be
simple harmonic of given period, it provides an exact
measure of the time, and thus enables the experimenter to
determine all the details of the other component, viz. the
vibration of the string. This apparatus for observing a
rapid vibration Helmholtz called a "vibration microscope."
In the simplest case when the bow bites well, and the prime
tone is powerfully produced, Helmholtz found that the motion
of any point of a horizontal string consists of an ascent
with uniform speed followed immediately by a descent at a
uniform speed. For the middle point of the string these
two speeds are equal, for other points they are unequal.
At the place of bowing the speed in the direction of bowing
appears to be equal to that of the violin bow. "During the
greater part of each vibration the string here clings to the
bow, and is carried on by it; then it suddenly detaches
itself and rebounds, whereupon it is seized by other points
in the bow and again carried forward." Thus, if the motion
of a point on the string is represented in a diagram with
time as abscissae and displacements as ordinates, we shall
have for the required "curve" a two-step straight line
zigzag, the slopes being in general different, see Fig. 87.

Reasoning upon these experimental results as a basis,

Helmholtz has given an analysis of the motion of a bowed string which, with slightly different notation, is followed here.

348. Theory of Bowed Strings by Helmholtz.—Let the motion of a point on the string be as represented in Fig. 87, and be also defined by the equations

$$y = ft - h \qquad \text{from } t = 0 \text{ to } t = a$$
and
$$y = g\,(\tau - t) - h \text{ from } t = a \text{ to } t = \tau \qquad (1),$$

where τ is the complete period of the compound vibration. Hence for $t = a$ we have

$$fa = g\,(\tau - a).$$

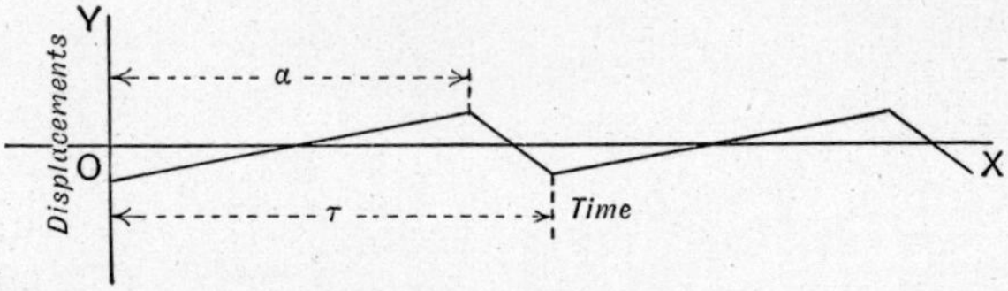

FIG. 87.—MOTION OF WELL-BOWED STRING.

Now let y be developed in the Fourier series,

$$y = a_1 \cos \omega t + a_2 \cos 2\omega t + \ldots + a_n \cos n\omega t + \ldots$$
$$+ b_1 \sin \omega t + b_2 \sin 2\omega t + \ldots + b_n \sin n\omega t + \ldots$$

where $\omega\tau = 2\pi$, and the values of the coefficients are to be obtained from the theorem by integration (see art. 52). Thus

$$a_n = \frac{2}{\tau} \int_0^\tau y \cos n\omega t\,dt = \frac{2}{\tau} \int_0^a (ft - h) \cos n\omega t\,dt$$

$$+ \frac{2}{\tau} \int_a^\tau \{g(\tau - t) - h\} \cos n\omega t\,dt,$$

whence
$$a_n = -\frac{(f + g)\tau}{2n^2\pi^2}(1 - \cos n\omega a).$$

Similarly $\qquad b_n = \dfrac{(f+g)\tau}{2n^2\pi^2} \sin n\omega a.$

Then, by substituting these in the Fourier expansion, we may write the results as follows:—

$$y = \frac{(f+g)\tau}{\pi^2} \sum_{n=1}^{n=\infty} \left\{ \frac{1}{n^2} \sin n\omega \frac{a}{2} \sin n\omega\left(t - \frac{a}{2}\right) \right\} \quad (2).$$

349. But this equation only refers to the point whose motion is delineated in the figure and expressed by equation (1). Now let x be the co-ordinate of a point on the string and l its length. Then, since in the general expression for the vibrating string the cosines of multiples of x/l are all absent, we obtain

$$y = \sum_{n=1}^{n=\infty} \left\{ c_n \sin \frac{n\pi x}{l} \sin n\omega\left(t - \frac{a}{2}\right) \right\} \quad (3).$$

By comparing (2) and (3), we have

$$c_n \sin \frac{n\pi x}{l} = \frac{(f+g)\tau}{n^2\pi^2} \sin \frac{n\pi a}{\tau} \quad (4).$$

Here $(f+g)$ and a are independent of n, but not necessarily of x. On putting $n=1$ and $n=2$ in (4) and dividing, we find

$$\frac{c_2}{c_1} \cos \frac{\pi x}{l} = \frac{1}{4} \cos \frac{\pi a}{\tau},$$

from which it follows that for $x = l/2$ and a finite ratio of c's, $a = \tau/2$. And since, by observation, a decreases with x, and both vanish together, we obtain

$$c_2 = \frac{c_1}{4} \text{ and } \frac{x}{l} = a/\tau \quad (5).$$

350. Thus, since x does not appear in the ratio of the c's, we find that $(f+g)$ is independent of x, but a is not. We shall see later that f and g are each functions of x, although their sum is constant.

Now let u be the amplitude of the vibration of the strings at the point x, then

$$fa = g(\tau - a) = 2u$$

$$\therefore \quad f + g = 2u\left(\frac{1}{a} + \frac{1}{\tau - a}\right) = \frac{2u\tau}{a(\tau - a)} = \frac{2ul^2}{\tau x(l - x)} \quad \left.\right\} \quad (6),$$

the last expression being found by (5). And, since $f + g$ is independent of x, we have, putting U for the amplitude at the middle of the string,

$$\frac{2ul^2}{\tau x(l - x)} = \frac{8U}{\tau} \; ;$$

or

$$u = 4Ux(l - x)/l^2 \quad (7).$$

Also (7) in (6) gives $\quad f + g = 8U/\tau \quad (8)$.

And from (5) it follows that a and $(\tau - a)$ are proportional to the corresponding parts of the string on each side of the observed point.

Put the value of $f + g$ from (8) in (4) and then the value so obtained of c_n in (3). We thus find, for the expression of the string's motion under the circumstances considered, the following equation:—

$$y = \frac{8U}{\pi^2} \sum_{n=1}^{n=\infty} \left\{ \frac{1}{n^2} \sin \frac{n\pi x}{l} \sin \frac{n2\pi}{\tau}\left(t - \frac{a}{2}\right) \right\} \quad (9).$$

Of course the ordinary relations for strings hold here, namely,

$$\frac{\omega}{2\pi} = \frac{1}{\tau} = N = \frac{v}{2l} = \frac{\sqrt{F/\sigma}}{2l} \quad (10),$$

where N is the frequency of the prime tone, v the speed of propagation of a disturbance along the string, F the force by which it is stretched, and σ its linear density.

351. It should be carefully noted that the analysis leading to equation (9) is based and built up on the assumed motion of the observed points being as specified at the outset, namely, the two-step straight line zigzag. That this is sometimes the case is the result of Helmholtz's experiments, and forms the foundation of the theory. But, as Helmholtz himself found, it is not always the case and then all this falls to the ground. Thus, when the motion of the observed point exhibits, as it sometimes does, little crumples superposed on the main zigzag, we should then have to use corresponding values of y instead of those in (1) to obtain by integration the coefficients which appear in (2). Hence equation (9) is not to be taken as a complete solution for a bowed string corresponding to that for a string plucked at a point (art. 143). Another way of showing that this must be so, is as follows :—The above expression contains no factor depending on the place at which the string is bowed, and all the partials are included and their relative amplitudes vary as $1/n^2$ simply. Whereas it is found that if a string is bowed exactly at any node of any partial, then that partial will not be elicited. Thus, if bowed very near to the point in question, the whole motion of the string would, in all probability, be slightly modified. Thus, in the full expression there should be a factor showing how the various partials fade away as the bow approaches any one of their nodes, and that they vanish when the bow precisely reaches any node.

352. Let us now proceed with the theory as developed by Helmholtz. If we put $\left(t - \dfrac{a}{2}\right) = 0$ in equation (9), then $y = 0$ for all values of x, and hence all parts of the string pass through their equilibrium position simultaneously. At that instant the velocity f at the point x is found by equations (6), (7), and (5) to be

$$f = 2u/a = 8\,U(l - x)/l\tau \qquad (11).$$

But this velocity only lasts for $a/2 = x\tau/2l$, after the instant when $y = 0$ everywhere. So, within this limit, we have the general expression for the displacement,

$$y = ft = 8\,U(l - x)t/l\tau \qquad (12),$$

and the extreme value of y reached, or the amplitude at x, will be

$$u = fa/2 = 4U(l-x)x/l^2 \qquad (13).$$

From this point the value of y diminishes at speed given by equations (6), (7), and (5), namely,

$$g = \frac{2u}{\tau - a} = \frac{8Ux(l-x)}{l^2(\tau - a)} = 8Ux/l\tau \qquad (14).$$

Hence, after time t from when $y = 0$ everywhere, y after increasing to its maximum value u will have been diminished for the time $(t - a/2)$, so will be less than u by the amount $g(t - a/2)$.

Thus we obtain by (13), (14), and (5),

$$y = \frac{4Ux}{l}\left\{\frac{l-x}{l} - \frac{2}{\tau}\left(t - \frac{a}{2}\right)\right\} = \frac{4Ux}{l}\left\{\frac{\tau - a}{\tau} - \frac{2t}{\tau} + \frac{a}{\tau}\right\}$$

or,

$$y = 8Ux\left(\frac{\tau}{2} - t\right)/l\tau \qquad (15).$$

353. Hence, at time t, the configuration of one part of the string through $x = l$ is given by equation (12), and, at the same instant, that of the other part passing through $x = 0$ is expressed by equation (15). Each equation shows that the form of the part to which it refers is a straight line. The point where these straight lines intersect is given by the condition that the two values of y are equal. Thus equating the right sides of (12) and (15), we obtain

$$(l-x)t = \left(\frac{\tau}{2} - t\right)x,$$

or,

$$\frac{x}{t} = \frac{l}{\tau/2} = v \qquad (16),$$

the v being identical with that occurring in equation (10). Hence the abscissa x of this point of intersection increases in proportion to the time and at the speed which enables it to traverse the length of the string in $\tau/2$. That the speed of any disturbance in running along the string must have this value might have been foreseen at the beginning, and so equation (16) serves as a check on the accuracy of the previous working.

354. Further, the point of intersection itself, which is at the same time the point of the string most removed from its position of rest, passes from one end of the string to the other, and during its passage describes the parabolic arcs, for which the equations, as seen from (13), are

$$y = \pm 4U(l-x)x/l^2 \qquad (17).$$

In these equations the y must not be confused with the y previously used for the displacement of a point x at time t. Of the two algebraic signs on the right side, the upper refers to the upper curve with positive ordinates, and the lower to the lower curve whose ordinates are all negative.

355. Hence the motion and the form of the whole string at any one instant may be thus briefly described. In Figure 88 the foot D of the ordinate of the highest point moves forwards (and D′ say, corresponding to the lowest point, then moves backwards) with the constant speed v along the horizontal line AB, while the highest (or lowest) point of the string describes in succession the two parabolic arcs AC_1B and BC_2A, and the string itself is always stretched in the two straight lines AC_1, C_1B or BC_2, C_2A. Further, the motion of the string at one point x is first

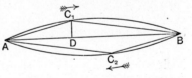

FIG. 88.—CONFIGURATION OF BOWED STRING.

upwards with constant speed f for the time a, and then downwards with constant speed g for the time $(\tau - a)$; where τ is the complete period of the compound vibration; $a = x\tau/l$, $f = 8U(l-x)/l\tau$ and $g = 8Ux/l\tau$, see equations (5), (11), and (14). Hence, although the numerical *sum* of the upward and downward speeds at any point of the string is the same as that at any other point $(f+g = 8U/\tau = \text{const.},$

see equation (8)), yet, the separate speeds and the fractions of the period during which each is maintained vary from point to point, and in such wise as to make the amplitudes at the different places differ from each other, and become indeed the ordinates of the two parabolic curves defined by equation (17).

356. As previously mentioned, Helmholtz also found that, in certain cases, the motion of the string at the bowed place was more complicated, consisting of little crumples superposed upon the main two-step zigzag. These little crumples he failed to keep steady enough to count until using an old Italian violin by Guadanini. This uniformity of vibrational form is evidently connected with the pure smooth flow of the tone heard, and shows the superiority of fine old instruments that have also been long played upon. Examples of motions of both characters are given in the next article. We thus see that the motion of the string itself may be modified by the resonator with which it is associated.

Now the foregoing investigation relates to the actual motion of the string when associated with a resonator. Yet still, as in the case of plucked and struck strings, we have to note that the effect on the ear from any instrument with bowed strings may be further modified by the action of the resonator, certain of the partial tones being preferentially reinforced (see arts. 361-363).

The physical intensities of the partials from the string itself when well bowed are shown in Table XXX.

357. Researches of Krigar-Menzel and Raps.—In 1891, O. Krigar-Menzel and A. Raps published (in the *Sitzungsber. d. Berl. Akad. d. Wiss.*) an account of a different method of observing vibrating strings. By this they obtained photographically a record of the motion at any point in the form of a displacement-time diagram. The essentials of the method are as follows:—Imagine a string stretched horizontally some distance in front of a vertical slit which is illuminated from behind by an arc lamp. By

means of a convex lens a real image of the slit is focused
on the string. This image crossed by the opaque string
now serves as object to a second lens, which focuses upon
a sensitive film the bright slit crossed by the string's
shadow. The photographic film is wound upon a drum
rotated uniformly by clockwork about its axis, which is
vertical. Then the up-and-down motion of the shadow
due to the string's vibration will be compounded with a
uniform horizontal motion due to the drum's rotation.
But this is what is required to give a displacement-time
diagram. On the original negatives these diagrams are
white on a black ground, and they are so reproduced in the
paper. This method obviously allows any point to be
chosen as the bowed point, and the same or other point
to be chosen as the observed point. These points were
variously chosen and combined by the authors, and sixty-
four photographs accompany their paper.

We can only reproduce a few of them here (Fig. 89).
For the sake of sharp photographs, fine metal strings were
usually employed, but they found that the effect was practically the same with strings of other materials.

358. In the first section of Fig. 89 we have cases of
special musical interest and also illustrative of Helmholtz's
theory. For here the bowing is at $\frac{1}{15}$th the length of the
string, which approaches to the practice of violinists. And
we see by the seven diagrams that at all the observed
points the motion is a pure straight line two-step zigzag;
and, further, that the times occupied on each step are proportional to the lengths of the two parts into which the
string is divided by the point of observation. In Section
II., on the other hand, the point of observation is the same
in all seven diagrams, and being the middle point, all evenly
numbered partials elude notice, as they have a node there.
But as the bowing passes from $\frac{1}{10}$ to $\frac{1}{3}$ the type of motion
changes considerably. In this section the symbol ϵ denotes
a small undetermined quantity of the order $\frac{1}{20}$. The last

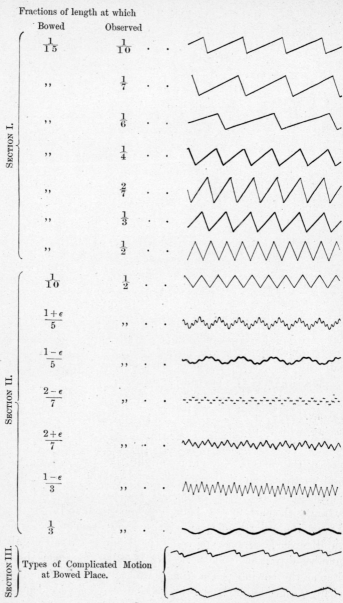

Fractions of length at which

Bowed	Observed		
$\frac{1}{15}$	$\frac{1}{10}$	.	.
,,	$\frac{1}{7}$	.	.
,,	$\frac{1}{6}$	.	.
,,	$\frac{1}{4}$	.	.
,,	$\frac{2}{7}$	.	.
,,	$\frac{1}{3}$	.	.
,,	$\frac{1}{2}$	.	.
$\frac{1}{10}$	$\frac{1}{2}$	.	.
$\frac{1+\epsilon}{5}$	,,	.	.
$\frac{1-\epsilon}{5}$	,,	.	.
$\frac{2-\epsilon}{7}$	,,	.	.
$\frac{2+\epsilon}{7}$	,,	..	.
$\frac{1-\epsilon}{3}$	,,	.	.
$\frac{1}{3}$	,,	.	.

SECTION I.

SECTION II.

SECTION III. Types of Complicated Motion at Bowed Place.

FIG. 89.—MOTION OF BOWED STRINGS OBSERVED BY KRIGAR-MENZEL AND RAPS.

diagram of this section is almost a pure sine graph. The reason for this can easily be seen. By bowing at $\frac{1}{3}$, the partials 3, 6, 9, 12, etc. are all absent from the motion of the string; and by observing at $\frac{1}{2}$, the partials 2, 4, 6, 8, etc. are all absent from this particular diagram of its motion, since they have a node at the centre. Thus the partials remaining in the diagram, up to the 16th inclusive, are those numbered 1, 5, 7, 11, and 13. And their respective amplitudes are of the order 1, $\frac{1}{25}$, $\frac{1}{49}$, $\frac{1}{121}$, and $\frac{1}{169}$. Hence we are practically reduced to the first and a very small fifth partial, the effect of the others being almost negligible. Section III. consists of two diagrams only, showing types of complicated motion at the place of bowing. It is clear that a theory of the whole motion of the string founded upon these motions at the bowed place would be more complicated than that of Helmholtz already given. For, in obtaining the coefficients for the Fourier series, we should be obliged to take y from these diagrams instead of from a simple two-step zigzag.

359. It should be especially observed in connection with bowed strings that it is no approximation to express their motion as a Fourier series. For, when the motion is properly maintained by the bow, it is strictly periodic, and therefore all the partials are compelled to be of commensurate periods, although the free natural periods of the same partials might depart slightly from the harmonic series. This slight departure would, of course, be allowed to assert itself when the violin is played " pizzicato."

Professor W. B. Morton and T. B. Vinycomb have also followed up the subject, and published results [1] illustrating plucking and resonance.

360. EXPT. 62. *Projection of String Vibration Curves.*—The displacement-time curves shown in the diagrams of Fig. 89 can easily be projected on a screen visible to an audience.

---

[1] *Phil. Mag.*, Nov. 1904.

This is attained by the following slight modification of the arrangement of Krigar-Menzel and Raps. The drum is replaced by a rotating mirror which is turned by one operator, while another bows the string. The ordinary metal "string" of a sonometer will do, but needs careful bowing. The light after reflection from the rotating mirror falls upon a suitably placed screen, and thus exhibits the curve while the sound is audible.

Yet another method of projection is due to S. Mikola (1906), and consists in replacing the drum-film of Krigar-Menzel and Raps by alternate black and white strips on the drum and parallel to its axis ; this then forms the screen on which the curves are seen.

361. Vibrations of the Various Parts of a Stringed Instrument.—As we have already seen, the vibrations of strings—whether plucked, struck, or bowed—are, in their main features, known to us through the work of Helmholtz and others. But, although the interest of the pure mathematician may cease at this point when the motion of the string is solved, and the musician's interest may only begin with the main body of sound leaving the instrument, yet the physicist may rightly inquire what happens between these two stages. For " the sound received by the ear from a stringed instrument does not come chiefly from the string direct. Indeed, if a string is mounted on very rigid and massive supports, scarcely any sound can be obtained from it, although the amplitude of its vibrations may be considerable (see Expt. 2, art. 2). Under the usual conditions the string moves the bridges over which it is stretched, they in turn move the belly, sides, and back of the sound-box, and the air within the box pulsates in response. Probably, therefore, the chief part of the sound received by the ear comes from the belly and other parts of the sound-box, as it has a larger surface, and is therefore better able to set the external air in vibratory motion.

" Now the question naturally arises, Are these vibrations of the same quality as those executed by the string itself ?

that is, may they be compounded of the same Fourier terms ? Probably not, for the worth of a violin does not lie in the strings, but in the sound-box.

"It appears, therefore, to be a matter of some importance to attempt to trace the changes in the character of the vibrations which occur as we pass through the series : string, bridges, sound-box, air within the sound-box, air outside the sound-box."

This aspect of the matter occurred to the writer some time back, and the above passage is quoted from the first instalment of work upon the subject.[1]

362. In these experiments vibration curves were *simultaneously* obtained from the sound-box and string of a monochord. This new feature had the advantage of exhibiting the relations of amplitudes and phases of the two motions, and also showed whether variations in the belly's motion were traceable to faulty bowing.

For the string's motion a modification of the method of Krigar-Menzel and Raps was adopted—their film on a drum being replaced by an ordinary glass negative shot along rails.

The motion of the belly, or upper face of the sound-box, was detected and recorded by means of a tiny three-legged optical lever. This lever received upon its mirror the light from an arc lantern after passing through a pin-hole and a focusing lens. The light is then reflected on to the photographic plate, where it makes a bright spot just below the image of the slit crossed by the string's shadow.

When the string is excited its shadow moves up and down the slit, and the belly moving in response the bright spot also oscillates vertically. If, however, in addition the plate is moving horizontally, we have both oscillations drawn out into displacement-time curves, the upper one for the string is, in the positive print, a black line on a white

---

[1] Barton and Garrett, *Phil. Mag.*, July 1905.

ground; the lower one for the belly being a white one on a dark ground (see Fig. 89A).

363. Further instalments of this work were carried out in 1906 by the writer and J. Penzer, in which the vibrations of the air [1] and those of the bridge vertically and lengthwise of the string [2] were dealt with. The methods for the vibration of the string were essentially the same throughout, its motion being, accordingly, always shown by a black line on a light ground. For the motions of the air the centre hole of the three on one side of the monochord was covered with a thin animal membrane, whose centre was connected by a light stalk of aluminium to a mirror capable of rocking on a horizontal axle, consisting of a needle working in vees on brackets fixed to the monochord itself. Thus, as the string was sounded, the air pulsated, and so by means of the membrane and stalk rocked the mirror. Consequently the spot of light reflected by the mirror and focused on the photographic plate rose and fell, and thus, as the plate moved horizontally, traced upon it a wavy line, showing the amplitude, phase, and character of the motions of the air. These proved to be of greater complication than those of the sound-box, the air apparently following more closely the highly complicated motions of the string itself (see Fig. 89B).

The motions of the bridge were obtained by special arrangements of the rocking mirror or optical lever, and were found to be intermediate in general character and complication between those of the sound-box and those of the air (see Fig. 89C). In Figs. 89B and 89C the string is shown in the lower part of the photograph. In all the three figures the frequency of the string is 130 per sec., and the bowing is at $\frac{1}{10}$ throughout.

364. Metal Reeds without Pipes.—Examples of this class of vibrator are presented by the harmonium, the American organ, and the concertina. In these cases the

---

[1] *Phil. Mag.*, Dec. 1906.	[2] *Phil. Mag.*, April 1907.

reed or tongue is a thin oblong metal plate or strip fastened
at one end to a block in which there is a hole behind the
tongue and of the same shape. In some examples of these
reeds the tongue, when in its position of rest, closes the
hole in the block with the exception of a very fine chink

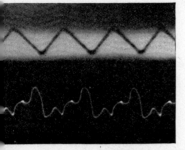

FIG. 89A.—BELLY'S MOTION.
Magnified 260 times that of string.

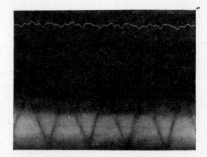

FIG. 89B.—AIR'S MOTION.
Magnified 1400 times that of string.

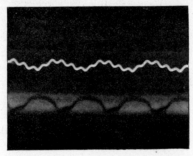

FIG. 89C.—BRIDGE'S MOTION LONGITUDINALLY.
Magnified 67 times that of string.

all round its margin. When in motion the tongue oscillates
so as to alternately open and (nearly) close the hole in the
block. This arrangement is termed a "free reed." Thus
the mode of producing a musical note with a free reed
resembles that in the siren. For in each, the passage for
the air being alternately opened and closed, its stream is

reduced to a series of separate puffs or rushes. On the siren this is effected by the rotation of a disc pierced at regular intervals, but in the case in question by the vibration of the elastic metal tongue or reed. Now, it is a result of mathematical analysis that, the more sudden the discontinuity of any periodic motion, the greater the relative importance of the high upper partials into which that motion may be resolved. Thus, the more sudden the action of the reed, the more obtrusive are the high upper partials, and the more cutting or grating is the quality of tone. Moreover, since, in the class of instruments under discussion, there are no pipes whose resonance can modify this quality, it remains of that cutting character which so soon palls upon the hearer.

365. As to the distinction between the harmonium and the American organ, the former has the wind forced from the bellows through the reeds, while the latter has it sucked through the reeds into the bellows.

The chief claim of the concertina to notice is the fact that it has fourteen notes to the octave, the two unusual notes occurring between D and E, and between G and A. There are thus separate notes for D♯ and E♭, and again separate notes for G♯ and A♭. We shall see in the next chapter to what this is due.

In the various instruments now under review the wind is the exciter and maintainer, the reed and the associated puffs of air form the vibrator of definite pitch, while the keys and their connections are the manipulative mechanism for producing the scale.

The reeds are tuned as follows :—To sharpen one, a little is scraped off the *tip*. This, while not materially weakening the spring, diminishes the mass where its effect is greatest, the frequency is accordingly increased. To flatten the pitch of any note a little is scraped off the root of the corresponding reed. This weakens the spring while scarcely altering the effective mass, and so the frequency is diminished.

366. The Organ.—For our purpose we must divide the stops of the organ into two classes, those with reeds and those without. We shall treat them in this order.

Metal Reeds with Pipes.—In passing from the reeds of the harmonium to those of the organ, we have to note, *first*, that the quality of the tone is now modified by the presence of a pipe; and, *second*, that the tuning is effected differently. Further, the reeds themselves may ·be of two kinds: *first*, free reeds like those in harmoniums; and, *second*, *beating* reeds which are too large to pass into the opening with which they are associated. They accordingly bend down upon the opening like a flap, and thus nearly close it. A beating or striking reed is "voiced" so as to come down with a rolling motion, and thus gradually cover the aperture. The harshness of quality consequent upon a sudden discontinuity is thus avoided. The free reed of an organ pipe is tuned by a wire clip which grasps it upon both sides near its root. The shorter that part of the reed left free to vibrate, the sharper is the pitch. The beating reed, on the other hand, has simply a wire pressing upon it near the root, and by an adjustment of this wire it is tuned.

By varying the make of the reeds and the shape of the pipes with which they are associated, various typical tone qualities can be obtained, imitating, more or less perfectly, the various instruments of the orchestra.

In these reed pipes or reed stops of the organ we have, therefore, the following classification of parts and functions: The blast of wind is the exciter, the reed of definite pitch is the vibrator, and the pipe with which it is associated is the resonator modifying the quality of the tone produced. The manipulative mechanism for the production of the notes of the scale, expression, and quality of tone, is represented by the keys, stops, bellows, etc.

367. Pipes without Reeds.—We now pass to the flue or flute stops of the organ. These consist of pipes, usually of parallel bore, and with a typical side-opening or "mouth" familiar to every one. They may be of wood, and are then usually of rectangular cross-section; or of metal, when they are usually cylindrical. Further, they may be either open at the end distant from the mouth or stopped. We have already seen (art. 175) that the open pipes have a full series of harmonic partials almost exactly in tune, especially if narrow, and that the stopped pipes, on the other hand, have only the odd series of partials.

It remains, further, to be noticed how the tone is excited and maintained, and the other details upon which the quality depends. Let us consider the latter first. The investigation of the tones natural to pipes (art. 180) referred to the tones of strongest resonance, as Helmholtz terms them. But, when the compound tone is maintained by blowing, the partials, though naturally forming a series nearly but not quite harmonic, are forced into the strict harmonic series, since according to Fourier's theorem any periodic motion has components of strictly commensurate periods. Now, in the case of narrow pipes the natural tones are very nearly the strict harmonic series. Thus, the components of any periodic motion whose frequency is that of the pipes' fundamental, will be almost exactly in tune throughout with the tones natural to the pipe. They will thus be all freely elicited, and the retinue of upper partials will be relatively full, the quality of tone from the pipe being accordingly fairly bright. In wide pipes, on the contrary, the upper partials natural to the pipe deviate considerably from the harmonic series founded on its prime. Hence, when a periodic motion of the frequency of its prime is forced upon it by blowing, the strictly commensurate components of this motion being considerably out of tune with the higher tones natural to the pipe, they are but slightly elicited. Hence, in this case, the retinue of upper partials is feeble, and the quality of tone is, in consequence, soft and mellow.

368. We have now to examine the action of blowing

itself. On this subject Helmholtz[1] wrote, " The means usually adopted for keeping pipes continually sounding is *blowing*. In order to understand the action of the process, we must remember that when air is blown out of such a slit as that which lies below the lip of the pipe, it breaks through the air which lies at rest in front of the slit in a thin sheet like a blade or lamina, and hence at first does not draw any sensible part of that air into its own motion. It is not until it reaches a distance of some centimetres that the outpouring sheet splits up into eddies or vortices, which effect a mixture of the air at rest and the air in motion. This blade-shaped sheet of air in motion can be rendered visible by sending a stream of air impregnated with smoke or clouds of sal ammoniac through the mouth of a pipe from which the pipe itself is removed, such as is commonly found among physical apparatus.

" Any blade-shaped gas flame which comes from a split burner is also an example of a similar process. Burning renders visible the limits between the outpouring sheet of gas and the atmosphere. But the flame does not render the continuance of the stream visible. Now the blade-shaped sheet of air at the mouth of the organ pipe is wafted to one side or the other by every stream of air which touches its surface, exactly as this gas flame is. The consequence is that when the oscillation of the mass of air in the pipe causes the air to enter through the ends of the pipe, the blade-shaped stream of air arising from the mouth is also inclined inwards, and draws its whole mass of air into the pipe. During the opposite phase of vibration, on the other hand, when the air leaves the ends of the pipe the whole mass of this blade of air is driven outwards. Hence it happens that exactly at the times when the air in the pipe is most condensed, more air still is driven in from the bellows, whence the condensation, and consequently also the equivalent of work of the vibration of the air is

[1] Ellis's Translation, p. 91.

increased, while at the periods of rarefaction in the pipe the wind of the bellows pours its mass of air into the open space in front of the pipe."

369. The above accounts for the maintenance of the vibrations when once started, but scarcely explains their initiation. Experiments have been made with a blade-shaped sheet of air directed (1) wholly without the pipe, and (2) wholly within. And it has been shown that in either case the pipe will not spontaneously speak. If, however, by a puff of wind the direction of the sheet of air were changed into its usual path, then the pipe commenced and continued to speak.

The phenomena of initiation and the theory of the exact adjustment of the mouth that ensures ready speech seem to be still obscure.

370. As to the dependence of quality of tone upon the special arrangements at the mouth, it must be remembered that the more sudden or discontinuous is the action of the blade-shaped stream of air, the more important are the higher components into which its periodic motion may be analysed by Fourier's theorem. And, obviously, this increase of the higher components of the impressed forces produces a corresponding increase in the upper partials elicited from the pipe. Thus Helmholtz says,[1] "Wooden pipes do not produce such a cutting windrush as metal pipes. Wooden sides also do not resist the agitation of the waves of sound so well as metal ones, and hence the vibrations of higher pitch seem to be destroyed by friction. For these reasons wood gives a softer, but duller, less penetrating quality of tone than metal." This extract also brings into notice yet another factor to be considered as to the quality of tone obtainable from a given pipe.

371. We may now sum up as follows :—The relative intensities of the various partials present in the compound tone of an organ pipe depend upon—

[1] Ellis's Translation, p. 94.

1. The relative intensities of the corresponding components into which, by Fourier's theorem, the periodic impressed force may be analysed.

2. The closeness of tuning between these . strictly commensurate components of the force and the tones natural to the pipe ; and

3. The possible more rapid diminution of intensity of the higher partials due to friction on the interior of the pipe.

The partials actually present in various pipes as determined by Helmholtz are shown in Table XXX.

372. It is also noteworthy that D. J. Blaikley finds that the pitch of the note emitted by a pipe when blown at practical pressures is a few vibrations per second sharper than its natural note of strongest resonance as determined by a tuning-fork.

By over-blowing organ pipes the pitch jumps somewhat suddenly to the next higher partial. This is, of course, avoided in the organ itself, each pipe being adjusted at the mouth, or " voiced " as it is termed, so as to speak freely its proper tone at the specified pressure at which the wind is to be supplied to it in the instrument.

373. Applying our usual classification to a flue pipe, we see that the blast of wind is the exciter as before, but the blade-shaped sheet of air and the column of air in the pipe had better be regarded together as the vibrating system. The blade-shaped sheet of air might be called the vibrator, but it is not of definite pitch, and is not by deliberate intention moved at the outset in any predetermined way. The settlement of the pitch lies almost solely with the pipe, which therefore can scarcely now be looked upon as a mere resonator to intensify the sound or modify its quality as in the case of the reed pipe. A stopped organ pipe is tuned by adjusting the piece which stops the upper end. An open pipe is tuned by moving a sliding ring or by adjusting a lead piece which shades the upper end.

374. The Flute Family comprises those well-known instruments, fifes and flutes of various pitches, and that smallest, highest-pitched kind termed a piccolo. In all these instruments we have a cylindrical pipe open at one end and pierced with a special side mouth hole near the other end. They are thus seen to be comparable to the open flue or flute pipes of the organ in the manner of exciting and maintaining the sound; though, in the case of the flutes and piccolo, the lips and chest of the performer replace the corresponding mechanism in the organ. The air blast may be regarded as the exciter, while the vibrating system comprises (1) the blade-shaped stream of air which passes from the player's lips and strikes the sharp edge of the mouth-hole, and (2) the column of air within the cylindrical pipe. The pitch is probably governed and kept steady chiefly by the air column which, by its vibration, causes the stream of air to enter or pass over the mouth hole. The manipulative mechanism for the production of the various notes of the scale consists of holes along the side of the tube. In the very simplest forms these may be reduced to six to be covered by the fingers. But, in all instruments intended to give the full chromatic scale, these six finger holes are supplemented by others provided with keys which remain closed except when the keys are pressed.

375. We have already seen from theory that an open cylindrical pipe gives the full retinue of harmonic partials. But the limit to which this retinue extends upwards and the prominence of the higher tones depends, as we have also seen, upon the width of the tube and other circumstances. Now, in the case of the flute, Helmholtz has shown that the overtones are very few and feeble. In fact, the lower notes of the flute when gently sounded are almost devoid of overtones. Thus, a very good imitation of such a flute tone is obtained from two tuning-forks, the higher being an octave above the other and very feebly sounded. It is well known that the quality of tone of the flute is sweet and pure, and in the lower register rather dull. This accords with Helmholtz's analysis of the flute's quality, and the fact that when few and weak overtones are present the quality is the opposite of strident and penetrating. The highest notes of the flute are, however, very bright and pleasing.

The piccolo is valuable for its power to emit such high notes with considerable power. Its highest notes are, however, harsh and tearing, and cannot well be endured except with a powerful accompaniment.

376. The compass of flute and piccolo are shown in Table XXIV., and the overtones of the flute in Table XXX. In the former the three notes, d', d'', and d''' are indicated as open notes. These are the prime, its octave, and double octave respectively, and are obtained with but slight modifications of fingering. We may, accordingly, regard the full chromatic scale as being built upon three of the tones natural to the whole tube or certain parts of it. Thus, beginning with d', we have the prime of the tube. Ascending note by note we have the primes of portions of the tube shorter and shorter as more and more of the side holes are opened. But, for producing d'', we have the same length of tube in use as for d', but the octave or second natural tone is now produced instead of the prime. The utterance of this higher note is favoured by opening the first hole of the six (that nearest the mouth hole), whereas for the prime all six holes were closed. We cannot profess to give any exact theory of the use of the holes and the pitches of the resulting notes. Indeed, the flute affords an excellent example of a case in which practice has outstripped theory. It is stated that the holes were originally made in the positions convenient for the fingers. Afterwards they were made in the positions and of the sizes found desirable for the notes to be produced. And the exact position and size appears still to be settled by trial and error.

377. The Oboe and Bassoon.—The family now to be dealt with consists of instruments characterised by double cane reeds and conical tubes terminated by bells. It comprises the oboe, the English horn (often called by its French name, *Cor Anglais*), the bassoon and the double bassoon. Of these the oboe and bassoon are most used. The relation of the four as regards compass is exhibited in Table XXIV.

The double cane reed vibrates transversely as well as longitudinally. In the course of this vibration the aperture at the end is alternately opened and closed. When open, the sides of the reed are curved, concave inwards; when closed, the two sides are straight and in contact. Thus, the player's breath, alternately passing and checked by the reed, forms the exciter. The vibrating reed and the column of air in the conical tube form the vibrating system. The pitch is settled by the tube, and is much lower than the tones proper to the reed itself. The manipulative mechanism consists of side holes and keys.

378. The strict theory of these openings, like that for those of the flute, is a matter for physicists in the future. Their general effect in raising the pitch by either shortening the tube in use or favouring the elicitation of a higher partial is obvious.

As to the pitch of the prime and the series of overtones which theory predicts for such an instrument as the oboe, we have seen in art. 186 that the tones proper to a conical tube closed at one end is the full harmonic series, as for a parallel tube of the same length open at each end, the lengths being the "corrected lengths" in each case. Helmholtz has shown that, when a reed is placed at the vertex of a cone, as in this case, then that end must be regarded as a closed end; for when it is not closed it opens to admit air into the tube. Hence, as regards the power of the end to resist pressure, it is either closed and does not yield, or when open, air enters instead of being permitted to escape. Thus, the oboe by overblowing gives the octave, twelfth, and double octave of its prime. Some of these natural or open tones are utilised on the instrument. The other notes required to fill the gaps and complete the full chromatic scale are obtained by the use of the holes and keys.

379. The quality of tone obtained from the oboe is somewhat penetrating. It would appear, therefore, to consist of an extended retinue of partials. And this Helmholtz has found to be the case, see Table XXX.

The bassoon, though differing greatly in appearance from the oboe, is, from the scientific point of view, simply a bass oboe. Because of its much greater length the tube of the bassoon is, for convenience, doubled on itself. Hence the very different appearance of the instrument. For convenience, also, the reed is fitted on a tube curved sideways. It is thus seen that the changes are in form only in order to adapt the bassoon to the performer, all the essentials being as in the oboe.

380. The Clarinet Family.—There are many clarinets in use similar to each other, but of different pitches. Thus, besides the clarinet proper in a variety of pitches, we have also the alto and bass clarinets. The basset-horn is like the alto clarinet, but has a small brass bell mouth. The compasses of the chief clarinets are shown in Table XXIV. All these instruments are characterised by their single cane reed and cylindrical pipe with a small bell mouth.

Thus, as with the oboe and bassoon, we may regard the air blast produced by the performer as the exciter, the reed and the air column forming the vibrating system giving a note whose pitch depends upon the length of the column, and considerably lower than those proper to the reed. The manipulative mechanism consists of the side holes and keys.

But since we have here a cylindrical pipe with a reed alternately opening and closing one end, the tones possible to the instrument form the *odd* harmonic series. The effect of this is twofold. Thus *first*, by overblowing, the first overtone obtained is a twelfth above the prime, and not an octave as in the case of the oboe and flute. Hence a sufficient number of side holes and keys must be provided to bridge this very large gap. *Secondly*, the quality of the tone produced is that characterised by the enfeeblement or extinction of the evenly numbered partials. It has been shown by D. J. Blaikley that some of the even partials are feebly present. The results of his experiments are shown in Table XXX. This is, however, no refutation of theory; for the clarinet, as Mr. Blaikley points out, is not cylindrical throughout; there is the bell mouth at the lower end, and a slight constriction near the mouthpiece or upper end. The characteristic quality of tone is no doubt also dependent to some extent on the form of reed used. This is a beating reed, applied to the sloping end of the mouthpiece which forms a table for it.

381. Brass Instruments.—In treating of brass instruments it will be convenient to take first a general survey and note the features common to all, leaving to later articles the more detailed examination of several important types. Thus, in the first place, all have cupped mouthpieces to which the player's lips are applied. Secondly, the tube is quasi-conical, or, more strictly, hyperbolical in shape with a bell mouth. If strictly conical with a closed vertex instead of a mouthpiece, the natural notes would constitute the full harmonic series of the same pitches as for a parallel tube of the same (corrected) length, and open at both ends (see art. 186). And although the vertex is not closed, and the tapering is, in some cases, interfered with by a parallel portion to allow of slides or valves, still the makers so proportion the tapering tube in other parts as to restore, as nearly as may be, the tuning of the natural or open notes to the harmonic series.

The various kinds of manipulative mechanism to bridge over these gaps and provide the chromatic scale differs in different instruments, and will be treated in subsequent articles.

382. The intermittent stream of air issuing from the player's lips may be regarded as the exciter, the lips themselves constitute a double membranous reed, and are alternately open and closed, thus constituting along with the air column the vibrating system. If we ask what parts are played by the air column and the lips in fixing the pitch, the answer requires a little care. It is the experience of players that the adjustment of the lips to the mouthpiece, the tension of the lips, and the pressure of the air used decide *which* of the various notes then natural to the instrument shall be elicited. But the exact pitch of that note depends chiefly upon the tube in use, and the temperature of the air within it at the moment. If the tube is small, the note can be forced a little above or below its natural pitch. Thus, on a cornet, it is said that some players can force the note a quarter of a tone flatter or sharper than its normal pitch. With the larger instruments this is not so easy.

383. Helmholtz has pointed out that membranous reeds circumstanced as the human lips are in playing brass instruments produce tones which are always sharper than their pitch if isolated. He classifies the lips in this case as membranous reeds *striking outwards*. It should be noticed that the opposite change of pitch occurs in the case of reeds which Helmholtz classifies as *striking inwards*. We have already seen illustrations of these in the case of the oboe and bassoon and the clarinet family.

384. We have seen that the tones natural to all brass instruments approximate closely to the full harmonic series. But the closeness of that approximation differs in different types of instruments. And this difference affects, not only the intonation of the instrument when the different notes are sounded separately, but also the quality of each such note. For, when any note is excited and maintained by the player, its various simple tones must be of commensurate periods, *i.e.* form a harmonic series. Now, if some of the

2 G

tones natural to the instrument are very nearly in tune with the corresponding tones of this harmonic series, they will be strongly elicited. If, however, some of the other tones natural to the instrument are considerably out of tune with the corresponding tones of the harmonic series, these will be but feebly elicited. In a badly made instrument, the tones strongly and feebly elicited might occur in any erratic fashion. But, in a carefully formed instrument, the tones more and more removed from the prime will be less and less strongly elicited. And this falling off should follow a regular law for all, though differing in each type. Hence the distinction between good instruments of various types probably lies chiefly in the extent upwards of the retinue of overtones sounding along with their prime. Or, in other words, the distinction may be said to depend upon the degree of prominence or subordination of the upper partials.

385. As to the cause of the greater or less prominence of these partials, it is perhaps to be sought mainly in the relation of the diameter of the tubing to its length, but also in part in the proportions of the bell. Much depends, too, on the shape of the mouthpiece itself. For an unsuitable mouthpiece spoils the tone of a good instrument. If the diameters of the tubing and bell are small in comparison with the length, as in the trumpet and trombone, the higher tones natural to the instrument are brought well into tune, and so are more strongly elicited. We thus have, from such instruments, an extended retinue of partials and a brilliant tone. This is also assisted by the somewhat shallow cup-shaped mouthpieces used. With deeper mouthpieces and either much wider tubing or larger bell, as in the euphonium and French horn respectively, we have the higher overtones less prominent and a softer quality results.

386. Mechanism for the Scale.—On some brass instruments no mechanism is provided for completing the scale, which is accordingly limited to the natural or open notes of the harmonic series. Examples of this class are afforded by the coach-horn, the bugle, and some trumpets. Thus, calls or fanfares performed on these instruments have a special character of their own owing to this limitation of scale, apart from the tone quality characteristic of each instrument.

387. The French Horn without valves comes next in order of simplicity. The tube of this instrument is coiled in a circular form, and is played with the left hand near the mouthpiece, the right hand being inserted in the bell, which is very large. When the natural or open notes of the instrument are required, the right hand is laid with the tips of the fingers so applied to the interior of the bell as not to materially obstruct the passage of the air. When, however, it is desired to obtain notes somewhat flatter than the open notes, the hand is placed so as to partially close the bell. This partial closing of the bell has a double effect. In addition to flattening the pitch it also deadens or muffles the tone. This latter effect may be at times of great artistic value. Sometimes, however, it is undesirable. This flattening of the pitch by the fist in the bell may be produced at the option of the player to the extent of a quarter of a tone, a semitone, three-quarters of a tone, a whole tone, or even more.

388. It might at first sight be supposed that even then only a poor approach to a complete scale could be obtained. It must, however, be noted that the French horn has a great length of tubing, but is played with a small mouthpiece. Hence the notes chiefly used are those in the higher part of the harmonic series; they consequently lie close together. Thus the slight flattening possible by closing the bell suffices to completely bridge some of these small gaps. This may be seen on reference to Table XXIV., which shows the first sixteen open notes for the French horn in F. The fundamental (F_1) is shown in brackets, as it is scarcely obtainable with the ordinary mouthpiece, and is rarely if ever used. It should be noted that the 7th, 11th, 13th, and 14th open notes are slightly different from any notes of the staff. They are accordingly only approximately represented by the notes given in the Table XXIV. As indicated by the full line in the table, the complete chromatic scale may be obtained for about an octave and a half, but certain gaps must occur lower down in the compass when only the fist is used in the attempt to bridge them.

389. But, in order to obtain notes in these gaps, and also to bring the more important notes of a given composition on the open notes of the horn, the instrument is put into different keys. This is done by means of a piece of detachable tubing of the right length, and called a *crook*. Thus, by taking off the F-crook and replacing it by another slightly longer one, we can put the horn into the key of E♭. Then all the sixteen notes shown in the table would be lowered by a whole tone. It may be urged that all the gaps in the scale are as large as before, which is true. But still the device is of great value, and very often a composer directs that some horns shall be in one key, and some in another, thus increasing greatly the open notes at his disposal. For the action of the French horn with valves, now so often used, the reader is referred to articles 393-4, where all the valved instruments are treated together.

390. The Trombone is the most familiar example of the next device for bridging the gaps between the open notes, and thus completing the scale. This device consists of the slide, a U-tube which fits upon corresponding straight parallel tubes of very slightly smaller bore. When the slide is closed up it is said to be in the first position. The instrument is then at its normal pitch, and yields the open notes shown in Table XXIV. When the slide is drawn out a few inches to what is called the second position, sufficient extra tubing is brought into use to put the instrument a semitone lower. We have thus at command another full series of open notes like the first, but all a semitone flatter. Hence, what was accomplished with the French horn by changing a crook during a rest in the music, is instantaneously accomplished on the trombone by means of the slide without any cessation of playing. The third position of the slide lowers the pitch a whole tone, the fourth a tone and a half, and so on, to the seventh and last position, which lowers the pitch three whole tones. Now the prime tone (called the pedal) is scarcely ever used. Thus the largest gap to be bridged is a musical fifth, occurring between the second and third open notes. Hence, the flattening extending to three whole tones, obtained by the seven positions of the slide, provides the full chromatic scale in this the largest gap to be dealt with.

391. But the slide in addition to this extends the compass by three whole tones below the lowest open note used (the octave of the pedal), and also gives useful alternative ways of playing some of the higher notes where the open notes are closer, and the gaps between them are consequently more than bridged by the three whole tones of the slide. These points are shown in Table XXV., which gives the scale for slide and valved instruments. Further, the slide has the great advantage of allowing an exact adjustment for each position so as to obtain the desired intonation. It also confers, from its continuous action, the power of gliding from one note to another.

392. But the acrobatic feats required to take in rapid succession distant positions form a drawback to this mechanism which unfits the slide trombone for the execution of rapid passages. It is noteworthy that these two advantages of the slide are possessed also by the violin, which, however, is free from the drawback inherent in the trombone. Indeed, to introduce the drawback of the slide trombone into a member of the violin family we ought to choose from the latter a violoncello, but restrict the instru-

ment to one string and the player to the use of one finger,
but allow him the power of eliciting the harmonics at will
without additional fingering. Thus in the violin family
the use of several strings and several fingers obviates the
difficulties of execution inherent in the slide trombone.
Turning again to the advantages of the slide, it is obvious
that, as in the case of the violin family, this mechanism
exacts from the player higher skill and greater care as a
compensation for its higher possibilities.

393. Valved Instruments.—We pass now to the consideration of the third and commonest kind of mechanism
for producing the scale in brass instruments, namely, valves.
Among the brass of the orchestra which usually have
valves, we may notice the trumpet with three valves, the
French horn with two or three valves, and the bass tuba
with three or four valves. The French horn is occasionally
fitted with only two valves, because it is chiefly used to
sound its higher notes which lie near together, hence the
gaps between them are easily bridged. Bass instruments,
on the other hand, sometimes have four valves in order to
bridge the largest gap occurring between the open notes,
namely, that between the prime and its octave.

394. But we may now confine attention chiefly to the
normal arrangement of three valves, which applies to the
instruments mentioned above, and in addition to nearly all
the valved instruments used in a purely brass band. On
depressing the piston of any valve an extra piece of tubing
is put into use. The valves are referred to as the first,
second, and third, and when depressed they flatten the
pitch by about a whole tone, a semitone, and a tone and a
half respectively. Thus they enable the player to bridge
the gap between the second and third open notes of the
instrument which are at the interval of a musical fifth.
The prime of the instrument, called the pedal, is not
usually employed. The mouthpiece is not suitable for
producing it, and its quality and intonation would probably

be faulty on most instruments. It is thus seen that the
use of these three valves (1) bridges the largest gap between
the open notes in use, (2) extends the compass downward,
and (3) supplies alternative fingerings for some of the
higher notes. In these respects the action of the valves is
closely analogous to that of the slide of the trombone.
This fact is clearly exhibited in Table XXV., which shows
the fingering for the scale on instruments with a slide or
with three valves. The notes are shown of the pitch of
the tenor trombone and euphonium; by altering them up
or down, but preserving the same relation, the table would
represent the scales for other slide or valved instruments.

TABLE XXV.—THE SCALE ON TENOR TROMBONE AND
EUPHONIUM

Order of Open Note in Use.	Positions of Slide on Trombone. / Valves depressed on Euphonium.	1st / None.	2nd / 2	3rd / 1	4th / 1 2	5th / 2 3	6th / 1 3	7th / 1 2 3
9		c''	b	$(b'\flat)$	(a')	$(a'\flat)$	(g')	$(g'\flat)$
8		$b'\flat$	a'	$a'\flat$	g'	$g'\flat$	(f')	(e')
6		f'	e'	$e'\flat$	(d')	$(d'\flat)$	(e')	(b)
5		d'	$d'\flat$	c'	b	$(b\flat)$	(a)	$(a\flat)$
4		$b\flat$	a	$a\flat$	g	$g\flat$	(f)	(e)
3		f	e	$e\flat$	d	$d\flat$	c	B
2		B$\flat$	A	A$\flat$	G	G$\flat$	F	E
(1)	(B$\flat$) Pedal, not often used on trombone, but a euphonium with four valves gives the chromatic scale down to this pedal B$\flat$.							

The notes in brackets indicate alternative fingerings, and
the dotted line divides them from the others. The seventh
open note natural to either instrument is flatter than the
corresponding note on the ordinary scale, hence this seventh

note is not generally used. Its omission is the reason why there are fewer alternative notes in the second line of the table, for the gap from the sixth open note to the eighth is larger than that from the fifth to the sixth, hence there is less overlapping.

395. Tuning a Brass Instrument and its Valves.— In order to tune brass instruments to the pitch of others of the same or different kinds, a tuning-slide is provided like the U-shaped slide of the trombone, but much smaller. This, on being drawn out, slightly depresses the pitch to any desired amount not exceeding the limit of the slide, which may be about a semitone. Suppose now the tuning-slide is pulled out to its extreme length, and so adds sufficient length of tubing to depress the pitch a diatonic semitone say, that is, the length of tubing in use is $16/15$ of its original amount with the tuning-slide closed. Then clearly, if the action of the valves put in just sufficient tubing to depress the pitch properly with the tuning-slide closed, their effect will now be too small. In fact, the length of tubing added by each valve should now be exactly $16/15$ of its original amount. To provide for this each valve is fitted with a little slide which may be drawn out sufficiently to tune that valve. This adjustment, or tuning of the valves, may be made as follows:—First, suppose that the tuning-slide has been drawn out to the extent necessary to put the instrument to the desired pitch. Then tune the first valve by drawing its slide until the note $b'\flat$ is obtained of precisely the same pitch, either as the eighth open note or with the first valve depressed, *i.e.* a tone lower than the ninth open note. This is another advantage of the alternative fingerings, see first and second lines in Table XXV. Next, tune the second valve until, by sounding d' as the fifth open note, and as derived from the sixth by depressing the first and second valves, precisely the same pitch is obtained. Similarly, the third valve may be tuned and tested by sounding the f as the third open note, and derived from the fourth by depressing the first and third valves.

396. The tuning of the valves here referred to as required after a slight extension of the tuning-slide of the instrument is required still more on the valves of the cornet, trumpet, or French horn after much longer or shorter crooks have been fitted to them. For whereas the tuning-slide can only depress the pitch by about half a tone, the crooks may depress it by one, two, or three tones or more.

397. Faulty Intonation of Valved Instruments.—It might now be supposed that all requirements had been met, and that the tuning of an instrument to the chromatic scale throughout its compass was correctly insured. Unfortunately this is not the case, as a little reflection will show. Let us sink, for the moment, the distinction between flats and sharps, and the niceties of just intonations (see Chapter IX.). But even this lower ideal is not met by the tuning of the valved instruments described so far. A glance at Table XXV. shows that while the first valve is required to depress the pitch one tone and the second a semitone, the two valves together are expected to depress the pitch by a tone and a half. But clearly, the second valve when used with the first should be tuned as though the instrument had a crook on depressing it a whole tone. In other words, the length of tubing in the second valve, which serves to depress the pitch exactly a semitone when the other valves are not in use, will be insufficient to depress the pitch a semitone when either the first or third valve is used simultaneously with the second. Again, if the first valve adds the right length of tubing to depress the pitch a whole tone when it is used alone, it will fail to depress it a whole tone when the instrument already has the second and third valves down, or the third alone. The faults we are dealing with now do not, of course, apply to the slide of the trombone. For the player is at liberty to take the positions increasingly farther apart, as the slide is more extended so as to preserve any intonation desired.

398. Compensating Pistons.—To obviate to some extent the blemish above noted in the tuning of valved instruments, compensating pistons have been devised. In one arrangement of this kind short tubes are attached to the first and second valves, with corresponding tubes in the pistons. But the whole system is so arranged that these additional short lengths of tubing only come into operation when their respective pistons are used in combination with the third valve, but not when played singly. These compensating pistons or valves are not, however, usually fitted to trumpets and French horns, for these play chiefly in the higher register, and consequently make but slight use of the third valve. Moreover, with the comparatively small volumes of air in these instruments the player can force the note into tune. But, with instruments that play in the lower registers, and so need the third valve much more, as the cornet, the compensating pistons are more desirable. But the improvement effected by them is of highest value in the case of the euphonium or bass tuba when used with four valves, and playing down throughout the pedal octave, *i.e.* down to the prime note of the instrument. For here the volume of air in motion in the instrument is too great to be easily forced into tune by the player, and with the larger fourth valve the discrepancy is of course greater than that mentioned in the three-valved instruments.

399. The Human Voice : Vowel Quality.—In endeavouring to subject to our previous classification the various parts of the marvellous mechanism which produces the human voice, we may on one view identify as follows : —The exciter is the air blast from the lungs, the vibrator is the double membranous reed called the vocal chords, the part of resonator is played by the mouth and the associated cavities, while the manipulative mechanism for the production of the scale consists of those muscles, nerves, etc., which serve to govern the frequency of vibration of the vocal chords. We have further the power to change the resonating cavities, and therefore to modify considerably the quality of the sounds produced.

Into the intricacies of the anatomy of the human voice we shall not enter here, neither can we dwell upon its manifold powers and subtleties. Apart from the singing of vowels, it must suffice to notice (1) that many of the consonants are the clicks or checks which occur at the beginning or ending of pure musical tone, (2) that speaking is characterised by a continual gliding change in pitch, (3) whereas singing, on the contrary, usually maintains the pitch at definite values for definite periods.

400. We are concerned chiefly, then, with the singing of vowels, that is, with the human voice as the tone of a *musical* instrument. The approximate compasses of each of the four main classes into which voices are usually divided are shown in Table XXIV. Within the limits of each compass certain subdivisions termed *registers* may be recognised. Emil Behnke defined a register as a series of tones which are produced by the same mechanism. He further stated that by the laryngoscope these registers may be demonstrated, and that they are, broadly speaking, as follows :—In the first, called the thick register, comprising the lowest series of notes, the vocal chords vibrate in their entire thickness. In the next, or thin register, the vocal chords vibrate only with their thin inner edges. In the highest, or small register, a portion of the vocal chink is firmly closed, and the vibration is confined to a small part of the vocal chords.

401. We must now inquire into the mechanism of the production of vowel sounds, the ability to pronounce which obviously puts the human voice in a class apart from all other instruments. Helmholtz points out that the vocal chords in a good voice close very completely in the course of their vibration, and that in consequence of the sharp discontinuity thus imposed in the passage of the air, the tone produced must have a full retinue of partials. Indeed, he has detected them in the human voice up to the sixteenth partial! This is the first factor towards the production of vowels. The second factor is the power possessed of setting the resonant cavities of the mouth and associated openings so as to reinforce tones of various pitches.

402. Suppose now the cavities are set to resonance with a certain definite pitch, and maintained unchanged in that position, while the vocal chords are set successively to different pitches and the voice produced. Then, according to the view of the matter which has received widest acceptance, one certain vowel, *the same throughout,* would be recognised as being sung at different pitches. For some vowels it is found that the cavities have a double resonance. To realise the full significance of the characteristics of vowel quality (on this view), let us contrast vowels with the other qualities hitherto noticed. Thus, all ordinary musical qualities of sound are characterised by a long or short series of partials belonging to the harmonic series, either full or with the even-numbered terms omitted. Further, the quality is recognised as remaining the same if the relation of intensities of the various partials remains the same. And this holds good whether the pitch changes or not. But the characteristic of vowels is that the partials near a certain *definite* pitch are favoured, whether they are near the bottom or the top of the series constituting the note in question. And if this pitch of favouring the partials remains the same, the vowel remains the same, whatever the relation (within reasonable limits) of this pitch to that of the note sung. This, at any rate, is the bare *outline* of the received theory of vowel constitution and production. No doubt many minor modifications are needed to bring it into complete accordance with facts in certain cases. Indeed, it is evident that, for the purposes of speech and song, we are accustomed to recognise as the same vowel anything within certain fairly wide limits.

403. Figure 90 shows a diagram of a few of the most important vowels on the plan quoted by Helmholtz from that originally given by Du Bois-Reymond.

(1) *From Helmholtz, German pro-nunciation being intended.*

(2) *With approximate English or French sounds.*

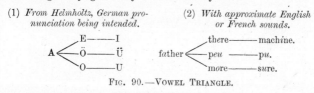

Fig. 90.—Vowel Triangle.

In the first form of the triangle it must be remembered that the vowels given are to bear the German pronunciation. In the second form the approximate equivalents in English or French words are given after Ellis. The common starting-point is the Continental A, to form which the mouth is fairly wide open and the tongue lies flat. Proceeding along the lowest line, the tongue remains flat, but the lips approach for the O and more still for the U (o͞o). Starting again from the A and proceeding along the top line, it is now the lips which remain quiet while the tongue is raised, for the E a little, and for the I (e͞e) much more. If we again start at the A and proceed along the middle line, we find both the previous movements have to be combined. Thus for the Ö (French *eu*, nearly) the lips approach and the tongue is raised, and for the Ü (French *u* nearly) both movements are carried to a further extreme.

404. Many other niceties may be entered into. For example, in 1867, Melville Bell recognised nine positions of the tongue, each of which might be associated with the ordinary or an increased distension of the pharynx, thus giving eighteen vowels. Then again, each of these eighteen vowels could be modified to various degrees by the approach of the lips. So that reckoning even two positions of the lips only, thirty-six distinct vowel cavities were obtained. Among these thirty-six vowels it was found that most of

the vowels in use in different nations could be placed.   Ellis
has shown that even this system may be materially extended.

The pitches of resonance for the cavities of the mouth,
etc., for the scheme of vowels in Fig. 96 are given by
Helmholtz as shown in Table XXVI.

TABLE XXVI.—VOWEL RESONANCES

Vowels (German Pronunciation)	U	O	A	E	I	Ü	Ö
Resonance Pitches	f	$b'\flat$	$b''\flat$	$\begin{cases} b''' \\ f' \end{cases}$	$\begin{cases} d^{iv} \\ f \end{cases}$	$\begin{cases} g''' \\ f \end{cases}$	$\begin{cases} c'''\sharp \\ f \end{cases}$

See also articles 611, 624, 625, and 630-632 for
further work respecting vowels.

405. Air Pressures used for Wind Instruments.—
Having sufficiently reviewed the characteristics of individual
instruments, or the families into which they may be
grouped, we now pass to the consideration of various topics
which affect at once several instruments or families.   And
of these let us first consider the range of air pressures used
in playing a number of different wind instruments.   In
1891, Dr. W. H. Stone described experiments made by him
on this subject some years previously.   His method consisted in playing the instrument while a tube in the mouth
communicating with a water gauge indicated the pressure
in use.   His results are given in Table XXVII.

TABLE XXVII.—STONE'S VALUES OF WIND PRESSURES

Instrument.	Range of Pressures in Inches of Water Column.
Oboe	9 to 17
Clarinet	15 to 8 [1]
Bassoon	12 to 24
Horn	5 to 27
Cornet	10 to 34
Trumpet	12 to 33
Euphonium	3 to 40
Bombardon	3 to 36

[1] Probably intended by Stone for 18.

406. In Stone's results no details are given as to the pressure used for each note, nor of the variations of pressure with loudness. To obtain information upon these points, experiments on Stone's method were made in 1901 on the trombone, cornet, and trumpet.[1] The chief results are exhibited graphically in the curves of Figs. 91 and 92. In these curves the ordinates are gauge pressures in cm. of water, and the abscissæ are proportional to the logarithms of the frequencies, so that equal distances denote equal musical intervals. The [C] in brackets in each figure denotes the middle C between the staves. The dotted line T T in Fig. 92 gives the results for the trumpet, the others for the cornet. In both figures *f*, *m*, and *p* denote *forte*, *mezzo*, and *piano*.

407. The general inferences to be drawn from the curves may be stated as follows: (1) The pressures increase with loudness and with pitch. Further, if the pitches are measured logarithmically, as in the diagrams, we see that the lines are for the most part straight. Hence (2) for a given instrument and intensity, the air pressure is approximately proportional to the pitch logarithmically measured. (3) The pressures used for loud low notes may exceed those for soft high notes, in some cases even where the notes are an octave apart.

408. Other experiments were made at the same time on the three instruments under notice, to test whether the pressures were the same for a given note obtained by alternative positions of the slide or alternative fingerings on the valves. In all cases it was found that it is almost indifferent as regards pressure required, whether a note is played on the given instrument as the third harmonic of a short tube, or the fourth of a correspondingly longer one, and so for other like examples. This result, though contrary to what is implied by some writers, is in accord with the experiments of Mr. D. J. Blaikley, who, in discussing the matter, added the following unique extension of the

[1] E. H. Barton and S. C. Laws, *Phil. Mag.*, April 1902.

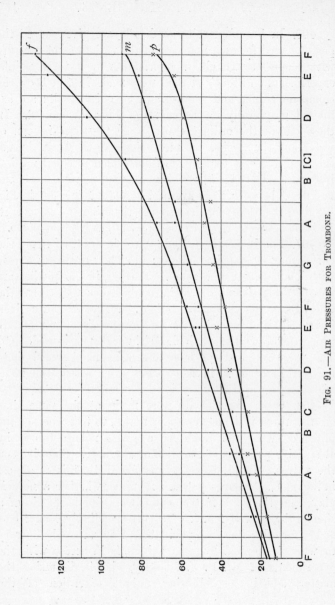

FIG. 91.—AIR PRESSURES FOR TROMBONE.

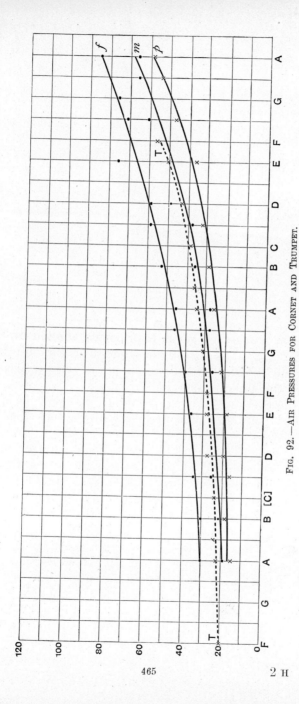

FIG. 92.—AIR PRESSURES FOR CORNET AND TRUMPET.

465

2 H

principle :—If notes are sustained with the *least possible* pressures, there seems to be no difference between the minimum pressure for " say B♭ (240 per second), as the second harmonic on the cornet and the same note as the fourth harmonic on the euphonium, an instrument of only twice the length, but of very much greater calibre, and played with a much larger mouthpiece." Mr. Blaikley's figures are given in Table XXVIII.

TABLE XXVIII.—BLAIKLEY'S MINIMUM PRESSURES

Note.	B♭.	F.	B♭.	
Frequency . . .	240	360	480	
Cornet, *pp.* ⎱ least	10·0	14·5	20	⎱ Pressures
Euphonium, *pp.* ⎰ possible	10·4	16·6	22·6	in cm. of water.

409. Pitches of Wind Instruments affected by Bore and Temperature.—It is important to remark here that the pitch of wind instruments is not necessarily calculable from the principles hitherto given. We have seen in a previous chapter (arts. 175 and 186) how the pitch depends on the length, the shape of the pipe, and the velocity of sound in the gas which fills it. We saw also (arts. 179 and 180) how to apply a correction for the open ends, and we have seen in the present chapter to which type of tube each brass or wood-wind instrument is to be referred. But the question still remains as to what is the velocity of sound in the tubes of actual musical instruments played with the mouth. The question really divides into two. For, upon examination, it is found that the velocity of sound is rather less in a small tube than in the free air. This matter will be dealt with in Chapter X. Further, the temperature of the air in a wind instrument played by the mouth is not necessarily that of the outside air. It will be practically so for an instrument of very large capacity. On the other hand, with an instrument of small capacity, it will be almost independent of the temperature of the outside air, but dependent chiefly upon the player's breath. These points, though too technical for full discussion here, are just mentioned to prevent the reader from drawing the mistaken conclusion that it is possible, from elementary theory alone, to predict the precise length of tubing for a flute, clarinet, or cornet of specified pitch.

It is also obvious, from what has been said, that the pitches of these different instruments will be unequally altered by a given change in external temperature. The results of observations on this subject by Mr. D. J. Blaikley ranging over some years are summarised in Table XXIX. They are taken from his lectures delivered at the Royal Military School of Music in 1887.

TABLE XXIX.—PITCH OF WIND INSTRUMENTS AND TEMPERATURE

Instrument.	Rise of Pitch due to a rise of 10° Fahr. in the external Temperature.	
	Percentage increase of Frequency.	Actual increase of Vibration per second in B♭ (479 per sec.).
Flute and Oboe . .	0·31	1·50
Clarinet . . .	0·43	2·06
Cornet and Trumpet .	0·51	2·45
French Horn and } Trombone } .	0·60	2·88
Euphonium . . .	0·66	3·16
Bombardon . . .	0·73	3·50
Mean of Full Wind Band	0·54	2·60
Organ Flue Pipes . .	1·05	5·04

410. Partials from Typical Musical Instruments.— We gather together in Table XXX. the list of partials constituting the musical tones of the various typical instruments which have been reviewed. Where the relative intensities are only known qualitatively they are denoted approximately by musical signs or X's of different sizes.

TABLE XXX.—PARTIALS OF TYPICAL INSTRUMENTS

Instruments	Partials and their Relative Intensities								Authorities and Remarks
	1	2	3	4	5	6	7	8	
Harp	100	81·2	56·1	31·6	13	2·8	…	…	Theory of Helmholtz for string plucked at one-seventh.
Piano	100	99·7	8·9	2·3	1·2	0·01	…	…	Theory of Helmholtz for string struck at ⅛th and like c'' on his grand piano.
Violin	100	25	11	6	4	3	2	1·5	Helmholtz theory and experiment.
Flute Pipes of Organ — Stopped Wide	X	…	x	…	…	…	…	…	Helmholtz theory and experiment.
Flute Pipes of Organ — Stopped Narrow	X	…	X	…	X	…	…	…	
Flute Pipes of Organ — Open Wide	X	X	x	…	…	…	…	…	
Flute Pipes of Organ — Open Narrow	X	X	X	X	X	x	…	…	
Flute	f	…	f	(p)	mf	(p)	mf	(pp.)	And beyond the 8th for 8 forks cannot match it.
Oboe	X	x	X	X	X	x	X	X	Helmholtz and Blaikley.
Clarinet; French Horn or Euphonium	X	X	X	X	X	X	X	x	
Trumpet or Trombone	X	X	X	X	X	X	X	X	
Human voice	X	X	X	X	X	X	X	X	And up to 16th detected by Helmholtz in bass voices.

411. EXPT. 62*a*. *Synthesis of Musical Tones by Forks.*—The facts of Table XXX. receive very valuable illustration if the respective instruments and performers are available, and also a set of forks tuned to the relative frequencies of the first eight partials. It is convenient to have the prime fork tuned to *c* (128), the eighth will then be *c‴* (1024). The seventh must be specially made the true trumpet-seventh, which is flatter than the ordinary *b″*♭. Its frequency is, of course, 896 if the prime tone *c* is exactly 128. These forks should be each mounted upon suitable resonance - boxes arranged in order before the operator. Then the *modus operandi* is as follows :—Having decided the instrument to be imitated and the pitch of the note, sound gently the fork to be used as prime, and let the performer tune his instrument to correspond. Next, beginning with the prime, sound loudly the combination of forks to build up the desired tone quality and with correct relative intensities according to Table XXX. Finally, let the performer sound the same note on his instrument.

With eight such forks carefully bowed one obtains extremely near imitations of the quality of tone of the flute, clarinet, euphonium, and trombone, which make a striking appeal to an audience. Eight forks are, however, insufficient to imitate the specially penetrating quality of the oboe.

The tone of the clarinet can also be well imitated by the longitudinal vibrations of a wire about ten metres long stroked with a rosined cloth at or near the middle, so as to practically eliminate the evenly numbered partials.

It is obvious that the experiment with the forks is open to the objection that the sounds of the higher forks die away quicker than those of the lower. Hence the relation of the intensities changes, and the tone consequently changes in quality. To test his theory and illustrate it experimentally in a manner free from this objection, Helmholtz performed the synthesis of the vowels by a set of electrically driven forks whose intensities were adjusted to and maintained at the desired values.

412. EXPT. 63. *Analysis by Helmholtz Resonators.*— The presence of the various partials in the tones of the voice or brass instruments can be well shown to an audience by the use of a set of Helmholtz resonators. There should be at least ten in number and mounted above one another. A monometric capsule is needed to each, and a tall rotating mirror, fixed on a vertical axis, near the jets. The whole arrangement is illustrated in catalogues of acoustic apparatus. Suppose the prime tone to be c (128), then a bass voice should be tuned precisely to this pitch as ascertained by blowing across the mouth of the largest resonator. The vowel *ah* (*a* as in *father*, but of pure Italian quality) at this pitch should then be sung forcibly and near the mouth of each resonator in turn while the mirror is rotated. It will be found that all the ten resonators pick out their respective partials for the tone produced by the voice. For lecture illustration of the presence of the partials in the tone of a brass instrument the trombone is most suitable. For, by means of the slide it can be instantly tuned to the right pitch as ascertained by another operator blowing across the mouth of the lowest resonator.

413. EXPT. 64. *Analysis of Vowels by Flames.*—The fact that vowel quality is a thing apart from the qualities of tone of ordinary musical instruments may be well shown by means of the manometric flame and rotating mirror (see art. 177). For this purpose it is well, for the sake of contrast, to have also some bell-mouthed instrument, say a cornet. On rotating the mirror and playing the scale or other passage on the cornet with its bell towards the manometric capsule, the flame images are seen to remain of the same pattern throughout, changing only in fineness as the frequency changes. When, however, any vowel is sung at different pitches in front of the capsule, it is noticed that the flame images usually change very much in type or pattern as well as fineness as the frequency changes. All the chief vowels, as shown in the vowel triangle (art. 403), should be used. The contrast between the effects of some of them and those of the instrument is in certain cases very striking. For this purpose the flame may be produced by acetylene instead of ordinary gas. By this means Mr. Merritt succeeded in obtaining an effect bright enough to photograph.

Another method of analysing vowels or detecting differences in different vowels is that of the specially long sensitive flame used by the late Prof. Tyndal, and called by him the vowel flame (see art. 280).

414. EXPT. 65. *Speech analysed by the Phonoscope.*— By means of the phonoscope already described (arts. 250 and 251) we may illustrate to an audience the different characters of the vibrations composing various vowels and even consonants. For this purpose the diaphragm must be very thin and rather slack, and the whole arrangement of mirror and connections light and free. When these details have been sufficiently attended to we obtain a very instructive illustration of the vibrations in question. All the chief vowels are well responded to by this arrangement, and such forcible consonants as *p* and *r* (if well trilled) are distinctly rendered on the screen. The words *papa* and *father*, uttered with a declamatory vigour, will be found particularly suitable.

415. EXPT. 66. *Analysis and Synthesis by Piano.*—A valuable experiment on the analysis and synthesis of sounds may be performed with a piano (preferably a grand piano). The front or top must be removed so as to lay bare the wires. Also all the dampers must be raised by depressing the loud pedal. Next choose a note on the piano of a suitable pitch for vigorous singing. Finally, sing to this pitch a full and well-sustained tone of a distinct vowel quality. When the sound of the voice ceases, the piano is then found to be giving forth a tone of the same pitch and of approximately the same vowel quality. Here, then, we have a case of analysis, resonance, and synthesis. For, first, the strings in tune with the various components of the tone sung, perform, as it were, the analysis, and responding to those vibrational components incident upon them give us the phenomenon of resonance. Then, on the cessation of the voice, all these tones, of approximately the right pitches and relative intensities, are blended, and produce upon the ear a very good imitation of the original vowel quality sung. All the chief vowels should be tried. It will be found that some succeed better than others. The better the piano, the better the result.

For some years Prof. M‘Kendrick of Glasgow has worked upon the subject of speech. His work will be introduced in Chap. XI.

CHAPTER IX

CONSONANCE AND TEMPERAMENT

416. Discord due to Beats.—The title of this chapter is to be understood broadly. Thus, we shall treat here of the various degrees of harmoniousness and dissonance present in different combinations of two or more tones, from the purest concords to the harshest discords. We shall afterwards inquire into the reasons which have led to a very general departure from just intonation, and shall then notice several important systems of approximate intonation or temperament, two of which have been widely adopted.

Before the Christian era the Greeks had studied musical concord and discord. They knew that the notes which produced consonance could be obtained from various lengths of a given string, and that between these lengths a very simple relation existed. This relation could be expressed by small whole numbers, as 1 to 2, 2 to 3, and so forth. Lengths in the relation of 64 to 81, on the other hand, produced dissonance.

417. Then Pythagoras propounded his celebrated riddle, "Why is consonance determined by the ratios of small whole numbers?" For over two thousand years that enigma remained unsolved. But in 1862, Helmholtz published the result of eight years' work on acoustics. This gave a masterly insight into the whole question, and resulted in the enunciation of Helmholtz's theory of concord and discord. Helmholtz showed that all dissonances or discords are due to unpleasant beats generated by the component notes. Consonances or concords, on the other hand, are formed by notes which fail to produce such beats. That is the theory in its bare outline. Many details must be supplied to define what constitutes the unpleasantness of the beats and to show how such beats may be produced.

418. First, let us ask why should beats be unpleasant in any case. Helmholtz's answer to this question is somewhat as follows:—During the loudest phase of the beats the ear is fatigued somewhat, but during the feeblest phase it is rested, and its sensibility restored. Hence, in this specially sensitive state the recurrence of the loud phase may be distressing. This effect on the ear Helmholtz likens to the effect upon the eye if one walks near a tall palisade when the sun is shining through from the other side, the flickering light being at times very irritating.

Another factor required to make the phenomenon of beats unpleasing, is that they should succeed each other at a frequency between certain limits. This holds good for the analogous case of flickering light also. The phenomena of fatigue of the eye and the irritation due to flickering at a certain rate may be illustrated to an audience by the following experiments:—

419. EXPT. 67. *Fatigue of the Eye.*—Let a sharply defined object in black or vivid colours be projected by the arc-light lantern upon a white screen in a dark room. A grotesque image in vermilion is particularly suitable. Let the eyes of the audience be intently fixed upon some point image for about twenty seconds, the time being counted audibly by the demonstrator. Then let the slide be removed so that the screen becomes pure white, the eyes being still fixed upon the same point of the screen as before (secured by the presence of a small cross at the point in question). Then an image, in shape like the first, but complementary in illumination and colour, soon appears on the screen. This shows that the parts of the eyes concerned in receiving the impressions of the original image and screen respectively become sufficiently fatigued by the process as to be unable to give equally vivid impressions of the various parts of the screen when entirely white. Thus, if the original image were black and the screen white, the parts of the eyes concerned with the white screen would become fatigued, and afterwards show a duller screen than that shown by those parts of the eye corresponding to the black image and which were accordingly unfatigued. In other words, the after image is in this case white upon a duller ground. If the original image were red, the after image would be green.

420. EXPT. 68. *Irritation due to Flickering.*—Introduce in front of the projection lantern an opaque disc having a number of radial openings, so that by rotating it the screen is alternately illuminated and darkened. Start with the screen illuminated, and then rotate the disc slowly ; the effect is not unpleasant. Rotate the disc quicker and quicker until the effect of a steady, uniform illumination is obtained ; this again is not unpleasant. But before this very high speed was reached there was an intermediate rate of alternate illumination and darkening of the screen which was particularly irritating. This rate may be again reached and maintained on slowing down. If properly done, the effect is so unpleasant as to cause many to avoid gazing at the screen for more than a few seconds at a time.

421. In Helmholtz's view the harshest effect of beats in the neighbourhood of c' is obtained when the beats are about 33 per second. But the frequency of the beats for the harshest dissonance varies in different parts of the compass. Another way of putting this is to say that it depends upon the interval between the two notes, for 33 per second corresponds to a semitone at one part of the compass, but to an octave at another part. Thus, we may say that the roughness arising from the sounding of two notes together depends in a compound manner on the magnitude of the interval between the two notes, and on the frequency of the beats produced by them.

EXPT. 69. *Beats by Helmholtz's Siren.*—We may illustrate the various degrees of roughness due to beats by the double siren of Helmholtz (see art. 296). Thus, opening circles of twelve holes in each chest and setting the siren rotating, the air blast being also turned on, we have unison. Then, on rotating the handle which turns the upper chest, we have a "mistuned unison" and beats produced. Now, just as in the case of the experiment with flickering light, it will be found that the beats are not unpleasant either when very slow or very quick, but that between certain limits they are distinctly disagreeable. Moreover, by having the siren driven at different speeds, it may be shown that the frequency of the beats must be correspondingly modified to give the roughest effect.

422. EXPT. 70. *Beats on Ellis's Harmonical.*—The effect of beats of the same frequency, but produced by notes at different intervals, can be very well illustrated on a specially tuned harmonium designed by Mr. A. J. Ellis, and by him termed the "harmonical." It has five octaves, of which the highest has very special tuning (see art. 465). The other four octaves have the white keys tuned to just intonation, the middle C (or c') being 264 per second. Of the black keys in these octaves, E♭, A♭, and B♭ are such as make ab, c', $e'♭$, and $e♭$, g, $b♭$ perfectly just major chords (*i.e.* with frequencies as $4:5:6$). To the D♭ digital is assigned the note which Ellis calls grave D, *i.e.* a note a comma $(81/80)$ flatter than D. Thus, the grave D is only the interval $10/9$ above C, whereas the D on the white digital is $9/8$ above C. The F♯ digital is also specially tuned, being ⁷B♭ as Ellis calls it. Thus, the relative frequencies of the notes c, e, g and that on the $f♯$ digital are 4, 5, 6, and 7.

Having explained so much of the special tuning of the harmonical, it will be seen that the following pairs of notes all differ by 33 vibrations per second. Hence, each pair gives beats of 33 per second, but the effects of the various pairs are very different, since their intervals range from a semitone to the interval of a fifth.

[TABLE

TABLE XXXI.—NOTES GIVING SAME BEATS

Pairs of Notes on Ellis's Harmonical, all giving beats of 33 per second.	c''	e'	d'	g	e	c	G
	b'	d'	c'	e	c	G	C
			(264)				

Intervals and Ratio of Frequencies.	Semitone.	Minor Tone.	Major Tone.	Minor Third.	Major Third.	Fourth.	Fifth.
	16/15	10/9	9/8	6/5	5/4	4/3	3/2

With the tuning usual in an ordinary harmonium, piano, or organ, the above effects may be approximately obtained by using the same notes. But the examination of the point at issue is in that case disturbed, since the frequencies of the beats are only approximately constant.

423. Various Ways of producing Beats.—In the preceding illustrations on the harmonical the frequency of the beats mentioned was that of the beats between the primes of the notes in question, as they would be the beats most noticeable. But it is easy to see that beats may occur in other ways. For a note of musical quality is a compound tone or a retinue of partials, and between any simple tone of one note and any one of the other, beats may occur. Further, as we have seen (in Chap. VII.), tones may, in certain cases, give rise to other tones called differential and summational tones. And between these and any of the components of the parent tones, beats may arise. But into all the conceivable intricacies we must not enter. We shall notice only the following more important cases: viz. beats arising between (1) two primes, (2) a prime and a differential, (3) a prime and an upper partial, and (4) two upper partials. We shall first illustrate these various ways by experiments, and then pass to the conclusions Helmholtz has drawn from a consideration of these various causes of dissonance.

424. EXPT. 71. *Beats between Primes.*—To illustrate the loudness of beats between two primes, use two large forks precisely similar and mounted on resonance-boxes. Make one

a little flatter by a piece of wax near the tip of one prong (or of both). Then on bowing the two forks the beats will be very plainly heard. It is well to have the forks of pitch c' (256). In this experiment we may safely conclude that the beats heard are between the primes, for, unless the amplitude is very large the octave is not appreciably produced, and if it were it would be overmasked by the resonance-box responding to the prime.

425. EXPT. 72. *Beats between Prime and Differential.*—For this purpose use forks an octave apart, say c' (256) and c'' (512), taken off their resonance-boxes. Plug the hole up on the c' resonance-box, and set it mouth up on the table, or use a water resonator set to respond to c' (256). Flatten one of the forks with wax, bow both and hold over the resonator, when beats will be distinctly audible throughout an ordinary lecture-room. We may explain how these beats are produced as follows :—*First*, Let the higher fork have the wax on, and suppose its frequency is thereby reduced by two vibrations per second from 512 to 510. (Verify this by another unaltered c'' fork, if available, both being bowed and held over a c'' resonator.) Then by the tones of the flattened c'' fork (510) and the c' fork (256) we have a differential tone generated of frequency $510 - 256 = 254$; and this differential tone gives *two* beats per second with the c' fork ($256 - 254 = 2$). *Secondly*, Let the lower fork be flattened with wax by two vibrations per second ; it has therefore a frequency of 254 instead of 256. (Verify again if possible by an unaltered c' fork.) We thus have tones from the two forks of frequencies 512 and 254. These give a differential tone of 258, which, with the 254 fork, yields *four* beats per second. This doubled rate of beats is a very striking confirmation of theoretical expectation.

426. EXPT. 73. *Absence of Beats between Fork and Mistuned Major Third.*—Taking two simple tones nearly at the interval 4 : 5, let us examine what might be expected as to the formation of beats. Suppose the tones are originally c' (256) and e' (320), and that the c' be flattened to 254, then between the 254 and the 320 we have a differential of 66, but nothing for it to beat with. If we pursue the formation of differentials of higher orders between the differentials themselves and the primes, we may, however, obtain beats as shown by Helmholtz.

Thus $320 - 254 = 66$, Differential Tone of the first order.

$$254 - 66 = 188 \qquad \text{,,} \qquad \text{,,} \qquad \text{,,} \quad \text{second ,,}$$
$$320 - 188 = 132 \qquad \text{,,} \qquad \text{,,} \qquad \text{,,} \quad \text{third ,,}$$
$$254 - 132 = 122 \qquad \text{,,} \qquad \text{,,} \qquad \text{,,} \quad \text{fourth ,,}$$

And between the differentials of the third and fourth orders we have beats of ten per second ($132 - 122 = 10$).

Scheibler claims to have heard beats between forks at intervals slightly differing from a major third, and Helmholtz believes he has heard them, but says that they are not of any importance in distinguishing consonances from dissonances. This statement can easily be confirmed by experimenting with the forks in the way mentioned above. It is specially striking to alternate this experiment with the previous one. Suppose the c' fork to be flattened two vibrations per second, it gives so plainly two beats per second with another c' fork, and four beats per second with the c'' fork. Whereas with the e' fork, the beats if audible at all in this mistuned major third, are extremely feeble in comparison with those of the mistuned octave. In the case of the mistuned major third, the writer, using good forks, could not detect any beats, whereas an organ builder present thought he could.

Lord Kelvin has made experiments on the "Beats of Imperfect Harmonies," [1] and claims that to hear beats of harmonies, other than the octave and fifth, is not so difficult as Helmholtz supposed. Thus it appears that the whole matter is involved in much difficulty, and at the present stage it seems unsafe to dogmatise.

427. EXPT. 74. *Beats between Prime and Upper Partial.*— The beats in this case are perhaps best shown by an imperfect octave on the harmonical. Use, for example, the grave D in one octave, and the ordinary D in the next octave above or below. Another pair of notes that also shows these beats is the ordinary and special forms of B♭ taken an octave apart. In either case the first upper partial of the lower note beats with the prime of the upper note, which is not exactly the octave of the lower. Of course it might be urged that these beats are due to the differential tones, as in the experiment No. 72, intended to illustrate that effect. And it must be admitted that the beats are of the same frequency, so cannot be distinguished. Probably the beats

---

[1] *Proc. Roy. Soc. Edin.*, vol. ix. p. 602, 1878.

heard are due to both causes. But the cause now under notice is fairly certain to be paramount. The effect may be illustrated, of course, upon any piano, harmonium, or organ which is out of tune, or very effectively by sounding a mistuned octave on the violin.

It may also be noted here that F. Lindig[1] has shown that on sounding two tuning-forks at a mistuned octave beats occur between the higher fork and the *asymmetry* octave of the lower.

428. EXPT. 75. *Beats between Two Upper Partials.*—For this purpose it is best to choose the interval of a mistuned fifth. For with a perfect fifth the primes are in the ratio $2 : 3$, hence the third partial of the lower note is exactly in unison with the second of the upper. But, if the fifth is a little out of tune, it follows that the two upper partials in question are not exactly in unison, but produce beats. And these partials being so near their respective primes, are usually fairly strong, and consequently give the desired effect in a marked degree.

Now on the harmonical we have a mistuned fifth ready to hand between the D and the A, and between the d and the a. For the following major chords are in exact tune : c, e, g; f, a, c'; and g, b, d; their relative frequencies being $72 : 90 : 108$; $96 : 120 : 144$; and $108 : 135 : 162$. Also d and d' make a perfect octave ($81 : 162$). Thus d and a ($81 : 120$) are a comma ($81/80$) less than a fifth apart, and give in consequence gritty beats. It requires the grave d (80) to make a perfect fifth with the a (120), and these notes should be found in perfect tune. The difference made in the harmony by the interval of a comma is very striking, yet, melodically considered, this interval is very small.

The beats of a mistuned fifth may also be heard with any fifth on the piano, harmonium, or organ, as ordinarily tuned. They may also, of course, be obtained by mistuned fifths on the violin.

The beats between two upper partials may also be

---

[1] *Ann. d. Physik*, 1̇1. 1, pp. 31-53, April 1903 ; *Science Abstracts*, p. 168, 1904.

illustrated on the harmonical by a mistuned fourth. For, although on this instrument the ordinary $b\flat$ makes a perfect minor third with g, it is too sharp by a comma to make a perfect fourth with f. Thus, the relative frequencies of f, g, and $b\flat$ are respectively 120, 135, and 162 ; hence the minor third, $162/135 = 6/5$, is true, but the fourth, which is $162/120 = (81/80) \times (4/3)$, is a comma too great. On the other hand, the special $b\flat$ provided on the $f\sharp$ digital is too flat to make a fourth with f. Thus, either of these notes for $b\flat$ will give beats with f. The beats heard are between the fourth partial of the lower note (f) and the third partial of the higher note ($b\flat$ or $^7b\flat$).

Again, we can obtain on the harmonical, beats between the upper partials of a mistuned major third. Take the notes e and $a\flat$, these are respectively perfect major thirds above c and below c'. But the interval between these two notes exceeds a major third by about a fifth of a tone. For the relative frequencies of c, e, $a\flat$, and c' may be denoted by 20, 25, 32, and 40, whence the first and third intervals are $25/20$ and $40/32$, and each equals $5/4$, a true major third ; but the second interval is $32/25 = 128/100 = (128/125) \times (5/4)$, and thus exceeds the just major third by the interval $128/125$, which equals 42 of Ellis's logarithmic cents. Thus, the notes in question on the harmonical yield very distinct beats, namely, between the fifth partial of the e and the fourth partial of the $a\flat$. This case is important in contrast with the absence (or faintness) of beats between forks at the interval of a mistuned third (see article 426).

429. Consonance or Dissonance of the chief Intervals.—We have seen that discord is due to beats, and also that beats arise in various ways. Again, these ways depend partly on the tones being powerful enough to produce differential tones, or rich enough in upper partials to give appreciable beats between the partials of one and the other note. Hence the degree of roughness due to the presence of beats will depend, not *solely* on the *interval* between the notes, but also and to a large extent on the *quality* of the compound tones in question. But, to simplify matters and keep to what is of chief importance, we shall usually confine attention to notes (or compound tones) of good musical quality with harmonic partials of gradually decreasing intensity extending up to say the sixth. We shall suppose also that the notes are not powerful enough to make the differentials of great importance, and that the summationals are practically inappreciable. In Table XXXII. is given a view of the chief intervals with the upper partials of each note and the beats arising between them. The differentials and summationals are also shown, but their power to produce appreciable beats is ignored. The numbers of the beats between upper partials are those for the pitch of the harmonical, for which middle c' is 264 per second.

TABLE XXXII.—SCHEME OF VARIOUS CONSONANCES

430. Helmholtz has calculated the degree of roughness of all the intervals comprised within two octaves. For this purpose he selected the quality of tone obtained from a good violin. To make the comparison quantitative, he was under the necessity of assuming a law as to change of roughness with number of beats, since the full details of the relation are not known. He chose, however, the simplest expression, which makes the roughness vanish when the frequency of the beats is either zero or infinity, and makes the roughness a maximum for thirty-three beats per second. The results of this calculation for a single

octave are represented in Fig. 93, in which the intervals
are plotted as abscissæ and the varying degrees of roughness as ordinates.   It is seen from this curve that a very
slight mistuning of the unison or octave produces a very
harsh dissonance, whereas the consonances of some other
intervals (notably the thirds and sixths) are far less
impaired by slight mistunings.

431. Expt. 76. *Consonances and Dissonances of all Intervals
within an Octave.*—The facts represented by the curve of
Fig. 93 may be very effectively illustrated on a violin if the
first or *e″* string be replaced by an *a′* string and tuned in
unison with the second or usual *a′* string.   Then, by

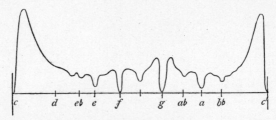

Fig. 93.—Degree of Roughness of Intervals within an Octave.

bowing the two *a′* strings together while sliding the finger
along the lower half of one of them, the other being meanwhile open, we reproduce the effects predicted by Helmholtz
and shown by his curve.   The great nicety of tuning
required to make either the unison or octave tolerable is
plainly noticed.   In fact, this characteristic of both these
intervals is well known to violinists and others.   To obtain
as strikingly as possible the effects shown in the diagram,
it is necessary at first to move the finger very slowly, and take
a small range of one or two semitones at a time, the hearers
being notified beforehand of the particular range of intervals
to be dealt with.   When the exact nature of the effect
to be noticed is better represented, it is possible to sweep
the whole octave with the finger at a single stroke, and follow
with the ear almost all the details shown in the curve.

432. Expt. 77. *Consonance of given Interval varies with
Pitch.*— But the consonance or dissonance of two notes

depends not only upon their quality and the interval between them, but also upon their position in the range of audible sounds, *i.e.* on their absolute pitch. This is conveniently shown by sounding notes at the interval of a major third in the bass octaves, and then in the other octaves in succession. It is at once noticed that the given interval sounds much rougher in the bass part of the compass than in the middle or higher octaves. Indeed, if we go high enough, the interval of a tone is but slightly dissonant; whereas if we go low enough in the compass, an octave is the only interval that can be tolerated.

These effects are preferably shown on the harmonical, but an ordinary harmonium or even piano will do.

433. But when an interval is chosen and the absolute pitch specified, the degree of roughness in some cases depends upon yet another circumstance. This case arises when the two notes composing the interval are assigned to different instruments whose tone qualities are distinctly different. It may then become a matter of moment as to which instrument takes the lower note. This has been pointed out by Mr. T. F. Harris,[1] who takes as examples the oboe, with the full harmonic series of partials, and the clarinet with (practically) the odd series only. Perhaps the most striking intervals for these instruments are the fourth, which is better with the oboe below; and the major third, which is better with the clarinet below. These cases are shown in Table XXXIII.

TABLE XXXIII.—CONSONANCES WITH OBOE AND CLARINET

Beats between upper Partials occur at Tones ⌒, and Semitones ⌒.

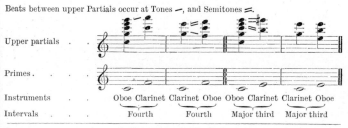

Upper partials . .				
Primes				
Instruments . .	Oboe Clarinet	Clarinet Oboe	Oboe Clarinet	Clarinet Oboe
Intervals . . .	Fourth	Fourth	Major third	Major third

[1] *Handbook of Acoustics.*

Among the upper partials the beats occurring at an interval of a whole tone are indicated by a single dash or bar, those occurring at the interval of a semitone by a double mark.

434. Chords and their Various Positions.—More than two separate compound tones, simultaneously produced, compose what is called a *chord*. If, with a given note, two others are sounded, each of which is consonant with the first, the consonance or dissonance of the chord will obviously depend chiefly upon the nature of the interval between the two added notes. If these two form a dissonant interval, the chord cannot be free from dissonance. If they form a consonant interval, then the chord will be to a corresponding degree consonant. Thus the triads (or chords of three notes) which lie within the compass of an octave and consonant are as follows :—

1. C E G.   2. C E♭ G.
3. C F A.   4. C F A♭.
5. C E♭ A♭.   6. C E A.

Of these, C E G, the major chord of C, and C E♭ G, the minor chord of C, serve as the representatives of all other major and minor chords. It is seen that each consists of two thirds, one a major and the other minor. But in the major chord the major third is below, while in the minor chord the minor third is below. The two chords can be simply represented by numbers giving the relative frequencies of their notes: thus 20, 25, 30 represent a major chord, while 20, 24, 30 represent a minor chord.

435. The various chords have been examined by Helmholtz, and also the various positions of the major and minor chords. It is thus found that, on scientific theory, the various positions or inversions of a chord may be arranged in an order of diminishing consonance. Thus Helmholtz gives twelve positions for the major triads, divided into two groups of six each, called respectively the

most perfect positions and the less perfect positions. These
are given in Tables XXXIV. and XXXV.

TABLE XXXIV.

THE MOST PERFECT POSITIONS OF MAJOR TRIADS

TABLE XXXV.

THE LESS PERFECT POSITIONS OF MAJOR TRIADS

In the first group the combinational tones (represented
by crotchets) do not disturb the harmony. In the second
group some of the combinational tones are unsuitable, and,
while not making the chords dissonant, put them in about
the same category as minor chords. The disturbing effect
of these combinational tones is indicated in the table by
dashes.

436. Of minor triads Helmholtz says that no position
can be obtained perfectly free from false combinational
tones. The three positions shown in Table XXXVI. he
gives as the best positions, the other nine are classed
as less perfect. As before, the minims denote the notes
of the chord, the crotchets representing the combinational
tones.

Table XXXVI.
The Most Perfect Positions of Minor Triads

Helmholtz views with favour that period of musical history when the simpler and smoother chords were used almost to the exclusion of the more dramatic effects of later times. Writing of that earlier period he has the following fine passage:—"Thus that expression which modern music endeavours to attain by various discords and an abundant introduction of dominant sevenths, was obtained in the school of Palestrina by the much more delicate shading of various inversions and positions of consonant chords. This explains the harmoniousness of these compositions, which are nevertheless full of deep and tender expression, and sound like the songs of angels with hearts affected but undarkened by human grief in their heavenly joy. Of course such pieces of music require fine ears both in singer and hearer, to let the delicate gradation of expression receive its due, now that modern music has accustomed us to modes of expression so much more violent and drastic."

We must omit notice of the various dissonant triads and of all chords of more than three notes, as lying rather beyond the scope of the present work. They are dealt with at great length by Helmholtz.

437. Reasons for Temperament.—We are now in a position to examine the number of notes to the octave which should be possessed by an instrument, and the exact tuning of these notes. In making this examination we must bear in mind the legitimate claims of the composer and the audience on the various musical instruments employed, and consider also the convenience of those who play the instruments. Each such claim or desideratum will involve certain consequences, and some of these we shall find to be conflicting. Hence, every practical solution of the problem before us is a compromise. These compromises consist in adopting a limited number of notes to the octave, and, by an approximate tuning called *temperament*, making them do duty for all the notes needed.

438. The claims may be grouped under three heads:— (1) purity of concords, (2) power to modulate, and (3) practical convenience. Let us deal with them in this order.

First, To satisfy the cultivated ear in the case of the simultaneous sounding of two or more notes, the chords of each instrument and combination of instruments should be pure. For the major diatonic scale, it will readily be admitted that this claim involves seven notes to the octave in what is called just intonation. This has already been referred to in the Introduction (art. 8), and is shown also in the present chapter (art. 430). But we may easily show that an eighth note is often needed, namely, the grave D, mentioned in art. 428. Let us now regard the matter from another point of view. In just intonation the whole tones are of two sizes, viz. 204 and 182 cents respectively; and the diatonic semitone, 112 cents, is larger than half of either of these tones. Now c and g are at the interval of a perfect fifth, but d is a large tone above c, while a is only a small tone above g. Hence the interval d to a in a justly intoned scale is not a perfect fifth. Thus, if it be required simultaneously to sound the pair d and a, or the minor chord $d f a$, we need an eighth tone, the grave d, which is a comma (22 cents) flatter than the ordinary d.

439. *Second,* In order to suit another instrument or a voice, each instrument must have the power to pitch a composition in any one of a number of keys differing by semitones only. Also, for the sake of artistic effect, the instrument must have the power to modulate into all such keys in the course of a composition. Further, in all these keys the intonation should be the same, that is, the intervals of the various degrees of the scale in any key into which we pass must be preserved the same as the corresponding intervals of the scale in the natural key of C. And to preserve the purity of the chords as claimed under the first heading, all these scales must be in just intonation. Now, to preserve just intonation during modulation involves the provision of *two* new notes in the octave for each sharp or flat remove. Thus, for the first sharp key, that of G, we need not only F♯ instead of F, but also the A must be made a comma sharper than for the key of C. For in the new scale beginning with G the first step from G to A must be a large tone (like C to D, 204 cents), whereas for the key of C the interval from G to A is only the small tone (182 cents). When these two new notes are provided we have a scale exactly like that in C, except that every note is a perfect fifth sharper than the corresponding notes of the original scale, *i.e.* the key-note G is a perfect fifth above C, the second note of the scale; the new A is a perfect fifth above D, the second note of the old scale, etc. Hence, the next sharp remove from G to D will again require *two* new notes for just intonation : these are C♯ instead of C, and in place of the ordinary E a new E a comma sharper is required.

440. Similarly, if we take the first flat remove from the natural key of C, we require *two* new notes beyond the ordinary seven in order to preserve just intonation. These are the B♭ in place of B, and the grave D a comma flatter than the usual D. These changes give us the key of F with notes in precisely the same relation to each other as those in the key of C. Hence, for the next flat remove, to the scale of B♭, we shall again need two new notes if just intonation is to be preserved.

Thus, for the natural key of C, seven sharp keys and seven flat keys, it appears that we require

$$7 + (2 \times 7) + (2 \times 7) = 35 \text{ notes to the octave.}$$

441. But this is on the supposition that none of the notes asked for coincide. Hence the question arises, Do any of them coincide? To answer this query, consider for a moment the keyboard of the piano or organ with twelve digitals to the octave. It is easily seen that on ascending by fifths through seven octaves, twelve steps are taken, and every note in the scale is used in some octave or another. Thus twelve fifths appear to equal seven octaves. Further, on ascending by major thirds, it is found that three major thirds appear to equal one octave. Now, do these relations hold in just intonation? Certainly not. Thus, take for simplicity's sake the frequency of the starting note, or 100, and ascend by octaves, by fifths, and also by major thirds, and see if any notes arrived at in these various ways ever tally. The intervals are shown in Table XXXVII.

TABLE XXXVII.—VARIOUS INTERVALS IN JUST INTONATION

RELATIVE FREQUENCIES OF NOTES.

Ascent by Octaves	100		200		400		800	1600	3200	6400	12,800
Ascent by Fifths	100	150	225	$337\frac{1}{2}$	$506\frac{1}{4}$	$759\frac{3}{4}$	.	.	.	.	13,218·79
Ascent by Major Thirds	100	125	$156\frac{1}{4}$	$195\frac{5}{16}$	.	.	.	.	.	.	.

442. It is seen by the even hundreds along the first line, and the odd numbers and fractions in the second, that no coincidence can ever be reached between them. Still less can any correspondence be ever attained between the first and third lines. The fact is the numbers 2 and 3 being prime, progress by octaves and by fifths from a given note can never lead to correspondence. Thus, twelve perfect fifths up gives the interval $(\frac{3}{2})^{12} = 531,411 \div 4096$; whereas seven octaves up gives the interval 2^7, which may be written $524,288 \div 4096$. Hence the discrepancy between them is the small interval $531,411 \div 524,288$ or about 24 cents. Accordingly, if this interval is ignored and the seven octaves divided into twelve equal fifths, all those fifths are mistuned. And, further, since in ascending by fifths every white and black note of the scale was used in some octave or other, all those notes differ from just intonation, which must have its fifths perfect. Similarly, since the numbers 5 and 4 are prime, progression by octaves and major thirds can never lead to correspondence if the intervals are maintained exact.

443. *Third*, For the sake of convenience to all concerned a reasonable simplicity is needed in the construction of each instrument, its tuning and keeping in tune, and in writing, reading, and playing the music. This claim is usually interpreted as involving a restriction to about twelve notes in the octave in the case of instruments whose notes are limited by separate mechanism. This includes such instruments as the piano and organ, the stringed instruments with fretted keyboards, and the various keyed and valved wind instruments. Obviously many more notes can be produced by instruments with a continuous adjustment of pitch, like the human voice, and instruments of the violin and trombone families. But the higher ideal possible to these instruments cannot be realised when they are used in conjunction with the others whose notes are limited to twelve in the octave. For, obviously, all must play the same scale, and thus the limitations of part become, for the time being, the limitations of the whole.

444. And, even when voices or violins are not fettered by association with instruments of a limited scale and fixed intonation, the difficulties of just intonation are probably greater than scientific writers have usually allowed. Take, for example, the case of a violin with strings tuned to g, d', a', and e''. Now suppose a composition begins in C natural and the strings are tuned to a justly-intoned scale of C. Then, if the piece modulate to the key of D, the a' string needs sharpening a comma to make a perfect fifth with d'. Of course this true, slightly-sharpened a' could be obtained from the d' string. But, if the use of the open strings were sacrificed, much of the sonority of the violin and its power of playing chords would be lost. In fact, the technique of violin-playing would then be greatly altered, and, probably, most players would feel a difficulty in maintaining the pitch true if they were driven to abandon the use of the open strings altogether.   For, obviously, they serve as a basis of reckoning after extended passages in which the hand is shifted far up the finger-board into the higher positions.   Thus, without the liberty to use the open strings, probably the intonation would be worse than now and not better.

445. Somewhat similar remarks would apply to an instrument like the trombone.   By the use of the slide it is true that the pitch can be varied continuously.   But take the case of the open notes ; let the instrument make two of these at the interval of a perfect fifth.   If the piece to be played were in such a key as to require these two open notes for the key-note and fifth respectively, then they are in perfect tune.   But suppose a piece were played in such a key as to bring these open notes on the second and sixth notes of the scale.   Then the perfect fifth pro-vided might not be required.   Here again, as on the violin, the required interval can be obtained, and with, perhaps, a smaller departure from the ordinary technique than in the analogous case of the violin.   But it would still entail a slight sacrifice, for although the note could be forced into tune by the lips, it would suffer, in consequence, some loss of brightness of tone quality.   Perhaps the nearest approach to just intonation that we ever realise in musical performances is in glee-singing without instrumental accompaniment.

446. But if the difficulties of just intonation are great in the case of violins and trombones, how much greater are they in instruments with digitals and fixed notes !   Suppose the number of notes to the octave to be increased con-siderably beyond the usual twelve, and the written music correspondingly complicated, then no doubt the difficulties of reading and playing could be overcome to some extent. Probably, however, the power of execution would be generally limited to simpler music than that now undertaken. Further, the number of notes to the octave need not be very great if only limited power of modulation were demanded. Whether music of a less florid nature, or confined within narrower limits of modulation, played in just intonation, would be preferable to very rapid passages and unlimited modulation, but in tempered intonation, is open to argument. Helmholtz greatly desired to see just intonation brought into general use. But did even he fully realise the difficulties in the way of its adoption? Many plans have been put forward by different authors and at various times with the view of obtaining an intonation practically just. Some of these plans involved over fifty notes to the octave. But, although devised with great ingenuity, they have never come into general use.

447. Hence, desirable as just intonation may be in the abstract, we seem as far as ever from its practical realisation for general musical purposes. Perhaps musicians usually underrate the desirability of just intonation. Scientists, on the other hand, may perhaps often lose sight of the enormous difficulties that lie in the way of its attainment. We must also remember that the right of science to dictate ceases where æsthetics begins. Thus, it may be safe to affirm that discord is due to beats between certain limits of frequency and concord to an entire or comparative absence of such beats. Further, it may be agreed that the intonation must be just for certain pairs of notes *simultaneously* sounded to be as free as possible from beats. But in florid music there is scarcely time for the beats to be heard. Further, in some passages it is desirable to have beats occurring only two or three times per second. Indeed, these are purposely introduced on certain stops of the organ.

448. Again, take the case of the flats and sharps.

For just intonation it is incontestable that the sharp, occurring between two notes a tone apart, is below the flat occurring in the same interval. Thus, for G$\sharp$ to make a just major third with E, which is itself a major third above C, we have an interval ratio from C to G$\sharp$ equal to $(5/4) \times (5/4) = 25/16 = 125/80$. Whereas for A$\flat$ a just major third below the upper C we have for the corresponding interval, *i.e.* from C to A$\flat$, the ratio $2 \times 4/5 = 8/5 = 128/80$. Thus, A$\flat$ is sharper than G$\sharp$ by the interval $128/125$, which equals 42 cents. Or, to reckon by cents direct, a major third in 386 cents, so from C to G$\sharp$ is double that, or 772 cents, whereas from C to A$\flat = 1200 - 386 = 814$ cents, or A$\flat$ is 42 cents sharper than G$\sharp$. But suppose now these notes, G$\sharp$ or A$\flat$, form a chromatic passage written for a single instrument. If descending, for the sake of avoiding needless accidentals, it would be written A A$\flat$ G, and if ascending G G$\sharp$ A. But in either case, if the instrument has the power of distinguishing between G$\sharp$ and A$\flat$, who knows what the composer wants? And if, in such cases, musicians sometimes demand that the G$\sharp$ should be sharper than A$\flat$ (or that B should be nearer to c than a diatonic semitone), has the physicist any right to complain? Surely the requirements here are matters of æsthetics, dependent upon the passage in question and the musical history and cultivation of the writer or hearer. Also the notation employed is, in many cases, purely a matter of convenience; and into this question the physicist, as such, has no title to enter.

449. As to the difficulty of tuning and keeping in tune, if just intonation is aimed at, the change of pitch with temperature should be borne in mind. This temperature variation for a number of instruments was given in the last chapter. From this it will be seen that, apart from the changes in a few weeks or months that cause instruments to need retuning, there is the more serious obstacle of this continuous variation which occurs as the room warms in the course of a single evening and affects different instruments to different degrees.

450. Granting, then, that we are usually almost driven to adopt comparatively few notes in an octave to represent the infinite number really needed, we shall presently consider in some detail two of the practical solutions that have attained a considerable vogue, namely, the mean-tone temperament and the equal temperament. The mean-tone temperament obtains a just major third, but at the expense of power to modulate (though this power may be increased somewhat by additional notes in each octave). The equal temperament has perfect power of modulation, but obtains it at the expense of flat thirds and sixths. Before, however, proceeding to these, we must say a little about the Pythagorean tuning or temperament, because it paves the way for the other, and our present staff notation still retains symbols to express its notes. And afterwards, as a specimen of a more ambitious system, we shall notice Bosanquet's cycle of fifty-three notes to the octave.

451. The Pythagorean Tuning.— In this ancient theoretical system all the notes used may be expressed by ascending in a series of twenty-six perfect fifths. These are represented in Table XXXVIII.

Table XXXVIII
Pythagorean Tuning by Perfect Fifths

A♭♭, E♭♭, B♭♭, F♭, C♭, G♭, D♭, A♭, E♭, B♭, F, C, G, D, A, E, B.
F♯, C♯, G♯, D♯, A♯, E♯, B♯, F×, C×, G×.

It will easily be seen that, on this system, the major thirds must be a comma too sharp. Further, it is clear, from what has been said, that the notes will never correspond to those obtained by ascending in octaves. Now, as shown in Fig. 93, a great increase of roughness is introduced by making a major third a comma sharp. Hence the above tuning is unfit for harmony. But violinists may be accused of still using this temperament, inasmuch as they tune their open strings to perfect fifths. It must, however, be observed that this does not commit them to sharpened major thirds, for the notes made by stopping the strings with the fingers can be varied at pleasure. Mr. Ellis gives the pitches of the above notes in cents as shown in Table XXXIX.

TABLE XXXIX.

PITCHES OF NOTES IN PYTHAGOREAN TUNING

Notes.	Cents.	Notes.	Cents.
c	0	$f\sharp$	611·7
$b\sharp$	23·5	$a\flat\flat$	678·5
$d\flat$	90·2	g	702·0
$c\sharp$	113·7	$f\times$	725·4
$e\flat\flat$	180·5	$a\flat$	792·2
d	203·9	$g\sharp$	815·6
$c\times$	227·4	$b\flat\flat$	882·4
$e\flat$	294·1	a	905·9
$d\sharp$	317·6	$g\times$	929·3
$f\flat$	384·4	$b\flat$	996·1
e	407·8	$a\sharp$	1019·6
f	498·0	$c'\flat$	1086·3
$e\sharp$	521·5	b	1109·8
$g\flat$	588·3	c'	1200·0

452. Mean-Tone Temperament.— This temperament owes its name to the fact that it sinks the distinction between the large and small tone, and adopts a tone which is the mean of the two. Thus it makes C to D and D to E, each 193 cents, instead of 204 and 182 respectively. It thus obtains the major third in just intonation. The fifths are, however, considerably out of tune, and its power to modulate is very small unless some additional notes are used beyond the usual twelve to the octave. This temperament may be regarded as derived thus. Ascend by four perfect fifths from C. Then the G and d are in just intonation, but the succeeding a and e' are each a comma sharp. Now, let the e' be made in just intonation, the necessary flattening being equally distributed over the four fifths used in ascending from C to e'. Thus each interval of a fifth is made a quarter of a comma too small. Thus, whereas the Pythagorean tuning kept the fifths perfect at the expense of greatly damaging the major thirds, the mean-tone temperament keeps the major thirds perfect at the cost of appreciably spoiling the fifths. The derivation of mean-tone temperament is exhibited in Table XL.

TABLE XL.—DERIVATION OF MEAN-TONE TEMPERAMENT

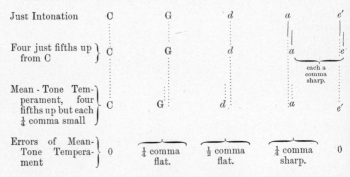

453. It is easy to see the power of modulation in mean-tone temperament is very restricted. For, having begun with a just major third in the scale of C, we naturally wish to keep it in all other keys. Thus, in the key of E major we need the justly intoned G♯. But in the key of A♭, in order to use the C's already provided, the A♭ must be a just major third below c. It is, accordingly, forty-two cents sharper than the G♯ as already referred to in art. 448. Hence the necessity for either more than twelve notes to the octave, or the restriction of modulation to the very few keys in which the original type of intervals is preserved.

The limitations of mean-tone temperament may be shown in another way as follows:—Let notes be written proceeding upwards by mean-tone fifths from C. Then from a C, seven octaves higher, descend by mean-tone fifths, and also ascend by fifths from the high C for a few notes. Now since the mean-tone fifths make the major thirds true, we never obtain again the notes from which we started, no matter how many intervals are taken up or down (see art. 442, where it was noted that octaves and major thirds involve ratios which are prime to each other). The scheme of notes just referred to is shown in Table XLI., in which the cents up from the lower C are also given. The notes in the bottom line are thus seen to be forty-two cents sharper than the corresponding notes in the top line.

TABLE XLI.—SCHEME OF NOTES IN MEAN-TONE TEMPERAMENT

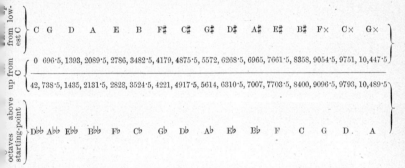

from lowest C	C	G	D	A	E	B	F♯	C♯	G♯	D♯	A♯	E♯	B♯	F×	C×	G×
up from C	0	696·5	1393	2089·5	2786	3482·5	4179	4875·5	5572	6268·5	6965	7661·5	8358	9054·5	9751	10,447·5
	42	738·5	1435	2131·5	2828	3524·5	4221	4917·5	5614	6310·5	7007	7703·5	8400	9096·5	9793	10,489·5
octaves above starting-point	D♭♭	A♭♭	E♭♭	B♭♭	F♭	C♭	G♭	D♭	A♭	E♭	B♭	F	C	G	D	A

454. This table clearly shows that for modulation into the seven sharp keys and the seven flat keys, we should need twenty-one notes to the octave, *i.e.* to B♯ inclusive in the top line and backwards to F♭ inclusive in the bottom line. With only twelve notes to the octave we should have power to play in six keys only, the key of C natural and five others, say two sharp keys and three flat ones or *vice versa*. And even then there would be no possibility of sounding accidental sharps when in the extreme sharp key, nor accidental flats when in the extreme flat key.

455. By reducing the above scheme to a single octave we obtain the notes of the mean-tone temperament in the compact form shown in Table XLII.

2 K

TABLE XLII.—SINGLE OCTAVE IN MEAN-TONE TEMPERAMENT

Diatonic Scale.		C		D		E	F		G		A		B	C
Cents up from C.	0		193		386	503·5		696·5		889·5		1082·5	120(0)
Notes.	C		D		E	F		G		A		B	C

Sharps and Flats.										
Notes.	C#	D♭	D#	E♭	F#	G♭	G#	A♭	A#	B♭
Cents up from C.	75·5	117·5	268·5	310·5	579	621	772	814	965	1007

It may be noted that the chief intervals in the mean-tone temperament are the diatonic tone and semitone of 193 and 117·5 cents respectively, the chromatic semitone of $(193 - 117·5 =)$ 75·5 cents and that between a sharp and the adjacent flat of $(2 \times 117·5 - 193 =)$ 42 cents.

To us now the mean-tone temperament derives its importance from the vogue which it once had, as shown by the following quotation from the late Mr. A. J. Ellis:—

"This was the temperament which prevailed all over the Continent and in England for centuries, and for this, and the Pythagorean, our musical staff notation was invented, with a distinct difference of meaning between sharps and flats, although that difference was different in the two cases. This temperament disappeared from pianofortes in England between 1840-1846. But at the Great Exhibition of 1851 all English organs were thus tuned. Handel in his Foundling Hospital organ had sixteen notes, tuned from *d♭* to *a♯*, 'ascending by mean-tone fifths.' Father Smith on Durham Cathedral and the Temple organ had fourteen notes from *a♭* to *d♯*, and the modern English concertina uses the same temperament and the same number of notes. The only objection to this temperament was that the organ-builders, with rare exceptions, such as those just mentioned, used only twelve notes to the octave, *e♭ b♭ f c g d a e b f♯ c♯ g♯*." Ellis thought that if it had been carried out with twenty-seven notes to the octave from $a\flat\flat$ to $g\times$ (as in Table XLI., omitting the $D\flat\flat$), it would probably have still remained in use. In his examination of fifty temperaments, Ellis found that this was decidedly the best for harmonic purposes. He con-. sidered that for simple melodic purposes the Pythagorean was preferred by violinists, but that was always absolutely impossible for harmony.

456. Equal Temperament.—The temperament now so widely in use is called the equal temperament, since it aims at dividing the octave into twelve equal intervals. It is clear that this temperament at once satisfies the requirements of practical convenience and, if attained with theoretical accuracy, secures perfectly the advantage of freedom in modulation. For, in the first place, it has the smallest number of tones that can be taken to represent the chromatic scale; and, secondly, whatever note is taken as the key-note, it is possible to proceed by precisely the same sequence of the standard intervals of tones or semitones to the octave above. Thus, on this temperament, twelve fifths make seven octaves, and three major thirds make one octave precisely.

We must now examine how far this temperament falls short in respect of supplying pure concords. The first step to this will be to find how far the various notes deviate from the corresponding ones in just intonation. We may do this in several ways, the following is perhaps the most suitable for our purpose.

457. Since only twelve notes are used in the octave and the steps made equal, we evidently fuse $C\sharp$ with $D\flat$, and $B\sharp$ with C, and so with the others. Hence, if we pass up by twelve fifths from C to $B\sharp$, the temperament required may be expressed by making the fifths all equal, and such as to bring $B\sharp$ into coincidence with C. Now on passing up twelve perfect fifths, we have the interval $\left(\dfrac{3}{2}\right)^{7}$ $= 531{,}441 \div 4096$; whereas, on passing up seven octaves, we have the interval $2^7 = 524,288 \div 4096$. Hence, to bring B$\sharp$ down to C, we must lower it by the interval $531,441 : 524,288$. This interval is known as the Pythagorean comma. To express it in cents, ascend the 12 perfect fifths, and descend seven octaves all measured in cents. Thus, we have the Pythagorean comma $= 12 \times 701 \cdot 955 - 7 \times 1200 = 23 \cdot 46$ cents, or say twenty-four cents nearly. Hence, the fifth used in equal temperament is smaller than the just or perfect fifth by one-twelfth of the Pythagorean comma, that is, by practically two cents or about one-eleventh of the ordinary comma.

458. Examine next the major third. This consists of two whole tones or four semitones of the standard equal-temperament size, so these major thirds must make an octave which contains twelve such semitones. Thus, if we ascend by the series of major thirds, A$\flat$ C E G$\sharp$, the equal temperament fuses G$\sharp$ and A$\flat$. Hence, if the deviation of this interval from just intonation be denoted by the ratio r or by c cents, we have the two equations

$$\left(\frac{5}{4}\, r\right)^3 = 2 \text{ and } 3\,(386 \cdot 314 + c) = 1200,$$

whence $r = \sqrt[3]{\dfrac{128}{125}} = \dfrac{126}{125}$ nearly, and $c = 13 \cdot 686$ cents.

These figures express the amount by which the equal-tempered major third is larger than the same interval in just intonation.

459. It is obviously convenient to measure intervals in cents when we wish to judge of the freedom for modulation which any temperament admits. On the other hand, when we wish to judge whether a consonance will be pure, it is often preferable to measure the intervals concerned by their frequency ratios. Further, when wishing to know how far a deviation from just intonation will damage the purity of any concord, we must refer to Helmholtz's diagram of degrees of roughness. To facilitate the comparison in various ways of the mean-tone and equal temperaments with just intonation, Table XLIII. and Fig. 94 are given. These show clearly that the mean-tone is superior to the equal temperament in its major thirds and sixths, but is worse in its fifths. Also, when restricted to twelve notes to the octave, the mean-tone is hopelessly behind the equal temperament in scope for modulation.

TABLE XLIII.—JUST AND TEMPERED INTONATIONS

Notes.	Intervals above C and Errors of Tempered Notes.					
	Just Intonation.		Mean-Tone.		Equal Temperament.	
	Frequency Ratios.	Cents.	Intervals.	Errors.	Errors.	Intervals.
C	1	0	0	0	0	0
			Cents.	Cents.	Cents.	Cents.
D	9 : 8	204	193	11♭	4♭	200
E	5 : 4	386	386	0	14♯	400
F	4 : 3	498	503	5♯	2♯	500
G	3 : 2	702	697	5♭	2♭	700
A	5 : 3	884	890	[1] 5♯	16♯	900
B	15 : 8	1088	1083	5♭	12♯	1100
C′	2 : 1	1200	1200	0	0	1200

460. EXPT. 78. *Effect of the Comma on the Violin.*—As an illustration of the effect which the comma produces in harmony, Helmholtz gives the following simple method open to any violinist. Tune the first, second, and third strings to *e″*, *a′*, and *d′*, as usual making the fifths perfect. Then stop the note *b′* with the first finger on the *a′* string. Obviously this will make a major sixth with the *d′* string and a major fourth with the *e″* string. And for melody, a single position of stop with the finger would make both the intervals passable. Try now the effect of harmony by sounding the *b′* along with the *d′* and with the *e″* respectively. It is at once perceived that no single position of the stop gives the best result both for the major sixth *d′ b′* and for the major

---

[1] All cents given are to the nearest whole number ; this line should really read 884·359, 889·7, 5·341, etc.

fourth b' e''. On the contrary, the position of the finger to stop the b' for a perfect major sixth with d' must be about 3/20 of an inch farther from the bridge than when stopping the b' to make a perfect major fourth with e''. On reference to the diagram Fig. 94 the reason for this is easily seen. For a major sixth (there represented by the A a sixth above C) we must have the sixth only a *small* tone (10/9) above the perfect fifth (G). Whereas for the perfect fourth (there represented by F a fourth above C) we must have the note a *large* tone (9/8) below the perfect fifth (G). Thus, to raise the pitch of the a' string from the perfect fifth to a major sixth with the d' we need to stop so as to sharpen it

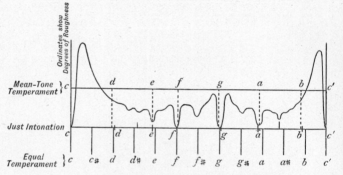

FIG. 94.—ILLUSTRATING DISCORD DUE TO TEMPERAMENT.

by only a small tone (10/9). Whereas, to diminish the perfect fifth between the a' string and the e'' to a perfect fourth, we need to raise the a' string by a large tone (9/8). And the difference between the two stops for these tones, expressed as a fraction of the string's length, is obviously $\frac{9}{10} \sim \frac{8}{9} = \frac{1}{90}$. So if the string is 13·5 inches long, this difference of stops is 3/20 of an inch, a nicety of stopping quite well within the range of a player's accuracy. It should also be observed from the diagram Fig. 94 that all the intervals on which this experiment depends, the perfect fifth, the major sixth, and the fourth, are intervals which are well defined or delimited. That is to say, a slight mistuning causes a large degree of roughness. Hence it is easy to get all these intervals tuned with sufficient accuracy by ear alone.

But although it is easy by this experiment to show that the best harmonies in the two cases referred to are obtained by the different stoppings, it will be found that an intermediate position gives a result which is tolerable, even for harmony, especially in a rapid passage and with a mellow-toned instrument.

461. Bosanquet's Cycle of Fifty-Three.—Although no temperaments but the equal and mean-tone have obtained much vogue, the cycle of fifty-three notes to the octave, invented and carried out by Mr. R. H. M. Bosanquet, deserves mention as the simplest of the many attempts to approach more nearly to just intonation. Indeed, Helmholtz says of it : " The ear cannot distinguish this scale from the just, and in its practical applications it admits of unlimited modulation in what is equal to exact intonation." But Mr. Ellis, the translator of Helmholtz, adds to the above passage a footnote. He allows that the intervals taken melodically might be indistinguishable from just intonation. But of the effect when used harmonically he says, " At least, as the intervals were tuned on Mr. Bosanquet's instrument, there was a decidedly perceptible difference to an ear accustomed as mine was to listen to just intonation."

462. This temperament divides the octave into fifty-three precisely equal degrees or steps, of which nine represent the large tone, eight the small tone, and five the diatonic semitone. All the fifty-three notes are provided, hence beginning at any one of them the diatonic scale can be played with the same sequence of the given standard intervals. Thus unlimited power of modulation is provided.

Let us next examine the degree of approximation to just intonation which this scheme offers. It is evident that each of the fifty-three degrees or steps will be equal to $1200 \div 53 = 22 \cdot 64151$ cents, whence the notes and intervals are easily calculated. Table XLIV. shows the comparison of this cycle with just intonation to the first place of decimals in cents.

TABLE XLIV.—Bosanquet's Cycle of Fifty-Three

Notes.	Just Intonation Cents up from C.	Bosanquet's Cycle.			
		Cents up from C.	Errors in Cents.	"Steps up from C.	Intervals in "Steps."
C	0	0	0	0	
D	203·9	203·8	0·1♭	9	9
E	386·3	384·9	1·4♭	17	8
F	498·0	498·1	0·1♯	22	5
G	702·0	701·9	0·1♭	31	9
A	884·4	883·0	1·4♭	39	8
B	1088·3	1086·8	1·5♭	48	9
C′	1200	1200	0	53	5

463. The table shows that throughout the diatonic scale the departure of Bosanquet's cycle from just intonation never reaches two cents. Accordingly, it has no interval so bad as the best in equal temperament, namely, the fourth and the fifth. Hence the scheme now under notice secures the advantage of practically just intonation together with that of freedom to modulate. But is it a practical temperament? We fear not. A harmonium on this plan was made and exhibited at South Kensington in 1876. In this instrument, for convenience of fingering, the fifty-three notes in the octave were distributed over eighty-four digitals. Passing from left to right the keys were arranged in the ordinary way, seven white keys and five black ones to the octave. But, passing upward from front to back, there were tier after tier of keys somewhat like seven manuals condensed into one. This may seem a formidable array of digitals. It is, however, noteworthy that with this keyboard the inventor secured the signal advantage of making the fingering of any given scale or chord precisely the same, no matter what the key or the names of the notes. Thus, given scale passages or chords have the *same form* to the hand in any key instead of *twelve* *different forms* according to the key as on the ordinary keyboard.

464. The notation suggested by Bosanquet for his instrument was the ordinary staff notation with the following slight modifications. The prefix of a backward-sloping line, thus \, indicated the flattening of a note by one of the "steps," of which fifty-three make the octave. Two such lines denoted the flattening by two steps, and so forth. The sharpening by the same amount was indicated by lines sloping the opposite way, thus /. The scale of c major would be $c \ d \ \backslash e \ f \ g \ \backslash a \ \backslash b \ c'$, but the notes represented by the staff notation instead of these letters. For the key of G the f is of course replaced by $f\sharp$ while the $\backslash a$ is replaced by a. It may be noted also that $///b$ is the same note as $\backslash\backslash c'$, since five of Bosanquet's "steps" make his diatonic semitone.

465. Ellis's Harmonical.—This instrument is a harmonium specially tuned according to the design of the late Mr. A. T. Ellis, the translator of Helmholtz's *Sensations of Tone*. Though already referred to in article 422, it requires a little additional notice in this place. One of these instruments was exhibited in London, and others have since been supplied by Moore and Moore to a number of universities and colleges. Its name is derived from the fact that the instrument furnishes a large number of harmonics. Thus, by special tuning, especially in the top octave, it has the first 16 partials of c, 132 per second. Whereas for C (66 per second) it provides 26 partials up to the 32nd inclusive, the 6 lacking being the 11th, 13th, 21st, 23rd, 27th, and 31st. It has what the inventor calls a "harmonical bar," by which the first 16 partials beginning at c can be played simultaneously; or, if desired, the 7th and 14th may be omitted. It is remarkable that the 7th and 14th, though not in the ordinary scales (either tempered or just), blend perfectly with the others, as theory predicts. Whereas harsh dissonances are caused by the use of the ordinary B♭'s, which are minor thirds above the G's. The instrument affords valuable illustrations of major and minor chords in just intonation (in the keys of C major and minor), but is not designed as a practical musical instrument, as it is incapable of modulation.

466. Character of Keys.—It is a matter of scientific interest to account for the special character of each key so often alleged by musicians. What is here referred to is, of course, the absolute character of the keys C, G, D♭, etc. and not the relative character of C and its dominant G into which the piece temporarily modulates. This matter is referred to briefly by Helmholtz and at considerable length by Berlioz. It appears that little if any difference of character can be attributed to the various keys for the organ or for voices with organ accompaniment or unaccompanied. But on pianos, violins, and brass instruments the difference is marked. Consider these classes of instruments in order. In the case of pianos it may be that the short, narrow, raised, black digitals are usually struck differently from the long, broad level, white ones. Hence, in the different keys these differences of touch are differently distributed throughout the degrees of the scale. Thus a different character may be imparted to the different keys. Again, in instruments of the violin family, the different keys bring into more or less prominence the open strings which sound fullest. Also the fingering varies considerably for different keys. So that here again we see how one key may be bright and ringing, another veiled and obscure. Similar remarks apply to the brass instruments. In one key the tonic and dominant may fall on open notes of the instrument, and in another key no open notes may be available for the diatonic scale. And the difference between open notes and valve notes is probably quite sufficient to give a character to the various keys which give or deny prominence to the open notes.

467. It may also be suspected that, in the case of the various instruments, by the ordinary method of tuning current in the musical profession, the various keys are unequally favoured although equal temperament is supposed to be aimed at. Thus, it may be that on a piano fresh from the hands of some able tuner the keys in most frequent use deviate slightly from equal temperament in the direction of just intonation, while the least used keys may deviate slightly in the opposite direction. If so, we should usually have something rather better than equal temperament, and only occasionally something rather worse. And this difference would be available for artistic effect by giving a different character to the various keys.

468. Orchestration.—Although many of the problems of orchestration are chiefly musical and beyond the scope of this work, there are a few points of scientific interest which demand notice here. In the first place, we may naturally inquire why in an orchestra there are several instruments of any given class but of different pitches and taking different parts. Thus, we have first and second violins, violas, violoncellos, and basses. Again, there are usually several flutes, several clarinets, an oboe, and a bassoon. So that each class of instruments furnishes several parts of the composition with its own special quality of tone. The same holds with respect to the brass. Thus we may have two or three trumpets, two to four French horns, and usually three trombones. Instruments of very distinct character may be used singly, as the triangle and others of like nature. Perhaps two reasons may be given for the grouping of instruments of one class but of different pitches into small bands in this manner. First, it enables the composer to give a harmonic rendering of a passage in the quality of tone of which these instruments are capable. Second, the employment of instruments of the same quality of tone is essential to the characterisation of the various consonances and dissonances. For we have seen that discord is due to beats, and usually for musical purposes these beats are between upper partials. Further, to make beats distinct, the sound at the minimum should be as weak as possible, that is, preferably of zero intensity. But, to secure this, the two beating tones must be of equal intensity. Hence, to secure this equality between upper partials, the two compound tones should have the same law of diminution in the retinue of upper partials, *i.e.* they should be of the same musical quality. Hence the necessity for having the various parts of a harmony executed in tones of the same or similar quality if the various shades of consonance and dissonance are to be clearly rendered.

469. Probably at one time only instruments of one class could be tolerated in harmony, because each class had its own style of tuning. Hence flutes might deviate from just intonation in one way, and be passable with each other, but intolerable along with some other family of instruments with different intonation. This may be the reason why at one period pieces were written for several instruments of the same class, say flutes only, or strings only, but no orchestration attempted.

470. Obviously orchestration implies standardisation both in pitch and temperament. We may thus regard an orchestra as an aggregation of small bands or families of instruments, each family being capable of harmonic utterance, but each having its own special character, disadvantages, and limitations. Thus, we may divide the orchestra and chorus broadly into the strings, the woodwind, the brass, and the voices. Hence, between these various parts, whether they are required for combined or successive utterance, there must exist a suitable balance. What this should be depends, of course, upon the character of the piece to be performed, and also upon the progress made in the art of providing instruments capable of rendering artistic music. Thus, the position of the orchestra at the present time is very different from that prevailing in Handel's time. The composition of an ordinary orchestra and chorus of the present day illustrates some of the preceding remarks. Of course the total number of performers differs very widely, and the relation of the constituents also varies greatly with the music to be rendered. Table XLV. gives a fair illustration of present practice for an orchestra and chorus of about three hundred for the purpose of oratorios and similar compositions.

TABLE XLV.

EXAMPLE OF MODERN ORCHESTRA AND CHORUS

Wind Instruments, etc.	Strings and Voices.
2 Flutes	12 First Violins
2 Oboes	8 Second Violins
2 Bassoons	6 Violas
2 Clarinets	6 Violoncellos
4 Horns	6 Double Basses
2 Trumpets	—
1 Alto Trombone	38
1 Tenor Trombone	
1 Bass Trombone	70 Sopranos
1 Bass Tuba	50 Contraltos
1 Pair Kettledrums	50 Tenors
	50 Basses
	4 Soloists
19	224

Band of 57 Performers, Chorus and Soli of 224, grand total 281.

471. Chief Intervals.—The chief intervals already referred to within the range of an octave are collected together for reference in Table XLVI. The values of the intervals are given in Ellis's logarithmic cents and by their frequency ratios. The references to the notes of the scale supposes that the key of C is being used.

TABLE XLVI.—CHIEF INTERVALS WITHIN AN OCTAVE

Values of Intervals.		Names and Examples of Intervals.		
Approximate Cents.	Frequency Ratios.	Just Intonation.	Mean-Tone Temperament.	Equal Temperament
22[1]	81 : 80	The Comma		
42	128 : 125	...	G♯ to A♭, etc.	
70	25 : 24	D to D♯, etc.		
76	70 : 67	...	C to C♯, etc.	
92	135 : 128	C to C♯, etc.		
100	89 : 84	...	...	Every Semitone
112	16 : 15	Diatonic Semitone		
117·5	107 : 100	...	Diatonic Semitone	
182	10 : 9	Small Whole Tone		
193	180 : 161	...	Every Whole Tone	
200	449 : 400	...	...	Every Whole Tone
204	9 : 8	Large Whole Tone		
300	44 : 37	...	...	Minor Third
316	6 : 5	Minor Third		
386	5 : 4	Major Third		
400	63 : 50	...	...	Major Third
498	4 : 3	Fourth		
500	303 : 227	...	...	Fourth
503	107 : 80	...	Fourth	
697	163 : 109	...	Fifth	
700	433 : 289	...	...	Fifth
702	3 : 2	Fifth		
800	100 : 63	...	...	Minor Sixth
814	8 : 5	Minor Sixth		
884	5 : 3	Major Sixth		
900	37 : 22	...	...	Major Sixth
969	7 : 4	Trumpet Seventh [2]		
996	16 : 9	Minor Seventh, a fourth above F		
1000	98 : 55	...	...	Minor Seventh
1018	9 : 5	Acute Minor Seventh, a Minor Third above G		
1088	15 : 8	Major Seventh		
1100	168 : 89	...	...	Major Seventh
1200	2 : 1	Octave	Octave	Octave

[1] The comma of the just intonation is strictly 21·506 cents ; each of the 53 intervals or "steps" of Bosanquet's cycle is 22·64151 cents, and the Pythagorean comma is 23·46 cents. [2] This is the note called 7B♭ in Ellis's Harmonical.

472. Historical Pitches.—We shall conclude the present chapter with Table XLVII., giving a few of the leading pitches that have been used at various times and places. These are extracted from the mass of details obtained and compiled by Ellis, and given by him in an appendix to his translation of Helmholtz's *Sensations of Tone*.

TABLE XLVII.—CHIEF PITCHES FROM LOWEST TO HIGHEST

Description of Pitches.		Rise of Pitch in Cents.	Frequency of c'.	Approximate Date.	Place.	Instrument or Authority identified with each Pitch.
Church Pitches.	Lowest.	0	370	...	...	Imaginary lowest pitch to reckon from.
		17	373·7	1648	Paris	
		33	377	1511	Heidelberg	
	Low.	66	384·3	1700	·Lille	Old Fork.
		129	398·7	1854	Lille	Old Organ.
Chamber Pitch (Low).		148	402·9	1648	Paris	Spinet.
		196	414·4	1776	Breslau	Clavichord.
Mean Pitch of Europe for Two Centuries.		199	415	1754	Dresden	Organ.
		230	422·5	1751	England	Handel's Fork.
				1820	Westminster	Abbey Organ.
				1877	England	Curwen's "Tonic Sol-Fa," Standard $c'' = 507$.
		243	425·8	1824	Paris	Opera Pitch.
		251	427·8	1788	Windsor	St. George's Chapel Organ (measured by Ellis, Feb. 1880, while still in "Mean-Tone").
Compromise Pitch.		260	430	1810	Paris	Fork.
		273	433·2	1828	London	Sir G. Smart's own Philharmonic Fork.
		285	436·1	1878	London	Fork to which Organ tuned at H.M. Theatre.
Modern Orchestral Pitches.		288	437	1859	Toulouse	Conservatoire.
		289	437·1	1666	Worcester	Cathedral Organ.
		305	441·2	1878	London	Covent Garden Opera.
		318	444·6	1877	London	St. Paul's Organ.
		323	445·8	1856	Paris	Opera.
		346	452	1885	London	International Exhibition of Inventions and Music.
		350	452·9	1878	London	Kneller Hall Military School.
		359	455·3	1879	London	Erard's Concert Pitch.
		380	460·8	1880	U.S. America	Highest New York Pitch.
Church and Chamber Pitches (High).		368	457·6	1640	Vienna	Organ.
		541	505·8	1361	Halberstadt	Organ.
		726	563·1	1636	Paris	Mersenne's Chamber Pitch.
		740	567·3	1619	North German	Church Pitch.

CHAPTER X

473. Velocity of Sound in Free Air.—Most of the methods of acoustic measurements hitherto developed aim at the determination of a velocity of propagation, absolute or relative, or a pitch. These will be taken in the order named. We shall then consider other problems, some of subordinate importance, whose treatment is less advanced, and in some cases has scarcely yet passed beyond the qualitative stage. Though much of the present chapter will be necessarily concerned with descriptions of classical determinations or researches, the simpler methods suitable for lecture illustration or laboratory exercises will not be overlooked.

We commence, then, with some of the classical determinations of the absolute velocity of the propagation of sound in free dry air at $0°$ C.

Paris Academy in 1738.—Cassini, Maraldi, and La Caille, three members of the Academy, made what appears to be the first exact determination of the velocity of sound in the open air. Their stations were the Observatory at Paris, Montmartre, Fontenay-aux-Roses, and Monthléry, the total distance involved being 17 or 18 miles. The experiments were made at night, and commenced on a signal being given from the Observatory. Alternately from each of the two end stations a cannon was fired at constant

512

intervals. At the other stations the times were observed which elapsed between seeing the flash and hearing the report. The distances in question were accurately measured and thus the speeds found. These observations were continued for some time and under different atmospheric conditions. The conclusions arrived at are as follows :—

(1) The velocity of propagation is independent of the pressure of the air.

(2) It increases with the temperature of the air.

(3) It is the same at each distance from the source of sound; that is, sound is propagated at uniform speed.

(4) With the wind sound is propagated quicker than against the wind, the speeds being in the first case the sum, and in the second the difference of those of sound and the wind.

(5) The velocity of propagation of sound in still dry air is 337 metres per second.

However, by the calculations of Le Roux applied to these same experiments, the velocity of sound at 0° C. was determined as 332 metres per second.

474. *Bureau des Longitudes, 1822.*—These experiments were also conducted at Paris, namely, between Monthléry and Villejuif. Cannons were fired from opposite ends of the line at intervals of five minutes. The observers were Humboldt, Gay-Lussac, and Bouvard at Monthléry, those at Villejuif being Arago, Mathieu, and Prony. At Villejuif were heard all the cannons fired at the other end, the mean time elapsing between flash and report being 54·84 seconds. The observers at Monthléry made the mean interval to be 54·43 seconds, but of the twelve firings at Villejuif only seven were heard, hence the correction for wind was not made so perfectly as desired. The mean time was, however, taken as the arithmetic mean of the above two values, namely, 54·63. The distance between the stations was determined by Arago as 18,622·27 metres. Thus, the speed

2 L

of sound at the temperature, when observed, was determined as

$$v = 18,622 \cdot 27 \div 54 \cdot 63 = 340 \cdot 8 \text{ metres per second.}$$

As the temperature was approximately $16°$ C., the speed at $0°$ C. was calculated to be

$$v_0 = \frac{340 \cdot 8}{\sqrt{1 + 0 \cdot 003665 \times 16}} = 331 \cdot 2 \text{ metres per second.}$$

Dutch Physicists, 1823.—A very careful determination made by Moll, van Beek, and Kuytenbrouwer, gave as the value of the velocity of sound in still dry air at $0°$ C.,

$$v_0 = 332 \cdot 26 \text{ metres per second.}$$

And from these observations a recalculation by Schröder van der Kolk afforded the value,

$$v_0 = 332 \cdot 77 \text{ metres per second.}$$

475. *Speed along a Slope.*—In 1823 Stamfer and Myrbach made determinations of the speed of sound between stations in the Tyrol differing in level by 1364 metres. In 1844 Bravais and Martins experimented between stations whose levels differed by 2079 metres. The upper station was on the Faulhorn and the lower one at the Lake of Brienz. The slant distance between the stations was of the order 9560 metres, and the slope of the straight line connecting them over $12°$. Reciprocal firing from each end was practised. On the mountain eighteen shots were fired during three days by A. Bravais and Martins. At the lake C. Bravais fired fourteen shots. The directly observed speeds of the sounds were upwards $337 \cdot 92$ m./sec., and downwards $338 \cdot 10$ m./sec., the mean value being $338 \cdot 01$ m./sec. Reduced to $0°$ C. and dry air this research gave the value,

$$v_0 = 332 \cdot 37 \text{ m./sec.}$$

The experiments in the Tyrol gave practically the same value. These are interesting as confirming the theoretical prediction that the speed of sound is independent of pressure. For the Lake of Brienz is 1857 feet above the sea-level, the top of the Faulhorn 8803 feet, and obviously at these altitudes the mean pressures would be very low compared with that generally observed at or near the sea-level.

476. *Experiments at Low Temperatures.*—Observations on the speed of sound at low temperatures have been made in Arctic expeditions. Parry determined the velocity at temperatures from $-38°·5$ F. to $-7°$ F., and again at $33°·5$ and $35°$. From the actual results the speed of sound at $0°$ F. would be about 1050 feet per second, and the temperature correction about 1 ft./sec. per $1°$ F. Thus, at $0°$ C. we should have a value between 1080 and 1090 ft./sec. A number of observations made by Greely at temperatures between $-10°$ and $-45°$ C. resulted in the expression,

$$v = (333 + 0·6t) \text{ metres per second,}$$

where v is the velocity of sound at $t°$ C.

477. *Stone's Experiments, 1871.*—This determination was made at Cape Town. Two observers were stationed, one 641 feet from the one o'clock time cannon at Port Elizabeth, the other at the Observatory 15,449 feet distant. The instants of hearing these reports by the observers were electrically recorded on the chronograph situated at the Observatory. There was no reciprocal firing, hence the wind velocity was measured and allowed for. The time taken by the electrical signals is negligible in comparison with the time taken by sound to travel. But the chronograph records were corrected for "personal equation." This is the term used by astronomers and others to denote the time lag or interval peculiar to any observer between his perceiving and recording an event. If, in the experiments under notice, the two observers possessed equal personal equations, however large or small, the results would have been unaffected by them. But, probably, each had a different personal equation, and especially a different

one for the given conditions in which one observer hears
a loud sound and the other a feeble one. To eliminate
this difference of personal equations, a smaller gun was
fired at distances from the two observers chosen, so as to
make the loudness for each observer the same as in the
actual experiment with the time gun. The time for sound
to travel over this distance, about one-tenth those in the
main experiment, was calculated provisionally from the
experimental value found by the neglect of the personal
equation. The recorded interval was greater than that
calculated by 0·09 second. Consequently 0·09 was subtracted from the intervals recorded in the main experiments,
as representing the excess of the personal equation of one
observer over that of the other. The value thus obtained
by Stone was

$$v_0 = 1090 \cdot 6 \text{ ft./sec.} = 332 \cdot 4 \text{ m./sec.}$$

478. *Variation of Velocity with Intensity.*—In 1864
Regnault experimented near Versailles on the velocity of
sound in the open air, two distances respectively, 2445 and
1280 metres being used. Reciprocal firing of guns was
employed. The instant of firing was recorded by the
rupture of a wire forming part of an electrical circuit, and
passing across the gun's muzzle. The arrival of the sound
at the distant station was also electrically recorded. The
sound-wave was received by a wood cone fixed to a cylinder
and closed at the far end by a thin india-rubber membrane.
The motion of the membrane due to the sound broke a
second electrical circuit. The two records were made upon
the same chronograph. But this apparatus had a time lag
just as truly as a human observer has his personal equation.
Regnault endeavoured to evaluate the error thus introduced,
and to correct for it. The mean values from a number of
experiments are as follows :—

For the distance of 1280 metres, $v_0 = 331 \cdot 37$ m./sec.
For the distance of 2445 metres, $v_0 = 330 \cdot 7$ m./sec.

This decrease of speed with diminished intensity of the sound is in accord with other experiments, and with theory. The value for the velocity of sound according to the ordinary theory professes to be valid only for infinitely small motions and variations of pressure. For finite amplitudes a larger value can be seen to hold; because with finite increases of pressure we have a finite rise of temperature, and hence an increased speed of propagation of the parts compressed. This fact of increased speed for great compressions is also well exemplified in the photographs of flying bullets due to Prof. C. V. Boys, see Fig. 29. In these photographs it is clear that the projectile, passing at a higher speed than that of ordinary sounds, compresses the air in front of it until a point is reached at which that shell of compressed air or wave can keep pace with the bullet.

In Regnault's experiment let us suppose that this lower limit or theoretical velocity was valid throughout the distance of 1165 metres between the first receiving station and the second. Then we have, for this lower limiting velocity,

$$v_0 = \frac{\text{difference of distances}}{\text{difference of times}} = \frac{2445 - 1280}{\dfrac{2445}{330 \cdot 7} - \dfrac{1280}{331 \cdot 37}}$$

$$= \frac{1165}{7 \cdot 3934 - 3 \cdot 8628} = 329 \cdot 9 \text{ m./sec.}$$

479. Jacques experimented with a cannon at Watertown, Mass., and showed (in 1879) that the velocity of sound is different in different directions round such a source. Membranes were used as receivers, and they recorded on a chronograph. Immediately in the rear of the cannon the velocity was less than the usual amount. A little farther back the velocity reached a maximum value distinctly above the ordinary velocity. Still farther away the velocity fell to about the usual value. Thus, with a charge of $1\frac{1}{2}$ lb. of powder, the velocity at the rear changed from about 1076 ft./sec. at about 20 ft. distance to a maximum of 1267 ft./sec. at about 80 ft. distance, and then decreased again. Other examples of variation of velocity with intensity will occur in connection with the propagation of sound in water and through pipes.

480. Velocity of Sound in Water.—In 1826, Colladon and Sturm measured the velocity of sound in water by experiments in the Lake of Geneva. Two boats were moored at a definite measured distance apart. From one a bell hung immersed in the lake. This was sounded by the stroke of a hammer fixed to a lever whose upper end by the same motion fired some gunpowder. Thus the instant of striking was known at the other boat by the flash. The sound travelling through the water was received at the distant boat by a tube whose lower end was immersed, the upper end being applied to the ear of the observer. Hence the interval between the starting and arrival of the sound was found. It was registered by a quarter-second stop-watch and the velocity calculated. This was determined to be 1435 metres per second, and the mean temperature of the water concerned was estimated at 8°·1 C. Now in water, as in air, the velocity of sound is theoretically given by the expression $\sqrt{\text{elasticity}/\text{density}}$. From the value of the elasticity of water at 8° C. determined by Grassi, and that of the density (0·999775) by Kopp, the velocity would be 1437 metres per second, a result in practical agreement with the experiment.

481. *Explosions under Water.*—In 1889 Threlfall and Adair published an account of experiments on the velocities of the sound-waves from explosions under water carried out in the harbour of Port Jackson, Australia. Various charges of gun-cotton were fired under water, and the times taken for sound to travel 150 metres or more were measured. The firing was electrical, and gave a signal recorded on a chronograph, which also afterwards recorded the instant when the sound reached an india-rubber diaphragm immersed in the water at the distant station. The calculated velocity of sound in the water was about 1500 m./sec.; the observed velocity of the explosion wave rose from 1732 m./sec. with 9 oz. of gun-cotton to 2013 m./sec. with 64 oz.

482. Method of Coincidences.—In 1853 J. Bosscha proposed a method of determining the velocity of sound by the apparent coincidence of sounds made simultaneously at points a measured distance apart. A rather simpler form of this method used by König in Paris in 1863 was as follows:—Two small electro-magnetic counters are actuated by a fork interrupter so as to give ticks at intervals of a tenth of a second. When the counters are close together the ticks heard coincide; but when one is removed farther and farther away the ticks heard are separated by an interval at first increasing and then decreasing, till coincidence is again established. This was found to occur at about a distance of 34 metres between the two counters. Hence the velocity of sound was determined to be of the order 340 metres per second. In 1864 D. Kahl further simplified this method by using only one counter, the second being replaced by the echo from a wall of the sound due to the first and only one now in use. It is obvious that this arrangement has the advantage of economising space, only 17 metres being now required between counter and the reflecting surface if the period is still one-tenth of a second.

483. Velocity of Sound in Pipes.—Regnault carried out an elaborate series of experiments on the velocity of sound in the water-pipes newly laid in Paris in 1862-63. The sources of sound used included a pistol, explosions, and musical instruments. The method of measuring the time was electrical. The shot broke that part of an electrical circuit which passed just in front of the pistol's muzzle. This caused a displacement of the mark on a smoked drum, thus registering the start of the sound on its course through the air in the pipe. The arrival of the sound at the far end of the pipe moved a very fine membrane. This made contact between a tiny platinum plate at its middle and a screw point near it. This contact completed an electric circuit, and caused the reversed movement of the same style that registered the instant of firing. The time between these two motions of the style was measured as follows :— Side by side with the mark in question were (1) a series of dots indicating seconds and actuated by a pendulum, and (2) a wavy trace due to a tuning-fork. Thus the whole number of seconds was given by the number of dots, and the fractions of a second, near the beginning and finish, estimated to thousandths of a second by the tuning-fork trace. Regnault found the membrane had a time lag increasing as the sound was fainter, and he endeavoured to allow for this. An accurate measure of the length of the pipe divided by the correct time furnished the value for the velocity under the conditions of the experiment. The pistol was inserted at the beginning of the pipe which was otherwise closed by a disc, the far end being also closed by the membrane. Hence the sound when once started could pass to and fro, being wholly or partially reflected at each end of the pipe. Pipes of three different diameters were used, and a number of lengths experimented on. The velocities found for the various lengths of the different pipes are shown by the curves in Fig. 95.

484. These results show plainly, first, that the speed of sound tends to a lower limit as the distances increase, *i.e.* as the intensities decrease ; and, secondly, that this limiting velocity is higher in wide pipes than in narrow ones. Regnault judged that in the pipe of 1·1 m. diameter the point was already reached at which the sides of the pipe were practically without effect. He therefore gave 330·6 m./sec. as the value of the velocity of the sound used in air at 0° C. in an infinitely wide tube. But, taking from the observations the speed of the sound in its last stages

before dying away, he obtained the slightly smaller value
of 330·3 m./sec.   Moreover, he found that the limiting
velocity was the same for all sources.   The humidity of
the air in these experiments was observed and corrected
for.

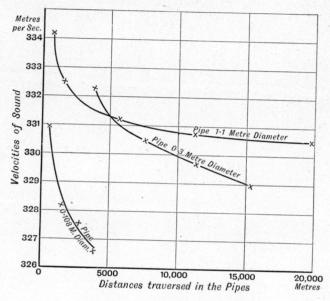

FIG. 95.—VELOCITIES OF SOUND IN PIPES.

485. Rink objected to Regnault's conclusions, and
pointed out that, in the first few coursings of the sound
along the pipes, not only the sound would pass along, but
also the air itself would move bodily.   Omitting, therefore,
the first and second coursings, we have the results for the
other passages of the sound along the tube 1·1 m. diameter
given in Table XLVIII., which exhibits Rink's view of the
matter.

[TABLE

Table XLVIII

Rink's Analysis of Regnault's Experiments

No. of Experiment.	Charge of Gunpowder in Pistol in gms.	Speed of each Passage of Sound along Pipe 1·1 m. diameter.						Mean Speed for given charge of Powder.
		3rd Passage.	4th Passage.	5th Passage.	6th Passage.	7th Passage.	8th Passage.	
1	0·5	330·02	330·29	330·15	330·21	330·11	330·13	330·152
2	1·0	330·36	330·59	330·57	330·61	330·44	330·42	330·498
3	1·5	330·29	330·57	330·54	330·60	330·47	330·53	330·433
4	2	330·60	330·51	330·84	330·39	330·44	330·30	330·513
5	1	330·04	330·26	330·26	330·23	330·15	330·22	330·193
6	1	330·36	330·37	330·50	330·67	330·55	330·50	330·492
Mean Speed for each Passage.		330·278	330·428	330·477	330·452	330·360	330·350	

From these data Rink deduced as the velocity of sound in a pipe 1·1 m. diameter the value 330·5 m./sec.

Le Roux, by methods similar to Regnault's, but for a tube 7 cm. diameter, found for the velocity of sound the value 330·66 m./sec

486. In other experiments as to the velocity of sound at different pressures, Regnault failed to detect any difference, though he used pressures varying from 247 mm. to 1267 mm., *i.e.* the pressure was increased to fivefold its original value.

He also used in the laboratory pipes containing different gases. He thus determined values of the velocity of sound for hydrogen and carbon dioxide with a tube 500 metres long, and for NO and ammonia with a tube 70 metres long. From the theoretical expression $v = \sqrt{\gamma p / \rho}$, the ρ being known and v determined, the value of γ, the ratio of the specific beats, is calculable. The results are shown in Table XLIX., in which the symbols with accents refer to the special gases and without accents to air.

TABLE XLIX.—REGNAULT'S EXPERIMENTS ON VARIOUS GASES

Gases.	$v'/v.$	$\sqrt{\rho/\rho'}.$	Ratio of Specific Heats.
Air	1	1	1·395
H_2	3·801	3·799	1·396
CO_2	0·8009	0·8087	1·368
NO	0·8007	0·8100	1·361
NH_3	1·2279	1·3025	1·239

487. Violle and Vautier, with a tube 70 cm. diameter and an improved form of Regnault's apparatus, showed in 1888 that the velocity of sound may be expressed by

$$v' = v(1 - c\sqrt{p}),$$

where p is the mean variation from the normal pressure in a wave, and c is a constant. They give 331·1 m./sec. as applicable to free air.

488. *Speed and Pitch.*—In 1905 the same physicists made experiments to test if the speed of propagation varied with pitch. " Musical notes were transmitted along a tube 3 m. in diam. and 2922 m. long, extending in a straight line from Argenteuil to Cormeilles, and closed at both ends by diaphragms which reflected them. On transmitting musical notes of different pitches along the tube, the authors found that the distance over which they are audible varies inversely as the square root of the pitch, a result which is in accordance with Rayleigh's theory. Notes produced by different musical instruments retain their rhythm, pitch, and quality unchanged. Within the whole range comprised between ut_1 and mi_4, the speed of propagation does not alter by 0·1 per cent." [1]

489. Velocity of Sound by Indirect or Relative Methods. — The methods now to be noticed for the

[1] *Science Abstracts*, 1905, p. 464 ; also *Comptes Rendus*, pp. 1292-1298, May 1905.

determination of the velocity of sound require the knowledge of either (1) the velocity of sound in some other
medium, or (2) the pitch of the source. They are
accordingly styled relative or indirect methods. Whereas
those already dealt with were direct methods on a large
scale, and involved only the measurement of a given length
and the time occupied by sound in traversing it, the
quotient thus furnishing the velocity sought.

490. Velocity of Sound in Iron.—A determination of
the velocity of sound in cast-iron was made by Biot. He
used 376 pipes, forming a total length of 951·25 metres.
A bell was mounted at one end and struck with a hammer.
The sound of the bell then travelled through the iron walls
of the pipes as well as through the air contained in them.
At the far end the separate arrivals of the sounds thus
propagated from the same source were distinctly audible.
From the time t elapsing between these sounds, the length
l of the pipes and the known speed v in air, the speed v'
in the iron may be found. Thus, we have

$$l\left(\frac{1}{v} - \frac{1}{v'}\right) = t \text{ or } v' = \frac{lv}{l - vt}.$$

The value found for the speed of sound in cast-iron was
approximately 3500 metres per second.

491. Dulong's Experiments with Organ Pipes.—In
1829 Dulong published the account of his researches on
the velocity of sound in air and other gases, organ pipes
being used in the determination. It is evident from the
theory given in Chapter V., art. 180, that if the pitch
and length of an organ pipe are known, the velocity of
sound in the gas used can be found provided the end
corrections are either known or can be eliminated. Indeed,
this method was suggested by D. Bernoulli so far back as
1762, but at that time it had not been discovered how to
deal satisfactorily with the ends. However, Dulong, to
eliminate the end corrections, used the following ingenious

device:—He found first the length of a very narrow tube which, with sufficient wind pressure, uttered a high overtone. He then obtained the same overtone with a shorter length of pipe, the alteration of length being the smallest possible to again yield a tone of the same pitch. The adjustments were made by a piston which closed the end remote from the mouth. This piston was carried on a graduated rod or shank, and might therefore be moved and set at will. If the two lengths mentioned were L and L' we obviously have

$$L + c + c' = \frac{\lambda}{4} + n\frac{\lambda}{2}$$

and

$$L' + c + c' = \frac{\lambda}{4} + (n-1)\frac{\lambda}{2},$$

where n is an integer, c and c' are the corrections for the two ends, one being applied to the closed end even lest it should not be perfectly tight and rigid.

Thus $L - L' = \lambda/2$, but by theory $v = N\lambda$, where N is the frequency. Hence we have

$$v = 2N(L - L'),$$

from which v is calculable if N is known. This was found by a siren set to unison with the tone of the pipe.

492. To operate with other gases, Dulong mounted the pipes horizontally in a wooden chest lined with lead. The graduated rod carrying the piston now passed through an air-tight opening in the side of the box, and so was capable of motion and adjustment as before. The pipe was in communication with a reservoir containing the gas to be examined. From this the pipe was blown and made to speak its tones, the gas then filled the chest, and all behaved almost as simply as in air. The values of v for air and other gases being determined, Dulong also calculated from them the corresponding values of γ, the ratio of the two specific heats ; indeed from the title of his memoir it appears that this was the chief end of his researches. His results are given in Table L.

TABLE L.—DULONG'S VALUES OF v AND γ FOR GASES AT $0°$ C.

Gas.	Velocity of Sound, v.	Ratio of Specific Heats, γ.
	Metres per second.	
Air . .	333·00	1·421
Oxygen . .	317·17	1·415
Hydrogen .	1269·50	1·407
CO_2 . .	261·60	1·338
CO . .	337·40	1·427
NO . .	261·90	1·343
C_2H_4 . .	314·00	1·240

But Dulong appeared to think that the absolute velocity of sound in the free air could not with certainty be ascertained from experiments on organ pipes. His results at different temperatures did not support the experimental value of the coefficient of expansion.

493. EXPT. 79. *Detection of Impurities in Gases by an Acoustic Method.*—For this test use two organ pipes of exactly the same pitch, and blow one with the gas in question in a state of known purity, and the other with the gas under test. If the second stock of gas is rendered impure by admixture with another gas of much different density, then, even though the γ's are the same for each, its presence to the extent of a few parts per cent will be sufficient to change the pitch by a comma, which would give distinct beats on sounding the two pipes simultaneously.

494. Wertheim's Researches with Organ Pipes.—In 1844 Wertheim published an account of his experiments with pipes which gave results in almost exact accord with theory. These results are shown in Table LI.

TABLE LI.

WERTHEIM'S VALUES FOR VELOCITY OF SOUND IN AIR

Temperature ° C.	Velocity observed in Metres per Second.	Derived Velocity at 0° C in Metres per Second.	Pipe used.	Mean Velocity at 0° C.
0·5	331·98	331·70		
2·0	332·74	331·53		
4·5	332·75	330·04		
8·0	335·43	330·62	Brass Pipe	332·10
8·5	338·05	332·91	40 mm.	m./sec.
9·0	338·01	332·54	diameter	
12·0	339·46	332·23		
12·3	343·01	335·53		
16·0	338·68	329·17		
26·6	247·82	332·01		
9·9	338·85	332·87	Brass Pipe	330·11
16·0	337·20	327·35	20 mm. diam.	
21·0	341·15	329·12	Brass Pipe 10 mm. diam.	329·12
9·3	334·65	329·09	Glass Pipe	330·23
11·5	336·50	329·61	20 mm.	
17·0	342·3	332·11	diam.	

The Mean of all these experiments was 331·33 m./sec.

One sees from this table that the velocities show a distinct diminution with diameter of pipe, whereas the two pipes of different materials but same diameter give about the same value of the velocity.

495. Velocities in Liquids by Organ Pipes.—In 1847 Wertheim published the account of his experiments on the velocity of sound in liquids, again made by the method of organ pipes. The primary difficulty in applying this method to liquids is that of causing the pipes to speak. The pipes provided with suitable mouth-pieces were immersed horizontally in the liquid, and were injected with a stream of the same liquid. The sounds thus obtained had the same character and yielded the same harmonics as in the air. But the sounds were accompanied by noises produced by the liquid striking against the lips of the mouth-piece. This circumstance, however, had no influence on the measures taken. By this method Wertheim found the value 1173 metres per second for the velocity of sound in the pipes when filled with water. Now this is much below the values found for the velocity of sound in water when in large bulk. Wertheim interpreted this result by supposing that the water in the pipe, during the longitudinal vibrations of his experiments, behaved like a solid rod. Or, in other words, he believed that such an isolated cylinder of liquid increased its cross section on the passage of a condensation, and contracted transversely in the presence of a dilatation. If, therefore, this were correct, there would be for water, as for a solid, one value for the velocity of sound through a cylinder, and another of higher value for the velocity of sound through the same substance in unlimited bulk (see Chap. IV. art. 129). The value already given as found from the pipes is then on this hypothesis the value for an isolated cylinder. For the velocity of sound in water in a practically unlimited mass Wertheim wrote

$$v = 1173 \sqrt{3/2} = 1437 \text{ m./sec.,}$$

which agrees practically with the experiments of Colladon and Sturm.

496. Thus the velocity of sound in liquids may be found (1) directly by large scale observations, (2) theoretically as the square root of (elasticity ÷ density), or (3) according to Wertheim, from experiments on organ pipes, a factor being then introduced to transform from velocity in a cylinder to velocity in bulk. Further, the theoretical method, where the elasticity is known, may be compared with Wertheim's organ pipe method. Or, what amounts to the same thing, the velocity being found by Wertheim's method, the elasticity may be deduced and compared with that found by direct experiment. If the results are concordant, our confidence in Wertheim's hypothesis is naturally strengthened. Following this plan, Wertheim made the determinations and comparisons set forth in Table LII., which show a very satisfactory agreement, considering the many difficulties of the work.

497. It may be noted the factor which in the case of solids transforms the square of velocity in a thin rod to that in the same substance in bulk is $(1 - \sigma)/(1 + \sigma)(1 - 2\sigma)$, and if this quantity has the value $3/2$, then σ, Poisson's ratio, has the value $1/3$ or $-1/2$. Thus, rejecting the negative value as inadmissible, we have n, the rigidity, $= \frac{3}{8}k$, where k is the volume elasticity. Hence, if Wertheim's factor $3/2$ is to be interpreted thus, it would be equivalent to attributing a certain rigidity or quasi-rigidity to a liquid when the vibrations are rapid.

TABLE LII.—WERTHEIM'S VELOCITIES OF SOUND IN LIQUIDS

Liquid.	Temperature in ° C.	Velocity of Sound in Metres per Second.	Volume Compressibility.	
			Inferred from Velocity of Sound.	Determined from the direct experiments by Grassi.
Seine Water . .	15°	1437·0	0·0000491	
Sea Water . .	20°	1453·0	0·0000467	0·0000436
Common Salt Solution . . .	18°	1561·0	0·0000349	0·0000321
Sodium Sulphate Solution . .	20°	1525·0	0·0000393	
Sodium Carbonate Solution . .	22°·2	1594·0	0·0000337	0·0000297
Sodium Nitrate Solution . .	20°·9	1669·0	0·0000301	0·0000295
Alcohol (common).	20°·0	1285·9	0·0000733	
Absolute Alcohol .	23°·0	1159·8	0·0000947	0·0000991
Ether . . .	0°·0	1159·0	0·0001002	0·0001110

498. Tyndal seemed convinced of the truth of Wertheim's hypothesis by the agreements shown in

2 M

Table LII. But in spite of this agreement or coincidence Helmholtz has shown (1848) that Wertheim's interpretation of his experiments cannot be correct. The distinction between the speeds of sound in a solid of unlimited bulk and in a rod lies in the fact that in the rod the cross section can alter. But in the case of a liquid in a pipe this cannot occur freely. And if it occurs at all, and so reduces the velocity, it must occur in a manner similar to that in an organ pipe with weak walls. Hence a reduction of speed so caused would depend upon the diameter of the tube, the thickness of its walls, and the elasticity of their material. This view of the matter, taken by Helmholtz, was afterwards confirmed experimentally by Kundt and others as we shall see presently.

499. Kundt's Tube and Dust Figures.—We have already described this method of experimenting in the chapter on resonance and response (art. 285). It now remains to notice, *first*, the results thus obtained by Kundt in 1868 ; and, *second*, to point out how the method may be used by students for laboratory determinations.

The methods for the velocity of sound used by Dulong and by Wertheim, and just described, depended upon the measurement of the wave length of a sound of ascertained frequency. It is to this measurement of a wave length that Kundt's method is directed. The earlier experiments were made with the single form of the apparatus, something like that described in Chapter VI. But, in Kundt's original form, the clamp for the middle of the smaller sounding tube (or rod) was a *cork*, which also formed a stopper in one end of the larger or wave tube. For the purpose of experimenting upon different gases some stopper was essential, but this stiff connection with the sounding tube seemed to interfere with the proper working of the apparatus, and an irregularity of the dust figures followed. Kundt, therefore, substituted for the cork layers of india-rubber tied round with silk. And, to obviate any errors through possible change of pitch of the sounding tube, he further adopted a double form of the apparatus, in which two wave tubes were simultaneously used, and the sounding tube or rod was clamped at two points each a quarter of its length from an end. These two nodal points formed the connections of the sounding tube with the two wave tubes. The sounding tube or rod was then excited by rubbing near the middle. This obviously evoked a tone whose wave length was the length of the rod. This double apparatus is shown in outline in Figure 96.

Another advantage of the double form of the apparatus is the elimination of temperature corrections which it automatically secures.

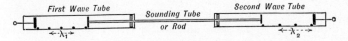

FIG. 96.—KUNDT'S DOUBLE APPARATUS FOR DUST FIGURES.

500. Kundt found that the velocity of sound in tubes depended not only upon the diameter of the tube, but also upon the frequency of the tone employed. The comparison in these two respects is shown in the values obtained by him, and set forth in Table LIII.

TABLE LIII.

RELATIVE VELOCITIES OF SOUNDS BY KUNDT'S TUBES

Diameters of Tubes.	Wave Lengths of Sounds used.		
	18 cm.	9 cm.	6 cm.
5·5 cm.	1·01010	1·00885	1·00584
2·6 cm.	1·00908	1·00842	1·00781
1·3 cm.	1·00000	1·00000	1·00000
0·65 cm.	0·98031	0·99170	0·99176
0·35 cm.	0·92628	0·96666	

501. Kundt could not detect any influence of intensity upon the velocity. He found, however, that the powder in a narrow tube, and especially if too much were present, decreased the velocity slightly. It was practically without effect in a large tube. Also a roughening of the interior of the tube was found to diminish the velocity. Indeed, Kundt considered that all the observed changes of velocity were due to friction and exchange of heat between the gas and the sides of the tube. It is obvious that when the gas is compressed, and in consequence warmed, any conduction of heat to the walls of the tube will diminish its temperature, and therefore diminish also the elasticity and velocity. Again, in the rarefied parts of the gas there is cooling. But here also conduction of heat, although this time from the walls of the tube, will, as before, produce a diminution of elasticity and velocity. Now, the quantity of the gas present varies as the square of the diameter of the tube, whereas the surface of wall presented for heat conduction varies only as the first power of the diameter. Hence the diminution of velocity from this cause must be greater with a smaller tube.

502. Ratio of Specific Heats by Kundt's Tubes.— Using the double form of wave tube apparatus, Kundt and Warburg (1876) determined the ratio of the specific heats of mercury vapour. The two wave tubes contained air and mercury vapour respectively, the latter being at a high temperature. Quartz sand was used to exhibit the dust figures, from which the wave length and velocity v for mercury vapour were found. But theoretical considerations give for the velocity $v = \sqrt{\gamma p/\rho}$ (see art. 121). The temperature and the molecular weight of mercury give the value of p/ρ for the vapour, and thus γ, the ratio of the specific heats, was calculated. Its value was determined to be 1·66.

Soon after the discovery of argon, the ratio of its two specific heats was determined by Lord Rayleigh using the method just described. The values 1·65 and 1·61 were found.[1]

503. Kundt's Tube for Liquids.—Using the tube method, Kundt and Lehmann succeeded in obtaining dust figures in liquids as in gases, after taking care that the liquids were absolutely free from air. As powder to form the figures, very fine iron filings were used. The results obtained agreed exactly with the criticism by Helmholtz on the hypothesis put forward by Wertheim, as to the latter's experiments on liquids in organ pipes (see arts. 495-498). In other words, as Helmholtz predicted, the speed of sound increased if the diameter of the liquid column decreased, and the strength of the walls of the glass tube used in the experiments increased. This is shown in Table LIV.

TABLE LIV.

SPEEDS OF SOUND IN WATER BY KUNDT'S TUBE

Diameter of Tube in mm.	Thickness of Wall in mm.	Temperature.	Speeds of Sound m./sec.
28·7	2·2	18·4	1040·4
34·0	3·0	17·0	1227·7
23·5	3·0	18·0	1262·2
21·0	3·5	18·5	1357·6
16·5	5·0	18·5	1360·2
14·0	5·0	22·2	1383·2

504. EXPT. 80. *Velocities of Sound in Solids by Kundt's Tube.*
—To determine in the laboratory the velocity of sound in a rod of metal or wood the single form of Kundt's tube will suffice. The description of this and the manner of using it are given in art. 285. A thermometer is needed to observe the temperature of the air in the wave tube. From this the speed of sound in the air may be calculated from the expression

$$v = v_0 \sqrt{1 + at} \qquad (1),$$

where v_0 may be taken as 331 m./sec., a the coefficient of

---

[1] See *Nature*, 7th February 1895.

expansion as $0\cdot003665$ per 1° C., and t is the observed temperature in degrees centigrade. Let the distances between the nodes as shown by the dust heaps or figures be l, and the length of the rod be l'. Then $l = \lambda/2$ and $l' = \lambda'/2$, where λ and λ' are the respective wave lengths in air and in the rod of the sound of frequency N say given by the longitudinal vibrations of the rod.

Hence for the speed v' of sound in the rod, we have

$$v' = N\lambda' = N2l' \qquad (2).$$

And for the speed of sound in the air, we have similarly

$$v = N\lambda = N2l \qquad (3).$$

Thus, on division, we obtain

$$v'/v = l'/l, \text{ or } v' = l'v/l \qquad (4).$$

And by (1) this may be written

$$v' = \frac{l'}{l} v_0 \sqrt{1 + at} \qquad (5),$$

which gives the speed sought in terms of the observed quantities and the constant v_0.

505. EXPT. 81. *Young's Modulus for a Solid by Kundt's Tube.*—The manipulation for this determination is just as in the foregoing experiment, except that we need, in addition, the density of the solid rod. For this purpose weighing and measuring will be most convenient if the rod is of wood. If it is of any well-known standard metal its density may be taken from tables of such constants. Thus, for cast-iron, wrought-iron, steel, or brass, the densities may be taken as $7\cdot25$, $7\cdot8$, 8, and 8 gm./cc. respectively.

We then use the ordinary approximate expression for v' (as proved in art. 123),

$$v' = \sqrt{q/\rho} \qquad (6),$$

where q is Young's modulus and ρ is the density of the rod. Thus v' and ρ being known, q is calculable.

506. EXPT. 82. *Speed of Sound and Ratio of Specific Heats in Gases by Kundt's Tube.*—For this determination the double form of apparatus described in article 499 is desirable. Then using air in one tube and the other gas in the other, and denoting by v and v' the respective speeds of sound in them, and by l and l' the observed nodal distances, we have

$$v'/v = l'/l, \text{ or } v' = \frac{l'}{l} v_0 \sqrt{1 + at} \qquad (1).$$

But, by theoretical considerations, we have

$$v' = \sqrt{\gamma p / \rho} \qquad (2).$$

Hence, the pressure and density of the gas being known, and v' determined from (1), γ is calculable from (2). This application of the method has already been referred to as used for mercury vapour and for argon.

507. Expt. 83. *Velocity of Sound in Liquids by Kundt's Dust Figures.*—For this purpose a modified form of Kundt's tube used by Dvořák is desirable, as it obviates the necessity for making sure that the liquid is absolutely air-free. Dvořák used a horizontal tube about 2 m. long, one end being turned up a little and closed, the other being turned up about 10 cm. and left open. The tube was then filled with water, except that at the closed end a large air bubble was left, the open end containing only water. This end is now to be blown as an organ pipe by blowing smartly across the pipe. The liquid is thus set in vibration, the nodal positions being conveniently shown by gunpowder free from saltpetre. By this method Dvořák obtained for water the results shown in Table LV., which are in good agreement with those due to Kundt and Lehmann and previously quoted.

TABLE LV.—SPEED OF SOUND IN WATER BY DVOŘÁK

Diameter of Tube.	Thickness of Wall.	Speed.
mm.	mm.	m./sec.
17·9	0·82	998
11·7	0·63	1046
8·46	0·52	1164
15	2	1213
11	2	1281

508. Calculation of the Mechanical Equivalent of Heat.—It is noteworthy that the value of the mechanical equivalent of heat may be obtained from acoustical determinations and theoretical relations. Thus, let the characteristic equation of a gas be written

$$PV = RT \qquad (1),$$

where P, V, and T denote respectively the pressure, volume, and absolute temperature of the gas.

Then
$$R = P_s \, a/\rho_0 \qquad (2),$$

in which P_s is the standard pressure, a the coefficient of expansion, and ρ_0 the density at 0° C. and standard pressure. Thus, the value of R in (1) is given by (2) and a knowledge of the tabular density.

But the theory of thermodynamics furnishes the relation

$$C_p - C_v = R/J \qquad (3),$$

where C_p and C_v are the specific heats in heat units at constant pressure and constant volume respectively, and J is the mechanical equivalent of heat.

Now, suppose that by any method the velocity v of sound has been determined. Then, from its theoretical expression

$$v = \sqrt{\gamma P/\rho} \qquad (4),$$

knowing P and ρ, we can calculate γ and use the relation

$$C_p/C_v = \gamma \qquad (5).$$

Hence, if C_p is known by Regnault's method of determination, C_v may be calculated, and on substitution in equation (3) J is thence determined.

If, on the other hand, neither specific heat for a certain gas is known, but only their ratio, then on assuming the value of J, equations (3) and (5) serve to determine both C_p and C_v.

509. Hebb's Telephone Method for Speed of Sound in Air.—At the suggestion of Michelson, T. C. Hebb in 1904 made an elaborate determination of the velocity of sound by means of telephones and parabolic reflectors. All methods involving the use of a tube were rejected on account of its attendant complications. Further, to all long-distance methods the following objections were made :—

(1) Very intense sounds must be used, thus involving a possible difference of speed near the source.

(2) It is almost impossible to correct accurately for wind, temperature, and humidity over such long ranges.

(3) The " personal equation " of an observer or of some recording device is involved.

510. The attempt was accordingly made to free the research from all these objections. The experiments were conducted in a room 120 feet long. The source of sound was a whistle blown so steadily as to maintain its frequency to 1 in 5000. It was placed at the focus of a parabolic mirror made of plaster of Paris, 5 feet in aperture and 15 inches in focal length. From this first mirror plane sound waves proceeded along the length of the room. These were received by a second precisely similar mirror and so converged to its focus. Near the whistle was a telephone transmitter connected to a battery and *one of two primaries* of a special induction coil. At the focus of the second mirror was placed a second similar telephone transmitter, also connected to a battery and the *other primary* of the special induction coil. Finally, to the secondary of this induction coil was connected a telephone receiver. When the whistle was sounding, the two transmitters were set in vibration with a definite phase relation depending on the distance between the mirrors. Further, the telephone receiver gave the resultant or vector sum of these two effects. Hence, by changing the distance between the mirrors the phase relation of these two effects was changed, and they accordingly gave alternate maxima and minima at the receiver. To make the minima as sharp as possible, the effects from the two telephone transmitters were adjusted to equality by resistances in their respective circuits. Thus, on obtaining the successive minima, the wave length of the sound issuing from the whistle was determined, and its pitch being found the velocity of sound easily followed.

511. In some of the experiments, instead of the whistle tone, waves of about 10 inches long were used from an e''' fork (1280 per second). Distances up to a hundred wave lengths were taken, and the minima could be located to an inch or one-tenth of a wave. Thus an accuracy of one in a thousand was reached, and this order of accuracy was aimed at throughout the experiment. The temperature was taken by six thermometers distributed along the space involved, and there was no disturbance from wind. It was feared that some little diffraction effect occurred with the ten-inch waves, so waves of six inches long were afterwards used. From these, which were considered quite satisfactory, the final value obtained for the velocity of sound in dry air at $0°$ C. was $331·29$ metres per second with a probable error of $0·04$.

The determination of the pitch of the whistle was made by tuning it to unison with a fork which was itself compared with a 512 fork by traces on a smoked glass disc. The 512 fork was then compared in the same way with a pendulum, and, finally, the pendulum with a clock.

512. Wertheim's Determination of Speeds of Sound in Solids.—By exciting longitudinal vibrations in a rod of measured length L, clamped in the middle, and observing the frequency N of its tone, we have for the speed of sound in it

$$v = N \lambda = N2L.$$

Using this method, Wertheim determined the speeds of sound for the whole series of metals. And the comparison of the values thus experimentally obtained with those theoretically calculated showed a good agreement. The results in question are given in Table LVI.

TABLE LVI.—WERTHEIM'S SPEEDS OF SOUND IN METALS

Metal.	Relative Speeds of Sound, that in Air being Unity.	
	Experimentally determined.	Theoretically calculated.
Lead (drawn) . .	4·257	3·787
Gold ,, . .	6·424	6·247
Silver ,, . .	8·057	7·940
Zinc ,, . .	11·007	10·524
Copper ,, . .	11·167	11·128
Platinum Wire . .	8·467	8·437
Iron (drawn) . .	15·108	15·472
Cast-Steel (drawn) . .	15·108	15·003
Steel Wire ,, . .	14·961	14·716

513. Velocity of Sound in Wax, etc.—The velocities of sound in wax and other soft solids which cannot be excited by stroking were determined by Stefan as follows. A rod of another material whose longitudinal vibrations could be excited was used to originate the tone, and to one end of this was fixed a piece of the softer material under examination. From the data thus afforded the velocity of sound in the soft body was determined by a somewhat complicated calculation.

In wax at 17°, Stefan found the speed of sound to be 880 m./sec. with a decrease of 40 m./sec. per 1° C. rise of temperature.

514. Warburg for the same determination used two rods, one of the soft substance under examination, and the other, say of glass or other ordinary solid. These were mounted so as to be capable of *transverse* vibrations, and an antinode of the hard rod was linked to an antinode of the soft one by a light wood connector fastened with wax. The nodal lines on each rod were shown by sand, and the distances between them measured. Then, if these similar nodal distances were l and l' in the hard and soft rods respectively, and their thicknesses h and h' in the plane of vibration, we have from theory (see art. 205) for the ratio of the velocities of sound in the two rods,

$$\frac{v'}{v} = \frac{l'^2 h}{l^2 h'}$$

To test this method Warburg first compared the velocities of sound in brass and glass. He found for the ratio the values 0·676 and 0·645, giving a mean of 0·660, whereas by Kundt's method he made the same ratio to be 0·668, which agrees with the other value within about one per cent. Warburg's results for the other bodies tested by this method are shown in Table LVII., which applies to temperatures from 15° to 17° C. Taking the velocity of sound in air at 16° C. as 340 m./sec., and that in glass as 15·65 times this, we have from Warburg's determination the velocity of sound in wax as 883 m./sec., which agrees well with Stefan's result.

TABLE LVII.

WARBURG'S SPEEDS OF SOUND IN SOFT BODIES

Material.	Speed relative to that in Glass as Unity.	Density.	Young's Modulus relative to that of Glass as Unity.
Glass . .	1	2·390	1
Stearine . . .	0·265	0·974	1/35
Paraffin . . .	0·251	0·908	1/42
Wax . . .	0·166	0·971	1/88
Tallow . . .	0·075	0·917	1/461

515. EXPT. 84. *Velocity of Sound in Wires.*—The method described by Tyndall for determining the velocity of sound in a wire is effective as a lecture illustration, and forms also a useful laboratory experiment where sufficient length is available. The wires under examination are fixed in any convenient manner at one end, the other end being attached perpendicularly near the centre of a wooden tray or board. When a rosined leather is passed gently along the middle of the wire it excites its fundamental longitudinal vibrations.

These move the sounding-board perpendicularly to its own plane, and thus produce powerful sound waves in the air. As we have seen before (art. 169), the relation between the frequency and the other constants is expressed by

$$N = \frac{v}{\lambda} = \frac{\sqrt{q/\rho}}{2L} \qquad (1),$$

where N is the frequency, λ the wave length, and v the speed of sound along the substance of the wire whose length is L, Young's modulus q, and density ρ. Thus, if N is known by comparison with a fork or siren, and L measured, v may be determined. Further, if ρ is known or determined, the Young's modulus q may be calculated. Or, if another wire of different material be used also for the sake of comparison, we may write for it

$$N' = \frac{v'}{\lambda'} = \frac{\sqrt{q'/\rho'}}{2L'} \qquad (2).$$

Hence for a comparison of the velocities of sound in the two wires we may vary the length of one until the N's are the same. In this case we obviously have

$$v'/v = L'/L \qquad (3),$$

from which the required ratio is at once obtained when the adjustment of lengths for unison has been effected. Further, writing (3) in the form

$$\sqrt{q'/\rho'} / \sqrt{q/\rho} = L'/L \qquad (4),$$

we see that the Young's modulus q' of the second wire may be obtained if that of the other and both densities are known.

The sounding-board may be screwed along its middle line to the edge of a firm counter or table, or a window-board. The wire should be attached near, but not quite at this middle line. It should be noted, also, that to shorten the wire it is not sufficient to place a bridge under it as in the case of strings vibrating transversely. The shortening may be arranged by clipping the wire with a heavy pair of thumb vice firmly attached to a large mass (say 56 lb.). In order to avoid unpleasantly high notes, it is also desirable to make the wires from 10 to 30 ft. long. Further, when experimenting with the wires there should be just sufficient longitudinal tension on them to take out any slight kinks and permit the rosined cloth rubber to pass smoothly along.

516. Further Researches on Sounds in Pipes.—We have already dealt with direct and indirect methods for finding the velocity of sound in pipes, but many other researches have been made in the endeavour to obtain a full insight into the phenomena concerned. The problem was theoretically attacked by both Helmholtz and Kirchhoff. The former took into consideration the friction alone, while the latter considered also the exchange of heat between the pipe walls and the contained gas. For the speed of sound in pipes both obtained like expressions, the difference between them consisting only in the significance to be attached to one of the constants. Thus both forms may be represented by

$$v' = v \left(1 - \frac{c}{2r\sqrt{\pi N}} \right) \qquad (1),$$

in which, according to Helmholtz, the constant c is the viscosity of the gas, while according to Kirchhoff it depends upon the heat conduction between the gas and the wall of the pipe. In either case v' is the speed of sounds of frequency N in a pipe of radius r, v being the speed in the open. Thus according to either physicist we have

$$(v - v') \propto \frac{1}{r\sqrt{N}} \qquad (2).$$

517. Since neither the researches of Regnault nor those of Kundt were extensive enough to test this relation, both Schneebeli and Seebeck undertook new experiments with this object. Both experimenters, like Kundt, set up stationary waves in the air of a tube closed at one end, but unlike Kundt, they determined *directly by the ear* the distances of the successive antinodes from the closed end. In the form of apparatus adopted by Seebeck the closed end of the tube was a movable position, which was shifted along a graduated bar so as to bring the antinodes one by one to a fixed point in the pipe. From this point a branch side pipe started which was connected to one ear by an india-rubber tube, the other ear being meanwhile closed. When the antinode is formed at the commencement of the branch pipe we have maximum changes of place, but minimum changes of pressure there, consequently no sound passes along the tube to the ear. Hence the adjustment in question is attested by the absence of sound. By this method Seebeck found that with wave lengths of 200 to 300 mm., the deviations from the mean were usually scarcely 1 mm.

518. Taking $v = 332 \cdot 77$, Seebeck found for the decrease of speed $(v - v')$ due to pipes the value shown in Table LVIII. In this table the calculated values are on the supposition that the Helmholtz and Kirchhoff law holds, the constant being chosen so as to give the speed experimentally found for the narrowest pipe.

TABLE LVIII.—SEEBECK'S RESEARCHES ON PIPES

Diameter of Pipe in Milli- metres.	c'', N=512 per sec. $(v - v')$.		g', N=384 per sec. $(v - v')$.		e', N=320 per sec. $(v - v')$.	
	Observed.	Calculated.	Observed.	Calculated.	Observed.	Calculated.
3·4	9·79	9·79	13·91	13·91	15·51	15·51
9·0	4·33	3·70	5·09	5·25	4·75	5·06
17·5	1·85	1·90	2·91	2·70	3·53	3·01

If we take the observations with the same tone in the various pipes and combine them, a value of the velocity v of sound in free air may be derived. Thus from equation (1) we may write for the same tone in two different pipes

$$v_1 = v\left(1 - \frac{c}{2r_1 \sqrt{\pi N}}\right) \text{ and } v_2 = v\left(1 - \frac{c}{2r_2 \sqrt{\pi N}}\right),$$

where v_1 denotes the speed of sound for the frequency N in the pipe of radius r_1, and v_2 the corresponding speed in pipe of radius r_2. Whence, on eliminating between these two equations the constant $c/2\sqrt{\pi N}$, we obtain

$$v = \frac{v_1 r_1 - v_2 r_2}{r_1 - r_2} \qquad (3).$$

519. Schneebeli combined in pairs in this way all his experimental results with pipes of diameters from 14 to 90 mm. and found the mean value

$$v = 332{\cdot}06 \text{ m./sec.}$$

But although the experiments supported the theoretical expressions of Helmholtz and Kirchhoff as to the variation of speed with *diameter* of pipe, both these experimenters found results in disagreement with the theoretical expression as to the dependence of the speed on *pitch* of the note. Thus, according to theory, the change in speed should be inversely proportional to the square root of the frequency, while according to the experiments of Seebeck the decrease of speed is inversely proportional to the square root of the *cube* of the frequency. Indeed, if in the table of his results (Table LVIII.) we multiply each value of $v - v'$ for a given diameter of pipe by $N^{3/2}$, the products for each line are approximately constant. But, from direct observations, the values of $v - v'$ for a given diameter of pipe seemed to vary inversely as the frequency itself. Hence from Seebeck's researches no definite conclusion could be drawn upon this point.

520. After this Kaiser used the method of dust figures to subject the Helmholtz-Kirchhoff theory to a further test. He experimented with three tones of 2357, 3895, and 5232 vibrations per second, in five tubes whose diameters were 25·8, 33·3, 44, 51·7, and 82 mm. From his experiments he concluded that the dependence of the velocity change both on the diameter of the pipe and the frequency of the tone agreed with the theory, provided that to the constant c of equation (1), instead of the theoretical value 0.00588 a value of about four times that, namely 0.0235, be assigned. The value for the speed of sound in free air derived by Kaiser from his experiments is 332.5 m./sec.

521. Wüllner's Experiments on Various Gases and at Different Temperatures.—Although the indirect methods above described have not cleared up the problems of pipes, and although it may be doubted whether they can afford a value of the speed so trustworthy as those carried on in the open air, still they certainly offer special advantages for dealing with different gases and at various temperatures. For different gases Dulong used organ pipes, as we have already seen. And, changing both gases and temperature, Wüllner used the method of dust figures. The wave tube used had a diameter of about 30 mm. The sounding tube was of glass one metre long and gave a tone of 2539 vibrations per second. This sounding tube was clasped at its middle by a rubber bung which fitted air-tight into one end of the wave tube. The other end of the wave tube was also closed air-tight by an adjustable stopper which was set so that between it and the fixed bung an exact number of half-wave lengths extended. Both stoppers were fitted with glass cocks so that the wave tube could be exhausted and filled again with any desired gas. The middle part of the wave tube for a length of about 1.1 metre was immersed in melting ice or in steam.

522. According to the Helmholtz-Kirchhoff theories, the decrease in the speed of sound due to enclosing the gas in a pipe is not independent of the nature of the gas. Yet for the diameter of tube and pitch of tone chosen by Wüllner, the correction on this account was so insignificant as to be usually negligible.

For air at $0°$ C., Wüllner found as the mean of six experiments,

$$v_0 = 331.898 \text{ m./sec.}$$

Now the theoretical expression for the speed of sound may be written $v = \sqrt{\gamma p(1+at)/\rho_0}$. But, if γ the ratio of the specific heats is supposed to change with temperature so that $\gamma = \gamma_0(1+\beta t)$, we may write

$$v = \sqrt{\gamma_0 p(1+\beta t)(1+at)/\rho_0}.$$

Finally, since $(1+\beta t)(1+at) = 1 + a + \beta t$ nearly for moderate ranges of temperature, we obtain the compact expression

$$v = v_0 \sqrt{1+\delta t}, \text{ where } \delta = a + \beta.$$

Wüllner found that δ was usually less than a, so that β seems generally to have a negative value. The results of Wüllner's experiments are shown in Table LIX., which also includes for the sake of comparison some of the determinations of Dulong and Regnault.

TABLE LIX.

WÜLLNER'S EXPERIMENTS ON GASES BY KUNDT'S TUBES

| Gases. | Relative Densities. | Relative Speeds of Sound according to | | | Speed of Sound at 0° C. by Wüllner. | Value of $\delta =$ Sum of Temperature Co-efficients a and β. |
		Dulong.	Regnault.	Wüllner.		
Air . . .	1	1	1	1	331·898	0·003646
Oxygen . .	1·1056	0·9524	...	...	...	...
Hydrogen .	0·06926	3·8123	3·801	...	...	...
Carbonic Oxide	0·9678	1·0132	...	1·0158	337·129	0·003588
Carbon Dioxide	1·5290	0·7856	0·8009	0·7812	259·383	0·003401
Nitrogen Oxide	1·527	0·7865	0·8007	0·7823	259·636	0·003307
Ammonia .	0·5967	...	1·2279	1·2534	415·990	0·003436
Ethylene .	0·9784	...	...	0·9518	315·90	0·003060

523. Blaikley's Experiments with Brass Tubes.—In 1883-4 D. J. Blaikley published[1] an account of his researches on the velocity of sound in air in smooth brass tubes. He felt that in the large scale experiments

[1] *Phil. Mag.*

the results were usually vitiated by uncertainties as to the mean temperature and hygrometric state of the air over the range in question. The Kundt's tube methods were also dismissed by him as being beautifully adapted for comparative results, but less suitable for absolute determinations. Blaikley remarks that in Regnault's experiments with pipes the diminution of velocity there found would, if extended to the diameters used in brass instruments, lead to smaller values than those actually experienced. This discrepancy is attributed to the roughness of Regnault's tubes. Further, it is pointed out that the membrane used by Regnault might introduce an error which would in every case lead to an under-estimation of the velocity. In illustration of this, Blaikley took a cylindrical tube with a membrane of gold-beater's skin at one end against which rests a bead hung by silk. Now, to respond to a vibration of 512 per second, this resonator needed to be 5 inches long only, whereas a pipe with a rigid stopped end must be $6\frac{1}{4}$ inches long to respond to the same note. Again, Dulong's experiments are objected to because in them care was taken to obtain a pipe producing a tone of good musical quality. This, Blaikley asserts, is the worst possible state of things for the purpose in view, and that for the following reasons:—In an organ pipe speaking a good musical tone the usual retinue of overtones is present. These upper partials when elicited separately are slightly inharmonic with the prime. Thus, on blowing the pipe, these naturally inharmonic overtones, on being forced into the strict harmonic series, constrain to some extent the pitch of the prime. The prime tone is in consequence slightly different in pitch from that which without such constraint corresponds to the true velocity of sound and the wave length under observation. Hence for the wave length and constrained pitch a vitiated velocity of sound would be inferred from such a pipe.

524. For these reasons Blaikley chose to experiment

with a special form of organ pipe. This had a bulb or pear-shaped portion introduced in the first quarter wave length near the mouth. Beyond this bulb the pipe continued cylindrical for a considerable distance, and in this part a sliding plug worked. With this plug adjustments could be made corresponding to the one-quarter wave length and three-quarters wave length with an ordinary cylindrical pipe. The bulb caused the natural overtones of the pipe to be quite inharmonic, and consequently they were not elicited by blowing. " By this means a pure tone was obtained. The blast was obtained from a fan, the wind from which passed through a regulating bellows with automatic-valve action, and it was found that great care was necessary on this point. The pressure in the bellows was 2·5 inches of water, and in the speaking mouth in every case very small. The temperature was observed by means of a thermometer entering the tube, so that the actual temperature during vibration might be recorded. The wet-bulb temperature and barometric pressure were also taken for moisture correction. The pitch was taken from a carefully tested Koenig fork of 256 vibrations, and the tubes were set to give a beating rate of about four per second, the lengths being read by a micrometer and standard rods. All the notes were exceedingly feeble, the pressure in the mouth being less than 1/10 inch of water, much under the lowest which Regnault found to influence the velocity."

525. Experiments were made with smooth brass tubes of five sizes, the frequencies of the tones ranging from about 131 to 323 per second. The results for the velocity are shown in Table LX.

[TABLE

TABLE LX.—BLAIKLEY'S SPEEDS OF SOUND FOR DRY AIR
AT 0° C. IN BRASS TUBES

Diams. of Tubes.→	11·43 mm.	19·05 mm.	31·71 mm.	52·91 mm.	88·19 mm.
	m./sec.	m./sec.	m./sec.	m./sec.	m./sec.
	324·533	327·09	328·72	329·90	330·29
	324·234	327·14	328·74	329·84	330·46
	...	326·98	328·78	329·84	330·02
	...	326·70	328·72	329·70	329·72
	...	327·09	328·72	329·95	329·99
	...	326·69	328·89	329·80	330·41
	...	326·99	328·76	329·53	330·09
	...	326·79	328·84	329·56	330·06
	...	326·70	328·84	329·65	330·10
	...	326·85	328·83	329·48	330·20
Mean speeds for each diameter	324·383	326·90	328·78	329·72	330·134

(left-side vertical label: Speeds of Sound from Separate Experiments.)

526. These values show that the diminution of speed is proportional to r^{-1}, and favour the view that it is also proportional to $N^{-\frac{1}{2}}$, r denoting the radius of the tube and N the frequency of the tone sounded in it.

Blaikley then applied to the above mean values of the speed for each sized tube a modification of Helmholtz's formula in order to obtain the speed of sound in free air. Taking these two by two, ten pairs were formed which yielded values ranging from 331·089 to 332·150. Of these the mean value was

$$v_0 = 331·676 \text{ metres per second,}$$

which constitutes Blaikley's final determination for the velocity of sounds of feeble intensity in free air at 0° C. and free from moisture.

Taking the Newtonian velocity of sound as 279·955 m./sec., Blaikley found for the ratio of the two specific heats for air the value

$$\gamma = 1·4036.$$

527. Later Work on Tubes.—In 1903 J. Müller

gave an account of experiments on tubes in which he
examined the equation of Helmholtz and Kirchhoff

$$v' = v\left(1 - \frac{c}{2r\sqrt{\pi N}}\right).$$

His apparatus was like Kayser's, and he concluded: (1) That
the above equation has no general validity, (2) That in a
tube the speed depends on the material, and c is not really
a constant.

F. A. Schulze published researches on the same subject
in 1904, testing again the validity of the formula just
quoted but for very narrow tubes. He used the double-
tube interference apparatus due to Quincke. The tubes
were of glass, brass, and caoutchouc, ranging in diameter
from 0·99 to 1·51 mm. Frequencies of 384 and 512
were employed, and v', the velocity of sound in the tube,
was found to range from 195 m./sec. to 290 m./sec. for
the high frequency. The influence of the nature of the
tube was marked. The so-called constant c in the formula
was found to range from 0·0075 to 0·025, according to the
diameter and nature of the tube.

**528. Speeds of Sound for Hot Gases by Resonance
Tubes.**—In 1898 E. H. Stevens [1] investigated at ordinary
and high temperatures the speeds of sound in air and
various vapours. The source of sound was a tuning-fork
mounted on its resonance-box, whose mouth was opposite
to the open end of a wide tube closed at the far end.
This contained the gas under test, and was termed the
interference tube, since by reflection at the stopped end
stationary waves were established in it. To find the
wave length of these stationary waves a much smaller
listening tube was introduced through the bung of the
interference tube, and connected by an india-rubber pipe
with one of the observer's ears, the other ear being closed.
The listening tube was adjusted so that its end in the

[1] *Ann. d. Physik.*, vii. 2, pp. 285-320, February 1902.

interference tube occupied successively the adjacent positions which gave the minimum sound. The wave length was then ascertained by an external scale. The chief results are given in Table LXI.

TABLE LXI.—STEVEN'S VALUES FOR SOUND

Substance.	Temperature.	Velocity.	Ratio of Specific Heats.
	C.	Metres per sec.	
Dry Air . . .	0°	331·32	1·4006
Dry Air . . .	100°	386·5	1·3993
Dry Air . . .	950°	686·0	1·34 ± 0·01
Ether . . .	99·7	212·6	1·112
Methyl Alcohol .	99·7	350·3	1·256
Ethyl Alcohol .	99·8	272·8	1·134
Carbon Disulphide .	99·7	223·2	1·234
Benzol . . .	99·7	205·0	1·105
Chloroform . .	99·8	171·4	1·150
Acetic Acid . .	136·5	...	1·147
Iodine . . .	185·5	140·0	1·303

The above values for velocity were obtained from experiments on different sized tubes, the effect of their finite diameters being eliminated, and the results professing to give the values for free space.

529. In 1902 this subject was attacked by A. Kalähne [1] but with a slightly different arrangement. The source of sound was now a telephone receiver membrane which was set opposite one end of an open resonance tube provided with a side branch and india-rubber pipe to conduct the sound to the observer's ear. The open tube was adjusted in effective length by sliding within it a disc to form the closed end. This was carried by a rod moving over a scale. As the disc was moved along and set at different places maxima and minima were successively produced at the position occupied by the side tube. Thus the wave length

[1] *Ann. d. Physik*, xi. 2, pp. 225-256, May 1903 ; *Science Abstracts*, p. 528, 1904.

was ascertained. Temperatures up to $900°$ C. were used, at which for dry air Kalähne determined the ratio of the specific heats to be $1·39$, being 6 or 7 per thousand less than its value for $0°$ C. From $0°$ to $450°$ C. no diminution in this ratio could be detected, and to $700°$ C. only a fall of about 4 per thousand.

530. Speeds of Sound at Liquid Air Temperatures.— In 1905 S. R. Cook[1] experimented on air and oxygen at very low temperatures. "The method used was that of the double Kundt tube, one sound tube being at ordinary temperatures, the other in a bath of liquid air contained in a Dewar bulb tube. The temperatures were read electrically by resistance thermometers. In air at $90°·7$ absolute, the speed of sound was found to be $18,152$ cm. per sec., whereas by the formula $u = u_0 \sqrt{1 + at}$ it would be 19,170 m./sec. Oxygen at $88°·4$ abs. showed a velocity of sound of $17,368$ cm. per sec. against the theoretical value of $18,000$ cm. per sec. In air at $90°·7$ abs. the ratio of the specific beats was determined as $1·342$, taking $1·408$ as the value at normal temperature and pressure. The velocities of sound in air and oxygen were also determined for a number of temperatures intermediate between those named and ordinary temperatures."

531. Correction for Open End of Tube Experimentally Determined.— In 1879 Blaikley made a careful experimental determination of the correction for an unflanged open end of a pipe. For this purpose a vertical tube of thin brass $5·3$ cm. diameter was used. The bottom part was immersed in water and thus formed the closed end. The length of the portion out of the water was adjusted till the resonance with a good fork was a maximum. Obviously the two shortest values of this length would be $\dfrac{\lambda}{4} - c$ and $\dfrac{3\lambda}{4} - c$, where c is the correction

---

[1] *Phys. Rev.* xxiii. pp. 212-237, September 1906 ; *Science Abstracts*, p. 623, December 1906.

sought for the open end. Thus, if the above lengths are respectively denoted by l_1 and l_2, we have

$$c = \frac{l_2 - l_1}{2} - l_1.$$

For the same tube resonating to various forks, Blaikley found the results given in Table LXII.

TABLE LXII.

BLAIKLEY'S EXPERIMENTS ON END CORRECTIONS

Pitch of Fork.		End Correction as Fraction of Radius.
Note.	Frequency.	
	Vibrations per sec.	
c'	253·8	0·565
e'	317·46	0·595
g'	380·81	0·564
$b'\flat$	444·72	0·587
c''	507·45	0·568
		Mean Correction 0·576

As previously remarked (see art. 179), this result is in very good agreement with the theoretical results of Helmholtz and Lord Rayleigh.

532. EXPT. 85. *Simple Laboratory Method for Speed of Sound in Air.*—Using the adjustable water resonator described in art. 237, we may easily determine the speed of sound in air if a fork of known frequency is available. Conversely, assuming the velocity of sound in air from the classical determinations, and correcting for temperature, we may ascertain the frequency of a fork. For either determination we may eliminate the end correction if the tube allows the use of resonance at lengths of about $\lambda/4$ and $3\lambda/4$, or failing this we may take for the end correction Blaikley's value, or say 0·6 times the radius of the tube. The fork must be used without a resonance-box, so as to allow the resonance of the pipe to assert itself as strongly as possible.

533. Determinations of Interval and Pitch.—In considering the various methods for determining the velocity of sound, we took first those which are absolute or direct, and, second, those which are comparative or indirect methods involving another velocity or other constant regarded as sufficiently well known. This seemed desirable, as in all cases the absolute value of the velocity in question was really desired, hence the indirect methods seem naturally to take a second place. But, in the case of determinations of frequencies, what we may call the reverse order seems preferable. For the simple ratio of the frequencies of two notes, that is, their interval, is sometimes desired for its own sake without any reference to the absolute values of the pitches of either. Moreover, this interval relation is often a subordinate factor in the determination of absolute pitch. We accordingly treat these comparative cases first.

534. In many of the methods for these determinations the human ear is the ultimate standard of appeal. Indeed, in some cases nothing is needed beyond the notes under examination either successively or simultaneously and the musical *ear* of the observer. Thus, if two notes of distinctly different pitches are successively sounded, most persons can perceive which is the higher. And if the interval between them is one of those recognised in music, a person with the slightest claim to be styled a musician easily and promptly judges with accuracy what that interval is. If the two notes are simultaneously sounded and of about equal intensity, then the exactness of any consonant interval can easily be ascertained by an ordinary observer from the absence of certain beats between the overtones and differentials. Of course, for this purpose it is necessary that the two notes should be of good musical quality. They must also be well sustained with considerable vigour if differential tones enter into the criterion. Further, to a musician any ordinary interval is at once recognisable when the notes composing it are simultaneously sounded.

If two notes are sounded together which are near enough in pitch to give beats between their primes, then it is easy for any one to detect the difference of frequencies by timing the beats. To do this we have simply to sustain without check the two notes and at about equal intensities, and count the beats for a period timed by a stop-watch. This important test by beats comes in again and again in many of the other determinations to be noticed later, and can fortunately be used by any one.

We shall now treat special methods for determining ratios of frequencies or intervals, taking elaborate or classical methods first, and simple ones suitable for ordinary lecture use and laboratory work afterwards.

535. The Vibration Microscope.—This instrument was proposed in its essential features by Lissajous, and was used by Helmholtz for the observation of a violin string (see art. 347). One prong of a tuning-fork carries a lens whose axis is perpendicular to the plane of vibration. This lens usually forms the object glass of a compound microscope whose eye-piece is held by a fixed support. Thus a stationary point viewed through the microscope is thrown into apparent simple harmonic motion of direction and period corresponding to that of the fork. Now let a bright point be carried by any body vibrating at right angles both to the vibration of the fork and to the axis of the microscope. Then on viewing this through the microscope we shall apparently view in the field the resultant of two rectangular vibrations, one of which is known to be simple harmonic. Hence, if the other vibration under examination is also simple harmonic, we may from the kinematics of the case recognise the relation of their frequencies, provided it is sufficiently simple to give a fairly stable figure. If the ratio is not expressible by simple whole numbers, the figure changes too rapidly to be recognised. Thus, if the periods are equal, the resultant is in general an ellipse which may become a circle or an oblique straight line according to the difference of phase. If the periods are not quite equal, then all the possible forms dependent on phase difference are successively assumed while one motion gains a period on the other. Hence the difference of frequencies can be ascertained by timing. For, if the frequencies are respectively N and N', and one gains a period on the other in t seconds, we have $Nt \sim N't = 1$, or $N \sim N' = 1/t$. Thus, if one frequency is known, the other can be ascertained. Further, if neither frequency is known, we have the ratio given by $N'/N = 1 \pm 1/Nt$.

536. If, as in the observations by Helmholtz on a violin string, the motion under examination is not simple harmonic, then the instrument may be used to infer the character of that motion. For, since the fork's motion is simple harmonic of given amplitude and period, the time may be inferred for each displacement. But the displacement of the body whose vibration is being observed is also shown in the field and at right angles to that due to the fork. Hence, the displacement-time diagram for the motion under consideration may be derived. In his classical researches on the violin, Helmholtz blackened the required spot of the string with ink, rubbed it when dry with wax, and then powdered this with starch, so that a few grains remained sticking. The violin was then fixed with its strings vertical opposite the microscope with the tuning-fork prongs horizontal, so that one of the starch grains could be clearly seen. Then on starting both vibrations every point of the string moved horizontally, while the objective of the microscope carried by the tuning-fork moved up and down vertically. Helmholtz used for this purpose the a' string, tuning it up to $b'\flat$, so that it sounded exactly two octaves higher than the tuning-fork of his microscope which sounded $B\flat$. In Helmholtz's experiment the fork of the vibration microscope was electrically driven.

Lord Rayleigh points out that " the vibration microscope may be used to test the rigour and universality of the law connecting *pitch* and *period*. Thus it will be found that any point of a vibrating body which gives a pure musical note will appear to describe a re-entrant curve, when examined with a vibration microscope whose note is in strict unison with its own."

537. Lissajous' Figures. — This is another optical method for the comparison of vibration frequencies and also due to Lissajous. It is susceptible of high accuracy, and forms in addition a striking lecture illustration, as the figures produced by the simultaneous perpendicular motions of two forks may be projected on a screen, and thus made visible to a large audience. It may be conveniently carried out as follows :—

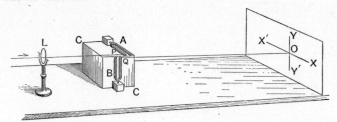

FIG. 97.—PROJECTION OF LISSAJOUS' FIGURES.

EXPT. 86. *Projection of Lissajous' Figures.* — For this purpose we require two tuning-forks tuned either to the same pitch or to some simple interval like an octave, a twelfth, or a fifth. These are provided with small plane mirrors, and are mounted on adjacent faces of a cubical box or framework CC, as shown in Fig. 97. From an electric-arc lantern a small beam of light I is derived, which passes through a focusing lens L, and is then reflected in turn at P on the fork A, and Q on the fork B, arriving finally in focus on the screen, where it makes a small bright spot at O. It is obvious that the vibration of the fork A alone will cause the spot on the screen to describe a horizontal line along XOX′. In like manner the vibration of the fork B alone will give to the spot a vertical motion along YOY′. Thus the simultaneous vibrations of both forks will give on the screen a curve executed by the bright spot which represents the resultant of the two rectangular simple harmonic motions ; in other words, the spot describes one of Lissajous' figures.

As seen from the previous discussion in the kinematical chapter, if the periods are precisely equal the figure is constant in type, its exact form depending on the relation of the amplitudes and phases of the component vibrations. If the forks are excited by bowing, both amplitudes diminish continuously after the cessation of bowing. If the forks are electrically maintained, the amplitudes can be adjusted to a desired value and kept constant.

If the periods are nearly, but not quite equal, the phase relation passes slowly through all its possible values. Thus, if at any instant the figure is an oblique line through the origin, it will change to an ellipse with axes along OX and OY, while the phase difference changes from zero to one-quarter of a period. This ellipse reduces to a circle if the amplitudes are equal.

538. Suppose now the method is used to adjust two forks to perfect unison, and let us note the accuracy obtainable. Let the forks have a frequency of the order 100 per second, and if bowed only suppose the vibrations are visible for a minute. We should then have 6000 complete vibrations executed, and in this number a gain of a quarter of a period of one fork on the other would be distinctly visible, since it involves the change of the figure from an oblique line to an ellipse with horizontal and vertical axes. We should, accordingly, in this simple case detect a lack of perfect unison expressed by one vibration in 24,000 ! The interval ratio would be 24,001 : 24,000, or, measured in cents of which 1200 go to the octave, the interval between the forks would be only 0·072 cent, or less than a thousandth of a semitone. With forks electrically driven this limit of accuracy could be much exceeded.

If the forks have frequencies in the ratio of 2 : 1, 2 : 3, or other ratios expressed by small whole numbers, the corresponding figure is produced and easily recognised. Further, it remains with or without change of form according as the tuning is approximate or precise.

539. Expt. 87. *Comparison of Forks by Graphic Records.*— This is a rougher, but still very instructive method of comparing the frequencies of two forks in which each carries a light style of aluminium foil, and thus traces a sine graph on a moving smoked surface. The surface may be smoked by exposure to the fumes from burning camphor. In the better form of the experiments this smoked surface is produced on glazed paper, which is then wrapped round the convex surface of a drum which may be kept uniformly rotating by clockwork. The vibration of the style is arranged so as to be parallel to the axis of the drum. The two forks are firmly mounted side by side near the drum so as to secure this relation. Then the drum being in rotation and the forks bowed, the two sine graphs are simultaneously described on the same paper, which is then removed and the records carefully examined. It may thus be found how many vibrations of one fork correspond to a given number of vibrations of the other.

A rougher method of obtaining this comparison is as follows:—The forks are mounted side by side, each fitted with a suitable style, and a piece of glass is smoked. Then while one operator bows the forks, another moves gently past them the smoked glass so as to receive the double trace. The direction of motion of the glass must be at right angles to that of vibration of the forks. If the motion of the glass is not uniform the accuracy of the result is not impaired, as only a comparison of the two frequencies is aimed at, and not any absolute determination of either.

540. EXPT. 88. *Comparison of Forks by Monochord.*—Another simple but instructive method of comparing two forks is afforded by the monochord. In this we either assume the relation that the frequency of a given stretched string is inversely as its length, or experimentally confirm it by comparison with forks of known frequencies. We must then carefully determine the different lengths of the string, which are exactly in unison with the forks to be compared. Thus, if the lengths are L_1 and L_2, and the frequencies of the corresponding forks are denoted by N_1 and N_2, we have

$$N_1/N_2 = L_2/L_1, \text{ or } N_1L_1 = N_2L_2 = \text{a constant.}$$

The adjustments to unison between string and fork in each case may be made by listening for the extinction of beats, as the bridge limiting the length of the vibrating portion of the string is moved along by steps of about one millimetre each. In this method of tuning the string should be plucked or struck and not bowed. The reason and importance of this when listening for beats were pointed out in article 294.

541. An alternative method of tuning is that of placing the stem of the vibrating fork on the bridge, and feeling lightly with the tip of a finger at the middle of that part of the string which it is desired to tune to the fork. If the two are in unison the string immediately responds. Indeed, while the fork's vibrations continue, the string, if well adjusted, may be repeatedly started after each check by the touch of the finger. This is on the principle of Helmholtz's resonance experiment described in article 243.

542. Absolute Value of Frequency.— *Determinations by Koenig and by Rayleigh.*—We shall now proceed to notice a number of methods for the absolute determination of frequency, taking first the classical methods which have been used by eminent investigators, and afterwards the simpler methods suitable for routine work in the laboratory.

To Koenig we are indebted for one of the most direct determinations of frequency which involves the use of a special instrument. This consists of a fork of sixty-four complete vibrations per second whose motion is maintained by a clock movement and escapement. This clockwork showed ordinary time and also the number of vibrations executed. The behaviour of the fork was tested by comparison between the instrument and any other clock known to be trustworthy. A standard fork of 256 complete vibrations per second was compared with this instrument by observation of the Lissajous' figure characteristic of the double octave.

543. Another celebrated determination of frequency is due to Lord Rayleigh, and is described as follows by the experimenter in his *Theory of Sound* :—

" An electrically-maintained interrupter fork, whose frequency may, for example, be 32, was employed to drive a dependent fork of pitch 128. When the apparatus is in good order there is a fixed relation between the frequencies, the one being precisely four times the other. The higher is, of course, readily compared by beats, or by optical methods, with a standard of 128, whose accuracy is to be tested. It remains to determine the frequency of the interrupter fork itself.

" For this purpose the interrupter is compared with the pendulum of a standard clock whose rate is known. The comparison may be direct, or the intervention of a phonic wheel [1] may be invoked. In either case the pendulum of the clock is provided with a silver bead, upon which is concentrated the light from a lamp. Immediately in front of the pendulum is placed a screen perforated by a somewhat narrow vertical slit. The bright point of light reflected by the bead is seen intermittently, either by looking over the prong of the interrupter or through a hole in a disc of the phonic wheel. In the first case there are thirty-two views per second, but in the latter this number is reduced by the intervention of the wheel. In the experiment referred to the wheel was so arranged that one revolution corresponded to four complete vibrations of the interrupter, and there were thus eight views of the pendulum per second, instead of thirty-two. Any deviation of the period of the pendulum from a precise multiple of the period of intermittence shows itself as a cycle of changes in the appearance of the flash of light, and an observation of the duration of this cycle gives the data for a precise comparison of frequencies.

544. " The calculation of the results is very simple. Supposing in the first instance that the clock is correct, let a be the number of cycles per second (perhaps $\frac{1}{40}$) between the wheel and the clock. Since the period of a cycle is the time required for the wheel to gain or lose one revolution upon the clock, the frequency of revolution is $8 \pm a$. The frequency of the auxiliary fork is precisely sixteen times as great, i.e. $128 \pm 16a$. If b be the number of beats per second between the auxiliary fork and the

---

[1] The *phonic wheel*, invented independently by M. La Cour and Lord Rayleigh, may be briefly described as a wheel whose rotation is electrically governed so that its speed remains practically constant.

standard, the frequency of the latter is $128 \pm 16a \pm b$. The error in the mean rate of the clock is readily allowed for; but care is required to ascertain that the actual rate at the time of observation does not differ appreciably from the mean rate. To be quite safe it would be necessary to repeat the determinations at intervals over the whole time required to rate the clock by observation of the stars. In this case it would probably be convenient to attach a counting apparatus to the phonic wheel."

545. Chronographic Method of A. M. Mayer.—In this method adopted by Professor Mayer the fork under examination carries a style and marks a sine graph upon a camphor-smoked paper on a revolving drum. A novel feature of the arrangement lies in the fact that the same style automatically records time upon the trace. This is effected as follows :—The pendulum of a clock at each swing makes electrical contact with a bead of mercury, and so makes and breaks the primary of an induction coil. Now the smoked paper and the style carried by the fork are included in the secondary of this induction coil. Hence at each instantaneous current in the secondary, a small spark occurs at the smoked paper which records the instant in question. If, by the comparison of the wavy and spark traces on the smoked paper it is found that n vibrations occur in t seconds, it is clear that the frequency sought is n/t per second.

546. Thus, in this method, although an absolute determination of the frequency is made, uniformity in the rotation of the drum is not essential. It must, however, be noticed that the true period of the fork is slightly interfered with by the friction of the style on the smoked paper. For, as we saw in the dynamical portion of this work, resistance to a vibration has not only a first order effect on the amplitude, but also a second order effect on the period. Accordingly this method must rank as inferior to those in which observations are conducted by optical or acoustical means, leaving the fork or other vibrator in its usual un-trammelled state.

It is obvious that a slight modification of this ex-perimental arrangement could be utilised for the inverse purpose of measuring small intervals of time, the sparks giving the seconds, and the sine graph tenths, hundredths, or thousandths of a second.

547. Scheibler's Tonometer.—Scheibler of Crefeld pre-pared a set of standard forks which constituted what is termed his *tonometer*; and by careful tuning and counting of beats the absolute pitch of each fork was determined. The principle of the method is as follows:—Suppose two forks are tuned exactly to an octave; let the frequency of the lower fork be denoted by N, then that of the higher is $2N$. Now let a number of intermediate forks be prepared, each making about four beats per second with the one below and the one above it in the series. Let the exact numbers of the beats per second between adjacent forks in the series be denoted by b_1, b_2, b_3, etc., then clearly we have

$$\left.\begin{array}{l} 2N = N + b_1 + b_2 + b_3 + \ldots \\ \quad\text{or } N = \Sigma b \end{array}\right\} \qquad (1),$$

where the summation extends over the octave. Thus knowing N we easily obtain the frequency of any other fork in the series. For obviously if the frequency of the nth fork in the series beginning at the lowest is N_n, we have

$$N_n = N + b_1 + b_2 + \ldots b_{n-1} \qquad (2).$$

548. Thus, the principle involved is to ascertain by beats the difference of frequencies whose ratio is known to be two. Lord Rayleigh points out that if a smaller interval like a fifth, fourth, or major third were obtained precisely by Lissajous' figures, the labour of bridging the larger interval of the octave would be much reduced. Scheibler's tonometer has not only the advantage of great accuracy, but also of portability. It is thus suitable for bell founders to take with them into belfries to ascertain the pitches of the various tones of any bell which they may have to replace. To determine the pitch of any tone by means of this tonometer it is only necessary to time the numbers of beats per second between that tone and each of the two forks in the tonometer to which the tone is nearest in pitch. Thus, if the forks of the tonometer have frequencies 64, 68·1, 71·9, 76 per second, etc., and the tone to be determined gives 5·6 beats per second with the 64 fork, 1·5 beats per second with the 68·1 fork, 2·3 with the 71·9, and 6·4 with the 76, then its frequency is obviously 69·6 per second.

549. In order that this method may be trustworthy it is essential that the pitch of each standard fork should be known to not vary when sounded with the one below and with the one above respectively. It is the lack of fulfilment of this condition which destroyed the value of the tonometer which was designed by Appun, and consisted of a number of harmonium reeds. And even with the tonometer of forks, it is necessary for extreme accuracy to know the pitch of each fork at the temperature of use, and its rate of variation of frequency with temperature. According to the observations of M'Leod and Clarke, the frequency of a fork falls by 0·00011 of its value for each degree centigrade of rise in the temperature. The value found by Koenig for the temperature coefficient of forks is $-0·000112$ per $1°$ C. Hence the frequency of a 256 fork falls 0·028672 of a vibration per second per $1°$ C. rise of the temperature.

550. Rayleigh's Harmonium Method for Pitch.—In spite of the fact just noticed that harmonium reeds vary a little in pitch according to whether they are sounded with the note above or below, Lord Rayleigh has utilised them for an absolute determination of pitch. Perhaps it is as well to consider first the method which must be rejected on account of this lack of permanence of pitch. Let the frequencies of the notes forming the interval of a major third on the harmonium be x and y. Then beats may be heard and counted between the fourth partial of the higher note and the fifth of the lower. Hence if the frequency of these beats is a per second, the fourth partial being the higher of the beating tones, we have

$$4y - 5x = a \qquad\qquad (1).$$

Now if the value of y/x were exactly that prescribed in the system of equal temperament, or were something else but accurately known, we should then be able to determine both x and y. But since we cannot be quite sure that the interval is correctly tuned, take the next major third, calling the frequency of this third note z, and the beats reckoned as before b per second. Then we have

$$4z - 5y = b \qquad\qquad (2).$$

Finally, let the beats between the fifth partial of this third note and the eighth of the first note be c, the latter partial being the higher. Then

$$8x - 5z = c \qquad\qquad (3),$$

whence from (1), (2), and (3) we obtain the values of x, y, and z in terms of a, b, and c. Thus

$$x = \tfrac{1}{3}(25a + 20b + 16c),$$
$$y = \tfrac{1}{3}(32a + 25b + 20c), \text{ and}$$
$$z = \tfrac{1}{3}(40a + 32b + 25c).$$

551. Now, as already mentioned, this plan would fail of high accuracy, because the frequency of the second note, say, would be slightly different when sounded with the first from that when sounded with the third note of the series, and similarly for the other combinations. In other words, the values of x, y, and z in the equations (1), (2), and (3) are not strictly identical, but have slightly different values in each equation.

To remove this source of error we must be able to check

the interval at the same time that the beats are being counted. That is to say, it is necessary to obtain *two* relations between the frequencies at a *single* simultaneous sounding of the two notes. Thus, let the equal tempered whole tone be selected as the interval, and call the frequencies v and w. Then it is slightly smaller than the large tone of just intonation $9/8$. Hence we may obtain between the eighth partial of the higher and ninth partial of the lower notes slow beats of frequency, say d per second. Then we shall have the relation

$$9v - 8w = d \qquad (4).$$

Again, this tempered interval is considerably larger than the small tone $10/9$. Hence there will be quick beats between the ninth partial of the higher and the tenth partial of the lower note. Thus, if these beats are e per second, we have

$$9w - 10v = e \qquad (5).$$

From (4) and (5) we obtain

$$v = 9d + 8e \qquad (6),$$

and $$w = 10d + 9e \qquad (7).$$

552. This was the plan followed by Lord Rayleigh in determining the pitch of the note C on a harmonium. The notes used were C and D, the interval being purposely reduced from the usual equal temperament. This made the quick beats slower, and so facilitated counting. Indeed, in the case noted below, what would naturally be the quick beats were so altered as to be slower than the others. Two observers were necessary, one to count the beats shown in equation (4), and the other to count those shown in equation (5). In one experiment, the time being ten minutes, the beats thus recorded were respectively 2392 and 2341. Hence,

$$d = 2392/600 \text{ and } e = 2341/600,$$

whence the pitch of C was given from (6) by

$$v = 67 \cdot 09 \text{ per second} \tag{8}.$$

But this result is true for the C only when sounding with the D.

553. Simple Determinations of Frequency.—We now pass to those methods for the determination of frequency which are of the simple class suitable for lecture illustration and ordinary experimental work in the laboratory. We shall commence with a few which are mechanical in nature, *i.e.* methods which assume no acoustical laws or constants. We shall afterwards notice several methods which may be styled acoustical in that they do assume such laws and constants.

    Expt. 88*a. Savart's Wheel.*—This method, as its name implies, is due to Savart, who first reduced it to a fair degree of accuracy. The apparatus consists essentially of a toothed wheel capable of rotation, a card or plate held so as to be caught by the teeth, a driving gear (or an electric motor could now be substituted) for setting the wheel in rapid rotation, and, finally, a counting arrangement to record the number of turns executed by it. In one apparatus used by Savart the wheel had 600 teeth, and could be driven at various speeds up to 40 revolutions per second. In this extreme case 24,000 taps per second would be given to the card by the teeth of the wheel, and hence a note of frequency 24,000 would be produced. On maintaining the speed of the wheel so as to exactly match the pitch of any note under examination, it is evident that from the counter and the time ascertained by a watch we can calculate the frequency sought. Thus, let the frequency of the note be N, and suppose that the wheel contains n teeth, and makes r complete turns in t seconds when matching this note.

Then obviously $N = nr/t$ (1).

This method is somewhat rough and may be regarded as inferior to the siren.

    554. Expt. 89. *The Siren.*—For the purpose of determining the pitch of a pipe or tuning-fork, the form of siren due to Cagniard de la Tour will be found convenient. It consists essentially of a vertical spindle carrying a disc pierced with a ring of holes which alternately open and close a similar ring of holes on the top of the cylindrical wind chest. At the upper part of the apparatus is added a counting mechanism with fingers and dials which record the number of rotations of the disc. The two rings of holes have opposite obliquities so that the pressure of the air as it escapes through them spins the disc. Thus, by suitable adjustment of pressure, the siren may be tuned to any desired note within certain limits. To determine a pitch by the siren we have obviously to tune the siren to the note in question, observe the indications of the dials at the beginning and end of a timed period, during which the siren is maintained at the right pitch, and then calculate the result as in the case of Savart's wheel, the number of holes in the disc replacing the number of teeth in the wheel.

555. But a little care is necessary both in the tuning and in the counting. For example, at some pressures the siren is distinctly flattened by putting the counting mechanism into gear. Hence, though the siren is usually provided with a sliding motion to put the counters in and out of gear, it is safer to keep them in gear throughout the experiments. If available, a stop watch may be used in conjunction with the siren to facilitate the timing when the counting mechanism is running the whole time. Again, in order to have the air blast sufficiently under control, either of the following arrangements will suffice :—

First, Derive the air blast from a large reservoir in which the air is maintained at a constant pressure by an automatic pump and safety valve, air pipes being laid round the laboratory as water pipes are. It is then desirable to connect the siren to the air tap by a rubber pipe fitted with a *screw* clip. This is the method in use at Nottingham, and acts very well. The screw of the clip can easily be moved an eighth of a turn at a time, and so the air pressure and consequently the pitch of the siren slowly changed. It should be noticed, however, that after even a very slight adjustment of the screw the pitch of the siren continues to creep up or down for, say, a minute or more. The fact that it is so changing is almost imperceptible, but it is better to time a minute by the watch before supposing the pitch to have reached its final value aue to the change in the position of the screw.

Second, If the above arrangement is not available, a foot bellows and wind chest with suitably weighted valve may be substituted. The final adjustment of pitch should still be made by a screw clip on the connecting tube manipulated as in the first installation.

In a preliminary adjustment of the wind pressure by the screw, when the pitch is rapidly altering, the experimenter may often feel uncertain whether the siren is sharp or flat, or by how much. It is then convenient to touch the disc or the spindle very lightly with the finger, thus decreasing its speed and so lowering the pitch. By this means the siren, if too sharp, can be brought down to the pitch required, or, if already too flat, the fact immediately ascertained.

556. When wishing to make a very exact determination of pitch, it is not safe to trust either that the siren is exactly tuned, or that it will remain constant in pitch during the counted interval, the better plan being to maintain the sound under examination during the whole time of counting, and to keep the siren the whole time slowly beating with it, the beats being counted also. This delicate adjustment may be preserved by lightly touching the axle with a feather. Thus, suppose the siren to be certainly sharper than the other sound the whole time, and let the total number of beats be b in the counted time of t seconds. Also, let the total number of revolutions of the disc in this time be r, and the number of holes in the disc be n. Then the frequency N of the sound under test is obviously given by

$$N = \frac{nr - b}{t} \qquad (2).$$

557. In order to be sure that the siren is throughout sharper than the other note, proceed as follows :—*First,* Make sure it is sharper to start with by ascertaining that increased pressure of the feather slows the beats. *Second,* Adjust the beats to about four per second. *Third,* Keep the beats at about this rate, taking special care that they never get slower and vanish. A typical example would be—

$$N = \frac{16 \times 326 - 76}{20} = 257 \text{ per second.}$$

Of course, if $b = 0$, equation (2) reduces to equivalence with (1) which was written for Savart's wheel.

558. Expt. 90. *Tuning-Fork and Fall Plate.*—In this experiment, instead of assuming the accuracy of some watch or clock, we assume the value of the acceleration due to gravity, *i.e.* the quantity usually denoted by g. The apparatus consists essentially of a smoked glass plate arranged to fall past the tuning-fork whose pitch is to be determined. The fork is mounted vertically in a block A, Fig. 98, which slides in a groove BB in the base board CC, which also carries a

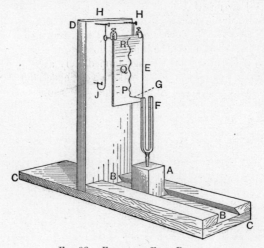

Fig. 98.—Fork and Fall Plate.

vertical board D to support the smoked plate E ready for its fall. The fork F carries on one prong a light style G of thin aluminium foil attached by soft wax. The plate may be conveniently smoked by the fumes of burning camphor. It is hung by a fine thread passing over two nails HH, and under screws at the *back* of the plate, which may be the side pinch screws of terminals used for the plates of Daniell's cells. This method of suspension causes the plate to tilt forward very slightly like pictures on a wall. Then, on adjusting matters so that to start with the style just touches the plate, on releasing the plate by burning the thread the style will be in gentle contact during the fall. To prevent breakage of the plate, a second loop, J, of stronger thread, may also be used, passing round a lower pair of nails on the board, and attached to the terminals on the plate so as to arrest it at the end of its fall. The arrangement will be understood from Fig. 98.

559. These details being arranged, the fork is set vibrating by a bow (or electrically driven if possible), and the thread burnt between the nails HH. Then as the plate falls, a wavy trace is marked upon it which is clearly the resultant of a simple harmonic motion horizontally, and a uniformly accelerated motion vertically. The acceleration g being assumed, we have thus the data for calculating the frequency N of the fork. But, owing to the very slow motion of the plate near the commencement of its fall, the corresponding wavy trace on the smoked surface will be very crowded, thus rendering a counting of the waves practically impossible. It is accordingly advisable to avoid this region and proceed as follows :—Select two portions PQ and QR where the waves can be readily counted, and each containing the same number n of waves, their lengths being l_1 and l_2 respectively. Further, let n/N the time of fall from P to Q or Q to R $= t$. Then, denoting by u the speed of the plate when P passes the style, we have by elementary kinematics

$$l_1 = ut + \tfrac{1}{2}gt^2 \qquad (1).$$

But the speed as the point Q passes the style is $u + gt$; hence for the portion QR we have

$$l_2 = (u + gt)t + \tfrac{1}{2}gt^2 \qquad (2).$$

Thus (2) – (1) gives $l_2 - l_1 = gt^2 \qquad (3).$

Whence, on writing for t its value n/N, we have

$$N = n\sqrt{\frac{g}{l_2 - l_1}} \qquad (4).$$

560. It may be noted here that the frequency of the fork is somewhat disturbed both by the mass of the style and its friction on the plate, and both these sources of error flatten the fork. These could be allowed for by tuning a second fork precisely to the one under test when without the style, and then counting the beats between the two when the first

was again provided with the style, and it was rubbing against
the smoked plate.   Thus if the beats between the two were
b per second, we should have for the frequency N_0 of the
undisturbed fork,

$$N_0 = N + b = b + n \sqrt{\frac{g}{l_2 - l_1}} \qquad (5).$$

If desired a correction to g may be made for the effect
of friction which retards the plate in its fall.   This could
be approximately obtained from a very good fork whose
frequency was accurately known, and finding g from equation
(4).   This value, slightly less than the true g, would then
be inserted in (5).

561 EXPT. 91. *Pitch from Stationary Waves.*—The procedure is as follows :—The source whose pitch is to be
determined is excited and sustained, the progressive waves
proceeding from it are reflected normally from a plane
surface so as to set up stationary waves.   The positions of
the nodes or antinodes are located, and their distance apart
measured along the line normal to the reflector.   Then
we have

$$l = \lambda/2 \qquad (1),$$

where l is the distance between successive nodes and λ
the length of the progressive waves.   But, if N is the
frequency of the tone and v the speed of sound in air, we
have

$$v = N\lambda \qquad (2).$$

Hence by (1), $v = 2Nl,$

or, $$N = v/2l = \frac{v_0 \sqrt{1 + at}}{2l} \qquad (3),$$

where v_0 is the speed of sound at $0°$ C., t the temperature
in degrees C., and a is the coefficient of gaseous expansion
($0·003665$ per $1°$ C.).   Thus, measuring l, observing t, and
assuming v_0, we may calculate N, the frequency sought.

In the practice of this method several precautions should
be noted.   In the first place, the reflecting surface must be
such as to insure adequate reflection.   Thus a light board
might only form a resonator, and a cloth would stifle
the sound.   A smooth plaster wall or a sheet of glass will

do. Secondly, the surface must be large enough in comparison with the length of the waves used to obviate diffraction. Again, the distance between successive nodal or antinodal positions must be measured along the normal to the surface through the source of sound.

562. Then to find the nodal positions the sensitive flame used must be chosen so as to have sufficient but not excessive sensibility. For a small organ pipe or tuning-fork of pitch in the treble staff, the sensitive flame obtained from an ordinary small Bunsen burner has been found suitable (see article 282). Again, in using the sensitive flame it is well to locate by it the places of least disturbance, as these are usually more sharply defined than the places of maximum disturbance. Sensitive flames are usually most affected by the places of maximum motion, *i.e.* by the antinodes. Thus, the places of least disturbance would be the nodes, and these occur at the reflector and at distances from it of $\lambda/2$, $2\lambda/2$, $3\lambda/2$, etc. If, however, the particular sensitive flame in use behaves in the opposite manner so that its places of least disturbance are the places of no variation of pressure, *i.e.* the antinodes, these would occur at distances from the reflector of $\lambda/4$, $3\lambda/4$, $5\lambda/4$, etc. Hence in this case the first distance from the reflector would be only $\lambda/4$, whereas all the intermediate distances in the first case and the others in the present case would be $\lambda/2$. It is also well to note that the position of a node or an antinode is fixed simply by that of the reflector and the length of the waves in use, and is quite independent of the exact distance of the source from the reflector.

563. EXPT. 92. *Pitch by Monochord from Difference and Ratio of Frequencies.*—For this method, in addition to the monochord and source of sound whose pitch is to be determined, we require a second source of sound to beat with the first. Hence by counting beats we obtain the difference of frequencies of the source under test and the auxiliary source. Also by finding the lengths of the string which at a given tension are in unison with the two sounds, we infer the ratio of their frequencies, which are inversely as the lengths observed. Thus, let the source under test (a fork or organ pipe say) and the auxiliary have frequencies N and N' and be in unison with lengths of the string L and L' respectively, L being greater than L'. Let the beats between the two sources be b per second. Then we have

$$L'N' = LN \qquad (1),$$

and
$$N' = N + b \qquad (2),$$

whence
$$N = \frac{bL'}{L - L'} \qquad (3)$$

gives the frequency sought.

564. In the practice of this method care must be taken that the tension of the string remains precisely the same when the lengths in unison with each source are determined otherwise equation (1) would not hold. Thus, in determining the lengths, the movable bridge used should be as accurately as possible of the same height as the fixed terminal bridges, and the requisite pressure of the string upon it must be supplied externally, say by the edge of a small coin pressed upon it at the place.

A little consideration will show that this is not a refined method, but rather interesting from its simplicity. Thus, if the number of beats per second were five (and quicker beats are difficult to count), we should need ten seconds uninterrupted flow of both sounds to give fifty beats, and enable the observer to determine b with an accuracy of one per cent. And equation (3) shows that the accuracy of the value obtained for N is not greater than that with which b is found. Again, if the pitches are high the method fails in accuracy, since then the five beats per second would correspond to a very slight difference of lengths L and L'. But for pitches of about 100, or say 128 (the c of the physical apparatus makers), the method succeeds fairly well. Further, the steel wire which usually forms the "string" of the monochord is more satisfactory at these pitches than when tuned much higher.

565. EXPT. 93. *Pitch by Vertical Monochord.*—In this experimental determination we assume the absolute relation between the pitch and all the circumstances of the case instead of the law of dependence of pitch on length simply as in the previous experiment. And in order to know precisely what the tension is, a vertical monochord is used, having a fixed bridge at the upper end of the string and a movable one to define the lower end of its vibrating portion.

Tension is then applied directly by a weight at the bottom of the string, and the vertical position of the monochord obviates the uncertainty of tension which in other positions would arise from the friction of the string over the bridge. It is as well also to pull the string away from the lower bridge before each determination, and then press it to the bridge by the rounded edge of a metal plate carefully applied, so as not to change the tension, but simply the length as desired. Further, to avoid complications due to the stiffness of the string raising the pitch, a thin wire should be chosen.

566. With these precautions the string is brought into unison with the source of sound under test, the first rough adjustments being made by changing the weights used and the final adjustment by sliding the bridge. The length is then measured, and the mass per unit length ascertained say by weighing a measured length of the wire or other cord in use. The frequency sought is then calculated from the equation developed in art. 165, viz.

$$N = \frac{1}{2l} \sqrt{F/\sigma},$$

where l is the length in cm. of the vibrating portion of the string, F is the tension in dynes, and σ is the linear density of the string in gm./cm.

For good work the value of σ must be known at the temperature at which the string is used in vibration. It may accordingly be determined at this temperature by direct weighing and measuring, or if a well-known standard substance, it may be calculated from its tabular density ρ_0 at $0°$ C., its radius r_0 at $0°$ C., and its coefficient of linear expansion z for $1°$ C. Thus, at $t°$ C. we have

$$\sigma = \pi r^2 \rho = \pi r_0^2 (1 + zt)^2 \frac{\rho_0}{(1 + zt)^3} = \frac{\pi r_0^2 \rho_0}{1 + zt}.$$

567. EXPT. 94. *Pitch by adjustable Resonator.* — An indirect method of finding the speed of sound in air from a fork of known frequency was detailed in article 532. This can obviously be used to find the frequency of a fork when the speed of sound is assumed. It is accordingly named here for completeness' sake, but need not be again described as the manipulation is just the same. The experimenter has merely to treat N as the unknown instead of v.

568. EXPT. 95. *Pitch from Transverse Vibrations.*—A strip of steel or other metal is used fixed at one end, free at the other, and set in vibration. It is then assumed from theory (see art. 205) that the frequencies of such strips are inversely as their lengths squared. A length L is found such that the pitch of this portion of the strip is then in unison with the fork or other source of sound whose frequency N is to be determined. The length of the vibrating portion is then increased to say L', so as to make its frequency N' so small that it can be counted and timed by a good watch, preferably a stop watch; thus N' is known. But from the theoretical relation, we have $NL^2 = N'L'^2$, or

$$N = N'L'^2/L^2, \text{ which determines } N.$$

The strip may be about 2 cm. wide, and say 1 mm. or less in thickness. It is conveniently clamped by an ordinary engineer's vice if such is available, in which case the bar may be horizontal but edge up, and the vibrations horizontal. Failing the vice, the strip may be laid on a strong table with an end projecting over the edge, and weights placed over that part on the table. In this case though the strip is horizontal the vibrations will be vertical, and hence gravity will enter as a disturbance.

569. Variation of Pitch and Decrement.—From the consideration of the determination of pitch simply we now turn to other matters intimately connected with it, taking first the variation of pitch and decrement with amplitude as investigated by R. Hartmann-Kempf. In this research the method of letting the vibrating body mark a sine graph upon a smoked surface was necessarily rejected, as the friction of the style upon the surface would change the damping and period, thus altering the very quantities which it was desired to measure. A photographic method was accordingly adopted in which the tuning-fork or other vibrator carried a mirror, thus reflecting light upon a sensitive film passing over a drum, and so yielding a wavy trace which shows the damping per wave. But it was also desired to obtain information as to the very slight change of period, as the vibrations died away, and for this very delicate purpose the uniformity of rotation of the drum could not be trusted. Hence, in the path of the beam was interposed a disc of yellow glass with a slit in its middle. This was carried by an auxiliary tuning-fork whose vibrations were electrically maintained. White light passed through the slit for about one ten-thousandth of a second each time this auxiliary fork was at its equilibrium position. And since this occurs twice in the period of the auxiliary fork, a series of bright dashes thus obtained on the photograph correctly indicated these intervals of time. During the remainder of the auxiliary fork's motion the actinic quality of the light was much weakened by its passage through the yellow glass disc, and its power of giving an intense photograph reduced accordingly. But in spite of this reduction the light was well able to give a good photograph at the *extremities* of the wavy curve where the full amplitude was reached, and the bright reflected spot *paused* in the film before making its return motion. And it is at this very place and there only that a good print was needed in order to register the amplitude of the fork's motion.

570. Thus, the white light through the slit gave a series of bright dashes occurring at instants separated by rigidly equal intervals of time, and so by their position on the film forming an accurate *time* record. While the yellow light passing through the disc not only showed quite distinctly those portions of the trace required of it, namely, the turning-points of the waves, thus recording the *amplitude* of each vibration, but also in the other parts of the wavy trace was faint enough to avoid obscuring the bright dashes.

Hartmann-Kempf found that the relation between logarithmic decrement and amplitude for three makes of tuning-fork is almost linear. The dependence of frequency

2 P

on amplitude was, however, found to be more complicated. Both are shown in the curves of Fig. 99. In all cases it is seen that the decrement increases and the frequency decreases with increasing amplitudes.

571. Reaction of Resonator on Pitch of Fork.—This subject was investigated by Koenig, who found that a certain fork of 256 per second sounded for about 90 seconds

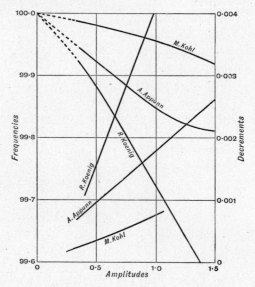

Fig. 99.—Variation of Pitch and Decrement.

without a resonator. An adjustable resonator was then brought near it, but its pitch set much lower than that of the fork. The resonator was then gradually raised in pitch, and when it was still a minor third below the fork the latter failed to sound quite so long as before, and at the same time received a slight increase of frequency. As the resonator was tuned more nearly to the fork this decrease of time and increase in frequency became each more pronounced. But, at the instant when unison was established between the natural tones of fork and resonator, the change in the fork's pitch suddenly disappeared. At the same time the sound was powerfully reinforced, but lasted only about 10 seconds. When the pitch of the resonator was still further raised, so that its natural tone was now sharper than that of the fork, the sound of the fork changed in the opposite direction, being now a little flatter than its proper pitch. The maximum disturbance of frequency found by Koenig was 0·035 complete vibration per second.

Lord Rayleigh has shown that the above phenomena are in accordance with theory, and that "on whichever side a slight departure from precision of adjustment may occur the influence of the dependent vibration is always to increase the error."

572. Subjective Lowering of Pitch.—Dr. C. V. Burton in 1895 called attention to the subjective lowering of pitch in the case of forks when first bowed. This was stated to occur to the extent of a semitone, a whole tone, or even a minor third in the case of large forks strongly bowed. The pitch recovers its normal value as the amplitude dies away. The phenomena were confirmed by other observers.

To account for them the following hypothesis was put forward :—It is known that large amplitudes of a vibrator may entail a slight rise of pitch if the elastic forces are not strictly proportional to the displacements (see *e.g.* Chap. IV., art. 114). Thus, for large amplitudes the microscopic structures in the internal ear might be as it were tuned up above their normal responsive pitch. Hence, in response to large external vibrations of say 100 per second, we might have appreciable motions in those structures whose natural frequency for small vibrations is less than 100, but whose frequency for these larger vibrations is 100 or thereabouts. There would, accordingly, be not one, but a number of these structures throughout a certain range affected, and the region of maximum disturbance would be among parts whose natural frequency for small vibrations is below .100. But on Helmholtz's theory our perception of pitch is fixed for each such structure and the mechanism by which it communicates with the brain. Thus, the pitch assigned to such a loud sound would be somewhat lower than the true pitch, being some kind of mean among the different pitches proper to the various structures stimulated. In the discussion at the Physical Society on this subject, Prof. C. V. Boys said " he found that by careful attention he could apparently persuade himself that the note in Dr. Burton's experiment was lowered or raised in pitch, or that it remained unaltered. A similar effect in the case of the eye could be obtained with stereoscopic pictures."

573. Total Number of Vibrations needed for Sensation of Pitch.—Experiments to determine this point have been made by a number of physicists, perhaps the fullest being by W. Kohlrausch. He used an arc of a circle carrying a limited number of teeth and attached to a pendulum. When the pendulum was let go the teeth struck a card suitably held. The sound thus produced was compared with that of a monochord. By varying the length the string was tuned till it was just perceptibly higher or lower than the sound from the card. The ratio of these lengths defined the characteristic interval which expresses the precision with which the pitch could be estimated from the given total number of vibrations. Some of the results of these experiments are shown in Table LXIII.

[TABLE

TABLE LXIII.—TOTAL VIBRATIONS AND ESTIMATE OF PITCH

Total Number of Vibrations in Sound from Card.	Characteristic Interval expressing Precision in Estimation of Pitch.	
	Ratio of Frequencies.	Value in Cents.
16	0·9922	14
9	0·9903	17
3	0·9790	37
2	0·9714	50

This shows that even with so few as two vibrations a fair estimate of the pitch can be formed.

574. Lowest Pitch Audible.—To determine the lowest sound audible, Savart used a bar about two feet long revolving on an axis between two thin wooden plates distant about a tenth of an inch from it. He maintained that a grave, continuous, very deafening sound was thus produced with 7 or 8 vibrations per second. Helmholtz, however, declined to accept this result, and attributed the sound heard to upper partials. In order to know exactly which tone was being heard, Helmholtz used his double siren. In this siren (as explained in article 296), when the rings of 12 holes are open in both wind-boxes, and the handle which moves the upper wind-box is rotated once, there are 4 beats for the primes, but 8 for the second partials, and 12 for the third partials. Now, when the pitch of the primes was 12 to 13 per second a tone could be heard, but the test by beats showed it to be the third partial. For, corresponding to each turn of the handle, 12 beats were heard. Thus, the tones actually heard were from 36 to 39 per second. Again, with primes of frequencies 20 to 40 per second, 8 beats occurred to each turn of the handle; thus showing that it was the second partial of frequency 40 to 80 that was audible. And it was not until 80 puffs of air occurred per second that the 4 beats of the primes themselves were heard. Helmholtz further tried experiments with wide-stopped organ pipes, as particularly suited for giving powerful primes with but little admixture of near partials. He found that the lower tones of the 16-foot octave, E_l to C_l, began to pass over into a droning noise so that the pitch was uncertain. He considered that in the case of the 16-foot C_l of the organ with 33 vibrations per second, although there was a tolerably continuous sensation of tone, it was almost possible to observe also the separate pulses of the air. Helmholtz also obtained deep tones free from all near partials by using a thin brass string weighted with a coin. In this case the partials were inharmonic, and those nearest to the prime were distant from it several octaves. For D_l, $37\frac{1}{8}$ per second, there was only a very weak sensation of tone, and for $B_{ll}\flat$, $29\frac{1}{3}$ per second, there was scarcely anything audible left. Helmholtz afterwards investigated the matter with two large tuning-forks by Koenig fitted with sliding weights. One gave from 61 down to 35 vibrations per second; the other from 35 down to 24. For 30 vibrations per second Helmholtz could still hear a weak drone, for 28 scarcely a trace, although the amplitude was 9 mm.

575. Preyer, using loaded tongues or reeds, considered that he heard down to 15 vibrations per second. But Helmholtz expressed doubts about such results unless checked by the counting of beats. This check, however, was supplied by Mr. Ellis, the translator of Helmholtz, in experiments in South Kensington Museum, on a copy of Preyer's instruments. Ellis heard the beats at 4 per second quite distinctly from the reeds of frequencies 15 and 19, and thus concluded that the lowest partial of the reed at 15 per second was effective. The lowest pair of reeds from which Ellis was able to hear the bell-like beat of the lowest partials distinct from the general crash, had frequencies 30 and 34. Probably the limit of low pitch for audibility varies from one person to another, and even with the same person may be subject to fluctuations from

time to time.   It would appear that not much continuous
tone is usually heard from vibrations slower than about 30
per second.

576. Highest Pitch Audible.—The highest pitches in
musical use are, on the pianoforte a^{iv}, say 3520 per second,
and in the orchestra, on the piccolo d^{v}, say 4752 per
second.   Appun and Preyer with small tuning-forks bowed
reached e^{viii} of 40,960 per second.   Ellis could hear these
100 feet away.   Lord Rayleigh has constructed bird calls
giving tones up to 50,000 vibrations per second.   But
these high frequencies were detected by sensitive flames,
nothing was heard from them above 10,000 per second.
Thus, the extreme limits audible by one means or another
may be assigned as about 15 to 40,000 per second, the
musical limits being about 40 to 4000 per second.   Thus,
whereas the eye sees a range of barely one octave (from the
extreme red of the spectrum of frequency say 400 billions
per second to about 760 billions per second at the extreme
violet), the ear has an extreme range of say eleven octaves,
about seven octaves being musically available.

To facilitate the determination of the difference of the
upper limit of audibility in different persons Galton's
whistle is very useful.   It is a miniature adjustable stopped
organ pipe whose setting can be read off from linear and
circular scales in the manner of a micrometer gauge.   The
air is supplied by an india-rubber bulb compressed in the
hand.   Sometimes the difference between two observers is
accidentally shown in a striking manner.   Thus, on one
occasion, a whistle was alternately sounded by air and by
ordinary coal gas.   With the coal gas put on one observer
exclaimed, " The pitch now rises about a minor third," but
the other replied, " Nay, the sound has ceased altogether."
The explanation, of course, being that to the second observer
the lower sound lay beneath his upper limit, but the higher
sound lay just above that limit, and so in consequence
entirely escaped his perception.

577. Harmonic Echoes.—It has sometimes been noticed that the echoes returned from groups of trees are apparently raised an octave. This phenomenon has been mathematically treated and explained by Lord Rayleigh. Let T denote the small volume throughout which the constant of compressibility m and the density of the medium σ experience changes whose mean values are respectively Δm and $\Delta \sigma$. Let the incident or primary waves be expressed by

$$s_0 = e^{ik(ut+x)} \tag{1},$$

where s_0 is the condensation, e the base of the Naperian logarithms, $i = \sqrt{-1}$, $k = 2\pi/\lambda$, and u is the velocity of sound. Then Rayleigh has shown that the effect due to the abnormal space T can be expressed by the equation

$$\frac{s}{s_0} = -\frac{\pi T e^{-ikr}}{\lambda^2 r} \left\{ \frac{\Delta m}{m} + \frac{\Delta \sigma}{\sigma} \mu \right\} \tag{2}.$$

In this s denotes the condensation of the secondary waves at the time t and at the distance r from the place of disturbance, μ being the cosine of the angle between x and r. "Since the difference of phase represented by the factor e^{-ikr} corresponds simply to the distance r, we may consider that a simple reversal of phase occurs at the place of disturbance." It should be noticed that the amplitude of the reflected or secondary waves is inversely proportional to the first power of the distance r but to the *square* of the wave length λ. Further, of the two terms on the right in equation (2), the first is symmetrical round the place of disturbance, but the second varies as the cosine of the angle between the primary and secondary rays. Thus, a place at which the compressibility m varies behaves as a point source or simple source. But a place at which the density σ varies behaves like what Rayleigh calls a *double* source. In other words, the first may be compared with radial oscillations of a single small sphere, but the second with equal and opposite oscillations of two neighbouring spheres with centres on the axis of x.

578. Lord Rayleigh derives equation (2) by analysis too advanced for introduction here, but he afterwards shows that the results may be inferred from the method of dimensions as follows:—Thus Δm and $\Delta \sigma$ being given, the amplitude of the secondary disturbance is necessarily proportional to T, and in accordance with the principle of energy must also vary inversely as r. Then the only quantities dependent on space, time, and mass, of which the ratio of amplitudes can be a function, are T, r, λ, u, and σ. But the ratio of amplitudes is a pure number, and hence cannot involve σ, as it is the only one of the five containing mass, nor u, as it is the only one of the five involving time. Thus, if λ be involved to the power a, $Tr^{-1}\lambda^a$ must be independent of the unit of length. That is

$$(L^3)L^{-1}L^a = L^0, \text{ or } 3 - 1 + a = 0.$$

Hence $a = -2$, or the amplitude of the secondary waves varies *inversely* as the *square* of the wave length λ. But the intensity of a wave varies as the square of the amplitude, accordingly the intensity of the secondary waves must vary inversely as the *fourth* power of the wave length. Thus, " the octave, for example, is sixteen times stronger relatively to the fundamental tone in the secondary than it was in the primary sound. There is thus no difficulty in understanding how it may happen that echoes returned from such reflecting bodies as groups of trees may be raised an octave." [1]   For, in the case just mentioned, the primary sound incident upon the obstacles would be estimated as of the pitch of its fundamental tone, whereas in the secondary waves sent out from the obstacle that fundamental would be practically masked by the exaggerated prominence of its octave, which would accordingly be taken as fixing the pitch.

[1] *Theory of Sound*, p. 153 of vol. ii.

579. Musical Echo from Palisading or Overlapping Fence.—We have just seen how the pitch may be apparently changed by a diffuse reflection or scattering. Another phenomenon, perhaps more remarkable though simpler in theory, is that in which the pitch may be said to be originated by reflection. To realise this effect a very sudden sound is needed near a palisading or overlapping fence presenting a number of equidistant and parallel reflecting surfaces. Then regarding the original sound incident upon the fence as a single impulse or small part of a wave, it is clear that we shall have a multiple reflection from the several bars or overlapping edges of the fence. Moreover, as these successive bars are at distances from the observer which increase by nearly constant amounts, the arrival of the successive reflections build up a tone of a definite frequency. On walking along a hard pavement in nailed boots past an overlapping wood fence this phenomenon may be readily observed, especially if the heels are purposely struck down at each step more forcibly than usual. In a case under the writer's notice it was clear that the distinct musical ring often noticed when walking near a certain fence was due to this cause. For, while the pavement consisted of asphalt along the whole of one side of a park, the overlapping wood fence forming the first section of its boundary was followed for some distance by a rough, irregular stone wall, after which came a third section consisting of wood fence as at first. On walking past this boundary the musical echo was well heard from the first and third portions where the wood fence formed the boundary, but refused utterly to come from the wall forming the second or intermediate portion.

580. The succession of surfaces offered to sound by a palisading and an overlapping fence may be compared with the optical arrangements known as the diffraction grating and the echelon respectively. But although the palisade and fence might conceivably be used acoustically as the grating and echelon are used optically, they are not so used in the case referred to. For in the optical case with monochromatic light the incident waves form a continuous train of definite frequency and wave length, and spectra are in consequence formed in certain definite positions depending on that wave length. In the acoustical case under discussion the original disturbance incident on

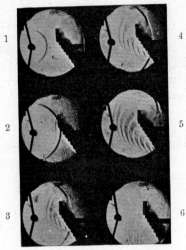

FIG. 100.—WOOD'S PHOTOGRAPH OF MUSICAL ECHO.

the successive bars is almost confined to a single pulse or part of a wave. Thus the frequency of the succession of impulses received at any point depends upon the difference in length of the paths traversed from the source to the observer by the waves incident upon the *various successive bars*. The actual formation of these waves by reflection from such a stepwise surface is shown in Fig. 100, which is from an instantaneous photograph by Prof. R. W. Wood of the waves in air from an electric spark.[1]

581. Æolian Tones.—Strouhal investigated the pheno-

[1] See *Phil. Mag.*, pp. 218-227, 48, 1899.

mena involved in the generation of the tones of the Æolian harp, which sounds when the wind plays upon the stretched wires. He found that the pitch of the Æolian tone was independent of the length and tension of the wire, but depended on its diameter and the speed of the wind. Thus denoting these quantities by d cm. and w cm./sec. respectively, he obtained for the frequency N the relation

$$N = 0\cdot185 \; w/d.$$

When, however, the Æolian tone coincided with one of the proper tones of the wire, the sound was greatly reinforced. Under the more extreme conditions the observed frequency deviated from the value of N given above. Strouhal showed also that with a given diameter and a given speed of wind, a rise of temperature was attended by a fall of pitch.

582. Minimum Amplitude Audible.—So far back as 1870, Toepler and Boltzmann made an estimate on this subject. Their method involved an application of Helmholtz's theory of the open organ pipe. They found that plane waves of frequency about 180 are just audible if the maximum value of the condensation s is $6\cdot5 \times 10^{-8}$. Now $vs_{max.} = \dot{y}_{max.} = \omega y_{max.}$, where y and $\dot{y}$ are the displacement and velocity of the vibrating particles, v is the speed of sound, and $\omega = 2\pi$ times the frequency N. Thus the amplitude is given by

$$a = y_{max.} = \frac{vs_{max.}}{2\pi N} = \frac{34,000 \times 6\cdot5}{2\pi \times 180 \times 10^8} = 2 \times 10^{-6} \text{ cm. nearly.}$$

583. *Rayleigh's Whistle Method.*—Lord Rayleigh carried out two methods for the determination of the minimum amplitude. In the first the source of sound was a whistle mounted upon a Wolfe's bottle. This was blown from the lungs so as to maintain a steady pressure measured by a water column $9\cdot5$ cm. high. This gave a sound heard without effort in both directions to a distance of 82,000 cm. A laboratory experiment showed that the air passing through the whistle at the above pressure was 196 c.c. per second. Hence the energy expended in the whistle was

$$E = 196 \times 9\tfrac{1}{2} \times 981 \text{ ergs per second} \qquad (1).$$

So this is the rate at which energy passed through the surface of a hemisphere whose centre is the whistle near the ground and whose radius is 82,000 cm. If the amplitude at this surface is a, we have as the expression for the activity per unit cross-sectional area (Equation 6, art. 146),

$$A = \tfrac{1}{2}\rho a^2 \omega^2 v \qquad (2),$$

where ρ is the density of the air and equals about $0\cdot0013$, $\omega = 2\pi N$ and v is the speed of sound which was in this case 34,100 cm. per sec., the frequency being about 2730 per second. Thus, for the hemisphere in question we have as the total activity $2\pi \times 82,000^2$ times the above expression (2). Hence equating this to (1) we have

$$2\pi \times 82,000^2 \times \tfrac{1}{2} \times 0\cdot0013 \times a^2(4\pi^2 \times 2730^2) \times 341,000$$
$$= 196 \times 9\tfrac{1}{2} \times 981 \qquad (3),$$

whence $a = 8\cdot1 \times 10^{-8}$ cm.

In this case the maximum velocity of the vibrating particles would be $0\cdot0014$ cm./sec., and the maximum condensation $s = $ max. vel. $\div$ speed of sound $= 4\cdot1 \times 10^{-8}$.

It should be noticed that the energy expended in blowing the whistle is not all converted into the energy of sound. Hence equation (3) is not strictly true, but gives an upper limit to the amplitude on the supposition that all the energy went into sound.

584. Rayleigh's Fork Method for Minimum Amplitude.—In this method the activity of the source is estimated from the decrement of the stock of energy possessed by it at a given standard amplitude. This activity is then equated to the usual expression for the activity in the wave front at the position of minimum amplitude for audibility. The details are as follows:—Let the amplitude of the ends of the fork prongs at time t be

$$\eta = \eta_0 e^{-kt/2} \qquad (1).$$

Then the law of the energy of the vibrating fork may be written

$$E = E_0 e^{-kt} \qquad (2).$$

For the energy varies as the square of the amplitude, hence its decrement involves a double index. To ascertain the value of k, let the time t_n be observed in which the amplitude sinks to $1/n$th of its initial value. Then, we have

$$\eta_0 = n\eta = n\eta_0 e^{-kt_n/2},$$

whence
$$k = \frac{2 \log_e n}{t_n} \qquad (3).$$

But since the activity A of the fork at any instant is its rate of loss of energy at that instant, we have

$$A = -dE/dt = kE_0 e^{-kt} = kE \qquad (4).$$

Thus, if E_0, k and t are known, A may be calculated.

585. But it is only the activity expended on sound that we require. So let k express the decrement of energy with the resonator in use and k_1 the corresponding decrement without the resonator. Then k can be divided into two parts as expressed by

$$k = k_1 + k_2 \qquad (5),$$

in which k_2 will represent the extra decrement of energy due to the presence of the resonator, and so covers that spent in producing sound, together with that which is dissipated in internal losses in the resonator. Thus the value k_2 is still only a superior limit for the decrement corresponding to sound-production, but must be taken as being the nearest approximation attainable.   Hence, for the activity producing sound we may write

$$A_2 = k_2 E_0 e^{-kt} = k_2 E \qquad (6).$$

Thus, by experiments with the resonator and without, k and k_1 are found by use of equation (3); k_2 is then inferred from (5). The values of k_2 and k are then used in (6). A little reflection will show that it is the k without a subscript that occurs in the index of e in equation (6).

In conducting the main experiment, one operator gives the fork a large vibration, and observes with a microscope till the standard amplitude is reached corresponding with E_0 in (6). He then gives a signal and withdraws. On receipt of this signal the other experimenter, who is stationed at a distance r from the fork, observes the time t for which the fork is still audible. Thus, from (6) the minimum value of A_2 is obtained in terms of E_0 and the k's. Now the value of E_0 for both prongs of the fork when the amplitude at their ends is η_0 is calculated by Rayleigh to be

$$E_0 = \sigma b l \pi^2 N^2 \eta_0^2 \qquad (7)$$

where σ, b, and l are the density, cross-section, and length of the prongs, and N their vibration frequency. Then, equating the expression for A_2 from (6) and (7) with the usual one for the wave front taken as hemispherical of radius r, we have

$$k_2 \sigma b l \pi^2 N^2 \eta_0^2 e^{-kt} = 2\pi r^2 . \tfrac{1}{2}\rho v (2\pi N)^2 a^2 \qquad (8),$$

where ρ is the density of the air, v the speed of sound, and a the minimum amplitude for audibility.

586. In an experiment on a fork of frequency 256, the vibrations fell from $0{\cdot}020$ cm. to $0{\cdot}010$ cm. in sixteen seconds without, and in nine seconds with, the resonator, whence $k = 0{\cdot}154$, $k_1 = 0{\cdot}0866$, and $k_2 = 0{\cdot}0674$ nearly. And for this fork $E_0 = $ about $4{\cdot}06 \times 10^3$ ergs. Thus $k_2 E_0 = 267$ ergs per second nearly.

But the t in equation (6) was here 12 seconds. Thus $A_2 = k_2 E_0 e^{-12k} = 267 e^{-12 \times 0.154} = 42.1$ ergs/sec. nearly. The amplitude of this minimum sound audible was found to be $a = 1.27 \times 10^{-7}$ cm., and the condensation $s = 6 \times 10^{-9}$.

587. Shaw's Determination of Minimum Amplitude Audible.

—Dr. P. E. Shaw[1] has applied his electrical micrometer to the question of the minimum amplitude audible. This determination consisted of two parts. First, the electrical micrometer was used to find the motion of the diaphragm of a telephone receiver due to steady currents of various values down to those too small to produce perceptible motion. This gave the relation between current and displacement of the diaphragm. Secondly, the telephone receiver was applied to the ear, and the same series of steady current values repeated, those values being noted at which the impulsive sound thus produced ceased to be audible. This gave the relation between current and audibility. Thus, on reference to the first set of observations, the relation between audibility and displacement of the diaphragm was at once found.

This investigation gave, as the mean result of a number, that the minimum motion of the diaphragm for audibility of an expected impulsive sound was 0.7×10^{-7} cm. for the right ear and 0.9×10^{-7} cm. for the left ear of the experimenter. Motions of the diaphragm less than a tenth of the above were measured but produced no audible effect. Dr. Shaw points out that the amplitude of the air vibrations would be probably (as calculated by Rayleigh) only one-fifth of those of the telephone diaphragm. Thus, taking this to be the case, audibility for an expected sound is possible from air vibrations whose amplitude is only 0.14×10^{-7} cm.

The above results were obtained under favourable conditions as to silence and steadiness, the work being carried out in an underground vault in University College,

[1] *Roy. Soc. Proc.*, vol. A 76, 1904.

Nottingham, and the finer observations made between midnight and 4 A.M.

588. The improved electrical micrometer used in this research, devised and developed by Dr. Shaw himself, was fully described in 1904.[1] Its essential parts may be classified under three heads as follows:—(1) The contact arrangements by which when a knob touches the object under test it completes an electrical circuit, and so announces the fact by a sound in a telephone. (2) A set of levers which magnifies the motion of the contact knob carried by the short arm of the first lever. (3) A micrometer screw and divided circle for reading the motion of the long arm of the last lever, and from which that of the contact knob can be deduced. The instrument is standardised and calibrated by observation of Newton's rings.

589. Long Range Transit of Sound.—When waves of sound are spreading in the open air from a powerful source, theory and experiment alike show that a number of causes operate to diminish their intensity or to prevent their ever reaching the regions geometrically open to them. Some of these causes have already been more or less dealt with. For completeness' sake they may be enumerated here with the others. We thus have the following:—

(1) *Radiation involves Attenuation.*—As already seen, if the radiation is spherical the intensity diminishes inversely as the square of the distance from the source.

(2) *Temperature Gradient produces Refraction.*—Lord Kelvin has shown that the air when undisturbed by winds and sunshine tends to a state which he calls *convective equilibrium.* In this state, if air be suddenly taken from one level to another, the adiabatic expansion or compression consequent on the change of pressure would just bring it to the temperature already possessed by that region. There is thus a lower temperature at higher altitudes since there the pressure must be less, and the air in ascending

---

[1] Royal Society, *loc. cit.*

2 Q

to it would suffer adiabatic expansion, and therefore cooling.

When this is the state of things, Lord Rayleigh has shown that the path of a ray of sound through the air is a catenary whose vertex is downwards. Moreover, if the ray is sent the reverse way the same catenary would be traversed.

590. (3) *Wind Gradient produces Refraction.*—As already seen (Chap. II. art. 65), if the wind is everywhere horizontal, but increases uniformly upwards, the ray of sound may describe a catenary or quasi-catenary. But in this case the path is not reversible. Thus, if the direction is against the wind the catenary has its vertex downwards. But if the sound passes with the wind the catenary described has its vertex upwards. Hence if cannons are fired at two stations A and B, it may happen that those fired at A will be plainly heard at B, whereas those fired at B may be inaudible at A. This may explain the facts of art. 474.

(4) *Regular Reflection.*—This may occur at large solid surfaces as a cliff, hill-side, etc., as in the case of the ordinary echo. This may also occur from large surfaces where the density of the air suddenly changes owing either to a sudden change in temperature or to a sudden change in the degree of humidity. The second and third examples may be called aerial echoes. According to Tyndall they are probably concerned in the rolling of the thunder.

591. (5) *Scattering or Irregular Reflection.*—Sometimes the air, though optically very transparent, is crowded with patches or layers of alternately different densities owing to sudden changes in temperature or humidity, or both. In this state of affairs, though no regular or distinct reflection may be obtained, the sound is scattered from each irregular surface, and so the intensity of the direct sound is thereby very much diminished. The phenomenon is analogous to the scattering of light from a milky glass or a turbid liquid. For these two optical media, while returning no light in the regular manner needed to form an image, yet intercept and scatter much of it, so that the portion passing on is considerably reduced.

This state of acoustic opacity or semi-opacity was carefully investigated by Tyndall, who also imitated it by lecture experiments. In one of these a number of alternate layers of carbon dioxide and coal gas were interposed between a bell and a sensitive flame. In this case the flame remained unaffected by the sound when the two gases were streaming from their respective sets of apertures, although the region in question was still quite transparent in the usual optical sense. When, however, the gases were turned off and the air allowed to diffuse into the region the flame responded well to the ringing of the bell.

592. (6) *Diffraction.*—The spreading of sound behind obstacles, which is one form of diffraction, must also slightly weaken the main or direct sound beyond that which is valid for spherical radiation simply.

We may now notice other states of the air which have been supposed prejudicial to sound, but which Tyndall by an elaborate series of experiments found are not so. These include the presence of rain, hail, snow, and fog, which Tyndall asserts have " no sensible power to obstruct sound." Lord Kelvin has shown that the temperature gradient which forms the limiting condition of equilibrium of the air in a warm fog is about half that in the limiting condition for fog-free air. It is, of course, a state in which temperature falls as we ascend. Thus on theoretical grounds we should expect that sound would radiate with less loss in a fog than when the air is clear. This inference is fully borne out by Tyndall's prolonged researches off Dover. He also arranged lecture experiments to show the very slight reduction in sound intensity caused by the presence of small obstacles. Thus sound passed with ease through layers of calico, cambric, silk, flannel, baize, and felt, in thickness sufficient to intercept the light of the sun.

593. The various diversions or losses suffered by sound in its progress were also carefully examined by Henry in America. But while he is disposed to attribute most of the vagaries of distant sounds to refraction, Tyndall attaches more importance to the scattering due to the patchy or flocculent state of the atmosphere. Reynolds has, however, shown that some of Tyndall's own observations admit of explanation on the principle of refraction.

594. Pressure of Vibrations. — The mechanical pressure exerted on a surface by waves incident upon them was first pointed out by Maxwell for electro-magnetic disturbances in connection with his electro-magnetic theory of light. The pressure of light has been experimentally confirmed and measured by Lebedew of Moscow, and with more refinement by Nichols and Hull of America.

According to theory the pressure in this case is equal to the volume density of light energy in front of the surface, and this was found to be so within the limits of experimental errors.

If this pressure of light was a phenomenon peculiar to light among all other known vibrations it would not concern us here. But it has been shown to be a general property of wave motion, and has recently aroused considerable interest. It therefore calls for notice in connection with sound.

In addressing the Physical Society of London in 1905 on Radiation Pressure in general, Prof. Poynting stated that up to then no general and direct dynamical theorem accounting for it had been given. In the meantime he considered the simple indirect method of proving its existence for waves of certain types given by Prof. Larmor was very useful. The general idea underlying this method is as follows :—Suppose radiation to fall normally upon a mirror which moves normally in the opposite direction so as to meet the incident waves. Then the reflected train will be of shorter wave length, and may be shown to have not only more energy per unit length, but to be pouring out more energy per unit time than the incident waves. This increase can only be accounted for by supposing that the moving mirror does work on the system. Hence the mirror must experience a pressure from the waves. To find the amount of this pressure we must treat the problem analytically. The following account is taken from Larmor's article,[1] but the notation is modified, and the analysis given in more detail in accordance with the plan of this work.

595. Larmor's Indirect Pressure Theorem.—Consider a wave train of any kind in which the displacement is given by

$$\xi = a \cos k(x + vt) \qquad (1),$$

so that it travels in the negative direction along the axis of x. Let it fall normally upon the reflector travelling towards it with velocity u, and whose position at time t is given by

$$x = ut \qquad (2).$$

There will be a reflected train of waves which may be denoted by

$$\xi' = a' \cos k'(x - vt) \qquad (3),$$

the speed of propagation v remaining of course the same as before. The disturbance does not travel into the reflector, and must therefore be annulled at its surface. Thus, at every instant we must have at $x = ut$, the relation

$$\xi + \xi' = 0,$$

which by (1) and (3) becomes

$$a \cos k(ut + vt) + a' \cos k'(ut - vt) = 0 \qquad (4).$$

And this is satisfied for all values of t by

$$a' = -a \qquad (5),$$

and

$$k'(v - u) = k(v + u) \qquad (6).$$

[1] *Encyclopædia Britannica*, vol. xxxii. p. 121.

Thus from (5) the amplitude of the reflected disturbance is numerically equal to that of the incident one. To interpret (6) we note from (1) that $k\lambda = 2\pi$, or the incident wave length is $\lambda = 2\pi/k$. Thus, if λ' is the wave length of the reflected train it is $2\pi/k'$, and (6) then shows that

$$\frac{\lambda'}{\lambda} = \frac{k}{k'} = \frac{v-u}{v+u} \qquad (7).$$

Or in words, by reflection at the moving reflector the wave length is shortened in the ratio $(v-u)/(v+u)$.

596. The energy in the wave train is half-potential and half-kinetic, and is given by the integration of $\rho(d\xi/dt)^2$ along the train, ρ being the density. Whence the energy per unit volume is found to be inversely as λ^2 (see art. 145). Let the energy per unit volume in the incident train be E, and that in the reflected train be E'. Then, since in the two trains the amplitude and density are the same, we have

$$\frac{E'}{E} = \left(\frac{v+u}{v-u}\right)^2 \qquad (8).$$

But in unit time the length $v+u$ of the incident train passes up to the reflector, and a length $(v-u)$ issues from it. Hence, if the energies per second or activities of the incident and reflected trains per unit cross-sectional area are denoted respectively by A and A', we have

$$A = (v+u)E \text{ and } A' = (v-u)E' \qquad (9).$$

Thus, by (8) and (9),

$$\frac{A'}{A} = \frac{(v-u)}{(v+u)} \frac{(v+u)^2}{(v-u)^2} = \frac{v+u}{v-u},$$

whence the increase of activity in the reflected train is given by

$$A' - A = \left(\frac{v+u}{v-u} - 1\right)A = \frac{2u}{v-u}A \qquad (10).$$

But this increase in the energy per unit time leaving the

mirror over that reaching it can only arise from work done
on it to cause advance against pressure exerted by the
radiation. And, just as the product of force and distance
equals energy, so the product of force and speed gives
activity. But the force per unit area is the pressure to be
evaluated which we will denote by P, and the speed of the
mirror is u. Hence we have

$$Pu = A' - A = \frac{2u}{v - u}A,$$

or,

$$P = \frac{2A}{v - u} \qquad (11).$$

597. It is convenient to express this pressure in terms
of the total volume density of energy just in front of the
reflector. Thus, from (8) we have

$$\frac{E + E'}{E} = \frac{2(v^2 + u^2)}{(v - u)^2} \qquad (12).$$

Then by (9) and (12) we obtain

$$A = (v + u)E = \frac{(v + u)(v - u)^2}{2(v^2 + u^2)}(E + E') \qquad (13).$$

Hence (13) and (11) give

$$P = \frac{2}{v - u} \cdot \frac{(v + u)(v - u)^2}{2(v^2 + u^2)}(E + E'),$$

or,

$$P = \frac{v^2 - u^2}{v^2 + u^2}(E + E') \qquad (14).$$

Or in words, the pressure on the reflector is $(v^2 - u^2)/(v^2 + u^2)$
times the volume density of the total energy of the
incident and reflected waves. If u is very small compared
with v this reduces to

$$P = (1 - 2u^2/v^2)(E + E') \qquad (15),$$

or, if $u = 0$, we have

$$P = E + E' \qquad (16)$$

That is, a reflector at rest experiences a *radiation pressure* equal to the *total energy density* of radiation in front of it.

Larmor illustrates this argument by the transverse vibrations of a tense cord along which, to act as a reflector, a pierced board or ring is made to slide. Lord Rayleigh [1] treats the string problem by a different method. Both show that the constraint, which acts as a reflector, is subject to a force which equals the total longitudinal density of the vibrational energy in front of it.

598. Direct View for Sound Pressure.—The above indirect theorem applies, of course, to sound waves, but it seems desirable to see if possible how for any particular kind of wave motion the pressure arises. For the case of sound this was shown very simply by Prof. Poynting in the address already referred to. He said, " In sound waves there is at a reflecting surface a node, a point of no motion, but of varying pressure. If the variation of pressure from the undisturbed value were exactly proportional to the displacements of a parallel layer near the surface, and if the displacements were exactly harmonic, then the average pressure would be equal to the normal undisturbed value. But consider a layer of air quite close to the surface. If it moves up a distance y towards the surface, the pressure is increased. If it moves an equal distance y away from the surface, the pressure is decreased, but by a slightly smaller quantity. To illustrate this, take an extreme case, and for simplicity suppose that Boyle's law holds. If the layer advances half-way towards the reflecting surface the pressure is doubled. If it moves an equal distance outwards from its original position the pressure falls, but only by one-third of its original value ; and if we could suppose the layer to be moving harmonically, it is obvious that the mean of the increased and diminished pressures would be largely in excess of the normal value. Though we are not entitled to assume the existence of harmonic vibrations when we

[1] *Phil. Mag.*, iii. 1902, p. 338.

take into account the second order of small quantities, yet this illustration gives the right idea. The excess of pressure in the compressed half is greater than its defect during the extension half, and the net result is an average excess of pressure—a quantity itself of the second order—on the reflecting surface. This excess in the compression half of a wave train is connected with the extra speed which exists in that half, and makes the crests of intense sound-waves gain on the troughs."

599. Again, using Boyle's law, Lord Rayleigh has shown [1] that for plane sound waves the total force is measured by the longitudinal density of total energy, and that the additional pressure is measured by the volume density of energy. If, however, the aerial vibrations are distributed equally all round, then the pressure due to them on a plane surface would coincide with one-third of the volume density of the total energy.

600. Experimental Confirmation.—The pressure of sound waves has been experimentally detected and measured by W. Altberg,[2] working in the laboratory of Lebedew. He employed a Kundt tube as the source of sound, and for the receiver a small wooden cylinder 21 mm. diameter. This was fixed at one end of the arm of a delicate torsion balance. One end of the cylinder passed through a hole in a plate with sufficient clearance to allow its free motion. The waves were then received on this plate and cylinder end. In some experiments the pressure rose to $0 \cdot 24$ dyne per sq. cm. The intensity of the sound was independently measured by a telephone plate in a manner devised by Wien. The results of the investigation showed that the pressure upon a reflecting wall is completely analogous to the pressure of light waves.

601. Pressure of Vibrating Membrane. — Lord

[1] *Phil. Mag.*, iii. 1902, p. 338.
[2] *Ann. d. Physik*, xi. 2. pp. 405-420, May 14, 1903 ; *Science Abstracts*, No. 1471, 1904.

Rayleigh also applied his methods of reasoning to other cases. Thus, if a vibrating membrane has a flexible and extensible boundary capable of shifting along the surface, and the vibrations are equally distributed in the plane, then the force outwards per unit length of contour is one-half the superficial density of the total energy.

602. Conception of Momentum of Radiation.—In the address already quoted Prof. Poynting also brought forward and emphasised the very valuable conception of momentum in connection with a beam of radiation. We cannot do better than again quote his own words, which run as follows:—

" Theory and experiment, then, justify the conclusion that when a source is pouring out waves, it is pouring out with them forward momentum as well as energy, the momentum being manifested in the reaction, the back pressure against the source, and in the forward pressure when the waves reach an opposing surface. The wave train may be regarded as a stream of momentum travelling through space. This view is most clearly brought home, perhaps, by considering a parallel train of waves which issues normally from a source for one second, travels for any length of time through space, and then falls normally on an absorbing surface for one second. During this last second momentum is given up to the absorbing surface. During the first second the same amount was given out by the source. If it is con-served in the meanwhile we must regard it as travelling with the train. Since the pressure is the momentum given out or received per second, and the pressure is equal to the energy density in the train, the momentum density is equal to the energy density ÷ wave velocity."

603. Thus, if the pressure be P, the momentum per unit volume M, and the energy density E, then the total momentum reaching a stationary surface per unit area per second would be

$$M\lambda/\tau = Mv = P.$$

But $\qquad\qquad\qquad P = E,$ as previously shown,

so $\qquad\qquad\qquad M = E/v,$ as stated above in words.

This refers to the incident beam only, and therefore represents the total pressure if the waves are completely absorbed as in the case of light at an absolutely black surface. When the radiation is completely reflected the pressure is doubled. When the incidence is oblique only the normal component is felt normally, but experiments by Prof. Poynting have shown that in the case of light the tangential component is felt tangentially and is of the amount predicted by theory.

604. Prompted by the remarks of Prof. Poynting, Lord Rayleigh[1] returned to the subject, but this time without the restriction to Boyle's law; he thus obtains "more general results," which, however, do not in all respects fulfil the anticipations of Poynting. The paper commences with a calculation similar to that given before, but applicable to a gas in which the pressure is any arbitrary function of the density. The general result obtained expresses the mean additional pressure upon the piston in terms of the mean kinetic energy as follows :—

$$\int (p_1 - p_0)dt = \left\{ \rho_0 + \frac{\rho_0^2 f''(\rho_0)}{2f'(\rho_0)} \right\} \int\int \frac{U^2 dx dt}{l} \qquad (1).$$

In this the p's denote pressures, the ρ's densities, $p = f(\rho)$, the accents to the f's denoting derived functions, U denotes the resultant velocity at point x at time t, and l is the length of the cylinder parallel to x. Among special cases that of Boyle's law is first taken, where $p = a^2\rho$. So that $f'(\rho_0) = a^2, f''(\rho_0) = 0$. Hence

$$\int (p_1 - p_0)dt = \rho_0 \int\int \frac{U^2 dx dt}{l} \qquad (2).$$

The expression on the right represents double the

---

[1] *Phil. Mag.*, x. pp. 364-374, September 1905; *Science Abstracts*, p. 35, January 1906.

volume-density of kinetic energy, or the volume-density of the whole energy; thus agreeing with the result of the former investigation. According to the adiabatic law, $p/p_0 = (\rho/\rho_0)^\gamma$, so that $f'(\rho_0) = \gamma p_0/\rho_0$ and

$$f''(\rho_0) = \gamma(\gamma - 1)p_0/\rho_0{}^2.$$

Thus, from (1) is obtained for this case—

$$\int (p_1 - p_0)dt = \frac{\gamma + 1}{2}\rho_0 \iint \frac{U^2 dx dt}{l} \qquad (3).$$

605. Hence the mean additional pressure upon the piston is now $(\gamma + 1)/2$ of the volume-density of the total energy. We fall back on Boyle's law by taking $\gamma = 1$. It appears, therefore, that the result is altered when Boyle's law is departed from. Still more striking is the alteration when we take the case treated in *Theory of Sound*, § 250, of the law of pressure—

$$p = \text{constant} - a^2\rho_0{}^2/\rho.$$

According to this, $f(\rho_0) = a^2$ and $f''(\rho_0) = -2a^2/\rho_0$. Then (1) gives for this case—

$$\int (p_1 - p_0)dt = 0 \qquad (4)$$

The law of pressure here used is that under which waves of finite condensation can be propagated without change of type. In (4) the mean additional pressure vanishes, and the question arises whether it can be negative. It would appear so. If, for example, $p = \text{constant} - a^2\rho_0{}^3/2\rho^2$; then $f'(\rho_0) = a^2, f''(\rho_0) = -3a^2/\rho_0$, and

$$\int (p_1 - p_0)dt = -\frac{\rho_0}{2} \iint \frac{U^2 dx dt}{l} \qquad (5).$$

606. The question of the momentum of wave trains is then considered, and it is shown that

$$\text{momentum} = \left\{ \frac{\rho_0 f''(\rho_0)}{4a^3} + \frac{1}{2a} \right\} \times \text{total energy} \qquad (6),$$

the a now denoting the velocity of infinitely small waves. This may be compared with (1). If we suppose the long cylinder of length l to be occupied by a train of progressive waves moving towards the piston, the integrated pressure upon the piston during a time l/a should be equal to twice the momentum of the whole initial motion. The two formulæ are thus in accordance, and (6) needs no detailed discussion. It may suffice to call attention, *first*, to Boyle's law, where $f''(\rho_0) = 0$, and, *second*, to the law of pressure leading to (4), under which second case progressive waves have *no momentum*. It would seem that pressure and momentum are here associated with the tendency of waves to alter their form as they proceed on their course.

607. Quality and Phase.—In the present chapter on acoustical determinations we have dealt with the velocity of propagation of sound, also, the pitch and amplitude of musical tones. There is but little to be said here about the third feature of a musical tone, namely, its quality. The two questions respecting quality that have not been already sufficiently discussed, and may be dealt with here, are the following :—

(1) Does quality depend on phase ?

(2) Are vowels characterised by a fixed or a variable pitch of resonance ?

To answer the first question Helmholtz experimented with a set of electrically maintained tuning-forks forming a harmonic series. In this set of forks he had two ways of weakening any individual tone. One way, that of placing the resonator a little farther away, had no effect on the phase. Whereas the other way, namely, that of shading the mouth of the resonator, and thus putting it a little out of tune with the fork, both weakened the tone in question and changed its phase also. By this means a difference of phase of one-quarter of a period could be obtained, and by reversal of the electric current a difference of half a period could be made. Thus full power over the phase was

attained. Speaking of the results of experiments conducted thus, Helmholtz said : " So far as quality of tone
was concerned, I found that it was entirely indifferent
whether I weakened the separate partial tones by shading
the mouths of their resonance chambers, or by moving the
chamber itself to a sufficient distance from the fork. Hence
the answer to the proposed question is : *The quality of the
musical portion of a compound tone depends solely on the
number and relative strength of its partial simple tones, and
in no respect on their difference of phases.*"

608. Helmholtz afterwards pointed out what he called
an apparent exception to the above rule. Koenig, however,
considered it a real exception. It is the case of two forks
sounding a slightly mistuned octave.

Koenig attacked the question as to the influence of
phase on quality by means of his wave siren. In this
instrument the wind issues from a slit-like aperture, and
encounters the margin of a disc whose departures from the
form of a circle consist of a set of regularly recurring waves
made of any desired pattern. The slit from which the wind
issues is in the position of a radius of the disc. Thus, as the
wave-formed margin passes round the air blast is alternately
increased or diminished according to a simple or compound
harmonic law corresponding to the shape of the particular
disc in use.

609. Speaking of these experiments by Koenig, Mr. Ellis,
the translator of Helmholtz,[1] says Koenig " compounded
harmonic curves of various pitches, and with various
assumptions of amplitude, under four varieties of phase :
(1) the beginning of all the waves coinciding ; (2) the first
quarter ; (3) the halves ; and, (4) the third quarters of each
wave coinciding—briefly said to have a difference of phase
of 0, $\frac{1}{4}$, $\frac{1}{2}$, $\frac{3}{4}$. These were reduced by photography, inverted,
and placed on the rim of the disc of a wave siren, and then
made to speak. He gives the remarkable curves which

[1] *Sensations of Tone*, p. 537.

resulted in a few cases, and instructions for repeating the experiments. The following are his conclusions:—

" ' The composition of a number of harmonic tones, including both the evenly and unevenly numbered partials, generates in all cases, quite independently of the relative intensity of these tones, the strongest and acutest quality of tone for the $\frac{1}{4}$ difference of phase, and the weakest and softest for $\frac{3}{4}$ difference of phase, while the differences 0 and $\frac{1}{2}$ lie between the others, both as regards intensity and acuteness.

" ' When unevenly numbered partials only are compounded, the differences of phase $\frac{1}{4}$ and $\frac{3}{4}$ give the same quality of tone, as do also the differences 0 and $\frac{1}{2}$; but the former is stronger and acuter than the latter.

610. " ' Hence, although the quality of tone principally depends on the number and relative intensity of the harmonic tones compounded, the influence of difference of (phase) is not by any means so insignificant as to be entirely negligible. We may say, in general terms, that the differences in the number and relative intensity of the harmonic tones compounded produces those differences in the quality of tone which are remarked in musical instruments of different families, or in the human voice uttering different vowels. But the alteration of phase between these harmonic tones can excite at least such differences of quality of tone as are observed in musical instruments of the same family, or in different voices singing the same vowel.' "

611. Vowel Pitches.—We now come to the second question, namely, as to the resonance pitch for a given vowel, Does it vary with the pitch of the note to which that vowel is sung or is it fixed? Or, in the words of Lord Rayleigh, is "a given vowel characterised by the permanence of partials of given *order* (the relative pitch theory), or by the permanence of partials of given *pitch* (the fixed pitch theory)?"

Willis decided the question in favour of the fixed

pitch theory, and Helmholtz seemed to hold the same opinion.

" If indeed, as has usually been assumed by writers on phonetics, a particular vowel quality is associated with a given oral configuration, the question is scarcely an open one. Subsequently, under Helmholtz's superintendence, the matter was further examined by Auerbach, who along with other methods employed a direct analysis of the various vowels by means of resonators associated with the ear. His conclusion on the question under discussion was the intermediate one that *both* characteristics were concerned. The analysis showed also that in all cases the first, or fundamental tone, was the strongest element in the sound."

" Hermann pronounces unequivocally in favour of the fixed pitch characteristic as at any rate by far the more important, and his experiments apparently justify this conclusion. He finds that the vowels sounded by the phonograph are markedly altered if the speed is varied." The theory and action of the phonograph is given in the next chapter in connection with which the subject of vowel pitches is again referred to.

612. Perception of Sound Direction.—Some years ago Lord Rayleigh [1] " executed a rather extensive series of experiments in order to ascertain more precisely what are the capabilities of the ears in estimating the direction of sounds. It appeared from these that, when the alternative was between right and left, the discrimination could be made with certainty and without moving the head, even although the sounds were pure tones. On the other hand, if the question was whether a sound were situated in front of or behind the observer, no pronouncement could be made in the case of pure tones. But with sounds of other character, and notably with the speaking voice, front and back could often be distinguished. The discrimination between the

[1] *Phil. Mag.*, xiii. pp. 214-232, February 1907, and *Science Abstracts*, p. 146, March 1907.

right and left situations of high sounds is easily explained upon the intensity theory, the head forming a fairly effective screen which places the averted ear in a sound shadow. But this theory becomes less and less adequate as the pitch falls. At a frequency of 256 the difference of intensity at the two ears is far from conspicuous. At 128 it is barely perceptible. But although the difference of intensities is so small, the discrimination of right and left is as easy as before.

613. " There is nothing surprising in the observation that sounds of low pitch are nearly as well heard with the further as with the nearer ear. When the wave length amounts to several feet it is not to be expected that a sound originating at a distance could be limited to one side of the head. This subject has been quantitatively examined in Rayleigh's *Theory of Sound*, § 328, whence it appears that for a frequency of 256 the difference of intensities is only about 10 per cent of the whole intensity. A fall in pitch of an octave reduces the difference of intensities 16 times. Thus at frequency 128 the difference would be decidedly less than 1 per cent of the whole ; and from this point on it is difficult to see how this difference could play any important part " in the lateral discrimination. In 1906-1907 Lord Rayleigh returned to the subject and carried out experiments " which have solved the above outstanding difficulty. By theory and experiments with forks it is concluded that above $c'' = 512$ the discrimination of right and left is made chiefly, if not solely, upon the difference of intensities at the two ears, but that at low pitch, at any rate below $c = 128$, phase-differences must be appealed to.

614. " To confirm this the obvious method was to conduct to the two ears separately two pure tones, nearly but not quite in unison. During the cycle, or beat, the phase-differences assume all possible values. This was realised by two forks of frequency 128, independently electrically

2 R

maintained, placed in different rooms and isolated. The observer in a third room listened with each ear to the sounds along gas-pipes led through holes in a thick wall from the resonators associated with each fork. The beat could be slowed down until it occupied 40 or even 70 sec., thus giving opportunity for more leisurely observation. The results were quite decisive; it was found that if the vibration on the right were quicker, the sensation of right followed agreement of phase, and the sensation of left followed opposition of phase—that is, the sensation of receiving a sound from the right was experienced when the sound received at the right ear had a lead in phase over that reaching the left ear.

615. " The conclusion, no longer to be resisted, that when a sound of low pitch reaches the two ears with approximately equal intensities, but with a phase-difference of one quarter-period, we are able so easily to distinguish at which ear the phase is in advance, must have far-reaching consequences in the theory of audition. It seems no longer possible to hold that the vibratory character of sound terminates at the outer ends of the nerves along which the communication with the brain is established. On the contrary, the processes in the nerve must themselves be vibratory, not of course in the gross mechanical sense, but with preservation of the period and retaining the characteristic of phase—a view advocated by Rutherford, in opposition to Helmholtz, as long ago as 1886. And when we admit that phase-differences at the two ears of tones in unison are easily recognised, we may be inclined to go farther, and find less difficulty in supposing that phase relations between a tone and its harmonics presented to the *same* ear are also recognisable. The discrimination of right and left in the case of sounds of frequency 128 and lower, so difficult to understand on the intensity theory, is now satisfactorily attributed to the phase-differences at the two ears.

616. " Observations with sounds of the frequency 256 are next dealt with, and it is concluded that when, by passing up in pitch, difference of phase fails, difference of intensity comes to our aid in the discrimination of right and left. In conclusion, it is pointed out that, in wishing to locate a fog-signal heard on board a ship, a combination of three or four observers facing different ways offers advantages. A comparison of their judgments, attending only to what they think as to right and left, and disregarding impressions as to front and back, should lead to a safe and fairly close estimate of direction."

The above conclusions as to lateral discrimination by phase-difference was further confirmed by Lord Rayleigh[1] by experiments with a revolving magnet and two telephones.

617. Architectural Acoustics.—According to W. C. Sabine,[2] " The problem of architectural acoustics requires for its complete solution two distinct lines of investigation : one to determine quantitatively the physical conditions on which loudness, reverberation, resonance, and the allied phenomena depend ; the other to determine the intensity which each of these should have, what conditions are best for the distinct audition of speech, and what effects are best for music in its various forms. Sabine's article contains contributions to each aspect of the subject. The question as to what conditions are best was attacked by investigating for a number of rooms what number of cushions and other absorbent articles were judged by musicians to give the best effect when hearing piano music. It was thus found that musical taste in such matters is very concordant and sensitive, a change of a few per cent making a room too resonant or too ' dead.' The other aspect of the question as to the physical dependence of reverberation on the presence of certain articles was elaborately investigated.

---

[1] *Phil. Mag.*, xiii. pp. 316-319, March 1907.
[2] *Amer. Acad. Proc.*, xlii. No. 2, pp. 51-84, June 1906, and *Science Abstracts*, p. 524, October 1906.

Tests were made of the absorbing powers of different substances, such as felt, curtains, an audience, and the usual
furniture of an auditorium. Further, the variation of these
absorbing powers with pitch was determined. Usually the
absorption increases with rise of pitch; or, in other words,
the duration of reverberation is diminished by a rise of
pitch."

·**618.** In 1906 a valuable paper appeared by Marage[1]
which "deals with the acoustic properties of six halls in
Paris, ranging from the Trocadero of volume 63,000 cub. m.
with an audience of 4500, down to the Physiological Theatre
of the Sorbonne, with an audience of 150, the volume being
890 cub. m. In a hall," according to this author, "the
audience hears three sets of vibrations: (1) those received
direct from the source; (2) those diffused or scattered by
the walls, ceiling, etc., thus producing the sound of resonance;
and (3) those regularly reflected by the walls which give
the distinct echoes. For a hall to be good from the
acoustical point of view there should be no echo, and the
resonance should be short enough to reinforce the original
sound to which it is due, instead of trespassing upon the
sound following. W. Sabine found from his experiments
that the duration of the resonance can be given by
$t = 0.171v/(a + x)$, where v is the volume of the room, a
is its absorbing power when empty, and x the absorbing
power of the spectators. Marage used as the sources of
sound the five vowels OU, O, A, É, I, each synthetically
produced by a siren in the place usually occupied by the
speaker, the listener being successively at different points
in the hall. In the largest hall, the Trocadero, holding
4500, the mean time of resonance was 2 sec. when empty
and 1·4 sec. when full. To make himself distinctly heard
in this hall a speaker must use a slow utterance, pausing
at each phrase. But it is not necessary to use more energy

---

[1] *Comptes Rendus*, **142**. pp. 878-880, 9th April 1906, and *Science Abstracts*,
p. 313, June 1906.

than in addressing 250 in the Physical Theatre of the
Sorbonne. In the large theatre of the Sorbonne, holding
3000, the resonance extended almost to 3 sec. empty, but
was only 1 sec. or less when full. The acoustic properties
of this hall are considered very good. Four other halls are
studied and details given.

619. " The author concludes (1) in agreement with
Sabine, that the resonance serves to characterise the acoustic
properties of a hall. (2) The duration of the sound varies
with the quality, the pitch, and the intensity of the primary
sound, hence a hall good for a speaker may be bad for an
orchestra. (3) With the formula before given we can
determine the duration of the resonance as a function of
the number of auditors. (4) For a hall to be good
acoustically, the duration of the resonance should be
practically constant at all parts of the hall, and for all
vowels, and fall between $\frac{1}{2}$ sec. and 1 sec. (5) If the
duration of the resonance much exceeds 1 sec., the speaker
can make himself understood only by speaking very slowly,
articulating distinctly, and avoiding giving to the voice too
much energy."

CHAPTER XI.

RECORDERS AND REPRODUCERS

620. The Phonautograph.—In this chapter we shall treat of various instruments which have been devised to record or reproduce sounds. Some of these involve applications of electricity to the subject of acoustics. Hence, for the full appreciation of these parts of the chapter it is necessary that the reader should possess some conversance with electrical theory and practice. But as it is clearly outside the scope of this work to teach elementary electricity, it will be assumed that the student has acquired from other sources a sufficient electrical knowledge to enable him to follow intelligently the descriptions and qualitative actions of the instruments dealt with.

For convenience' sake, however, a few notes will be given at the end of the chapter on those parts of more advanced electrical theory which are applicable to the subject in hand and are needed for its quantitative study.

We commence with the phonautograph of Scott and Koenig. This instrument was introduced in 1864, and yields a record of sounds in the form of a wavy trace on smoked paper. The paper is fixed on a rotating drum, and the curves are made by a style attached to a membrane. This membrane is set in vibration by the sounds which it receives after concentration by passage through a conical or paraboloidal funnel. By means of this instrument many curves have been obtained due to single sounds or to a combination of sounds. Its interest is now chiefly historical. For examples of curves originally due to the phonautograph, see Fig. 13, Art. 31.

621. The Phonograph.—The phonograph was invented by Edison in 1877. It not only records sounds as the phonautograph did, but also reproduces them. Thus it may be held to solve in the domain of acoustics a problem closely analogous to that achieved by photography in the domain of optics. For in each case a record is made, and then an imitation of the original facts may be in a sense reproduced from that record at will and after the lapse of time. But in the case of an ordinary photograph the form and light and shade are imitated, but the colour is lost. With the phonograph, however, not only may the pitch and relative intensities be correctly repeated, but even the quality also is reproducible and with astonishing though not perfect fidelity.

622. The essentials of the first instrument are briefly as follows :—The original sound falls upon a diaphragm whose consequent vibrations move a style which appropriately indents a sheet of tinfoil wound on the surface of a rotating drum. This indented tinfoil constitutes the record of the sound in question. To reproduce it the drum is adjusted to the starting-point, and again rotated at the same speed as before. The style and diaphragm are thus caused to repeat approximately their original motions, and thereby reproduce what is recognisable as an imitation of the original sound.

The details of the apparatus may be understood by reference to Figs. 101 and 102.

623. Supported upon a suitable base and bearings we have the horizontal axle aa, Fig. 101, carrying the drum or cylinder cc. Both axle and cylinder have a screw thread of the same " hand " and the same pitch. Thus, on turning the handle h, a point in one of the threads of the drum will

remain in the same thread although the drum is advancing.
The thin diaphragm d, made of mica, animal membrane, or
metal, is placed just below the mouthpiece m, see Fig. 102.
Both are carried on the bar b pivoted at pp, and adjustable
by the screw s, so as to make right contact with the tinfoil
round the cylinder. At the centre of the diaphragm is
cemented a small plate l, Fig. 102, which carries a little
style t. This presses on the steel spring r, which bears
a little rounded steel point n, which indents the tinfoil.
After taking a record the screw s is unfastened, and the

FIG. 101.—HISTORIC PHONOGRAPH.

bar b swung up so that the point n clears the tinfoil.
The handle is then turned backwards until the cylinder is
brought to its original position. The bar b is then brought
down again, the screw s adjusted, and the funnel f fitted on
to the mouthpiece. The handle is now turned at the
same speed as at first, and the original sound is thereby
approximately reproduced.

The original design of the instrument just described,
and in which the record was made upon tinfoil, was followed
by a modified form in which a wax cylinder replaces the
tinfoil. Further, in the improved forms of the instrument
uniformity of rotation is secured by clockwork, or an electro-

motor, both in taking the record and in reproducing the sounds from it.

624. We have already referred to the use of the phonograph by Hermann to settle the question as to whether vowels are characterised by a fixed or a variable pitch. We may now notice in detail how the phonograph lends itself to this determination. Suppose, for example, the vowel ōō to be sung into the phonograph at the pitch *F*,

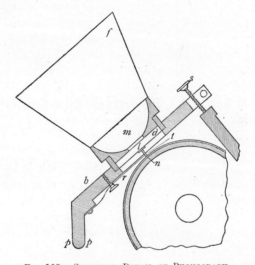

Fig. 102.—Sectional Detail of Phonograph.

the chief resonance being *f* an octave higher. Then the second partial *f* would be specially reinforced, and this special reinforcement would be registered in the phonograph's record. Now, if the vowel ōō is characterised by a special reinforcement of its second partial, the phonograph when reproducing the sound at any speed would retain and reproduce correctly this reinforcement of the second partial, the whole compound tone being raised in pitch if the handle was turned quicker than in taking the record, and the whole lowered in pitch if the handle were turned slower.

625. But if the vowel *ōō* is characterised by the special reinforcements of the partials near the fixed pitch *f,* then, on turning the phonograph either quicker or slower in reproducing the sound than in taking the record, we should have the special reinforcements of a pitch sharper or flatter than *f,* and accordingly a different vowel produced. And this was the result found by Hermann, hence his adherence to the fixed-pitch theory.

" Other forms of phonographs, some termed gramophones, have been invented, in which the records are taken on a flattened disc rotating horizontally, and so arranged that the recorder describes a series of spirals diminishing from the circumference to the centre of the disc ; but they are all constructed on the general principle of the phonograph." [1]

626. M'Kendrick's Phonograph Recorder.—Dr. J. G. M'Kendrick, professor of Physiology at Glasgow, has for years past carried out extensive researches with the phonograph. In addition to its powers for amusement or practical purposes, he regards the phonograph in its present state as a " scientific instrument worthy of a place in physical and physiological laboratories beside other instruments of scientific research, and those employed for demonstration in teaching." Professor M'Kendrick has studied " the marks on the wax cylinder in three different ways—by casts, by photographs, and by mechanical devices." The method of casts was not satisfactory ; it had the disadvantage of flattening out the marks. Numerous microphotographs were taken of portions of the wax cylinder on which were records of the voice and other instruments. But from these not very much could be inferred. Finally, M'Kendrick overcame the many difficulties met with in designing and using a mechanical device for tracing out a curve showing the depths of the indentations in the wax cylinder. This perfected instrument he calls a *phonograph recorder.*

[1] *Encyclopædia Britannica,* vol. xxxi. p. 679.

627. The chief difficulties encountered in the construction of such an instrument were due to (1) the inertia of the moving parts, (2) the extreme shallowness of the indentations to be copied, and (3) the disturbance caused by friction of the recording pen or pencil. The difficulty as to inertia was overcome by driving the wax cylinder about one thousand times slower when operating the phonograph recorder than when it was used to give out tones. To represent the indentations on a scale large enough to be appreciable, the depths of the minute indentations in the wax cylinder were in the curves magnified nearly a thousand times by a series of levers, the lengths of the indentations being magnified about thirty-five times only. The difficulty as to friction of the pen was overcome by using a fine glass syphon like that in Kelvin's syphon recorder. The strip of paper which is uniformly passing lengthwise past this pen is made alternately to approach and recede. Thus, on each approach it takes a minute drop of ink at the end of the fine glass tube. Hence, without appreciable friction, a series of dots is made on the paper sufficiently representing the curve sought. In the curves so obtained one foot of paper represents the fortieth of a second. With this apparatus Professor M'Kendrick was able to record the vibrations of the tones of several instruments, and also the tones of the human voice, both in speech and in song. Some of the results are shown in Fig. 103, taken from the Science Lecture for 1896 before the Philosophical Society of Glasgow.

M'Kendrick has also published his record of the spoken word " Constantinople," but owing to its extreme length and complexity it is not reproduced here.

628. Referring to the records of spoken words Professor M'Kendrick writes as follows:—" There is not for each word a definite wave form, but a vast series of waves, and, even although the greatest care be taken, it is impossible to obtain two records for the same word precisely the same in character. A word is built up of a succession of sounds, all usually of a musical character. Each of these sounds, if taken individually, is represented on the phonograph-record by a greater or less number of waves or vibrations, according to the pitch of the sound and its duration. . . . . The speech sounds of a man vary in pitch from 100 to 150 vibrations per second, and the song sounds

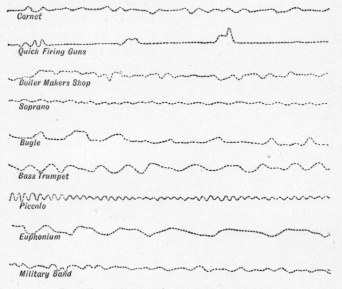

FIG. 103.—M'KENDRICK'S PHONOGRAPH RECORDS.

of a man from 80 to 400 vibrations per second. The sounds that build up a word are chiefly those of the vowels. These give a series of waves representing a variation in pitch according to the character of the vowel sound: In the record of a spoken word the pitch is constantly moving up and down, so the waves are seen in the record to change in length. It is also very difficult to notice where one series of waves ends and where another begins. . . . . In 'Constantinople' there may be 500, or 600, or 800 vibrations. The record of the words 'Royal Society of Edinburgh,' spoken with the slowness of ordinary speech, showed over 3000 vibrations, and I am not sure if they were all counted.

629. " This brief illustration gives one an insight into *nature's* method of producing speech sounds, and it shows clearly that we can never hope to read such records in the sense of identifying the curves by an inspection of the vibrations. The details are too minute to be of service to us, and we must again fall back on the power the ear possesses of identifying the sounds, and on the use of conventional signs or symbols, such as letters of the alphabet, vowel symbols, consonant symbols, or the symbols of the Chinese, which are monosyllabic roots often meaning very different things according to the inflection of tone, the variations in pitch being used in that language to convey shades of meaning.

" When human voice sounds are produced in singing, especially when an open vowel sound is sung on a note of definite pitch, the record is much more easily understood. Then we have the waves following each other with great regularity, and the pitch can easily be made out. Still, as has been well pointed out by Dr. R. J. Lloyd, of Liverpool, a gentleman who has devoted much time and learning to this subject, it is impossible by a visual inspection of the vowel curves to recognise its elements. Thus two curves, however similar, possibly identical to the eye, may give different sounds to the ear, that is to say, the ear, or ear and brain together, have analytical powers of the finest delicacy."

630. Bevier's Phonograph Analysis.—In 1900-1902 L. Bevier,[1] junr., carried out in America a series of experiments with the phonograph designed to throw light on the composition of vowel sounds. The analysis was carried

---

[1] *Physical Review*, also *Science Abstracts*, p. 541, 1900 ; p. 778, 1902 ; pp. 113 and 301, 1903.

out by the optical enlargement of phonograph records, ordinates and abscissæ being then microscopically examined, and Fourier components to the tenth harmonic looked for. Bevier " concludes that the vowels, as produced by the human organs of speech, are composed in the first place of two elements: that due to the vibration of the vocal chords, and that due to the resonance of the mouth and nose cavities. It is not always possible to separate clearly these two elements, but the problem is quite simple for the vowel *a* (as in *father*). The fundamental is due to the vocal chords, and the overtones that are strongly reinforced are due to the mouth and throat resonance. This vowel *a*, at any pitch, and pronounced by any clear voice, contains the following partial tones: (1) The fundamental to which it is sung, with the first two or three overtones. (2) The overtone or overtones whose frequencies of vibration chance to fall between 1000 and 1300 vibrations per second. This is the main characteristic of *a*, which serves to identify it to the ear, and remains remarkably constant, no matter what the fundamental may be. (3) The overtone or overtones whose frequencies of vibration chance to fall between 575 and 800 per second for men's voices, with a maximum at about 675; or between 675 and 900 with a maximum at about 800, for the voices of women and children. This is presumably the resonance of mouth and throat cavities resounding as one vessel, and is not as constant as the main resonance described above."

631. For the vowel *a* (as in *hat*), three resonance regions were found near frequencies 1550, 1050, and 650, the first being by far the most important one.

For the vowel *e* (as in *pet*), the strongest resonance was found for frequency 1800, there being also two centres of weaker resonance at 1050 and 620.

The vowel *i* (as in *pit*) showed a strong resonance characteristic of the vowel at about 1850, with another resonance at about 575, there being comparatively little distributed resonance between the above pitches.

The vowel *i* (as in *pique*) was found to be characterised by a powerfully-reinforced upper partial at about 2050, a chord-tone present with large amplitude, there being very little intermediate resonance. See Fig. 103*a*.

This I. Resonance curve was plotted by Bevier from *all* the records computed for this vowel, and was added to show the matter in convenient shape to the eye. He states, however, that this *average* result gives a too gradual rise and decline for the region of strong resonance, as had previously been noted by him for the corresponding curve

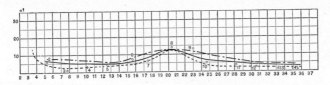

Fig. 103*a*.—I. Resonance Curves.

for the vowel *i* as in p*i*t. For the strong resonance at frequency 2048 see the last two curves of Fig. 104, which show so clearly the eighth partial of 256 and the fourth of 512.

632. Bevier considers that both physiologically and acoustically these vowel sounds, as in f*a*ther, h*a*t, p*e*t, p*i*t, p*i*que, form a true series.

And in concluding the study of this series a sheet of curves was exhibited giving examples of all these palatal vowels side by side. The pitches were chosen to make the comparison most instructive, viz.: one of each at 512 per second, and one of each at or near 256, the octave below. No good example of *a* being available at 256, one a semitone higher was substituted.

Fig. 104 is from this plate of Bevier's in the *Physical Review*, Nov. 1902, and shows curves for the five vowels in question, at two pitches for each. The vowels are indicated by a special notation at the left margin, the numbers near, 1, 4, 6, and 7, refer to the voice by which the vowel was sung, while the numbers 272, 512, 256, etc., at the right margin indicate the frequencies.

633. The Telephone.—The salient points in the history of the telephone are briefly as follows:—

In 1876, Graham Bell, of Edinburgh, Montreal, and

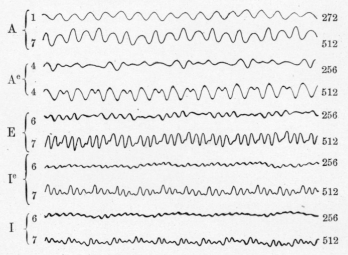

FIG. 104.—BEVIER'S VOWEL CURVES.

Boston, patented in the United States the speaking telephone. The invention was favourably reported on by Lord Kelvin at the British Association in 1876, and the telephone itself was exhibited at the Association's meeting at Plymouth in 1877. At that time Bell's telephone acted both as a *transmitter* and as a *receiver*. That is to say, the instruments at each end of the line were identical. What is termed the transmitter is the one which transmits to the line the signals corresponding to the sounds spoken into it. While the other instrument which receives these signals and reconverts them into sounds is called the receiver.

634. Sir William Preece says, " So far as the receiver is concerned, the telephone has remained virtually the same as it is described in Bell's patent; alterations have been made, but in essential principle every successful receiver hitherto introduced is covered by Bell's invention.

" It is, however, quite a different matter with the transmitter. The original Bell instrument, which was identical with the receiver, has been almost completely superseded as a transmitter. In its place some form of *carbon transmitter* is now generally used."

The first carbon transmitter was constructed by Edison in 1877, who ascribed its action to a variation of electrical resistance of the carbon due to pressure.

In 1878 Hughes discovered the *microphone,* and showed that the effect of Edison's carbon transmitter was dependent on loose contact.

635. The action of Bell's telephone both as transmitter and receiver may be understood from Figure 105, which shows a section of one of the later forms.

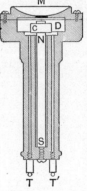

FIG. 105.—BELL'S TELEPHONE.

In this Figure NS is the permanent bar magnet of steel with one pole towards the vibrating plate or diaphragm D, which is of very thin iron. On the end of the magnet next the diaphragm is the coil of wire C, whose ends are connected to the outside terminals TT'.

In order to telephone, two such instruments may be connected by a pair of wires constituting what is known as a metallic circuit, or one terminal of each instrument may be put to earth, and the remaining terminals of the instruments connected by a single wire.

2 s

636. Consider first the action of the transmitter, that is, the instrument which receives the spoken sounds and transmits the signals to the line. The waves falling upon the saucer-shaped mouthpiece M are concentrated on to the diaphragm D and set it in vibration. Each change in position of the disc changes the magnetic field between it and the magnet NS, and each change in this field sends a transient induced current through the coil and the wires connected with it, called the "line." Thus, an approach of the diaphragm strengthens the field and sends a current one way, a recession of the diaphragm weakens the field and sends a current the opposite way. Moreover, these currents are approximately proportional to the motions of the diaphragm to which they are due. Thus the features of the spoken sounds are represented by the undulatory currents started by the transmitter.

637. Let us now trace out what happens to these currents. They are propagated very rapidly along the line, whether it consists of a pair of parallel wires or a single wire overhead and the conducting earth below. On their arrival at the other end we are concerned with the action of the receiver. These undulatory currents, by passing through the coil of the receiving instrument, serve according to their direction to increase or decrease the magnetisation of its magnet, and thus cause the diaphragm to be more strongly or less strongly attracted than when no current passed. It is thus set in vibration, and accordingly generates in the air sound-waves which are the approximate counterpart of those which originally fell upon the diaphragm of the transmitter.

Thus the transmitter acts like a tiny dynamo of a special form, in that currents are generated by it from the mechanical motion of the diaphragm. Further, the receiver is a tiny electro-motor, in that on receipt of electric currents it produces the approximate motions of the diaphragm.

In the arrangement just described, since the transmitter is itself a generator, no battery is needed.

638. Sensitiveness.—The ordinary explanation of the action of the receiver as outlined above is known as the "push and pull theory." But some physicists have objected to this, and have supposed that some special molecular action occurred, believing that the forces otherwise available are inadequate to produce in the diaphragm sufficient motion to generate audible sounds. But Lord Rayleigh's experiments on this point support the ordinary received theory. He also points out that the minimum amplitude for audibility is extremely small (see Arts. 582-587). Thus it is not so surprising to find that a Bell receiver will respond to a current of the order $4 \cdot 4 \times 10^{-8}$ ampère as determined by Rayleigh. Indeed, Tait found 2×10^{-12} ampère, and Preece 6×10^{-13} ampère as the currents to which a telephone receiver can respond.

639. Permanent Field Indispensable.—In the telephone receiver it is important to note the necessity explained by Heaviside for the field due to the permanent steel magnet. Suppose the field due to the magnet near the diaphragm is denoted by H, and let a very small change in it due to currents in the coil be denoted by $\pm h$. Now the induced magnetism in the diaphragm is proportional to this field, and the attraction is proportional to the product of the two. Hence we have an attraction varying between the limits $k(H \pm h)^2$, where k is some constant. Thus the difference of attractions available for motion of the diaphragm is $4kHh$. That is, the force available is proportional to the product of the permanent field and the change which can be produced in it. Hence the sensitiveness of the apparatus is much increased by the presence of a strong permanent field, provided it is not such as to lessen the possible changes in it due to the currents received. Here it must be noticed that there is a practical limit to the intensity of the permanent field which it is wise to use. For, if the magnet is nearly saturated, very little change could be made in the field. Hence, in that case, the gain in making H large would be balanced by a consequent diminution of h for a given current. But this limit is not reached with ordinary steel magnets, hence their value in the instrument.

640. Edison's Carbon Transmitters.—The first carbon transmitter constructed by Edison in 1877 passed through various stages, and afterwards received the form shown in Fig. 106.

When using for telephony a carbon transmitter, a battery is needed to generate the current, and it is the

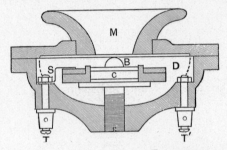

FIG. 106.—EDISON'S CARBON TRANSMITTER.

function of the transmitter, by the variation of its own resistance, to vary the current thus independently produced. How it does this may easily be seen from Fig. 106. The sound-waves pass through the mouthpiece M, fall upon the vibrating plate D, and set it in motion. This vibratory motion acts upon the rounded ivory button B and the adjoining platinum plate, which thus makes a variable contact with the disc of carbon C. The electrical circuit through the instrument is from the terminal T through the spring S to the platinum plate, thence through the carbon and the case of the instrument to the second terminal T'. Hence a downward motion of the diaphragm improves the contact with the carbon, lessens the electrical resistance, and therefore increases the current. An upward motion makes the carbon contact worse, increases its resistance, and hence decreases the current.

641. Suppose now that for sounds of a given intensity the change of resistance in the transmitter is one per cent of the total resistance in the circuit. Then a one per cent change in the current is produced and the telephone receiver affected accordingly. Next, let a longer line be used so that the total resistance in the circuit becomes ten times its former value. Then if the same battery is used, and sounds of the same intensity fall upon the diaphragm of the transmitter, we have two changes to notice. First, the current is only *one-tenth* of its original value; and, second, the changes which the transmitter can produce are only about *one-tenth* per cent of that reduced current, because the changes in resistance of the carbon contact remain of the same absolute value as at first, while the total resistance is made tenfold. Thus to maintain the changes in current at the receiver the same when the total resistance in circuit is made tenfold, we need to increase the voltage of the battery to one-hundredfold. Or, to generalise: when the line changes in length in order to maintain unimpaired the efficiency of the circuit, we should need to make the voltage of the battery vary as the square of that length. And this would be quite out of the question in practice on a large scale.

642. To obviate this necessity Edison passed the current from the transmitter through the primary of an induction coil, whose secondary was connected to the line. The transmitter then acts in connection with a small resistance due to the battery, the transmitter itself, and the primary wire of the induction coil. Hence the variations of resistance of the transmitter have a considerable relative magnitude, and produce correspondingly large relative changes in the current through the primary of the induction coil. And these changes, by induction, give rise to corresponding periodic currents in the secondary of the induction coil, their voltage (or *E. M. F.*) being very high. Hence the line may be fairly long without prejudice to the action of the circuit.

643. Hughes' Microphone.—In 1878 Professor Hughes introduced what he called the microphone, which is really a form of telephone transmitter. Its action depended on a loose contact whose resistance varied with the sounds incident upon it. The changes in resistance thus produced affected the currents derived from a battery whose circuit included both the microphone and a telephone receiver. One of the earliest forms of the apparatus consisted of two

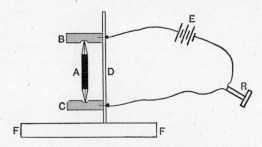

FIG. 107.—HUGHES' MICROPHONE.

nails laid side by side, but not in contact, across which a third nail was laid. The effect is, however, better when carbon pencils are used, and the apparatus employing carbon may be regarded as the standard type of the microphone, and is with modifications still retained. One form of it consists of a small pencil of gas carbon A, Fig. 107, with pointed ends resting lightly in small circular holes in the two pieces of carbon B, C, so that the pencil takes up a vertical position between them. The pieces B and C are fixed to a thin sounding board or diaphragm D, fitted into a frame and mounted on a solid base F F. A battery E and a telephone receiver R are included in the circuit with the pieces B and C. The instrument, though apparently so rough, is of surprising delicacy, the movement of a fly on the diaphragm serving to produce in the receiver audible effects.

644. The true nature of the action at the loose contact is perhaps not yet fully understood, though of late years much research has been done upon the contacts in the case of the coherers used in wireless telegraphy. Possibly the phenomena in the two cases are somewhat analogous.

For the loose contacts of the microphone Shelford Bidwell considered carbon is the best material, because it is unoxidisable and infusible, a poor conductor, and has a lower resistance when heated.

The difference between Edison's carbon transmitter and Hughes' microphone does not seem great, but the Edison form has disappeared, and the carbon transmitters now generally in use may be regarded as modifications of Hughes' microphone.

The details of these various instruments and all the intricacies of current practice are outside the scope of this work. The reader interested in them should consult one of the technical treatises, such as the *Manual of Telephony* by Preece and Stubbs.

645. Trunks and Transformers.—We may, however, with advantage mention here the following devices used for long-distance telephony:—For transmission to any considerable distance, free from the disturbances due to induction, the double wire or metallic circuit is imperative. It is therefore invariably used for the so-called trunk lines connecting towns at any great distance apart. But suppose a subscriber at one end is on a single wire circuit only, and desires to communicate with the distant town reached by the metallic circuit of the trunk-line. To admit of this, transformers or translators are used at the ends of the trunk or double line between the two central stations. These translators are induction coils of special construction. The National Telephone Co. have used coils of 290 ohms

resistance for the trunk, and 140 ohms for the local
sections. The core is of the softest iron, and the coils
wound closely and regularly. In the most approved forms
the cores are more than double the length of the coils, and
after the completion of the winding, the projecting ends of
the iron wires constituting the core are folded back over
the windings of the coil. Since the use of a translator
involves some loss of effect it is desirable to avoid having
more than two in use at any one time in any given speaking
circuit. Indeed, in some districts it has been the rule with
the National Telephone Co., that of the two subscribers
using a trunk wire one must have a metallic circuit, so
that only one translator is in use.

646. Vibrations of a Telephone-Membrane.—In 1902
R. Kempf-Hartmann [1] experimented on the vibrations of a
telephone-membrane, obtaining many interesting results.
Vibration curves were photographically produced by the
light reflected to a moving film from a mirror fixed on the
membrane of a telephone receiver. It was thus shown
that the membrane very quickly takes up the vibrations
impressed upon it, one-thousandth of a second in some cases
sufficing for the steady state to be reached. Curves are
given in the original paper for vowels and consonants at
different pitches and intensities. The effect of the frequency
natural to the membrane is also shown in a special set of
curves.

647. Rhythm Electrically perceived.—Prof. M'Kendrick, pursuing the researches mentioned before (Arts. 626-
629), arranged the following combination of apparatus :—
To the glass plate diaphragm in the reproducer of the
phonograph was attached a tube connecting it with a
microphone transmitter. This transmitter was connected
in series with a battery and the primary of an induction
coil. The wires from the secondary of this induction coil

---

[1] *Ann. d. Physik.* viii. 3. pp. 481-538, June 1902. *Science Abstracts*, p. 27,
1903.

ended in platinum plates dipped in weak salt solution. The phonograph was then set going and the fingers put into the beakers containing the salt solution. By this means the intensity of every note could be felt; indeed the variation of intensity, the rhythm, and even the expression of music were all felt.

M‘Kendrick writes, " This experiment suggests the possibility of being able to communicate to those who are stone deaf the feeling, or, at all events, the rhythm of music. It is not music, of course, but, if you like to call it so, it is music *on one plane and without colour*. There is no appreciation of pitch or colour or of quality, and there is no effort at analysis, an effort which, I believe, has a great deal to do with the pleasurable sensation we derive from music. In this experiment you have the rhythm which enters largely into musical feeling. On Saturday last (Dec. 1896) through the kindness of Dr. J. Kerr Love, I had the opportunity of experimenting with four patients from the Deaf and Dumb Institution, one of whom had her hearing up till she was eleven years of age, and then became stone deaf. The girl had undoubtedly the recollection of music, although she does not now hear any sound. She wrote me a little letter, in which she declared that *what she felt was music*, and that it wakened in her mind a conscious something that recalled what music was. The others had no conception of music, but they were able to appreciate the rhythm, and it was interesting to notice how they all, without exception, caught up the rhythm, and bobbed their heads up and down, keeping time with the electrical thrills in their finger tips."

648. The Speaking Arc.—In 1898, H. Simon showed that the continuous current electrical arc could be used as a telephone receiver. His experiment, as quoted by Duddell in 1900, was as diagrammatically represented in Fig. 108. Such arrangements are now referred to as the speaking arc.

In this figure M denotes the microphone, E the battery, A and B the primary and secondary of an induction coil. When the microphone is spoken into, its varying resistance changes the current in A, and thus produces in B induced currents which are superimposed on the main current in the arc derived from its source of supply. Thus the current through the arc suffers periodic variation. This variation is accompanied by corresponding changes in the vapour column between the carbons, and so produces sounds which are the duplicate of the original ones incident upon the microphone. In order to obtain louder and clearer speech, Duddell, who brought this subject before the Institution of

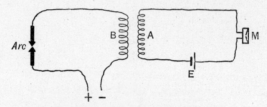

FIG. 108.—SIMON'S SPEAKING ARC.

Electrical Engineers in 1900, prefers the arrangement shown in Fig. 109.

649. In this arrangement M and E denote as before the microphone and its battery; A and B are the primary and secondary of the induction coil by which the microphone affects the current in the arc. But the secondary B is now placed in shunt with the arc instead of being in series with it. The main current of the arc is prevented from passing round B by the presence of the condenser S in the shunt circuit. Also, the alternate currents induced in B are practically prevented by the inductance L from flowing through the cells which supply the arc. Thus in the arc, and in the arc only, have we the superposition of the steady current supplying it, and the periodic currents due to the microphone and the sounds falling upon it. The variations of current in the arc are consequently greater than if the microphone had to affect the currents flowing through a steadying resistance, such as R, and any inductances that may occur in the main circuit of the arc, as in Simon's arrangement.

650. The details of Duddell's arrangement of speaking arc are given by him as follows :—

"The microphone M was supplied by the National Telephone Co. and was intended for long-distance transmission. E shows two accumulators used in series with it. The induction coil A B had an iron wire core about 15 mm. diameter. A had 600 turns, resistance 1·52 ;

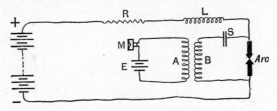

Fig. 109.—Duddell's Speaking Arc.

B 400, resistance 1·53. Mutual induction 0·0253 henry. The condenser S had a capacity of 2 or 3 microfarads, for the arc cored carbons were used 11 to 13 mm. diameter, the current being 10 to 12 ampères, and the arc length 20 to 30 mm. To obtain these long arcs with ease the carbons must be cored, or some other means taken to introduce foreign bodies, such as salts of potassium and sodium, into the arc. These salts may be introduced by soaking the carbons in their solutions instead of using them as cores."

Duddell also described an arrangement by which the arc could be used as a telephone transmitter, an ordinary telephone receiver being used in conjunction with it.

651. The Musical Arc.—Because of its close connection with the speaking arc, we mention here the musical arc, though perhaps it is not strictly within the scope of this chapter as a recorder or reproducer of sound. It seems to be rather a case in which the sound originates owing to the extreme excitability or sensitiveness of the arc, and the presence of conditions favourable to the continuance of the sound when once produced. It seems to have been first observed by Elihu Thomson in 1892, but was independently discovered and brought forward by Duddell in 1900, whose arrangement for producing it is shown in Fig. 110.

652. In this arrangement the arc consists of solid carbons, and there is simply a shunt circuit to the arc containing a condenser S and an inductance L. Now it is

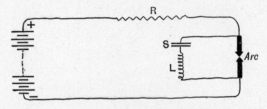

FIG. 110.—DUDDELL'S MUSICAL ARC.

well known that in electrical matters an inductance and a capacity are respectively analogous to a mass and the reciprocal of a spring in mechanical matters. Thus in this shunt circuit we have the possibility of electrical oscillations of a definite frequency and period (viz. $\tau = 2\pi \sqrt{LS}$ as shown in article 656). Duddell, commenting on this arrangement, writes: "It must be remembered that although we have an alternate current through the condenser and self-induction, the source of supply is not an alternating one, and that *it is the arc itself which is acting as a converter and transforming a part of the direct current into alternating, the frequency of which can be varied between very wide limits by altering the self-induction and capacity.* The upper limit I find to be about 10,000 ∿ per second, and the lower limit, if such exists, is well below 500 ∿ per second."

653. In the discussion on Duddell's paper the close analogy of this interesting electrical phenomenon to some acoustic ones was very aptly brought out as follows by Prof. Ayrton :—Mr. Duddell "has shown us that an ordinary so-called perfectly silent arc supplied with current from accumulators is, if the carbons be solid, like the mouth-piece of a flageolet or flute but not blown. The application of a shunt to that arc, consisting of a capacity in series with a self-induction, performs two operations. It starts vibrations in the arc, just as blowing a flute gives rise to vibrations of many different rates. Just as one of these rates of vibration is picked out and reinforced in the case of a flute or flageolet by the form of the resonance chamber dependent on the position of your fingers or keys, so in this musical arc the particular one of the many vibrations that are probably started which is picked out and reinforced depends on the capacity of the condenser and the value of the self-induction which is in series with it."

654. Oscillatory Discharge of a Condenser.—We now pass to the electrical theory which is applicable to the phenomena dealt with, but not found in the more elementary text-books on electricity. Some of this theory, besides being useful for its application to tele-phony and other examples of electrical oscillations, will also be found interest-ing as affording analogies to some of

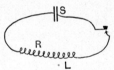

Fig. 111.—Oscillatory Discharge.

the acoustic phenomena already dealt with, such as free and forced vibrations.

We commence with the oscillatory discharge of a condenser, the mathematical theory of which was given by Kelvin in 1853. Let a condenser of capacity S and charge x_0 be connected at time $t = 0$ with a coil of resistance R and inductance L, as shown in Fig. 111.

Also at time t let the charge on the condenser be x and the current u. Then the current $u = -\dot{x}$ and the electrostatic electromotive force or voltage driving it is x/S. But this voltage must equal the sum of Ru and the back *E.M.F.* of self-induction which is $L\dot{u}$. We thus obtain the equation of motion for the system, which may be written

$$L\ddot{x} + R\dot{x} + x/S = 0 \qquad (1).$$

655. This equation has two types of solution, the one or other applying according as R is above or below a certain critical value. If R is above that value, the corresponding solution indicates a gradual subsidence of the charge, and with this case we are not here concerned. If R is below this critical value the general solution expresses oscillations, and may be written

$$x = Ae^{-qt} \cos{(nt + a)},$$

where n and q have definite values, A and a being dependent only on the initial conditions. This may be verified by differentiation and comparison with (1). To fit the given initial conditions we may write the solution in the form

$$x = x_0 e^{-qt} \left(\cos{nt} + \frac{q}{n} \sin{nt} \right) \qquad (2),$$

where $\quad q = R/2L, \; n^2 + q^2 = 1/LS,$ or $n^2 = \dfrac{1}{LS} - \dfrac{R^2}{4L^2}$ (3).

From these it is seen that the condition for oscillations is that n should be real, or, in other words, that we should have

$$R < 2\sqrt{L/S} \qquad (4).$$

On differentiating (2) we have the current expressed by

$$u = -\dot{x} = \left(\frac{n^2 + q^2}{n} \right) x_0 e^{-qt} \sin{nt} \qquad (5).$$

656. The period of oscillation is obviously given by

$$\tau = 2\pi/n, \text{ or } \tau = 2\pi\sqrt{LS} \text{ nearly} \qquad (6),$$

the second form being a sufficient approximation when R is very small, as seen from (3).

This is then an exact analogue to the case of damped simple harmonic motion dealt with in Chap. IV. (articles 89 and 90).

On reference to equation (1) above, or to the solution, we see that in the electrical case the self-induction or inductance L is like the inertia in the mechanical case, the ohmic resistance R is like the resistance per unit speed, and the reciprocal of the electrical capacity is like the mechanical restoring force per unit displacement.

657. Forced Electrical Vibrations.—Now, suppose that, instead of the condenser circuit being simply made by putting down the contact key, a source of simple harmonic *E.M.F.* of period $2\pi/p$ is introduced in place of the key. The equation of motion may then be written

$$L\ddot{x} + R\dot{x} + x/S = y_0 \cos pt \qquad (7),$$

where y_0 is the amplitude of the E.M.F. But this is the equation of motion of an elastic system subject to an harmonic impressed force. The response is accordingly what we have previously noticed, namely, a forced vibration of the period of the force impressed (see Chap. IV. Art. 91). Thus, the solution for the forced vibration alone may be written

$$x = \frac{y_0 \sin \epsilon}{2pq} \cos(pt - \epsilon) \qquad (8),$$

where
$$\tan \epsilon = \frac{2pq}{L(n^2 + q^2 - p^2)} = \frac{2pq}{L\left(\dfrac{1}{LS} - p^2\right)} \qquad (9).$$

As before, q is here written for $R/2L$ and $(n^2 + q^2)$ for $1/LS$.

Thus here, as in the mechanical case, the impressed harmonic force maintains the vibration with a certain definite and constant amplitude associated also with a certain definite phase. The magnitude of each of these quantities depends on the difference of frequencies of natural and forced vibrations.

658. To complete the expression for the possible vibrations in the condenser circuit we must add to equation (8) the free vibrations of the system as given by equation (2). This addition would enable us to fit the solution to any initial conditions. But, as in the case of mechanical vibrations, those natural to the system would die out, and after a time leave the forced vibrations in sole possession of the field. When this state is reached it is important to notice that the effect of the condenser is comparable to a negative inductance. Thus, on fitting the solution as expressed by equation (8) in the left side of equation (7), the first term of (7) yields $-Lp^2x$ and the third term x/S. Hence $1/S$ may be annulled by $-Lp^2$ if they are numerically equal. Or, as we shall afterwards find more convenient, Lp may be annulled by $\left(-\dfrac{1}{Sp}\right)$. Or, at the given frequency, $-1/Sp$ represents the effect of a condenser of capacity S, and Lp represents the effect of an inductance of value L. When $p^2 = 1/LS$, it is seen from (9) and (8) that the vibrations are at a maximum.

659. Impedance of a Circuit.—Suppose now the capacity of a condenser is made infinite, or that it is short-circuited, or removed altogether. Then, in any of these cases, the term involving the condenser disappears from the equation of motion, for if present the potential difference of its terminals is always zero. Thus, supposing the impressed *E.M.F.* to be as before, the modified equation of motion derived from (7) would be

$$L\ddot{x} + R\dot{x} = y_0 \cos pt.$$

But since the charge x has now lost its meaning, we may desirably pass from charge to current. Accordingly, writing for $\dot{x}$ and $\ddot{x}$, $-u$ and $-\dot{u}$ respectively; and for convenience changing the sign of the impressed force, we obtain as our equation of motion

$$L\dot{u} + Ru = y_0 \cos pt \qquad (10).$$

The solution of this may be written

$$u = u_0 \cos (pt - \epsilon), \left.\vphantom{\begin{array}{c}a\\b\end{array}}\right\}$$
where $\quad u_0 = y_0 / \sqrt{R^2 + L^2 p^2}$ and $\tan \epsilon = R/Lp \qquad (11).$

Thus, if the alternations are very slow, the amplitude of the current is related to that of the *E.M.F.* almost according to Ohm's law, *i.e.*

$$u_0 = y_0 / R \text{ nearly.}$$

But if the alternations are very quick, then we have

$$u_0 = y_0 / Lp \text{ nearly.}$$

In any intermediate case the amplitude of the current is found from that of the *E.M.F.* on dividing the latter by $\sqrt{R^2 + L^2 p^2}$. This quantity has been called by Heaviside the *impedance* of the coil for the frequency $p/2\pi$. He defines impedance as "the ratio of the amplitude of the impressed force to that of the current when their variations are simple harmonic."

660. Another method of representing the results contained in (11) by means of the imaginary quantity $i = \sqrt{-1}$ is sometimes more convenient. It may be written as follows:—Let the impressed *E.M.F.* be given by

$$y = \text{the real part of } y_0 e^{ipt},$$

then, the current is expressed by

$$u = \text{the real part of } \frac{y_0 e^{ipt}}{R + Lip} \qquad (12).$$

On rationalising these expressions for *E.M.F.* and current, they will be found equivalent to those in (10) and (11) above.

661. Resistance and Inductance modified by Alternations and Damping.—It is further to be noticed that not only must the impedance be substituted for the ordinary ohmic resistance in the case of alternating currents in a coil of appreciable inductance, but also that the values of the resistance and inductance to steady currents become themselves modified when the currents are alternating. When the current is steady it is uniformly distributed throughout the cross-section of the conductor. But when the current is simple harmonic it is more concentrated at the surface than at deeper or more internal parts of the cross-section. This causes the resistance to increase and the inductance to decrease. Following on the theory of Maxwell, this case for a straight cylindrical conductor has been worked out by Lord Rayleigh [1] who obtained the following results :—

$$R' = R\left(1 + \frac{1}{12}\frac{p^2 l^2 \mu^2}{R^2} - \frac{1}{180}\frac{p^4 l^4 \mu^4}{R^4} + \ \ldots \ \right) (13),$$

$$L' = lA + l\mu\left(\frac{1}{2} - \frac{1}{48}\frac{p^2 l^2 \mu^2}{R^2} + \frac{13}{8640}\frac{p^4 l^4 \mu^4}{R^4} \ \ldots \ \right)$$

or,

$$L' = L - l\mu\left(\frac{1}{48}\frac{p^2 l^2 \mu^2}{R^2} - \frac{13}{8640}\frac{p^4 l^4 \mu^4}{R^4} \ \ldots \ \right) \Bigg\} (14).$$

In these equations R and L are the ordinary values of the resistance and inductance for steady currents, R' and L' their special values when the currents are simple harmonic of period $2\pi/p$, l is the length of the wire, μ its magnetic permeability. The mathematical analysis by which the above results are derived is far too long for introduction here, especially as the matter is only on the border-line of the subjects treated.

662. When the alternations are *damped* simple harmonic,

---

[1] *Phil. Mag.*, May 1886.

instead of being uniformly sustained, a further change sets in. Both resistance and inductance are increased by the damping. Indeed, the inductance may rise to a higher value than that for steady currents. Let the values of the equivalent resistance and inductance for this case be denoted by R'' and L'' when the currents vary as $e^{-kpt} \cos pt$. Then it has been shown [1] that for a straight cylindrical conductor the following relations hold :—

$$R'' = R\left(1 + \frac{1 + k^2}{12} \, p^2 a^2 \mu^2 + \frac{k(1 + k^2)}{24} \, p^3 a^3 \mu^3 \right.$$
$$\left. - \frac{1 - 2k^2 - 3k^4}{180} \, p^4 a^4 \mu^4 \; . \; . \; . \right) (15).$$

$$L'' = L + l\mu\left(\frac{k}{6} \, pa\mu - \frac{1 - 3k^2}{48} \, p^2 a^2 \mu^2 \right.$$
$$\left. - \frac{k(1 - k^2)}{45} \, p^3 a^3 \mu^3 \; . \; . \; . \right) (16),$$

where $a = l/R$ is the conductivity for steady currents of unit length of the wire.

Prof. W. B. Morton and the writer have shown [2] that the criterion for the oscillatory discharge of a condenser is slightly modified when these new values of the resistance and inductance are introduced, the condition that corresponds to the critical state when R and L are used becoming an oscillatory discharge with the values of R'' and L''. And further, they showed [3] that in the case of damped or decaying currents we may have *axial* concentration instead of the surface concentration due to harmonic currents of sustained amplitude.

663. Alternating Currents in Parallel. — Consider now the case of two currents in parallel, each possessing resistance and self-induction, their mutual induction, however, being negligible. And let an harmonic *E.M.F.*

---

[1] E. H. Barton, *Phil. Mag.*, May 1899.
[2] *Phil. Mag.*, July 1899 ; *Phys. Soc.*, March 1899.
[3] *Phil. Mag.*, July 1899 ; *Phys. Soc.*, May 1899.

be applied to the system. The problem of determining the currents has been treated by Prof. J. A. Fleming in his *Alternate Current Transformer*, from which the following is derived. The circuits are represented in Fig. 112.

The main current, before dividing at A into the two coils, and again after reuniting at B, is denoted by $U \sin pt$. Let u denote the current at time t through the upper coil of resistance R and inductance L. Similarly let w denote the current at the same instant in the lower coil of resistance S and inductance N. It is accordingly required to find u and w in terms of U, p, and the constants of the coils.

664. By tracing through the upper coil we see that

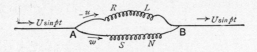

FIG. 112.—PARALLEL INDUCTIVE CIRCUITS.

the potential difference between A and B at time t is expressed by $Ru + L\dot{u}$. At the same instant a corresponding expression holds for the lower coil. But this gives the same potential difference, namely, that between A and B. We thus have the equation

$$L\dot{u} + Ru = N\dot{w} + Sw \qquad (17).$$

But, since there is no accumulation of electricity at either A or B, we have

$$u + w = U \sin pt$$
or,
$$w = U \sin pt - u \qquad (18).$$

Thus, on substituting for w from (18) in (17), and performing the differentiation, we obtain

$$(L + N)\frac{du}{dt} + (R + S)u = U(Np \cos pt + S \sin pt) \qquad (19).$$

And this equation, on dividing by $(L+N)$, is of the type

$$\frac{du}{dt} + Pu = f(t) \qquad (20),$$

whose solution is

$$u = e^{-Pt}\left\{ \int Qe^{Pt}dt + \text{constant} \right\} \qquad (21).$$

On substituting and evaluating the integrals for our case, the solution of (19) may be written

$$u = \frac{U}{(R+S)^2 + (L+N)^2p^2}\{(S^2 + N^2p^2 + RS + LNp^2)\sin pt$$
$$+ (RN - LS)p\cos pt\} \qquad (22).$$

By the symmetry of the case we can at once write down the expression for w by interchanging the constants of the coils. Thus

$$w = \frac{U}{(R+S)^2 + (L+N)^2p^2}\{(R^2 + L^2p^2 + RS + LNp^2)\sin pt$$
$$+ (LS - RN)p\cos pt\} \qquad (23).$$

665. For single and branching circuits under harmonic *E.M.F.'s*, Fleming expresses the results as follows:—

"When an impressed electro-motive force acts on a circuit which branches into two, having each self but no mutual induction, the main current lags behind the impressed *E.M.F.* in phase, but the branched currents respectively *lag behind* and are *pressed ahead* of the phase of the main current."

Fleming goes on to show that if the inductance in one branch is precisely zero, that then the current in it is in phase with the impressed *E.M.F.*, or in other words, that the current in it is unaffected by its being joined in parallel with an inductive circuit.

Suppose now that either the inductances or the frequencies are low, so that the terms involving them are negligible in comparison with those involving the resistances. Then from equations (22) and (23) we derive those expressing the usual subdivision of steady currents, namely

$$u = \frac{S}{R+S} U \sin pt \text{ and } w = \frac{R}{R+S} U \sin pt \qquad (24).$$

If, however, the reverse holds, the inductances or frequencies being so high that the terms involving the resistances are negligible in comparison with the inductive terms, we then find

$$u = U \left\{ \frac{N}{L+N} \sin pt + \frac{RN - LS}{(L+N)^2 p} \cos pt \right\} \qquad (25),$$

and

$$w = U \left\{ \frac{L}{L+N} \sin pt + \frac{LS - RN}{(L+N)^2 p} \cos pt \right\} \qquad (26).$$

666. These equations express the subdivision of the current according to the inductances of the circuits, which have now become paramount.

Lord Rayleigh has treated the case where the two branches of the circuit have mutual as well as self-induction. This brings out the striking result that the current amplitude in each branch may exceed that of the main current. Thus, in a case cited, a main current of amplitude unity may divide into currents of $3/5$ and $2/5$ in the two branches, their phase difference being small or zero. Or, the main current, still of amplitude unity, may divide into currents of amplitudes 3 and 2 in the branches, their phases being opposite. Or, to express both the amplitudes and phases algebraically, we may say that in the first case $+1 = +3/5 + 2/5$; whereas in the second case, the subdivision of the main current is expressed by $+1 = +3 - 2$. In the first case the two coils are connected so that steady currents would circulate in them in opposite directions, M the mutual induction being then negative. In the second case the opposite state of things holds good and M is positive. Such a case of the branch currents exceeding the main current has been experimentally verified by Lord Rayleigh and shown to an audience.

667. Electric Waves along Parallel Leads.—One of the most important of telephonic phenomena is that of the propagation of the currents along the line, or, in other words, the propagation of electric waves along its parallel leads. These parallel leads may, of course, be the two parallel wires constituting the metallic circuit now almost always used, or they may be the nearly obsolete system of a single wire and the earth's surface. We now often refer to these phenomena as the propagation of electric waves, since by Maxwell's theory and the experimental confirmation of Hertz and his successors, we know that the currents in the wires are only a small portion of the general phenomena of the electro-magnetic field between and round them, and its propagation along the line with the speed of light. It is fairly obvious that the resistance of the line will cause the waves and currents to diminish as they proceed along it. Further, since for periodic currents we have the ohmic resistance replaced by the impedance $\sqrt{R^2 + L^2 p^2}$, it would appear that the diminution or attenuation of an alternating current would depend upon p, that is upon its frequency.

668. Thus, if no special pains are taken to avoid it, we should expect the various partial tones composing any note or vowel to be diminished in different ratios by their passage over the same length of the line. This selective diminution is called *distortion*, since it distorts the relation between the partials of any composite tone, and by which it is characterised, and so alters its quality, or if a vowel changes it to some slightly different vowel. Accordingly both attenuation and distortion are to be avoided as far as possible in the currents passing along a telephone line. This matter has been very fully treated by Oliver Heaviside, who showed mathematically how to make a line which would not involve any distortion of the signals sent along it. This he called a *distortionless* circuit. Heaviside showed that if in a line without resistance or leakage a resistance be inserted, then, at the spot in question there is a reflection of the incident waves in which the current is reversed. If, however, this resistance be removed, and a conducting bridge be placed across the pair of leads constituting the line, then, in the reflection which occurs at the bridge it is the potential difference of the wave that is reversed instead of the current. Now let there be both a resistance inserted, and a conducting bridge placed across, and let them be so proportioned that the waves reflected in virtue of each are *equal* as well as *opposite*, the reflected wave is accordingly abolished. Part of the original wave is absorbed in the resistance and bridge, and the rest passes on without distortion. This explains the pith of the matter in words. We now pass to the mathematical theory, following Heaviside's method, though with slightly modified notation.

669. Heaviside's Distortionless Circuit.—Let the line consist of two parallel conducting leads, of which R, L, K, and S are respectively the resistance, inductance, leakance (or leakage conductance), and permittance (capacity), all reckoned in electro-magnetic units per unit length of the line. At the time t and place z along the line let y denote the transverse voltage, and u the longitudinal current. Then the potential gradient along the line expresses the *E.M.F.*, and may be equated to the usual function of the current when resistance and inductance are present. Thus

$$-\frac{dy}{dz} = Ru + L\frac{du}{dt} \qquad (27).$$

Again, the space rate of decrease of current would express the time rate of increase of charge if leakage were absent. Accordingly, making the requisite correction for leakage in the present case we may then equate to the product of capacity and rate of increase of potential. We thus obtain an equation symmetrical with the first, namely

$$-\frac{du}{dz} = Ky + S\frac{dy}{dt} \qquad (28).$$

670. We have now to eliminate u between these two equations. Thus on differentiating (27) to z we find

$$\frac{d^2y}{dz^2} = -R\frac{du}{dz} - L\frac{d^2u}{dtdz}.$$

And, substituting in the right hand side of this from (28) differentiated where necessary, we obtain

$$\frac{d^2y}{dz^2} = KRy + (KL + RS)\frac{dy}{dt} + LS\frac{d^2y}{dt^2} \qquad (29).$$

We now introduce Heaviside's condition for the distortionless circuit, namely

Let $\qquad\qquad R/L = K/S = q,$ say $\qquad\qquad (30).$

Also for brevity let $\qquad LSv^2 = 1 \qquad\qquad (31).$
Then (29) becomes

$$v^2\frac{d^2y}{dz^2} = q^2y + 2q\frac{dy}{dt} + \frac{d^2y}{dt^2} \qquad (32).$$

671. Now take a new variable Y defined by

$$y = e^{-qt}Y \qquad (33).$$

Equation (32) now reduces to

$$v^2\frac{d^2Y}{dz^2} = \frac{d^2Y}{dt^2} \qquad (34).$$

And this is the familiar equation of undisturbed wave propagation, whose solution is

$$Y = f_1(z - vt) + f_2(z + vt) \qquad (35).$$

Hence by reference to (33), we have as the solution sought,

$$y = e^{-qt}\{f_1(z - vt) + f_2(z + vt)\} \qquad (36).$$

From equations (28), (30), and (31), we find that the corresponding current is given by

$$u = e^{-qt}\left\{ \frac{f_1(z - vt)}{Lv} + \frac{f_2(z + vt)}{-Lv} \right\} \qquad (37).$$

672. Or, in words, the current in the positively travelling waves is given by potential $\div Lv$, and the current in the negative wave by potential divided by $(-Lv)$. Equations (36) and (37) express waves proceeding right and left at speed v without distortion, but with logarithmic attenuation. The symbols f_1 and f_2 denote arbitrary functions which must be chosen to fit any given initial conditions.

It is not to be expected that the distortionless circuit can be attained in actual telephone practice, but it is the ideal to be kept in view and approached as nearly as possible.

As to the value of v, the speed of propagation, its limiting value may be found thus. Let the line consist of parallel wires of radius a and at a relatively large distance apart b. Then we have approximately, $L = \mu 4 \log_\epsilon(b/a)$, and $S = \kappa/4 V^2 \log_\epsilon (b/a)$, where μ and κ are respectively the magnetic permeability and dielectric constant of the medium between the wires, and V is the speed of light in vacuo. Thus by (31) we obtain

$$v^2 = 1/LS = V^2/\mu\kappa,$$

or, for air, $\mu = \kappa = 1$, and $v = V$, the speed of light, say 3×10^{10} cm. per second.

673. Reflections at Terminal Bridges.—An important problem in connection with telephonic practice is the determination of the reflection occurring when the waves along the line reach a bridge of any kind across the two leads. This bridge may be considered as having resistance only, resistance and inductance, capacity only, or all three. Also, the bridge may be at the end of the line or at some intermediate position.

Consider first a bridge without inductance or capacity,

but of resistance R_1, and situated at the end of the line. Let the transverse voltage of the incident wave be expressed by y_1 and that of the reflected wave by y_2, the corresponding currents being respectively u_1 and u_2.

Then by (37) we have

$$u_1 = y_1/Lv \text{ and } u_2 = -y_2/Lv \qquad (38).$$

Since the bridge is devoid of capacity there is no accumulation of electricity there. Hence, applying Ohm's law to the current through it, we have

$$u_1 + u_2 = (y_1 + y_2)/R_1 \qquad (39).$$

Thus, on substituting from (38) in (39) we obtain

$$\frac{y_1 - y_2}{Lv} = \frac{y_1 + y_2}{R_1},$$

whence $\qquad\qquad y_2/y_1 = \dfrac{R_1 - Lv}{R_1 + Lv} \qquad (40).$

674. This equation applies to waves of any form, and is not restricted to those of simple harmonic type.

Three special cases of terminal bridge reflection call for notice. These are as follows :—

(i.) Ends of line insulated, $\qquad R_1 = \infty$, $y_2/y_1 = +1$ $\left.\right\}(41).$
      (current reversed by reflection)

(ii.) Ends of line short circuited, $R_1 = 0,\ y_2/y_1 = -1$ $\left.\right\}(42).$
      (voltage reversed by reflection)

(iii.) Bridge of critical resistance, $R_1 = Lv,\ y_2/y_1 = 0$ $\left.\right\}(43).$
      (incident wave entirely absorbed)

Cases (i.) and (ii.) are obviously analogous to the reflections occurring at the stopped and open ends of organ pipes. These results were predicted by Heaviside in treating waves of telephonic frequency. For high-frequency waves from condenser discharges as introduced by Hertz, the first two cases were experimentally confirmed by V. Bjerknes in 1891. For oscillator waves of about thirty-five million per second, the third case of total absorption was experimentally confirmed in 1896 by the writer and Dr. G. B. Bryan.[1]

675. As Heaviside points out, it is this property of total absorption that should be possessed by the telephone receiver which constitutes a special form of terminal bridge. Such a telephone at the end of a line which is itself one of Heaviside's distortionless circuits would afford an ideal arrangement.

But a telephone receiver is not a pure resistance without either capacity or inductance. The theory accordingly needs extension to include such bridges. Heaviside has shown that in the case of simple harmonic waves incident upon a bridge the single symbol R_1, in equation (40) for a pure resistance, may be replaced by a certain function of all the constants concerned for a bridge of the most general type.

676. Generalised Bridge.—Thus let the bridge have resistance R_1, inductance L_1, and permittance (capacity) S_1, and let the incident waves be of frequency $p/2\pi$, so that y_1 is the real part of $y_0 e^{ipt}$, where $i = \sqrt{-1}$. Then R_1 in (40) is replaced by the generalised *resistance operator* Z, expressed by

$$Z = R_1 + L_1 ip + 1/S_1 ip \qquad (44).$$

The reason for R_1 being replaced by $R_1 + L_1 ip$ is seen from equation (12). Further, the fact that capacity opposes inductance has been pointed out at the end of article 658.

Thus equation (40) becomes in the general case

$$y_2 = \text{the real part of } \frac{Z - Lv}{Z + Lv} y_0 e^{ipt} \qquad (45),$$

or, with the understanding that only real parts are taken, this may be abbreviated into

$$\frac{y_2}{y_1} = \frac{Z - Lv}{Z + Lv}.$$

[1] *Phil. Mag.*, January 1897.

In either form Z is given by (44); of course if any of the quantities represented by the right side of (44) are absent, their symbols are to be omitted from the expression for Z, which holds good for any one or more of them.

It should be noticed that if L_1 or S_1 occur, then a change of phase is introduced in the reflected wave.

677. Intermediate Bridges.

Consider now an intermediate bridge whose resistance operator is Z defined by equation (44). Suppose the incident waves and consequently all the others are simple harmonic. Let the transverse voltages of the incident, reflected, and transmitted waves be denoted respectively by y_1, y_2, and y_3, and let the corresponding currents be u_1, u_2, and u_3. Then by equation (37) we have

$$u_1 = y_1/Lv, \ u_2 = -y_2/Lv, \ u_3 = y_3/Lv \qquad (46).$$

At the bridge itself we have

$$u_1 + u_2 - u_3 = (y_1 + y_2)/Z \qquad (47).$$

Lastly, we see that $\qquad y_3 = y_1 + y_2 \qquad (48).$

Hence (46) in (47) gives

$$\frac{y_1 - y_2 - y_3}{Lv} = \frac{y_1 + y_2}{Z} \qquad (49).$$

Whence by (48) we obtain

$$\frac{-2y_2}{Lv} = \frac{y_1 + y_2}{Z},$$

which yields $\qquad \dfrac{y_2}{y_1} = \dfrac{-Lv}{2Z + Lv} \qquad (50).$

Then by (48) and (50) we have

$$\frac{y_3}{y_1} = \frac{2Z}{2Z + Lv} \qquad (51).$$

These last equations give the reflected and transmitted waves in terms of the initial and the constants of the bridge and line; in using them $y_0 e^{ipt}$ should be written for

y_1, and, finally, real parts only retained, *i.e.* the abridged notation following (45) is here employed.

678. It may be noticed that for a bridge of pure resistance R_1, the above become

$$\frac{y_2}{y_1} = \frac{-Lv}{2R_1 + Lv} \text{ and } \frac{y_3}{y_1} = \frac{2R_1}{2R_1 + Lv} \qquad (52).$$

Again for a bridge of permittance S_1, the resistance and inductance being both negligible, Z becomes $1/S_1 ip$, and we accordingly obtain

$$\frac{y_2}{y_1} = \frac{-Lv}{(2/S_1 ip) + Lv} = \frac{-LvS_1 ip}{(2 + LvS_1 ip)} \frac{(2 - LvS_1 ip)}{(2 - LvS_1 ip)}$$

$$= \frac{-(LvS_1 p)^2 - 2iLvS_1 p}{4 + (LvS_1 p)^2} \qquad (53),$$

and $\dfrac{y_3}{y_1} = \dfrac{2/S_1 ip}{(2/S_1 ip) + Lv} = \dfrac{2(2 - LvS_1 ip)}{(2 + LvS_1 ip)(2 - LvS_1 ip)}$

$$= \frac{4 - 2iLvS_1 p}{4 + (LvS_1 p)^2} \qquad (54).$$

679. It is noteworthy that the reflected and transmitted waves differ in phase by a quarter of a period whatever be the capacity of the condenser, although their respective phase differences from the incident waves depend on the value of that capacity. This may be seen as follows:—If the expression for y_2/y_1 be put in the form $A + iB$, the change of phase being called ϵ_2, we have

$$\tan \epsilon_2 = B/A = \frac{-2}{-LvS_1 p} \qquad (55).$$

Similarly the change of phase for the transmitted wave being ϵ_3, we have from (54)

$$\tan \epsilon_3 = -LvS_1 p/2 \qquad (56),$$

whence, apart from sign, $\epsilon_2 \sim \epsilon_3 = \pi/2$.

Experiments with high frequency waves by the writer and Dr. Louis Lownds as to the amplitude and phase of reflection and transmission at an intermediate bridge consisting of a condenser only[1] gave results in harmony with the above theory of Heaviside.

[1] *Phil. Mag.*, October 1900.

EXAMPLES ON CHAPTER I

1. DESCRIBE and explain the three requisites for the production of sound waves.

2. Distinguish between the propagation of waves and the actual transit of matter, giving experimental illustrations.

3. Enumerate the three features possessed by any musical tone, and explain the physical basis of each.

4. Prove *experimentally* that pitch depends upon frequency, and that interval depends upon and is fixed by ratio of frequencies.

5. Establish mathematically that it is only when measuring pitches logarithmically that a resultant or composite interval is measured by the sum of the measures of its component intervals.

6. Calculate for each of the other six notes of the scale the number of logarithmic cents up from the keynote C.
Ans. 204, 386, 498, 702, 884, 1088.

7. If the keynote C is made of frequency 66 per second, determine the frequencies of the other notes of the scale.
Ans. 74·25, 82·5, 88, 99, 110, 123·75.

8. Write a short essay on the production and propagation of sound.

EXAMPLES ON CHAPTER II

On Arts. 13-31.

1. Define Simple Harmonic Motion, and find expressions for the velocity and acceleration of a point executing it.

2. If a point executes a simple harmonic motion of period

4π seconds and amplitude 3 cm., find its maximum velocity and that at half its full displacement, also the acceleration at its turning-points and when the displacement is 1 cm.

Ans. Velocities $\pm 3/2$ and $\pm 3\sqrt{3}/4$ cm./sec.

Accelerations $\pm 3/4$ and $\pm 1/4$ cm./sec.^{2}

3. Plot to scale a displacement curve or "graph" for the motion of Question 2, and verify by its aid the results previously obtained. (This and other like exercises may be done on squared paper.)

4. Enunciate the chief characteristics of transverse progressive waves of simple harmonic type.

5. Draw a displacement curve for longitudinal progressive waves and explain the significance of each feature of the curve.

6. Define the phase of a vibration, and explain and illustrate by equations the various ways of measuring it.

7. Write equations for the following progressive waves :—

  (*a*) Amplitude 0·1 cm., period 1/64 sec., wave length 450 cm.

  (*b*) Amplitude $1\cdot27 \times 10^{-7}$ cm., frequency 256, velocity of propagation 33,000 cm./sec.

8. Find the maximum "condensation" s in Question 7 (*b*).

Ans. $s = 6 \times 10^{-9}$.

9. Compound two collinear simple harmonic motions of equal periods, their amplitudes being 2 and 3 cm. and their epochs $\pi/4$ and $\pi/3$ respectively.

10. Compound two simple harmonic motions of equal amplitudes, their frequencies being as 15 : 16, and exhibit graphically the resultant for eight of the shorter periods.

11. By the method of displacement curves compound two simple harmonic vibrations of periods and amplitudes each as 2 : 1.

12. Write a short essay on progressive waves.

On Arts. 32-50.

13. By means of a ball hung by a thread fixed at its upper end, illustrate *experimentally* the composition of rectangular vibrations of equal periods, their phase differences being successively zero, half, and quarter.

14. Compound analytically or graphically two rectangular vibrations of equal amplitudes, both vibrations starting with no displacement and their periods being as (a) 2 : 1 and (b) 2 : 3.

15. By *experiments* with a Blackburn's pendulum make sand traces to verify the results found for Example 14.

16. State the chief characteristics of stationary waves, showing particularly how they differ from progressive waves, and writing the equations for each.

17. Enunciate and explain Huyghens' Principle of Wavelets and Envelopes.

18. Apply Huyghens' principle to the reflection of plane waves at a plane surface, and show that the angles of incidence and reflection are equal.

19. In the case of refraction at a plane surface treated by Huyghens' principle prove that the known laws of refraction of light are confirmed.

20. State and explain the conclusions to which Huyghens' principle leads as to the passage of waves through small openings and large ones.

21. How may the principle of Huyghens be experimentally illustrated?

On Arts. 51-59.

22. Express y as a function of t by Fourier's theorem given that from $t = 0$ to $\tau/2$, $y = 0$ and that from $t = \tau/2$ to τ, $y = 2k$.

$$Ans. \quad y = k - \frac{4k}{\pi} \left\{ \frac{\sin \omega t}{1} + \frac{\sin 3\omega t}{3} + \frac{\sin 5\omega t}{5} + \ldots \right\}$$

23. From $t = 0$ to a, $y = ft - h$, and from $t = a$ to τ, $y = g(\tau - t) - h$; expand y by Fourier's theorem.

Ans. See art. 348.

24. From Example 22 plot to scale the first three terms of the Fourier series, compound them, and compare with the original conditions.

25. In Example 23 put $a = \tau/3$, and plot curves to scale for the first four terms of the Fourier series, comparing the result of composition with the terms of the question.

26. Plot the equiangular spiral r cm. $= 4b^{-\theta}$, choosing b so that the radius vector shrinks to half in each complete revolution.

(*Note.*—$b = 1 \cdot 1166$ nearly.)

27. If a point describes the spiral of Example 26 at the rate of 50 revolutions per second, what are its linear velocity and accelerations at the start ?

> *Ans.* Velocity = 1264 cm./sec., accelerations are 399,424
> centrally, and 87,974 cm./sec.² opposite to velocity.

28. The motion of the point in Example 27 is projected upon a fixed straight line parallel to the initial radius vector. Write the equation of this projected point, and find expressions for its velocity and acceleration at time t.

> *Ans.* See equations (11) and (12) of art. 58, in which
> write $a = 4$ cm., $\kappa = 34\cdot8$ per sec. nearly,
> $q = 314\cdot16$ radians per sec., and $p = 316$
> radians per sec.

On Arts. 60-70.

29. Explain Doppler's principle, and show that, in the absence of wind, a given speed of approach of source raises the apparent pitch more than the same speed of approach of the recipient.

30. A cyclist riding at 15 miles per hour meets a carriage with bells proceeding in the opposite direction at 5 miles per hour. How many logarithmic cents will the pitch appear to fall on passing ?   (Take speed of sound 1100 ft./sec.)

> *Ans.* 92·34 cents nearly.

31. Make a diagram showing the refraction of sound by a wind whose speed is 100 miles per hour, the original wave front being inclined at 45°, and distinguish between the refraction of the wave front and the refraction of the direction of propagation.

32. Establish the law of refraction of sound by an abrupt change of wind speed, and account for a possible total reflection.

33. Define Strain, Strain Ellipsoid, and Simple Shear. Obtain the fractional change of volume consequent upon a general strain.

34. Show that one uniform dilatation and two simple shears are able to build up any specified general strain.   Hence resolve the strain $(0\cdot03, 0\cdot02, 0\cdot01)$ into a uniform dilatation and two shears.

35. Resolve into axial strains each of the three following strains :—

> (*a*) The simple elongation $(0\cdot01, 0, 0)$;
> (*b*) The uniform dilation $(0\cdot02, 0\cdot02, 0\cdot02)$;
and   (*c*) The simple shear $(0\cdot03, -0\cdot03, 0)$.

> *Ans.* See equations (7), (8), and (9) of art. 69.

36. Explain fully with diagrams that a simple shear may be regarded as a progressive sliding of undistorted planes. Also show that the amount of an indefinitely small shear is double of its fractional elongation or contraction.

EXAMPLES ON CHAPTER III

1. Explain the nature of Elasticity, and give an equation showing how it is measured.

2. Draw up a tabular statement of the chief elasticities, showing by symbols the stresses and strains characteristic of each, and also the class of substance to which each applies.

3. Define Rigidity. Explain by aid of a diagram that a second view of the corresponding stress may be taken, and find the relation between the two.

4. Express Young's modulus and Poisson's ratio for an isotropic substance in terms of the volume elasticity and rigidity.
Ans. See Table V.

5. Find the value of the elongational elasticity of a solid in terms of (*a*) its Young's modulus and Poisson's ratio, and (*b*) its volume elasticity and rigidity.   *Ans*. See Table V.

6. Express in terms of the volume elasticity and rigidity of an isotropic solid the values of (*a*) the Ratio of elongation to tension, and (*b*) the Ratio of lateral contraction to tension.
Ans. See Table V.

7. *Experimentally* verify Hooke's law by tension of a vertical wire provided with scale and vernier, plot a curve with loads and elongations as co-ordinates, and deduce Young's modulus.

8. Repeat the *experiment* of Example 7 by one of the finer methods, and note the higher accuracy obtained, and express it by retaining more figures in the answer.

9. Treat mathematically the torsion of a cylinder of isotropic substance, and obtain an expression for the equal and opposite couples applied at the end faces.

10. Determine *experimentally* the Young's modulus, rigidity and volume elasticity of the substance of the given short piece of wire or fibre (glass or quartz), only the ordinary apparatus of a physical laboratory being available.

METHOD.—*First* for *Young's modulus* by bending. Let the fibre rest on supports a distance l cm. apart, and be observed microscopically to be depressed a depth a cm. at the middle in consequence of a load of m gm. suspended there. Then if the radius of the fibre or wire is r and the Young's modulus q, it may be shown that

$$q = mgl^3/12\pi r^4 a \qquad (1).$$

Second for *Rigidity* by torsional oscillations. Prepare a base board of wood about 10 cm. long, 2 cm. wide, and 2 mm. thick. Make a hole at the centre to admit one end of the wire or fibre, which is then fastened off underneath, the main part of the fibre standing at right angles to the board. Clip the far end of the fibre so that it hangs vertically with the board horizontal at the bottom, and free to oscillate by torsion of the fibre. On the board set two ordinary laboratory weights, each of M gm. (say 50 gm.) at a distance $2b_1$ apart, centre to centre, and suppose the period of complete torsional oscillations is found to be T_1. Next, place the weights nearer, a distance $2b_2$ apart say, and let the period of oscillation be T_2. Then if the length of fibre in use is L and the radius r, it may be shown (see arts. 81 and 85) that the rigidity is given by

$$n = \frac{16\pi LM}{r^4} \cdot \frac{(b_1{}^2 - b_2{}^2)}{(T_1{}^2 - T_2{}^2)}.$$

Third, having the Young's modulus and rigidity, the *Volume Elasticity* is found by the relation $k = nq/(9n - 3q)$ in Table V.

The above is the method referred to at the end of art. 83. It has been carried out by students at Nottingham, one of whom (Mr. T. J. Richmond) obtained for a fibre of soda glass

$$q = 5\cdot 61 \times 10^{11} \text{ dynes per sq. cm.}$$
$$n = 2\cdot 33 \times 10^{11} \text{ dynes per sq. cm.}$$
whence $\qquad k = 3\cdot 15 \times 10^{11} \text{ dynes per sq. cm.}$

These are very fair values for such a simple method, capable of being worked in an hour or two, and without any special apparatus.

11. Write an essay on Strains, Stresses, and Elasticity.

EXAMPLES ON CHAPTER IV

On Arts. 84-90.

1. Give a general expression for the period of a vibrating mass. Show that a weight at the middle of a stretched string has a period in accord with this. What must be the tension in a string a yard long in order that a mass of 4 lb. at the middle vibrates with a period of 2 seconds?

Ans. 29·58 poundals, or 0·92 lb. weight nearly.

2. What is the total energy of the mass in Example 1 while the amplitude is 3 inches?

Ans. 1·23 ft. poundals, or 0·0382 ft. lb. wt.

3. Calculate the total energy possessed by a cubic centimetre of steel at the end of a steel tuning-fork where the amplitude is 2 mm., the frequency being 64 per second. (Take the density of steel as 8 gm. per cc.)

Ans. 25,870 ergs, or 26·37 cm. gm. wt.

4. In the case of a mass M suspended from an elastic cord or spring of mass m find the period of vertical oscillations, correcting for the mass of the spring and establishing the expressions used.

5. Obtain, either with or without the calculus, the motion of a particle subject to a resistance proportional to its velocity as well as a restoring force proportional to its displacement.

6. Plot a displacement-time curve showing the damped vibration of a particle under conditions such that the friction lowers its pitch by one logarithmic cent to the value 40 per second, the initial amplitude being one centimetre and velocity zero.

Ans. The required curve is $y = e^{-9t} \cos 80\pi t$ nearly.

7. If in Example 6 the particle in question is a cubic millimetre near the end of a large steel bar, calculate the values of the restoring and frictional forces acting upon it. (Take the density of steel as 8 gm./cc.)

Ans. Restoring force = 506 dynes per cm. Frictional force = 0·144 dyne per unit speed (*i.e.* 1 cm./sec.); this gives a maximum resistance of 36 dynes as the particle passes through its equilibrium position with a speed of about 250 cm. per second.

On Arts. 91-111.

8. Treat the problem of the vibrations forced upon an elastic system by an impressed harmonic force, using either the calculus or an elementary method.

9. Show how the vigour of forced vibrations depends upon the closeness of tuning between the frequency of the force and that natural to the system. What prevents their indefinite increase ?

10. Discuss the phenomenon known as the "sharpness of resonance," and explain upon what quantity it depends.

11. An elastic system under the influence of an harmonic impressed force often exhibits two sets of vibrations, the "forced" and the "natural." Explain exactly how each set arises, and how one may be withdrawn or fail to appear.

12. If an impressed harmonic force begins to act upon an elastic system at rest, what motion immediately ensues, and how is it modified as time goes on ?

13. A small bullet is hung by a fine silk thread a metre long to a large mass which is itself suspended by a strong wire 110 centimetres long. All being initially at rest the large mass is struck horizontally by a hammer so that it begins to oscillate with an amplitude of 1 cm. Describe in general terms what happens to the bullet. Also obtain an equation expressing its displacement as a function of the time, supposing it is subject to resistances which would reduce the amplitude of its own vibrations to one-half in 100 vibrations.

14. Set up apparatus in *experimental* illustration of Example 13, and confirm or disprove the conclusions theoretically reached.

15. Write an essay on Forced Vibrations.

On Arts. 112-116.

16. Write and solve the equations of motion of an elastic system in which the value of the restoring force involves the square of the displacement.

17. Explain carefully under what conditions the octave and the twelfth of an original tone may be produced when the amplitude is large.

18. If an asymmetrical elastic system is under the simultaneous action of two periodic impressed forces what is the nature of its response ? Prove your statements mathematically.

19. Write a short essay on the Principle of Superposition, pointing out the limitations of its application and giving a numerical example.

On Arts. 117-129.

20. Establish the expression for the speed of waves along a stretched cord, and explain how it may be experimentally confirmed.

21. Derive a general expression for the speed of sound in a gas, also discuss the formulæ due to Newton and to Laplace.

22. How does the speed of sound in gases vary with pressure and temperature? Establish an approximate formula for the speed in air at various temperatures.

23. Discuss the possibility of waves of sound of permanent type advancing through the air, and show why, in the case of intense sounds, the condensed portions overrun the rarefied portions.

24. Obtain the speed of longitudinal waves in a solid rod, and show that no available tension will make transverse waves go so fast.

25. Derive the differential equation for small transverse disturbances along a stretched cord.

26. Establish the differential equation for plane waves in a gas.

27. Treat, by the calculus, the case of small longitudinal disturbances in a solid prism and in an extended solid.

28. Write an essay on the propagation of small disturbances, treating typical cases in detail.

On Arts. 130-144.

29. Solve the differential equation for small disturbances, and apply the solution to the case of any initial disturbance without velocity.

30. Treat the case of the propagation of small disturbances in an elastic medium with an initial motion but no displacement, the differential equation being assumed known.

31. Obtain expressions for the reflections occurring at a "fixed" and at a "free" end.

32. Make a series of diagrams showing the state of things at various instants in a stretched cord ten metres long, in which there was initially a small displacement without velocity between the points distant three and four metres respectively from one end.

33. Treat, both analytically and graphically, the motion of a stretched string pulled aside by a sharp point at one-seventh of its length and then let go.

34. Solve the differential equation for small disturbances in a manner directly applicable to a stretched string with fixed ends and without explicit mention of waves and their reflection.

35. Give a solution by Fourier's series for a plucked string, making a diagram showing the decreasing law followed by the different overtones.

36. Discuss the motion of a struck string, using Fourier's theorem, and treat the convergence of the partials and its dependence upon the place of excitation.

On Arts. 145-155.

37. Obtain expressions for the energy (per unit volume) and energy current (per unit area) of plane sound waves in air.

38. In the case of a musical tone of frequency 256 per second, the sound waves in the air being plane and having an amplitude of one-thousandth of a millimetre, find (*a*) the energy of the radiation per cubic centimetre, and (*b*) the energy current per square metre, the speed of propagation being 33,200 cm. per second. (Take the density to be 0·00129 gm. per c.c.)

> *Ans.* (*a*) 0·0000167 erg/c.c. nearly.
>
> (*b*) 5540 ergs per square metre per second.

39. Obtain the general differential equation for small vibratory disturbances in a light compressible fluid medium in space of three dimensions.

40. Transform the general differential equation for vibrations in a compressible fluid (obtained in answer to Example 39) so as to express spherical radiation.

41. Discuss the reflection of spherical waves at the origin.

On Arts. 156-163.

42. Obtain expressions for the reflection and transmission coefficient of sound waves on reaching the surface of separation of two gases.

43. If a sound wave originates in hydrogen gas and passes by normal incidence into air, what fraction of the initial energy emerges ? (See art. 161 for method.)

44. If a wave disturbance travels along a thick stretched cord till it reaches a junction with a thinner cord, show what happens and that the result is in harmony with the conservation of energy.

45. Establish expressions for the partial reflection and transmission of longitudinal waves along solid rods at a junction where some change in dimensions or properties suddenly occurs. Examine and justify by general considerations the changes of phase, if any, in the reflected wave (a) when the Young's modulus does not change at the junction, and (b) when the density does not change; the cross section being constant for the two rods under each supposition.

> *Ans.* (a) Displacement reversed by reflection from denser rod in which waves travel slower.
>
> (b) Displacement not reversed by reflection from rod in which Young's modulus is lower and waves travel slower.

46. A longitudinal wave is started in a solid rod whose cross section, density, and Young's modulus are respectively s_1, ρ_1, and q_1. It then reaches a place at which the rod changes suddenly in cross section and material being now characterised by s_2, ρ_2, and q_2. Show that the fraction of incident amplitude reflected at the junction may be represented by

$$\frac{b}{a} = \frac{s_1 \sqrt{\rho_1 q_1} - s_2 \sqrt{\rho_2 q_2}}{s_1 \sqrt{\rho_1 q_1} + s_2 \sqrt{\rho_2 q_2}}.$$

Also devise for specified materials a junction at which no reflection can occur.

> *Ans.* See art. 158, equation (8). For no reflection make $s_1 \sqrt{\rho_1 q_1} = s_2 \sqrt{\rho_2 q_2}$.

EXAMPLES ON CHAPTER V

On Arts. 164-181.

1. Determine the notes which may be emitted by a stretched string of given length, diameter, and density.

2. *Experimentally* verify the laws of vibrations of strings by a monochord and suitable tuning-forks.   (See art. 166.)

3. Discuss the modifications introduced into a string's vibrations by its own stiffness or the lack of fixity of its ends.

4. Obtain expressions for the possible tones yielded by rods in longitudinal vibration when fixed at the middle. How may they be elicited ?

5. Establish the frequencies of the possible tones of open and stopped parallel pipes.

6. How may the vibrations of organ pipes be experimentally demonstrated ?

7. Write an essay on organ pipes, dealing especially with the modifications introduced into the elementary theory by the necessary corrections for the open end and mouth.

On Arts. 182-197.

8. Obtain equations expressing the stationary vibrations in conical pipes, and apply them to the cases of a complete cone with base closed and base open.

9. Find the positions of the nodes and antinodes in a complete open cone whose corrected length is one metre, when responding to a tuning-fork whose pitch is the fifth partial of the cone.

> *Ans.* Measuring from the vertex throughout :—Nodes, 0, 28·61, 49·18, 69·42, and 89·49 cm. Antinodes, 20, 40, 60, 80, and 100 cm.

> (See Table VIII. and art. 188.)

10. Establish the differential equation for small disturbances of a stretched membrane.

11. Treat the vibrations of a square membrane dealing with at least three of its possible tones and sketching some of the possible nodal systems.

On Arts. 198-220.

12. Calculate the bending moments required to bend a given bar to a specified curvature, illustrating your answer by two numerical examples.

13. Obtain the relations between applied forces, shearing stress and bending moments in a bar at rest.

14. Derive the differential equation of transverse motion of an elastic bar, also the conditions which apply at the ends under various circumstances.

15. Assuming the differential equation for the lateral motion of a bar, solve the equation and show how the frequencies of the possible tones of the bar depend upon its dimensions and properties.

16. Discuss the lateral vibrations of a free-free bar, giving a graphical solution of the equation found for the series of partials of which it is capable.

17. Show that a slight modification of the graphical method referred to in Example 16 will solve the equation defining the sequence of tones which may be elicited from a fixed-free bar vibrating laterally.

18. *Experimentally* obtain the lateral vibrations of a bar free at both ends, and of a bar fixed at one end and free at the other.
(See arts. 210 and 212.)

19. How has it been shown experimentally that the simple static theory of Lord Rayleigh gives a close approximation to the period of lateral vibrations for a fixed-free bar ?

20. Describe the change in position of nodes which progressively occurs as a bar is bent more and more from the straight form to a U-shaped bar.

21. The temperature variation of a steel tuning-fork being shown by Koenig to be *minus* 0·000112 per 1° C., and the linear expansion being 0·000012 per 1° C., show that the temperature variation of the Young's modulus for steel is *minus* 0·000236 per 1° C.   (See art. 220.)

On Arts. 221-234.

22. Describe what are known as Chladni's figures, giving sketches of a few for a square plate with free edges.

23. Obtain *experimentally* four or more Chladni's figures with the plate provided.

24. Explain by diagrams and general reasoning the derivation of a simple Chladni's figure.

25. Discuss the vibrations of a ring, a cylindrical shell, and a bell.

EXAMPLES ON CHAPTER VI

On Arts. 235-244.

1. Enumerate at least ten examples of resonance and allied phenomena, classifying them in tabular form according to the nature of the interactions occurring.

2. *Experimentally* tune the given flask to resonance with each of the forks provided.

3. Determine *experimentally* by the adjustable water resonator the relative frequencies of the prime and second tone of the given fork.

4. Give a simple theory of a resonator, obtaining an expression for the frequency of its prime tone.

5. Write a short essay on resonance, pointing out how the subject may be experimentally illustrated.

On Arts. 245-258.

6. Describe the two forms of Melde's experiment, and give a specimen set of loads to exhibit the various numbers of segments.

7. *Experimentally* obtain the vibrations of a thread attached to a tuning-fork as in Melde's experiment, one, two, and three segments being exhibited in each of the two modes.

8. Explain the action of Dr. Erskine-Murray's phonoscope.

9. Describe by aid of diagrammatic sketches the salient physical features of the human ear.

10. Follow in detail the various chief occurrences in the act of hearing in the case of simple and compound tones.

11. What reasons have we for believing that the vibrations received at the outer ear are modified as they pass through the train of aural mechanism?

On Arts. 259-278.

12. Describe the action of a violin bow and also that of Goold's generators.

13. Write an essay on the theory of singing flames.

14. Explain the paradox that a vibration maintained by a harmonic impressed force is most encouraged if the force is at its maximum when the displacement is *zero*, whereas a vibration maintained by sudden heating and cooling is most encouraged if these effects occur when the displacements are at their *maximum*.

15. Explain the arrangements for driving a tuning-fork electrically, showing particularly how it is that the electro-magnetic action helps the vibrations one way more than it hinders it the other.

On Arts. 279-287.

16. Describe several forms of sensitive jets and flames, pointing out the special advantages of each.

17. Explain the phenomenon of the setting of a disc normally to motions in the air, and describe how to demonstrate this effect.

18. Give the theory underlying the production of Kundt's dust figures, and particularise some of the precautions essential to success.

19. *Experimentally* obtain a set of Kundt's dust figures.

20. Explain the occurrence of the striations in Kundt's dust figures.

EXAMPLES ON CHAPTER VII

On Arts. 288-296.

1. Describe several methods of experimentally demonstrating the phenomena of interference.

2. Explain precisely the distinction between interference and beats.

3. State how the law of the frequency of beats may be established.

4. How may the phenomena of beats be demonstrated to a single observer, and how to a large audience ?

On Arts. 297-306.

5. What is meant by the term combinational tones ?   Give two or more methods by which they may be experimentally demonstrated.

6. Draw up a table showing the pitches of the differentials and summationals produced by given generating tones.

7. Do you suppose the vibrations corresponding to combinational tones to occur first in the ear itself, or to occur independently of the ear altogether ?   Give reasons for your belief.

On Arts. 307-321.

8. How may tones of higher order arise in an elastic system from the influence of a loud simple tone ?   Account mathematically for the production of some one higher partial in this manner.

9. Give an experimental example of the octave being heard from a vibrating body which has no parts whose frequency is that octave.   Discuss the possible ways of production of this upper partial.

10. Summarise the researches of Koenig on beat notes, and give Bosanquet's views on the subject.

11. Explain the methods and results of the researches of Rücker and Edser on combinational tones.

12. Describe the recent work by E. Waetzmann on combinational tones.

13. State the theory put forward by Everett to account for resultant tones.

14. Write an essay on the objectivity of combinational tones.

EXAMPLES ON CHAPTER VIII

On Arts. 322-363.

1. Analyse the essential parts of a musical instrument regarded from the view-point of the physicist.

2. Give a tabular classification of the chief musical instruments showing the approximate compass of each.

3. Discuss the quality of tone from plucked strings. Can the vibrations be represented by a Fourier expansion ?

4. Compare the qualities of tone from strings struck (*a*) with a sharp, hard edge, and (*b*) with a soft rounded hammer.

5. Enumerate and explain the chief points of scientific interest in instruments of the violin family.

6. How has the problem of bowed strings been treated by Helmholtz ?

7. State in general terms the nature of the motion, as determined by Helmholtz, of a well-bowed string when emitting a note of good musical quality.

8. Describe the researches of Krigar-Menzel and Raps on bowed strings.

9. How may the characteristic motion of a bowed string be optically demonstrated to an audience ?

10. Does the motion of the string alone of a stringed instrument determine the quality of the sound heard ? If not, state why not, and describe any work undertaken to throw light on the subject.

On Arts. 364-380.

11. Discuss the arrangement and tuning of organ pipes with and without reeds.

12. Explain how organ pipes without reeds "speak," and account for the different qualities of tone of various pipes.

13. Describe the typical "wood-wind" instruments, explain their action, and account for their characteristic qualities of tone.

On Arts. 381-398.

14. How is the sound produced in a brass instrument? Explain also how the various possible notes are obtained on the French horn (without valves) and on the slide trombone.

15. Explain the production of the various notes of the chromatic scale on a brass instrument with three valves.

16. Show that the intonation of the ordinary three-valved brass instruments must be faulty, and explain its improvement by compensating pistons.

On Arts. 399-404.

17. Explain the production of musical tones by the human voice.

18. Give a classification of the chief vowels, and explain the modifications of the mouth cavity and opening on which they depend.

19. Explain the ordinary view as to what characteristics in a compound tone impart to it the vowel quality, and state the resonance pitches for the leading vowels.

On Arts. 405-415.

20. Discuss the experimental results that have been obtained as to the pressures used in playing wind instruments.

21. How are the pitches of orchestral and other instruments affected by temperature changes?

22. Compare the special qualities of tone from various wind instruments, and state how you could demonstrate their individual composition by experimental synthesis.

23. Describe the analysis of the voice by a set of Helmholtz resonators.

24. *Experimentally* examine by Koenig's manometric capsule and flame a series of vowels, each sung at several different pitches.

25. How may vowels and consonants sung or spoken be analysed and their characteristic vibrational forms exhibited to an audience?   (See arts. 414, 250, and 251.)

2 x

EXAMPLES ON CHAPTER IX

On Arts. 416-428.

1. Give an account of Helmholtz's theory of concord and discord.

2. State several ways in which beats may arise, and describe experiments to illustrate two or more of these cases.

3. Explain the absence of obtrusive beats between two tuning-forks whose interval is a mistuned major third.

On Arts. 429-436.

4. Describe, with passages in musical notation and a graph, how the degree of harmoniousness varies for the chief intervals within an octave, the tone being of violin quality.

5. How may the variation of harmoniousness of two notes within an octave be experimentally demonstrated in confirmation of Helmholtz's theory ?

6. Give an example of a concord between instruments of different quality of tone, which is changed in degree of consonance if the instruments interchange parts. Why is this so ?

7. Write down a few of the major triads in the scale of C, give some of their best positions and some of their less perfect positions, accounting for the difference.

8. Explain why minor triads are usually less harmonious than major triads.

9. Write an essay on concord and discord.

On Arts. 437-450.

10. Enumerate the chief reasons for temperament in the tuning of musical instruments with fixed notes and keys.

11. It is often stated that human voices, instruments of the violin family, and slide trombones can easily perform in just intonation. Critically discuss this statement.

12. What difficulties would be entailed if just intonation were demanded from instruments with fixed notes like the piano and organ ?

On Arts. 451-464.

13. Explain the derivation of mean-tone temperament, its tuning, its advantages and disadvantages.

14. What pairs of notes in the Pythagorean tuning become fused in the equal temperament and why ? State also what advantage is fully obtained in the equal temperament and what drawbacks are involved.

15. Show precisely how the effect of the " comma " (22 cents) may be illustrated harmonically on the violin by sounding successively a fourth and a major sixth.

16. What was the tuning adopted in Bosanquet's cycle of fifty-three, and what were the advantages aimed at by it ? How do you account for its failing to attain any vogue ?

On Arts. 465-472.

17. How may the special musical character of certain keys be scientifically explained ?

18. State the frequency ratios of the following intervals, also their measure in logarithmic cents.

> Just Intonation : the comma, diatonic semitone, trumpet seventh.
>
> Mean-tone Temperament : whole tone, diatonic semitone, fifth.
>
> Equal Temperament : semitone, major third, fifth.
>
> > (See Table XLVI. in art. 471.)

19. Trace the changes of pitch which have occurred in the course of musical practice.

> (See Table XLVII. in art. 472.)

20. Write an essay on Consonance and Temperament.

EXAMPLES ON CHAPTER X

On Arts. 473-488.

1. Give an account of the classic determinations of the velocity of sound in free air, and state the results obtained.

2. How have the velocities of sounds in water been obtained by large-scale experiments ?

3. Describe Regnault's celebrated researches on the velocity of sound in pipes. What was the view of Rink respecting this work ?

4. What has been done to test the dependence of speed of sound on pressure and pitch ?

On Arts. 489-508.

5. How was the speed of sound in iron found by Biot ?

6. Describe Dulong's experiments with organ pipes and various gases, indicating the results obtained by him.

7. What did Wertheim find as to the speed of sound in different-sized organ pipes ?

8. Explain the experiments by Wertheim as to the speed of sound in liquids, also the erroneous views held by him and exposed by Helmholtz, Kundt, and Lehmann.

9. Give an account of Kundt's researches by means of his method of dust figures, and state the chief results obtained by him.

10. Explain what other determinations can be made by Kundt's tube besides the relative speeds of sound in air and other gases.

11. *Experimentally* obtain the speeds of sound in brass, oak, pine, etc. by Kundt's tube.

12. Obtain an *experimental* determination of the values of Young's modulus for various solids by Kundt's tube.

13. How may the value of the mechanical equivalent of heat be deduced from acoustic and thermal data ?

On Arts. 509-532.

14. Describe Hebb's telephone method for the speed of sound in air.

15. How may the speeds of sound in soft bodies be determined ?

16. Write a *résumé* of the theoretical and experimental work which has been done on the dependence of speed of sound in pipes upon pitch and diameter.

17. Describe Wüllner's researches on the speed of sound in various gases and at different temperatures.

18. Explain carefully the reasons which led Blaikley to adopt a bulbous tube for his experiments on the speed of sound, and state the results thus obtained by him.

19. What do you know of recent work as to the speed of sound in hot gases and in gases at liquid-air temperatures ?

20. Give an account of Blaikley's experimental determination of the correction for an open end, and state how a simple repetition of this may be carried out in any laboratory.

On Arts. 533-568.

21. Describe the vibration microscope, and state the uses to which it has been put.

22. How may Lissajous' figures be optically projected and utilised to determine the relative frequencies of two forks ?

23. *Experimentally* determine the ratio of the frequencies of two forks by the monochord.

24. Explain the method of tuning and the manner of using the set of forks which constitute Scheibler's tonometer.

25. How did Lord Rayleigh determine the absolute pitch of a note on a harmonium ?

26. Determine *experimentally* the pitches of the given fork and organ pipe by use of the siren of Cagniard de la Tour.

27. By means of the fall plate *experimentally* determine the frequency of the given fork, the value of " *g* " being assumed.

28. By *experiments* with the vertical monochord obtain the absolute frequency of the given tuning-fork.

29. Assuming the speed of sound in air at 0° C., *experimentally* determine the pitches of the forks provided.

On Arts. 569-581.

30. Explain the methods adopted by Hartmann-Kempf in examining the variation of pitch and decrement of a fork with amplitude, and state also the results obtained.

31. When a resonator responds to a fork, in what way is the pitch of the fork itself modified ?

32. Give an account of the various experiments as to the lowest pitch which constitutes a humanly-audible sound.

33. What do you know as to the highest pitches audible, and how would you test any person's upper limit of audition ?

34. Give a general explanation of harmonic echoes, the sound returned being apparently an octave (or more) above the original sound.

35. How may a musical sound arise by the successive echoes of a very sudden sound of extremely short duration ?

36. Upon what conditions does the pitch of an Æolian tone depend ?

On Arts. 582-593.

37. Explain, with equations, Rayleigh's fork method for determining the minimum amplitude audible.

38. Describe Dr. Shaw's electrical determination of the minimum amplitude audible.

39. Enumerate and explain the various deflections and losses suffered by sound in its transit over long ranges.

On Arts. 594-606.

40. Explain generally why sound waves incident upon a surface produce a pressure, and describe the experimental confirmation of this phenomenon.

41. Establish Larmor's radiation pressure theorem.

42. Discuss Poynting's conception of the momentum of radiation, adding an outline of the work of Rayleigh on this subject.

43. Write an essay on the pressure of sound.

On Arts. 607-619.

44. Discuss the dependence of the quality of a musical sound upon the phase relation of its component simple tones.

45. Give the evidence for and against the fixed-pitch theory of vowels.

46. Explain the work of Lord Rayleigh on our perception of sound direction.

47. Describe the work of Marage, and that of Sabine, upon architectural acoustics.

EXAMPLES ON CHAPTER XI

On Arts. 620-632.

1. Describe the construction and action of some form of phonograph.

2. Which theory as to the characteristic quality of vowels is favoured by Hermann's experiments with the phonograph ?

3. Review M'Kendrick's researches with the phonograph, pointing out the difficulties met with and how they were finally overcome.

4. Give a brief outline of the results obtained by M'Kendrick as to the character of the vibrations present in the sounds from various instruments and the voice.

5. Explain the methods followed by Bevier in his phonograph analysis, and give a *résumé* of the chief results thus obtained.

On Arts. 633-647.

6. Give an account of the introduction of telephony and a sketch of Bell's receiver.

7. Explain the action of a telephone receiver, and account for its high sensitiveness.

8. Prove that in the ordinary telephone receiver a permanent magnetic field is indispensable.

9. Describe, with a sectional sketch, the construction and working of an Edison carbon transmitter.

10. Show that to insure constant efficiency with a telephone circuit, consisting of line, carbon transmitter, battery, and receiver, the voltage would have to vary as the square of the length of the line. How is this drawback obviated?

11. Describe a simple form of the device known as Hughes' microphone.

12. Explain the use of transformers in long-distance telephony.

13. How have some of the elements of music been electrically communicated to patients who are stone deaf?

On Arts. 648-653.

14. Explain with sketches the electrical arrangements which constitute the "speaking arc."

15. How does the "musical arc" act, and to what familiar musical instrument may it be compared?

On Arts. 654-666.

16. Discuss mathematically the oscillatory discharge of an electrical condenser, and show that charge and current are each damped harmonic functions of the time.

17. Describe in general terms what happens when an electric condenser is allowed to discharge through a circuit containing both resistance and inductance. To what may the various electrical quantities be likened in the case of a mechanical vibration?

18. An electrical condenser of capacity a hundredth of a microfarad[1] is charged, insulated from the battery, and then connected to a circuit whose resistance is one thousand ohms and inductance one henry; determine the ensuing phenomena.

Ans. The period τ is 0·00063 second nearly, and the damping factor q (of art. 655) is 500 per sec., so that the amplitude is reduced to less than two-fifths in three periods.

---

[1] The analysis in the text (art. 654 *et seq.*) is valid for *c. g. s.* units. In solving this problem note that a microfarad $= 10^{-15}$, an ohm 10^9, and a henry 10^9 of these *c. g. s.* electro-magnetic units.

19. For Example 18 plot discharge curves for (*a*) quantity and (*b*) current.

20. Discuss the subject of forced electrical vibrations, showing their analogy to mechanical vibrations.

21. Show that in the case of electrical vibrations a condenser may be likened to a certain *negative* inductance.

22. Define the *impedance* of a circuit, and determine its value for a specified circuit and alternations of given frequency.

23. Explain in general terms how the resistance and inductance of a given circuit are modified by high-frequency alternations and by rapid damping respectively.

24. How is the criterion for the oscillatory discharge altered by the modifications referred to in Example 23 ? Explain also under what circumstances *axial* concentration of the current may occur.

25. Discuss the division of alternating currents in parallel circuits, showing what this reduces to (*a*) when the frequency is very low, and (*b*) when it is very high.

On Arts. 667-679.

26. State in general terms how attenuation and distortion are produced in the electro-magnetic waves passing along a telephone line, and show how the distortion may be obviated.

27. Give the mathematical theory of Heaviside's distortionless circuit.

28. Determine the reflections occurring at the terminal resistance bridge of a telephone line, pointing out the three critical cases analogous to " open " end, " stopped " end, and total absorption.

29. How may a bridge be dealt with when it presents resistance, inductance, and capacity ? Which of these quantities involves changes of phase ?

30. Consider the case of an intermediate bridge on a line of parallel electric leads, and show that if the bridge is a pure capacity the reflected and transmitted waves differ in phase by the angle $\pi/2$.

INDEX

THE END

Printed by R. & R. CLARK, LIMITED, *Edinburgh*